PHYSIOGRAPHY OF
EASTERN UNITED STATES

A Companion Volume

BY

NEVIN M. FENNEMAN

•

PHYSIOGRAPHY OF
WESTERN UNITED STATES

This book presents a comprehensive sum-
marization of the physiographic features
of western United States, covering the
Great Plains, the Rocky Mountain System, the Intermontane Plateaus, and the
Pacific Mountain System.

534 pages, 6 x 9, 173 illustrations and maps

PHYSIOGRAPHY

OF

EASTERN UNITED STATES

BY

NEVIN M. FENNEMAN

Professor of Geology, University of Cincinnati

FIRST EDITION
SECOND IMPRESSION

McGRAW-HILL BOOK COMPANY, INC.

NEW YORK AND LONDON
1938

THE MAPLE PRESS COMPANY, YORK, PA.

PREFACE

The term *physiography* as used in the United States is the approximate equivalent of *geomorphology*. The latter term is used more in Europe and is growing in favor in this country. Geomorphology is definitely limited to the genetic study of land forms. Physiography has often been made to include treatment of the atmosphere and ocean. In that broad sense it is essentially the scientific study of physical geography. In this book the atmosphere and ocean are mentioned only as related to the land surface.

As a study of processes, principles, laws, and types, physiography is a branch of geology. In its areal or distributional phase it is a branch of geography. Since the study of the distributional phase is inseparable from that of principles, physiography may be said to represent the overlap of the two major sciences. The data entering into this book are in very large measure the product of geological investigations. The ultimate description based on these data should be the basis of geography.

It has been the hope of the author to produce something more than a mere compilation from the vast field of geologic literature. If it can be claimed that knowledge within the stipulated field has been *organized* rather than merely assembled, the author's hope will have been realized. The aim has been to establish order rather than to describe the United States. It seems regrettable that so large a proportion of the total text should be occupied by descriptive material. The purely geographical reader may find these descriptions desirable on their own account, but that is not the basis on which space has been allotted. The ultimate justification of any description except the briefest is its evidential value in the interpretation of physiographic history.

In the treatment of so large an area, the degree of generalization, allowable and advisable, is a constant problem. It is too much to hope that the distribution of space to different regions and to different problems will meet the wishes of all readers. As an illustration, relatively little space has been given to concrete cases of change in drainage. Probably no other one thing so epitomizes the history of a region's physiography as the history of its rivers. Volumes might be filled with their records; yet the policy of this book is to describe drainage changes by classes where general causes can be assigned, and to discuss individual streams only by way of illustration, or on account of some special interest.

The treatment of geomorphic history in terms of erosion cycles is no doubt simpler than the actual story. It is inherently probable that many cycles were initiated by minor uplifts; also, some extensive peneplains may have been largely destroyed. The policy in this matter is to treat the evolution of topography in terms of a few major erosion cycles, demonstrated beyond doubt, even though known to be composite. In casting the present account into large molds, in which only a few cycles are recognizable, the complications are deferred rather than denied. Intensive local studies will continue to reveal episodes which will find their settings in the relatively simple framework used here. For the present it seems better to err on the side of simplicity rather than complexity. Incompleteness in this matter is regarded as better than error.

In all sciences involving areal discussion, divisions, often called provinces, are outlined to suit the needs of the discussion. There are faunal provinces, and climatic and petrographic and various other kinds, in addition to physiographic provinces. The boundaries differ for each science, and, even in the single science of physiography, two men, or the same man at different times, may wish to emphasize different elements of the picture and, accordingly, to divide the total area in a different manner. The only reason for using one set of divisions rather than another, or for adhering to one scheme for general use, is that it most often fits the needs of the discussion. This is about equivalent to saying that the best scheme of division into provinces is the one which makes possible the largest number of general statements about each. To illustrate, it is impossible to make any true or valuable statement about the topography of Pennsylvania, except that it is varied. Yet a group of true and significant statements may be made about the Allegheny Plateau. though it is larger than Pennsylvania. The system used by the United States Geological Survey is understood to be tentative and subject to refinement. Most of it is doubtless permanent. It is followed in this book, with minor changes, each of which is mentioned and explained.

Various places might be pointed out in which the contrast between adjacent provinces is less marked than the contrast between minor divisions. There are several states in which lines, treated here as subordinate, would have been given higher rank, and *vice versa*, if those states were to be treated alone. In each case, however, the substitute plan for that particular state is found to be unworkable when a larger area is considered. The problem would be simpler if each unit area were topographically homogeneous and obviously different from its neighbors. However, it is necessary to come back frequently to the thought that the goal of science is *explanation* rather than mere description, and that the limits of an area under discussion are chosen to fit the logical explanation, not the superficial appearance. It is fortunate that in most cases the application of these two criteria yields similar results. If it were not so, it would be necessary to use one set of divisions for purposes of description and another set for the discussion of origins.

Some of the boundary lines are almost as sharp in nature as on the map. Some of them represent broad generalizations which are highly important in a rational discussion, even though the lines themselves are hard to locate in the field. They may be extremely crooked in nature, or they may represent zones of gradation rather than sharp limits. No one can be so conscious of the limitations of such a map as the men who labor to produce it. No geological reader will be misled by its seemingly definite commitments.

Attention must be called to the fact that the names of the several provinces and sections are proper names. They have in most cases been suggested by the most general feature of the area, but in many cases they cannot be applied as descriptive terms to the entire unit. Thus, the Appalachian Highland is not all high, and the Coastal Plain province is not all coastal plain, and the Driftless section of the Upper Mississippi Valley is not all driftless. In most cases such inconsistencies are inherited and are not of the author's making. In all cases they are in accordance with the ordinary use of language when large areas are being discussed.

No attempt is made to give a complete bibliography. So large a part of the data has come from reports and papers written for other than physiographic purposes that to list them here would be misleading. Some of the footnote citations are given to support statements in the text; others to aid the serious student in following up the subject. The most helpful references in the latter category are to relatively late publications which are themselves well documented. The student of a problem is assumed to know how to follow a clue.

The illustrations, without exception, are designed to clarify the text, not to ornament it. No preference whatever is given to recent photographs over older illustrations already published. Assistance in building an adequate mental picture is the sole criterion. The maps at the end of the volume are designed primarily to enable the reader to find the localities mentioned in the text. Some of them are also topographically expressive. For that purpose some generalizations are better shown on Lobeck's Physiographic Diagram of the United States. The serious reader will profit by keeping that map constantly at hand. To have inserted enough geologic maps to meet all the needs of the earnest reader would have expanded the book unduly. The geologic map of the United States should always be kept within easy reach by the serious student.

NEVIN M. FENNEMAN.

CINCINNATI, OHIO,
January, 1938.

ACKNOWLEDGMENTS

The obligations of the author to his fellow geologists are large. The chapter on each province was read in manuscript by one or more geologists having first-hand knowledge of the area through many years of field work. L. W. Stephenson and C. Wythe Cooke each read the chapter on the Coastal Plain. The Piedmont province was read by M. R. Campbell, the Blue Ridge province by Arthur Keith, and the Ridge and Valley province by George W. Stose. Richard F. Flint read the chapter on New England and the section on Long Island. Howard A. Meyerhoff reviewed New England, the Adirondacks, and the Hudson-Champlain Valley. The part relating to the Taconic section was also read by George W. Bain. L. C. Glenn read the chapter on the Interior Low Plateau. All parts pertaining to the glaciated sections of the Central Lowland were read by Frank Leverett. F. T. Thwaites read the treatment of the Driftless Area and the Superior Upland. The Western Young Drift and the Dissected Till Plains were read by A. C. Trowbridge. The manuscript on the Osage section was committed to Raymond C. Moore, and that on the Ozark Plateau to Josiah Bridge, while H. D. Miser reviewed the chapters on both provinces of the Interior Highland. The long-sustained interest and substantial cooperation of Richard F. Flint, Howard A. Meyerhoff, and F. T. Thwaites call for greater recognition than the brief mention made above.

The time and study devoted by these colleagues to constructive criticism of the chapters sent them were such as to prompt the author to share with them whatever credit the book may merit. Yet the freedom with which it was necessary to treat the many valuable suggestions requires that the author assume full responsibility for all statements for which no authority is cited.

In the matter of illustrations, it would be a pleasure to acknowledge all the friendly assistance of various persons and organizations. In addition to mere permission to publish (acknowledged in the several captions), the author is indebted for generous cooperation to Mrs. E. B. Knopf on Fig. 39; to George H. Ashley on Figs. 55, 66, and 69; to the Maryland Geological Surveys on Fig. 79; to Frank J. Wright on Fig. 98; to Richard F. Flint on Figs. 108 and 123; to F. T. Thwaites on Figs. 129 and 145; to the Wisconsin Geological and Natural History Survey on Figs. 138 and 139; to W. W. Atwood on Fig. 146; to A. C. Trowbridge on Fig. 158; and to R. C. Moore on Fig. 172.

Special mention must be made of Louis H. Desjardins, who drew the general maps for Plates I to VII, and of Mrs. Anneliese S. Caster, who drew, or redrew, nearly all the sketch maps, diagrams, and sections, beside reading all page proof and preparing the index. The assistance of Miss Lillian Smith, secretary of the Department of Geology and Geography in the University of Cincinnati, went far beyond the routine performance of duty and is correspondingly appreciated.

CONTENTS

PAGE

CHAPTER VII

CHAPTER VIII

CHAPTER IX

CHAPTER X

CHAPTER XI

CHAPTER XII

CHAPTER XIII

LIST OF MAPS FOR REFERENCE

xiii

PHYSIOGRAPHY OF
EASTERN UNITED STATES

CHAPTER I

THE COASTAL PLAIN PROVINCE

GENERAL DESCRIPTION AND DISCUSSION

The Continental Shelf

Relation of Sea and Land.—The eastern and southern margin of the United States is a lowland which passes under the sea almost without change of its very gentle slope. The plain continues under shallow water for a distance varying from a few miles to a few hundred miles. Then the slope steepens and descends rapidly to the abyss. In studying the larger problems of the earth and its history this steep slope is taken to mark the edge of the continental mass. The plain under shallow water, generally less than 600 feet deep, is treated as part of the continent. It belongs there just as the Mississippi Valley does, both having been dry land and shallow sea repeatedly. Even now, throughout most of the coast, shallow sea is changing to lowland or the reverse is taking place.

The submerged portion of the gentle slope is the *Continental Shelf* and the emerged portion is the *Coastal Plain*, which might be defined as that portion of the continental shelf which has emerged without substantial deformation. Together, these two provinces constitute the *Atlantic Plain*, one of the major physiographic divisions of the United States.

From Newfoundland to Florida, and around the Gulf of Mexico, the Atlantic Plain does not vary greatly in width, except for the long southward extension in Florida, and another long northward extension up the Mississippi Valley. At the northern end it is all submerged at present, thus making the Banks of Newfoundland, 300 miles wide. South of New York

1

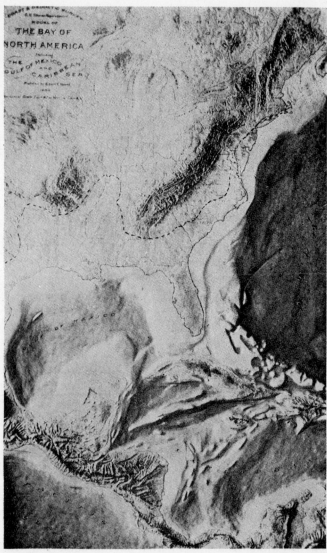

FIG. 1.—Map of the eastern coast of North America showing the Coastal Plain and Continental Shelf.   (*Photograph of model by Edwin F. Howell.*)

the Continental Shelf is only a third as wide, and off the east coast of southern Florida it narrows to 5 miles.

The dry land portion of the Atlantic Plain begins south of New England with narrow islands and increases in width to more than 300 miles in Texas, even aside from the extensions named above. This apportionment of the area between dry land and shallow water is both recent and temporary. The ease and frequency of change from one state to the other is in marked contrast with the enduring limits of the Atlantic Plain as a whole.

Offshore Profile.—The broad seaward slope is only slightly interrupted by details of the shore. One of these details is a slight steepening of slope on the beach front (Fig. 2). It

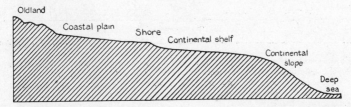

Fig. 2.—Profile of the margin of the continent. Coastal plain and continental shelf are part of a single plain whose slope is only slightly interrupted by a concave zone due to shore processes.

affects the shallow bottom to a depth of 5 or 6 fathoms, beyond which depth the gradient is frequently not over 2 feet per mile. A narrow offshore band, perhaps 1 or 2 miles in width, is therefore concave upward. At depths varying from 20 to 50 fathoms the gradient begins to increase slightly, but generally a marked slope, such as would be noticed on land, is not attained until much farther out, often not until the 100-fathom line is approached. Farther out, the sea floor declines rapidly, but "rapidly" in this connection is quite as apt to be less than 1 foot in 20 as more than that amount. One foot in ten is decidedly steep. Where the land has risen at a time not very remote, as is the case with Southern United States, the steep descent begins at smaller depth.[1]

Seen in cross section, therefore, the sea bottom is concave within a mile or two offshore, then sensibly flat for most of its

[1] JOHNSON, DOUGLAS, "The New England-Acadian Shoreline," pp. 297*ff.*, John Wiley & Son, New York, 1925.

width, beyond which it becomes convex until at great depths it flattens again, making the profile concave.

Function of the Barrier Beach.—This distribution of slopes, small as they are, has important bearings on shore-line development when the land rises or sinks and a new shore line is adopted. The behavior of breakers, undertow, and shore currents requires a steeper gradient near shore than that which prevails farther out at depths of 5 or 6 fathoms.   Hence, if the water level falls several fathoms, the offshore gradient will be too small and a barrier or "sand reef" will be constructed at a suitable distance from shore to restore the proper gradient (Fig. 3).   The same would occur if the land sinks, bringing the sea in over a coastal

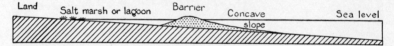

Fig. 3.—Diagram of marginal sea bottom with barrier beach. It is assumed that the original slope is too gentle for the profile of equilibrium required by the waves and undertow. By building a barrier offshore the seaward slope is steepened and becomes concave near shore. (The steepness of all slopes is greatly exaggerated.)

plain like that of Texas and Louisiana where the slope is only 1 or 2 feet per mile.

Most of our Atlantic and Gulf Coast is now sand-reefed for the simple reason that the general slope of the Atlantic Plain is too gentle to afford a profile of equilibrium for shore processes.   The same would be true should the land either rise or fall by a moderate amount.   We re the present barriers removed, the slope would, at many places, be essentially uniform.   As it is, the relatively steep slope in front of the barrier about compensates for the flat lagoon behind.   With long-enduring stability the barriers would shift landward and become normal beaches, but always the slope of the marginal sea bottom would be steeper than farther out.   Should the Coastal Plain be broadened by uplift, the old shore line, perhaps many miles from the sea, would appear in the landscape as a faint escarpment by reason of which the level of the plain might be raised 10 to 20 feet in a single mile. Successive uplifts would cause the plain to be terraced (compare pages 24, 27).

The faint escarpment here described is not a sea cliff.   The latter is made above the water level where the offshore slope is steep enough. In the terracing of our Coastal Plain both kinds of steeper slopes are no doubt represented. They should not be confused, as the restored sea level belongs at the top of the one and at the foot of the other.

Sediments from the Land.—The Continental Shelf is the great dumping ground for terrigenous sediment. Near shore, sand is far the most abundant material. An occasional sea cliff

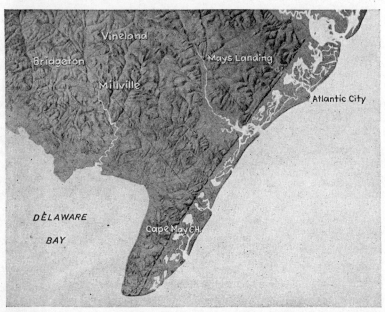

FIG. 4.—Coast of New Jersey, showing the edge of the dry land slightly cliffed by the waves; also the barrier beach on which Atlantic City stands. The intervening area is partly lagoon and partly salt marsh. The relief of the land is badly exaggerated. (*Geol. Survey N. J.*)

or stream flood may supply gravel, but even where present on the beach it does not generally go out far on the bottom. Sand may extend well out on the shelf and, where there has been a complicated history of ups and downs, or where a strong current sweeps the bottom, both sand and gravel may appear even in deep water. Generally, however, mud is the dominant sediment on the outer part of the shelf and in deeper water. Broken shells are widespread both in sand and mud.[1] Where the coast has

[1] The general charts of the coast, prepared by the United States Coast and Geodetic Survey, indicate the material of the bottom.

been deeply embayed by subsidence, as in the northern part of our Coastal Plain, very little sediment gets beyond the estuaries.

Life and Lime on the Continental Shelf.—The Continental Shelf affords one of three great realms of marine life, the other two being the surface zone and the bottom of the deep sea. The surface zone, whether of deep water or shallow, is preeminently the home of fishes and other swimming forms. It swarms also with minute vegetable forms which constitute the basic food supply of all marine animals except for such food as is washed outward from the land. The bottoms of the deep-sea basins, totally dark, are inhabited by various types, for the most part curious and often bizarre, but not to be compared in abundance with the fauna near the surface. Between these two realms the great cold dark mass of the ocean is desert.

Life on the Continental Shelf is vastly more important geologically than that of the other realms. It consists largely of "shell fish," corals, and other invertebrates, resting on, or attached to, the bottom. Most of them use lime in their shells or other hard parts which, after death, are contributed to the marine sediments. Such remains may merely mingle with sand and mud, making them calcareous, or they may predominate and thus form the limy mud which after consolidation becomes limestone. The reasons for this excess of marine life on the Continental Shelf are to be found partly in the greater warmth and light of the shallow waters, and partly in the food supply brought down by streams.

Structure and Origin of the Continental Shelf.—The abovementioned sediments lie in layers, some of which may be several hundred feet thick and constantly thickening. Beneath the beds now forming are others to a depth of thousands of feet as inferred from drillings near shore. As might well be expected from the fact that the drainage area fronting the Atlantic is much smaller than that which fronts the Gulf of Mexico, the depths of sediments along these two shores differ greatly. From southern New Jersey to Florida, known depths of sediment at or near the water's edge range from 1600 to 2500 feet.[1] Along the Gulf Coast the maximum thickness is at least 15,000 feet and

[1] Shaw, E. W., Ages of Peneplains of the Appalachian Province, *Bull. Geol. Soc. Amer.*, vol. 29, p. 583, 1918.

may be much more.[1]   As most of these sediments were laid down under relatively shallow water, it is plain that the margin of the sea has been sinking in the meantime.

It might be inferred from the form of this great mass of sediments that the Continental Shelf is primarily a shore terrace due to deposition by the undertow which drags out detritus to a depth not reached by wave motion.   Where the sediments have their greatest thickness, the whole shelf may have been built in this way.   Where the sediment is relatively thin, it is still impor-

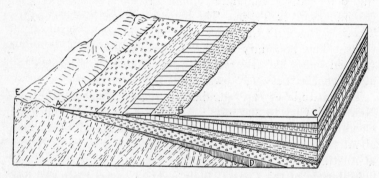

Fig. 5.—Diagrammatic cross section to illustrate the structure of the Coastal Plain.   *E A*, old land; *A B*, Coastal Plain; *B C*, ocean; and *A D*, original surface on which the first coastal plain sediments were laid down.   The heavy line below *B C* represents the surface of the Continental Shelf.   Bedding planes are represented by straight lines diverging seaward.   Angles of dip are seen to increase from the youngest formation to the oldest.   Dips are necessarily so exaggerated as to vitiate the diagram for other purposes.

tant in smoothing the surface of the shelf and in establishing the correlation sometimes observed between the depth of its edge and that of wave action.   Hence it may be that the sediment is a mere trimming of the Continental Shelf rather than its constituent mass.   Ignoring sediments entirely, continental shelves would probably still be widespread.   Two thirds of the earth's crust has sunk (approached the center) more than the other third, and the ocean basins thus produced are somewhat more than full, so that the water spreads over the edges of the higher segments where the rise is not too abrupt.   Constant

[1] STEPHENSON, L. W., Major Marine Transgressions and Regressions and Structural Features of the Gulf Coastal Plain, *Amer. Jour. Sci.*, 5th ser. vol. 16, p. 294, 1928.

loading of these inundated edges causes them to sink but the extent to which the major features are changed is poorly known.[1]

THE COASTAL PLAIN IN GENERAL

Inner Boundary.—The landward limit of the Coastal Plain depends on the definition of the term. It is not merely a plain along the coast. For reasons more fully explained under Structure its extent is limited to formations of Cretaceous and younger age. However, the requirement that these be without substantial deformation eliminates much of the Lower Cretaceous (Comanchean) in Texas. The boundary from New England to Texas is therefore the inner edge of Cretaceous (or younger) rocks. The boundary south of the Brazos River in Texas (treated somewhat arbitrarily for convenience) is approximately at the contact between Lower and Upper Cretaceous.

The altitude of the boundary increases from sea level near New York City to 300 feet in Maryland and nearly 800 feet in Georgia, declining again to 360 feet near the mouth of the Ohio, about the same at Little Rock, and rising once more to 700 feet at Austin and 1000 feet on the Rio Grande.

Materials of the Coastal Plain.—The Coastal Plain still bears a strong resemblance to the Continental Shelf. It consists of the same materials stratified in the same way, and had, on emergence, the same featureless surface. Necessarily, sediments now exposed and subject to erosion are older than those on the sea bottom which are still accumulating. Some of the formations beneath the Coastal Plain, perhaps the larger part, are partly consolidated. A few are firmly consolidated into sandstone or limestone, but many of them are in their original condition, sand, gravel, clay, or marl, not sandstone, conglomerate, shale, or limestone.

Structure of the Coastal Plain.—Like the offshore slope of the Continental Shelf, the slope of the newly emerged surface near

---

[1] A preliminary study by seismic methods, in 1935, indicates that the surface of hard rock beneath the coastal plain sediments of Virginia slopes outward almost uniformly to the deep sea, and that the "shelf" of younger sediments is merely superimposed on this slope. See M. Ewing, A. P. Crary, and H. M. Rutherford, Geophysical Investigations in the Emerged and Submerged Atlantic Coastal Plain, part 1, Methods and Results, *Proc. Geol. Soc. Amer.* p. 75, 1935; also B. L. Miller, part 2, Geological Significance of the Geophysical Data, p. 93.

shore is generally very small, 2 to 4 feet per mile being common. This represents the dip of the newest and topmost beds. Wherever the surface is parallel to the topmost bed, there are, of course, no other outcrops. Commonly, however, the uppermost formation occupies only a narrow belt near the sea. Farther inland older beds outcrop, dipping seaward beneath the youngest. These are succeeded by older and still older beds, the several formations outcropping in parallel belts, the oldest being farthest inland (Fig. 5).

The order here described can occur only where the dip of the lower formations is steeper than the slope of the surface. Both surface observation and drilling show that this is the case. In general, the older and lower the stratum the steeper the dip. Throughout most of the Atlantic and Gulf Coastal Plain the dip of the lowest bed does not vary greatly from 30 feet per mile. Locally it is a little less or much more.[1]

The steeper dips of the older beds give the obvious suggestion that the margin of the continent has progressively or intermittently tilted seaward as its outer edge under the sea was buried under a load of sediment, while the dry land portion was being lightened by erosion.[2] This is in accordance with the principles of isostasy[3] now generally received. The coast during any one tilting should be a kind of hinge line between the downturned sea bottom and the upturned land. In a very general way the coast (hence also the hinge line) has shifted seaward in successive geologic epochs. Continued uptilting of the landward edge of the Coastal Plain has been considerably in excess of erosion.

Growth of the Coastal Plain.—The Coastal Plain is often spoken of as the newer margin of the continent, a relatively recent addition to a growing mass. In a sense this is true, but it is also true that the growth of the continent has been intermittent. There were many ups and downs, alternations of land and sea, during the accumulation of the coastal plain sediments. Moreover, before the oldest of the present formations was laid down, there were times at which the continent not only extended

[1] SHAW, *op. cit.*, p. 582.

[2] STEPHENSON, L. W., Major Features in the Geology of the Atlantic and Gulf Coastal Plains, *Jour. Wash. Acad. Sci.*, vol. 16, p. 471, 1926.

[3] A criticism of the current theory is given by R. T. Chamberlin, *Jour. Geol.*, vol. 39, pp. 1–23, 1931.

seaward, probably to the edge of the Continental Shelf, but was higher, perhaps even mountainous. Just previous to the deposition of the Cretaceous beds, the entire Atlantic Plain was probably a seaward-sloping peneplain on older rocks not unlike those of the adjacent provinces toward the interior.[1] Although this was a plain bordering the coast it was not a coastal plain in the accepted sense of that term, as already defined. When this peneplain was submerged, covered by sediments, and uplifted for the first time, the Coastal Plain came into being.

Fig. 6.—View in the lower and flatter part of the Coastal Plain, eastern shore of Maryland. The foreground is on the Wicomico terrace. The dark trees and the buildings are on the Talbot terrace. (*Md. Geol. Survey.*)

Distribution of Erosion.—As explained above under Structure, the present seaward slope of the Coastal Plain is not that of the former sea bottom unless it be in a narrow belt near the coast. Inland toward the older land the gradient generally steepens, the rise having more than kept pace with erosion. This increase of altitude, though moderate, has important topographic effects because the general slope of the land is steeper than the gradient required by streams. Generally this is not true on the flatter parts along the coast. Wherever the surface lies above stream grade it is dissected, or in process of dissection, into hills.

[1] STEPHENSON, Major Marine Transgressions, etc., *op. cit.*, p. 281. Many of the facts here cited belong to historical geology and the evidence for them cannot be discussed here. Much of the data comes from drilling.

In general the surface near the coast is in the infancy of its erosion cycle, if indeed erosion can be said to have begun at all. With increasing distance inland, tributary streams increase in number and in size. Youth and maturity follow in the order of distance from the sea. At places where weak rocks underlie the landward margin, an entire erosion cycle has been gone through and a peneplain produced (page 71). Not only does advancement in the cycle increase with distance from the coast, but relief increases also, so that the inner margin of the Coastal Plain may be a country of hills 200 or even 300 feet high, though generally not steep because the rocks are weak. Two principles

Fig. 7.—Rolling surface near edge of the Sunderland formation, Calvert County, Maryland, illustrating mature dissection of parts of the Coastal Plain. The material is soft, the slopes gentle, and the forms well rounded. (*Md. Geol. Survey.*)

are involved in this contrast between inner and outer margins of the province: (1) Altitude is necessary to valley cutting, since streams cannot cut below their base level; (2) time is equally necessary, and the inner edge has been out of water longer.

Belted Coastal Plains.—If all the rocks of the Coastal Plain offered equal resistance to erosion there would be a nearly uniform rise from the infant plains along the coast to the mature, or even old, erosion surface on the inner margin. On the other hand, where a series of dipping rocks contains strata of unequal strength, erosion produces low belts on the outcrops of weaker rocks, with intervening ridges, or rather, slightly higher belts, on the outcrops of the stronger rocks (Fig. 22, page 69). Ridges of this character on the Coastal Plain are usually broad, low, and inconspicuous, representing, as they do, the outcrops of nearly horizontal formations which are strong only by comparison with others that are weaker. The highest ridges rise several hundred feet above the lowlands. The more conspicuous side is the so-called scarp, *i.e.*, the inward-facing slope which cuts across the outcropping beds. Even this, when viewed as a whole, is very gentle. The high belt owes its rougher character not to its height directly, but to the fact that its greater altitude makes local valleys possible. The belt therefore becomes a hill country which may contrast strongly with the smooth lowland at its inner foot. Especially is this true when the difference in rocks results in a difference of soils, and therefore of cultural features. Concrete examples are included in the local descriptions of the Gulf Coastal Plain. Toward the sea the altitude of the hilly belt declines gently with the dip of the harder stratum until it passes under others.

For high and low belts thus described, the terms *cuesta* and *inner lowland*[1] are generally used in the United States. The terms *wold* and *vale*[2] were borrowed, with a little change of sense, from England but have not come into general use. Coastal plains marked by such contrasts are said to be *belted*. The most prominent belting in this province is in Alabama and Texas.

Coastal plains are most typical where the records of sedimentation and emergence are least complicated with those of submergence. If the latter is complete no complication need ensue. But usually it is only partial, disturbing the orderly progress of the erosion cycle, and with it, the normal gradation from low featureless plain near shore to greater altitudes and higher relief inland. Pronounced uplift followed by depression, as in the northern part of this province, may indent the coast with far-reaching bays, or may dismember the plain into islands, sometimes leaving high hills near the coast as in the Navesink Highland of New Jersey.

Drainage.—Most that can be said here about the character of the drainage might be inferred from the origin of the Coastal Plain. Where the rise of the entire plain above the sea has taken place as a single act, no matter how slowly, *i.e.*, without

[1] Terms introduced by W. M. Davis. The first is a Spanish (Mexican) term pronounced *questa*.

[2] Proposed by A. C. Veatch, U. S. Geol. Survey, *Prof. Paper* 44, 1906.

serious interruption by sinking and without serious modification by tilting in other directions, the streams from the old land merely elongate themselves in a direction transverse to the new belt of dry land. Such "extended consequents" become the master streams of the Coastal Plain. Excellent examples are seen in Texas and in the Carolinas. Between them will be other consequent streams, heading on the new-made land and flowing to the sea in courses parallel to the master stream. Dendritic tributaries branching from both of these types will dissect the intervening plain. The length and number of such tributaries will increase from the shore inland.

On a belted coastal plain, strike streams like the Tombigbee in Mississippi tend to develop on weak strata. A vigorous development of such streams would bring about captures of the transverse streams, and a trellised drainage pattern would result. (*Cf.* Fig. 56, page 202.) Such a condition on our coastal plain is largely hypothetical, there being no distinctly trellised drainage in this province. Parts of certain streams, Delaware, Potomac, and others, do indeed follow weak belts in a striking manner, but not necessarily for the reasons here suggested (see page 35).

EMBAYED SECTION OF THE COASTAL PLAIN

General Character.—From Cape Lookout (lat. $34\frac{1}{2}°$) northward the Atlantic Coastal Plain is so deeply indented by branching bays or estuaries that it is little more than a fringe of peninsulas, narrowing to zero at New York and represented beyond that by islands. Coincident with this narrowing and disappearance of the Coastal Plain is a broadening of the Continental Shelf, which farther north includes the Banks of Newfoundland.

A casual view of the map leads to the inference, confirmed by geological investigation, that the edge of the continent has here been depressed and that the amount of depression increases toward the north. The rivers of this section as far south as the James and Appomattox in Virginia are drowned to the Fall Line.[1] Farther south this is not true; farther north the sea covers not only the whole width of the coastal plain formations but apparently broad areas of older rocks.

[1] The term Fall Line, as used here, means the inner edge of the Coastal Plain province. The line is discussed in Chap. 2.

The Gulf of Maine.—It is plain that the Cretaceous substratum of Long Island is the crest of a cuesta whose inner lowland is submerged in Long Island Sound.   East of this are other islands,

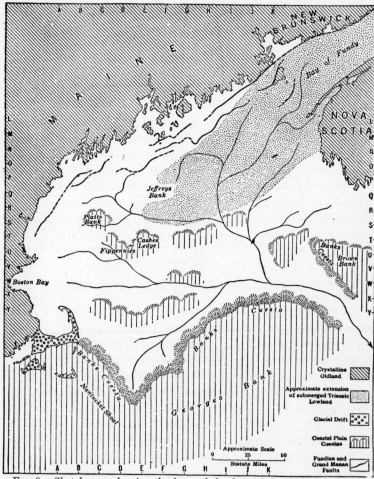

FIG. 8.—Sketch map showing the form of the floor of the Gulf of Maine and hypothetical preglacial drainage. (*Douglas Johnson, "The New England-Acadian Shoreline."*)

and farther east are widespread shoals, the largest being Georges Bank, 10 to 40 fathoms under water and reaching to the longitude of Nova Scotia (Fig. 8). It is believed that these shoals represent submerged cuestas developed on a coastal plain.[1] The name Gulf of Maine is applied to the deeper waters between the banks and the shore. The basin of the Gulf of Maine, with depths from 100 to 200 fathoms, represents not only the inner lowland analogous to Long Island Sound, but probably also a wide area of soft rocks analogous to the Triassic lowlands from New Jersey to Virginia (page 145). It is believed that the former stream valleys in this inner lowland can still be traced by soundings, some of them nearly 1200 feet below the water surface. Necessarily, this drainage reached the sea through a gap in the cuesta. The lowest gap, which is near Nova Scotia, is less than 900 feet below the surface. If not due to unequal sinking, it may well have been filled in part by shore processes while sinking, or perhaps in part by glacial material[2] or slumping of the relatively steep slopes. Newfoundland has now no coastal plain, yet fragments of rock have been dredged from the Banks which are of the same age and character as the coastal plain sediments of New Jersey.[3] Stetson has dredged fragments of bedrock similar to the rocks of New Jersey, broken from the outer slope of Georges Bank 1000 to 2000 feet below the surface of the water.[4]

LONG ISLAND

The northern end of the Coastal Plain is the least typical part of the province. Long Island, Martha's Vineyard, and other islands, as well as Cape Cod, consist largely of glacial deposits resting on submerged banks. Some of these islands would be represented by smaller land masses of Cretaceous or Tertiary sediments, rising above water if all glacial deposits were removed. Presumably these higher remnants of an old coastal plain, in large part drowned, had something to do with the movements of the ice and therefore with the accumulation of the drift that constitutes the bulk of the islands.

[1] JOHNSON, DOUGLAS, "The New England-Acadian Shoreline," pp. 265–312, 1925, John Wiley & Sons, Inc., New York.

[2] SHEPARD, F. P., and others, Origin of Georges Bank, *Bull. Geol. Soc. Amer.*, vol. 45, pp. 281–302, 1934.

[3] JOHNSON, *op. cit.*, p. 301.

[4] STETSON, H. C., Geology and Paleontology of the Georges Bank Canyons, *Bull. Geol. Soc. Amer.*, vol. 47, pp. 339–366, 1936.

Cretaceous Core.—Long Island with its glacial deposits removed would have from a fourth to a third of its present area and a possible sixth of its present volume above sea level. This would consist of a low ridge 10 to 12 miles wide, extending on the north to the limit of the present island but falling short of those limits on the east, west, and south.[1] The maximum height of this mass is more than 250 feet and its slopes to the north and south are about equally steep. It is an extension of a similar ridge in New Jersey on Cretaceous rocks known there as the Monmouth group (or Marl series) just as the lowland submerged in Long Island Sound is the extension of the New Jersey lowland on the Raritan and Matawan formations,[2] stretching from near New York southwestward past Trenton. To state the matter more strongly, a single cuesta and a single inner lowland stretch from the Connecticut shore to the Delaware, the former being interrupted by transverse valleys and buried at the north by glacial drift, the latter being partly submerged.

Plain of Glacial Deposits.—Superimposed on the partly submerged belted coastal plain east of the Hudson are glacial and interglacial deposits of various stages, mainly the last. The master feature of the topography of Long Island is a plain which slopes southward from an altitude of 200 feet or less at the north shore and occupies the entire width of the island. It was constructed in the main of glacial outwash. Some boulder clay is found with the outwashed material, but the two are so interbedded that their discrimination is not attempted on available geologic maps except in limited areas. The outwash is much in excess, especially toward the south.

Terminal Moraines.—Two belts of terminal moraine, traversing the island almost from end to end, rise above the plain here described. The northern of these two, called the Harbor Hill moraine, runs along or near the north shore throughout its length; the Ronkonkoma moraine runs through the middle of the island. The two belts, united at the west, become distinct about 20 miles east of New York and gradually separate eastward, until at the extreme east end they are 12 to 14 miles apart, each

---

[1] VEATCH, A. C., and others, Underground Water Resources of Long Island, New York, U. S. Geol. Survey, *Prof. Paper* 44, Pl. 3, 1906.

[2] *Idem*, Pl. 2. The identity of these formations in Long Island is inferred from analogy. It is not established by fossils.

moraine forming the crest of one of the long peninsulas or "flukes."[1] Southward from each moraine, spreads an outwash plain of the same age.

In the eastern half of the island (east of long. 73°) the plain rarely rises above 100 feet, and it is much lower toward the eastern extremities. West of the middle, considerable areas are above 200 feet, but the level falls off toward the west end. The maximum heights of the moraines are also west of the middle, 391 feet in the Harbor Hill and 410 feet in the Ronkonkoma belt. East of the middle the northern moraine borders the shore and is being undercut by the waves. West of the middle it leaves the shore. At places its steep north slope is separated from the Sound by a 6-mile strip of plain, approximately 200 feet high and at places terraced.

Outwash Plains.—Most of the outwash plain from the Harbor Hill moraine and a part of that lying south of the Ronkonkoma moraine present the normal features of such plains. Considerable areas are flat, having a gentle southward slope. Kettles are common. In both cases the latest sheet of outwashed sand and gravel thins toward the south and may fail at places to cover the higher swells or divides on older deposits. Concerning the origin of much of the southern plain there has been some difference of opinion. In the two most comprehensive studies of Long Island made by the U. S. Geological Survey[2] the plain on the south is treated as subaerial outwash, though certain exceptional features are pointed out. Others have maintained its subaqueous origin[3] while conceding the absence of certain expectable features.

The character of the valleys crossing this southern plain has been remarked by all observers. They are shallow, indefinite depressions variously designated as "dry rivers," "creases," or

---

[1] Long Island presents roughly the outline of a whale, Brooklyn being at the head and the two peninsulas at the east end forming the flukes.

[2] VEATCH, A. C., and others, U. S. Geol. Survey, *Prof. Paper* 44, 1906. FULLER, MYRON L., U. S. Geol. Survey, *Prof. Paper* 82, 1914. In any careful study of Long Island the maps contained in these two professional papers should be at hand for reference.

[3] FAIRCHILD, H. L., Postglacial Marine Submergence of Long Island, Geol. Survey Amer., *Bull.*, vol. 28, pp. 279–308, 1917. This paper recognized both types, conceding also that the subject is controversial. Its history is to some extent discussed. Note Pl. 10.

"furrows," which seem not to owe their forms to the work of ordinary streams.[1] The variety of explanations offered indicates that their appearance is peculiar.

The lower crests of the morainic ridges in the eastern half of the island are described as strikingly softened in contour and are believed by Fairchild to have been formed below sea level.[2] That the land should have risen on the northeast with the withdrawal of the ice is quite in harmony with well-known facts concerning the region of the Great Lakes and St. Lawrence.

Shores of Long Island.—The shores of Long Island show the effects of recent sinking. There is some evidence that this is still going on, but this is not a necessary inference. It is not even necessary to assume that the last movement was downward. Partial recovery from a greater submergence is compatible with the present shore features if sedimentation in the meantime has been limited.

The northern shore in its western half is deeply notched by steep-sided bays which are related to valleys carved in the scarp slope of the old Cretaceous cuesta when the land stood higher. This surface is cut into peninsulas and islands, all cliffed on their exposed sides, while bars have come to span minor indentations, and to tie islands to one another or to the headlands. The amount of shore erosion and beach construction increases from west to east as the narrow and protected sound widens from 1 or 2 miles to more than 50, and the sweep of the wind is correspondingly increased. The eastern half of the north shore is retreating before the waves and is almost straight, as it was even before the Harbor Hill moraine was built. The last ice sheet did not greatly alter either the smooth shore in the east or the valleys in the west.

The south shore is determined by the intersection of an exceedingly gentle slope with the surface of the sea. Accordingly, a fine barrier beach parallels the shore for three fourths of its length. In the easternmost fourth, which is most exposed, the beach, which may, or may not, have been offshore at the start,

[1] SHALER, N. S., Report on the Geology of Martha's Vineyard, U. S. Geol. Survey, *7th Ann. Rept.*, p. 317, 1888. While this description was not written for Long Island, writers agree that the problem on Martha's Vineyard is the same.

[2] FAIRCHILD, *op. cit.*, p. 296. The same opinion was held by Shaler and many of the older writers.

has been pushed landward and lies at the foot of actively cutting cliffs. The best known barriers at the west are Coney Island and Rockaway Beach. The space between the barriers and the south shore increases in breadth toward the west, becoming 6 miles in Jamaica Bay. Salt marsh and open, shallow water share the space about equally.

Back of the lagoon and marsh are small drowned valleys, indicating sinking of the main island. The smallness of these on the south shore as compared with those on the north may be partly explained by the fact that the south shore is too low to admit of much valley cutting.

Summary History of Long Island.—The making of the present topography of the island begins with a relatively late uplift, probably after the Miocene,[1] which made possible the degrading of the Sound lowland. This lowland was necessarily cut out largely by streams from the north and their subsequent tributaries which followed the softer rocks. The actual courses of these streams have not been definitely determined.[2]

The Sound lowland and the Cretaceous cuesta had almost their present forms (now covered by water and glacial drift) before the advent of the Glacial Epoch. In the older studies of Long Island geology,[3] the sloping plain described above as the dominant feature of the island was ascribed mainly to the work of pre-Wisconsin ice sheets. On this plain, after mature erosion, the moraines were said to have been built in the Wisconsin stage, while the last contribution of outwash partly restored the flatness of the plain. Later studies[4] indicate that all glacial and inter-

---

[1] VEATCH, A. C., *op. cit.*, pp. 28 and 50.

[2] The matter is discussed by A. C. Veatch, *op. cit.*, pp. 31–32, 51 and Pl. 6, and by Fuller, *op. cit.*, p. 58.

[3] VEATCH, A. C., *loc. cit.*, and Fuller, *loc. cit.* See also WOODWORTH, J. B., and EDWARD WIGGLESWORTH, Geography and Geology of the Region Including Cape Cod, the Elizabeth Islands, Etc., *Mem. Harvard Museum Comp. Zool.*, vol. 54, 1934.

[4] CROSBY, W. O., Outline of the Geology of Long Island, N. Y., *Ann. N. Y. Acad. Sci.*, vol. 18, pp. 425–429, 1928. WELLS, F. G., Reconsideration of the Pleistocene Geology of Long Island, *Proc. Geol. Soc. Amer.*, p. 121 abs., 1934. FLEMING, W. L. S., Glacial Geology of Central Long Island, *Amer. Jour. Sci.*, vol. 30, pp. 216–238, 1935. Thesis supervised by Prof. R. F. Flint and accepted by the Department of Geology, Yale University. FLINT, RICHARD FOSTER, How Many Glacial Stages Are Recorded in New England?, *Jour. Geol.*, vol. 43, pp. 771–777, 1935.

glacial deposits older than Wisconsin are of small volume and that the Wisconsin ice sheet found the island not differing greatly in form and size from the preglacial cuesta.   The major part of the volume of the island is thus ascribed to late glacial till and outwash, mainly the latter.   Even in the morainic ridges the proportion of till is small.   They owe their relative height partly to the fact that outwash is thickest along the ice front. In addition, the morainic belts are made higher and given local relief by hummocks, ridges, and local plateaus which represent deposits in the crevasses and interspaces of a ragged edge of stagnant ice.

The full picture of events, as described by Fleming, is some-what more complex and may best be deciphered by a study of

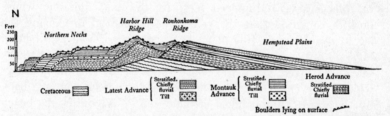

Fig. 9.—North-south section through Long Island, showing diagrammatically the relations of the Pleistocene deposits as inferred by W. L. S. Fleming.   The diagram is to be interpreted as an expression of generalizations, not as a record of measurements.   Total length about 20 miles, height 250 feet.

Fig. 9.   The ice front advanced three times.   The morainic belts owe most of their height to the first advance but their features of varied relief to the second.   In the third advance, hills were rounded and boulders strewn widely over the surface. The time intervals between the three advances were short. Erosion and weathering were negligible and masses of dead ice continued to occupy the obsequent valleys on the northern slope. Between these masses, outwash built that part of the plain that lies north of the Harbor Hill moraine, most of it comprised in the "necks" or peninsulas.

That the numerous indentations of the shore on all sides originated in the drowning of valleys is obvious.   It does not necessarily follow that this drowning was due to the last crustal movement, though recent sinking of at least 25 feet is inferred from the occurrence of fresh-water peat below sea level and containing buried stumps and trunks.[1] If the last great crustal movement was the postglacial rise affirmed by Fairchild, then the sinking that preceded must have been still greater since a recovery of several hundred feet still left the valleys drowned. The submergence must also have been of short duration since it left no distinct record by way of shore lines or sediments.

Martha's Vineyard.—Underlying Martha's Vineyard and its neighbor Naushon Island to the northwest are low ridges of Tertiary rock, for the most part well masked by glacial deposits. These ridges are parallel to the coast and have all the appearance of cuestas on a belted coastal plain.   They are 5 to 8 miles apart, being separated by the submerged lowland of Vineyard Sound. The outer of the two ridges underlies the northwestern side of the triangular island of Martha's Vineyard.   It is deeply buried (at places several hundred feet) by terminal moraine, whose position suggests that the ridge was influential in causing the ice to terminate at this place.[2]   South and east of this belt of hills are outwash plains or true marine plains,[3] stretching to the sea and fringed along the southern coast by drowned valleys whose intervening fingerlike peninsulas have been trimmed back by the waves to an almost straight line.[4]   A continuous beach along this line separates the bays from the ocean, converting the former into "ponds."

Geologically, Martha's Vineyard is interesting because of its brightly colored Miocene clays exposed at Gay Head.   The chief interest is not in the colors but in the sharp anticlinal folding, which is quite exceptional in coastal plain deposits.   Frequent dips of 25° and occasional dips of 45° are known.   Probably the drag of the glacier, or its push against a steep valley side, deformed the beds in this manner.[5]

[1] FULLER, M. L., *op. cit.*, pp. 184 and 215.

[2] For a description of these features see N. S. Shaler, Report on the Geology of Martha's Vineyard, U. S. Geol. Survey, *7th Ann. Rept.*, pp. 303–360, 1886.   See especially the maps, Pls. 20 and 21.

[3] SHALER, *op. cit.*, p. 316.   Shaler's description of this plain is believed to apply equally well to most of the plain on Long Island south of the Ronkonkoma moraine.   He states that the same type of plain is shown even better on Nantucket.

[4] The Martha's Vineyard topographic sheet of the U. S. Geological Survey should be examined.

[5] Shaler (*op. cit.*, p. 344) gave consideration to this and other surficial

General Features South of New York

West and south of the Hudson River the embayed section of
the Coastal Plain gradually broadens to 175 miles in North
Carolina. Deep embayment by drowned river valleys is its
most obvious characteristic throughout. Glaciation is absent
except on Staten Island and a few square miles of the adjacent
mainland. A striking feature from the Hudson to the Potomac is
a lowland, 5 to 20 miles wide, at the landward edge of the province.
At places the lowland abuts against the noticeably steep slope of
the adjacent Piedmont province, a feature which has attracted
much attention and has been variously interpreted (page 35).

Lowland on the Raritan Clay.—The surface features of this
section are closely related to the character and age of the geological formations. At the base, outcropping farthest inland,
are the Raritan clay (Cretaceous) in New Jersey and the sandy
clays of the Potomac group in Maryland. It is the wasting of
these easily eroded beds that has caused the lowland. The
outcrop of the Raritan clay, partly submerged beneath Long
Island Sound and buried by glacial drift on Staten Island, is a
smooth strip of lowland from New York Bay to Trenton, beyond
which it is followed by the Delaware River to below Wilmington
where the river course, now drowned, turns seaward. The lowland is less perfect around the head of Chesapeake Bay but it
continues, partly on the Raritan, partly on Potomac, covered in
part by the waters of the Chesapeake. The continuous lowland
on these weak beds embraces the cities of Wilmington, Baltimore,
and Washington. Northeast of Baltimore it is occupied by the
head of Chesapeake Bay, which is the drowned valley of the Susquehanna. Southwest of Washington for 30 miles it embraces
only the immediate valley of the Potomac estuary. Where that
turns east, the lowland ends, its development farther south being
precluded by an effective cover of Miocene which there extends
to the Piedmont.

Central Cuesta.—The weak clays and sands outcropping in
the axis of the lowland and dipping seaward are overlain by others
of Cretaceous and Tertiary ages, less easily eroded. In the main
these are marl formations, commonly three in number, alternat-

---

forces but concluded that the deformation was truly orogenic. Veatch
(*loc. cit.*) accepts the glacial explanation.

ing with sands.[1] At many places the marls are indurated into firm limestone, while both marls and sands have suffered local cementation by iron oxide. As the general result of such strengthening there is a fairly continuous cuesta rising at many places 200 feet above the lowland and bearing the highest hills in the section. These higher lands are located on the outcrop of the Upper Cretaceous formations, generally of the marls. Among these high points in New Jersey are Beacon Hill (373 ft.), Pine Hill (372 ft.), Mount Laurel (173 ft.), and Woodbury Heights.[2] Apparently the Mannetto Hills of Long Island, though of glacial material, rest on a similar Cretaceous ridge. Taken together these high points mark the crest of an uneven cuesta, the most outstanding topographic feature of southern Jersey, though its crest line bears no close relation to the main divide. These two main features, the lowland and the cuesta, are designated by Veatch as the Hightstown Vale and the Perrineville Wold. The latter is prominent only in New Jersey. The lowland, partially drowned, extends to the Potomac, but the higher land of the "Eastern Shore" in Maryland and Delaware is not a cuesta but a partially dissected plain at a maximum altitude of about 80 feet.

Topography on the Miocene.—East of the above-described cuesta on Cretaceous marls, there is at places an indefinite escarpment rising to a broken ridge on Miocene beds.[3] In New Jersey this is a kind of secondary cuesta on the seaward slope of the main one. In the absence of the main cuesta in Maryland and Delaware the Miocene underlies a low plain. Whether because the system thickens, or because it has been less elevated and thus preserved from erosion, it overlaps and protects the Cretaceous more and more until, south of the Potomac, it reaches the Piedmont and affords no chance for the Raritan lowland to develop.

---

[1] WELLER, STUART, The Classification of the Upper Cretaceous Formations and Faunas of New Jersey, *Jour. Geol.*, vol. 13, p. 76, 1905.

[2] Veatch, A. C., (*op. cit.*, Pl. V) shows structural and topographic cross sections of New Jersey and Long Island.

[3] MANSFIELD, GEO. R., Potash in the Greensands of New Jersey, U. S. Geol. Survey, *Bull.* 727, 1922. Plates 1, 2, and 3 are a geologic and topographic map of a strip about 20 miles wide from Sandy Hook Bay to Delaware Bay, embracing the margin of the Tertiary. Two stratigraphic and topographic cross sections are shown in Pl. V.

Pleistocene Terraces

General Description.—Throughout the Coastal Plain south of the glacial border, the surface is more or less terraced. Seven or more levels may be distinguished. Along much of the Atlantic Coast this terracing extends approximately to the Fall Line. Toward the south, where the inner margin is higher, the terraces fail to reach it. The age of these terraces decreases and their distinctness increases from the highest to the lowest. The lower ones embrace many extensive uneroded plains. At places a low scarp separates one plain from another, and the inference seems warranted that these lower terraces are former sea bottoms and the scarps shore lines. Remnants of such plains and scarps are sufficiently numerous and consistent in elevation that at least the lower terraces may be said with confidence to result from intermittent rise of the land or falling of the sea level. The

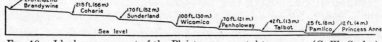

Fig. 10.—Ideal arrangement of the Pleistocene coastal terraces.   (*C. W. Cooke.*)

elevation of each terrace is uniform for long distances and its original boundaries may be drawn.

The boundaries are not straight but to some extent resemble the present shore line though they are not parallel to it. A terrace may surround and slope toward an estuary and merge at its head with a stream terrace of the same age. The slope of a terrace toward a neighboring estuary is quite as steep as its seaward slope, or even steeper.

In the southern states the terraces form broader, straighter and more continuous bands than among the numerous estuaries around Chesapeake Bay (*cf.* Figs. 11 and 13). In the south the upper members of the series, although more eroded, seem to have been originally quite as clear as the lower ones and of the same origin. All are treated together as a single series of marine terraces caused by intermittent (or oscillating) withdrawal of the sea.

Among the numerous estuaries around the head of Chesapeake Bay the terraces above 100 feet are much less clear and their boundaries are often vague. There are short stretches in which the change from one level to the next is by a noticeable slope, but there are also wide expanses of faintly sloping plain within which the passage from one level to the next is not marked by any steepening of the grade. However, it was in Maryland that the terraces were first described and explained as marine,[1] and this has been the prevailing interpretation in the literature of the subject. Chamberlin and Salisbury,[2] however, would regard them as mainly the work of streams, and the upper members of the series are so regarded by Campbell[3] who finds terraces at the higher levels in the Maryland Coastal Plain to be the work of meandering streams, and the local scarps to be bluffs. The descriptions in the following paragraphs, so far as they relate to the higher and less perfect terraces, are necessarily somewhat empirical. No escarpments are continuous. In some localities the names of the several terraces are applied to zones merely on account of their agreement in altitude with clearly marked terraces elsewhere.

Material Underlying the Terraces.—The material underlying these flat, or formerly flat, surfaces consists of poorly stratified, sometimes cross-bedded, sheets of sand, gravel, and clay. Loam predominates at the surface. Coarse material is said to predominate below,[4] while near the large rivers in the northern part of the section, glacial erratics may occur at any level. For the higher levels it would be difficult to make a generalization, except that thick beds of gravel tend to uphold and preserve flat surfaces.

The question of materials is closely connected with the origin of the terraces. In the absence of fossils, however, the deposits on a series of terraces (whether marine or fluvial) may be essentially alike unless the older ones are distinctly weathered. It

[1] SHATTUCK, GEO. B., The Pliocene and Pleistocene Deposits of Maryland, Md. Geol. Survey, 1906; see also CLARK, WM. B., and B. L. MILLER, Physiography and Geology of the Coastal Plain Province of Virginia, Va. Geol. Survey, *Bull.* 4, 1912; STEPHENSON, L. W., The Coastal Plain of North Carolina, *N. C. Geol. Econ. Survey*, vol. 3, 1912.

[2] CHAMBERLIN and SALISBURY, *Geology*, vol. 3, pp. 347–350.

[3] CAMPBELL, M. R., The Alluvial Fan of Potomac River, *Bull. Geol. Soc. Amer.*, vol. 42, pp. 182 and 825–852, 1931. WENTWORTH, CHESTER K., Sand and Gravel Resources of the Coastal Plain of Virginia, Va. Geol. Survey, *Bull.* 32, abs. p. XIII, 1930.

[4] SHATTUCK, *op. cit.*, pp. 87 and 93; C. K. WENTWORTH (Va. Geol. Survey, *Bull.* 32, 1930) describes the material in detail.

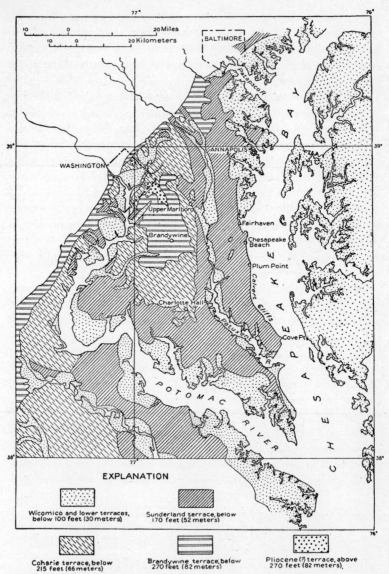

FIG. 11.—Sketch map of Pleistocene terraces in or adjacent to southern Maryland. (*C. W. Cooke, XVI Internat. Geol. Congress, Guidebook.*) Compare the terrace pattern with the drainage pattern.

may even be that the waves and currents of the sea, advancing upon and reworking a gravelly formation, may leave a deposit not very different from what they found. At places they might even leave none at all but merely cut down the surface of the material originally present.

List of Pleistocene Terraces.—The terraces of Maryland were originally described as four in number. Several additional levels have since been distinguished. The full series on the Atlantic Coast now comprises seven, but it does not follow that any single line could be drawn across the province on which all would appear. The following table lists the terraces by name and the present altitude of the inner margin of each, *i.e.*, of the assumed strand line at the time of its making. The geologic ages assigned represent the present working hypothesis of Dr. C. Wythe Cooke.

PLEISTOCENE TERRACES IN SOUTHEASTERN UNITED STATES[1]

Approximate altitude of strand lines		Name of terrace	Tentative age (Cooke)
Feet	Meters		
		....	Nebraskan glacial stage
270	82	Brandywine (Hazlehurst)	Aftonian interglacial stage
?	?	....	Kansan glacial stage
215	66	Coharie (Claxton)	Yarmouth interglacial stage
170	52	Sunderland (Okefenokee)	Yarmouth interglacial stage
?	?	....	Illinoian glacial stage
100	30	Wicomico (Newberry)	Sangamon interglacial stage
70	21	Penholoway (Tsala Apopka)	Sangamon interglacial stage
42	13	Talbot (Chowan, Pensacola in part)	Sangamon interglacial stage
?	?	....	Iowan glacial stage
25	8	Pamlico (Dismal Swamp, Satilla, Pensacola in part)	Peorian interglacial stage
		....	Wisconsin glacial stage

[1] COOKE, C. W., Tentative Ages of Pleistocene Shore Lines, *Jour. Wash. Acad. Sci.*, vol. 25, p. 333, 1935. For fuller discussion of the terraces see C. W. Cooke, Seven Coastal Terraces in the Southeastern States, *Jour. Wash. Acad. Sci.*, vol. 21, pp. 503–513, 1931.

Surface Higher than the Terraces.—Much of the surface adjacent to but above the highest terrace, even on the edge of the Piedmont province, is underlain by a formation of gravel,

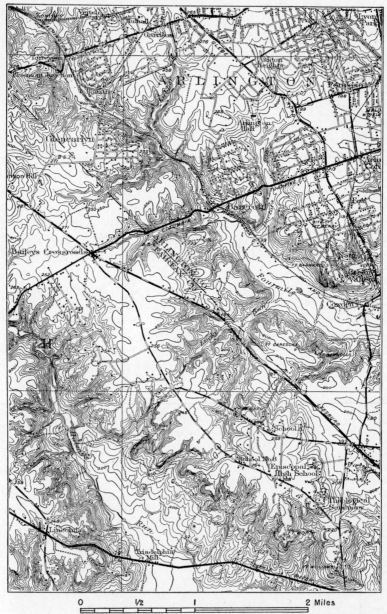

FIG. 12.—Parts of the Brandywine and Coharie terraces 3 to 14 miles south-
west of Washington.   The flat upland, 260 to 270 feet high, is Brandywine.
Flat areas below 215 feet on the eastern margin are Coharie.   The Episcopal
High School in the southeast corner stands at the top of a typical escarpment
separating the two terraces.   The same relations appear in the northeast corner.
Contour interval, 10 feet.   (*U. S. Geol. Survey.*)

sand, and loam, much like that which covers the nearby terrace. All was formerly called Lafayette and treated as Pliocene. That part of the "Lafayette" which is not terraced is higher, more eroded, and more weathered. All of the terraces are now regarded as Pleistocene. Near the Potomac there is no obvious "shore line" or scarp to mark the limit of the highest (Brandywine) terrace, but farther south in the Carolinas the limit is clear. There a considerable portion of the Sand Hill belt intervenes between the highest terrace and the Fall Line.

Brandywine Terrace.—Most of the gravel once called Lafayette lies beneath the terraces. Between streams, at least in the North, the Brandywine terrace on this formation embraces some remarkably smooth, seaward-sloping plains. The preservation of these is favored by the porous character of the material which favors percolation and thus hinders erosion. These flats grade into mild undulations and, near streams, into hills of steeper slope. At places the gentle slope is continuous to the level of the lower terraces. At other places steep slopes and hills intervene. In southern Virginia and North Carolina the Brandywine terrace lies only in part on these Tertiary gravels. Locally it truncates older formations, among which are Eocene rocks which give rise to the Red Hills. Under such conditions the Brandywine terrace is much wasted by erosion, the underlying materials being more readily washed than the "Lafayette" gravels. Most of this terrace in North Carolina comes within the strip familiarly known as the Sand Hill district.

Coharie and Sunderland Terraces.—At an altitude of about 215 feet another level appears, sparingly in the north but prominent in the Carolinas. This is the Coharie terrace. It is succeeded in turn, either gradually or abruptly, by the Sunderland at 170 feet or less. Tributary streams leave no large part of the Sunderland terrace untouched by erosion, but in one sixth (more or less) of the area the valleys are young and do not appear in a wide view over what seems to be a continuously flat landscape. In five sixths of the area, erosion is further advanced. The level of the Sunderland terrace declines seaward, locally, to the 100-foot contour line without a break before it gives way to the Wicomico, whose maximum height is at that level. In Virginia and North Carolina it is cut off by the Surry escarpment, at which the level may drop abruptly 30 feet or more to the

Wicomico, or perhaps to the Penholoway level. This is the most noticeable steep slope in the Virginia and Carolina Coastal Plain. It separates what is popularly called the "uplands" (older terraces) from the "lowlands."[1] The Sunderland and Coharie form a broken belt through Virginia and North Carolina.[2]

FIG. 13.—Map showing distribution of surficial formations in North Carolina (*After L. W. Stephenson, N. C. Geol. Econ. Survey*, vol. 3, Pl. 13, 1912). Doctor Stephenson, in granting permission to use this map, comments as follows: "This map, made in 1909 partly from data furnished by B. L. Johnson, is in need of revision. The units mapped correspond in a general way with the Pleistocene terraces now recognized: *L*, Lafayette, corresponds to the Brandywine and to higher unnamed terraces and may include some Cretaceous gravels; *Co*, Coharie, includes some Brandywine; *S*, Sunderland; *W*, Wicomico, includes also the later defined Penholoway; *Ch*, Chowan, a synonym of Talbot as restricted by Cooke; *P*, Pamlico."

Much of the area is underlain by late Tertiary gravel, not easily distinguished from that which may have been deposited by the waters of the sea that cut the terrace.

[1] WENTWORTH, *op. cit.*, p. 8.

[2] For description of terraces in North Carolina, see B. L. Johnson, Pleistocene Terraces in the North Carolina Coastal Plain, *Science*, vol. 26, pp. 640–642, 1907; L. W. Stephenson, The Coastal Plain of North Carolina, *N. C. Geol. Econ. Survey*, vol. 3, 1912. Note geologic map, Pl. 17, and map of surficial formations (terraces), Pl. 13.

Wicomico and Penholoway Terraces.—Against the Surry escarpment the Wicomico terrace abuts at an altitude of 80 to 100 feet. It is succeeded in turn by the Penholoway whose limiting altitude is 70 feet. North of North Carolina the two have not been distinguished in mapping. These terraces are still less eroded, but their surviving flats, though broader than those at higher levels, are none the less isolated one from another. The Wicomico appears, and the Penholoway is widespread, in the interior of the peninsula east of Chesapeake Bay comprising the "Eastern Shore" of Maryland and including Delaware. The two pass southward through Virginia and North Carolina with little change of altitude or character. In the latter state are some extensive swamps.

Talbot and Pamlico Terraces.—The Wicomico and Penholoway surfaces decline faintly seaward to a scalloped boundary marked at many places by a decided slope, the Suffolk escarpment in Virginia and North Carolina, by which the level is dropped a small amount to the Talbot (Chowan) terrace or, it may be, 20 to 30 feet to the Pamlico where the Talbot is absent.

It has been customary in Maryland to assign to the Talbot terrace all land below the Wicomico. As the result of more recent work this terrace is now divided into two in North Carolina[1] and three in Virginia.[2] The Talbot succeeds the Wicomico at 42 feet A.T., making a prominent belt in North Carolina but mainly confined to valley terraces in Virginia. Below it is the Pamlico (Dismal Swamp) terrace, which is widespread south of the James River and Chesapeake Bay. As the Talbot is absent here, the Pamlico terrace abuts against the Suffolk escarpment whose height west of Dismal Swamp is 30 feet or more. The lowest land along the shore is called by Wentworth the Princess Anne Terrace (included here in the Pamlico). At places a distinct rise, perhaps a former sea cliff, separates the Princess Anne from the next higher level (Fig. 14). This lowest terrace fringes the peninsulas in Chesapeake Bay and shares with the Dismal Swamp (Pamlico) terrace most of the ground between the great estuaries of North Carolina, where the name Pamlico stands for both Dismal Swamp and Princess Anne terraces. While the greatest swamps are on these two, the Talbot, Pen-

[1] STEPHENSON, *loc. cit.*
[2] WENTWORTH, *loc. cit.*

holoway, and even the Wicomico, have their shares of swamp, and there is much solid ground in the two lowest members of the series.

Pleistocene Terraces in New Jersey.—The corresponding terraces in New Jersey are similar in kind to those of Maryland though not satisfactorily correlated. The Bridgeton, Pensauken, and Cape May correspond in their order to the Sunderland, Wicomico, and Talbot,[1] but their equivalence in time has been

Fig. 14.—Escarpment separating the latest terrace at the level of the beach on the right from the next higher terrace, called Princess Anne in Virginia and not distinguished in the text from the Pamlico. (*Virginia Geol. Survey.*)

questioned. The two lower terraces (generally less than 100 feet above the sea) cover most of the Coastal Plain in New Jersey, wrapping around the central cuesta and extending up the Delaware Valley. As in Maryland, the lowest terrace is flattest. Aside from this, the flattest surfaces in the state are remnants of the Bridgeton terrace just under 150 feet in height and lying south of Philadelphia.[2]

[1] CHAMBERLAIN and SALISBURY, *Geology*, vol. 3, p. 450, 1906. Shattuck (*op. cit.*, p. 137) says, "Comparison with the work of Salisbury in New Jersey shows lack of harmony throughout."

[2] SALISBURY, R. D., Physical Geography, *Geol. Survey N. J.*, vol. 4, p. 63, 1895.

Topographic breaks separating one so-called terrace from another in New Jersey are local and rare. The Cape May terrace is nowhere bounded by an unequivocal shore line.[1] Among the fairly clear stretches of boundary line between terraces, some are not horizontal, indicating that if they ever were shore lines, they have been affected by crustal movement. A line interpreted as the upper limit of the Pensauken (Wicomico?) rises locally to 150 to 160 feet,[2] though elsewhere it agrees in level with the corresponding line farther south, 90 to 100 feet. Tertiary gravel, whether terraced or not, is topographically unimportant in New Jersey. Above all terraces rise the crests of the cuestas bearing the exceptional high points mentioned above.

Origin of the Coastal Plain Terraces.—The question of marine *versus* fluvial origin of these terraces does not vitally affect their present-day physiography, except as one origin or the other is necessary to explain existing forms. In suggesting that doubt exists with reference to some localities, it may be stated that evidence from fossils is everywhere meager and generally wanting; also that lack of good assortment of materials has been a leading factor in the discussion. The conception of most workers has been that of intermittent uplifts, between some of which (not all) the eroded surface was partly submerged beneath the sea and, to the extent of its submergence, leveled up anew by wave erosion and sedimentation. Assuming a net gain in land area with each oscillation, this would result in a series of terraces with local seaward-facing scarps, all crossed by estuaries if the amount of recent sinking is suitable.

A corresponding series of terraces in the river valleys, due mainly to stream planation or stream deposition, may be combined with the picture described above, each river terrace merging imperceptibly with a contemporary marine terrace. Such a combination of marine and fluvial agencies would produce the essential forms of the present topography. There is no doubt that both of these factors enter into the result. There remains, however, some question as to whether streams may at times have brought down so much sediment as to fill their valleys before

[1] SALISBURY, R. D., Glacial Geology of New Jersey, *Geol. Survey N. J.*, vol. 5, p. 205, 1902.

[2] *Idem.*, p. 60.

reaching the sea and to spread their detritus fanlike over inter-stream areas.[1]

The Pleistocene terraces have been to some extent correlated in age with the several glacial invasions. The Talbot of Mary-land (Cape May in New Jersey) was thus assigned by Salisbury to the last (Wisconsin) glacial stage.[2] The usual assumption has been that the terraces represent deposition at times when the continent was depressed, perhaps in part by the weight of ice, and that some of the material in them is reworked glacial out-wash. Leverett has recently connected the Wicomico terrace directly with the train of outwash along the Susquehanna coming from what is believed to be Illinoian drift.[3]

More consideration is now being given to the opposite means of submergence, namely, the intermittent rise of the sea level. It is commonly agreed that such rises occurred in the interglacial epochs, when the water which had been withdrawn to form glaciers was restored to the sea. On this hypothesis the terraces are interglacial. A systematic attempt to assign all coastal terraces to their places in glacial history, each to an interglacial epoch, is found in the work of C. Wythe Cooke.[4] This writer assigns each terrace to an interglacial stage on the assumption that the sea stood higher at such times (see table, page 27).

[1] Roughly speaking, this is the condition assumed by Chamberlin and Salisbury (*Geology*, vol. 3, p. 452). Though asserting that each land phase no doubt had its corresponding marine phase, formed at the same time, these authors may be regarded as the chief representatives of the fluvial hypothe-sis. The Maryland geologists, and C. Wythe Cooke, of the U. S. Geological Survey, may be regarded as extending the marine factor to its maximum. Recent studies by C. K. Wentworth (cited above) in Virginia have classified the Brandywine formation and a large part of the Sunderland as fluvial, the lower terraces being regarded as mainly marine. In the main the decision rests on the character and internal structure of the terrace forma-tions, the topography not being decisive.

[2] SALISBURY, R. D., Physical Geography of New Jersey, *Geol. Survey N. J.*, vol. 4, p. 170, 1895.

[3] LEVERETT, FRANK, Results of Glacial Investigations in Pennsylvania and New Jersey in 1926 and 1927, *Bull. Geol. Soc. Amer.*, vol. 39, p. 151. He finds the Pensauken closely associated with Kansan drift, hence probably not the equivalent of the Wicomico.

[4] COOKE, C. W., Correlation of Coastal Terraces, *Jour. Geol.*, vol. 38, pp. 577–589, 1930.

SPECIAL FEATURES OF THE EMBAYED SECTION

Offsetting of Rivers at the Fall Line.—It is a striking fact that the rivers from the Delaware to the James, on reaching the Coastal Plain, turn and follow its inner edge for some miles before crossing to the ocean. The Connecticut may have done the same from Pliocene to Late Glacial time.[1] The Hudson alone seems to have held a straight course. All these rivers jog toward the south or southwest. South of the James two smaller streams, the Appomattox and the Nottoway, are offset somewhat toward the north.

Various explanations have been offered. That the Cretaceous beds are specially weak along this line is sufficient to account for longitudinal valleys but not for the diversion of transverse streams unless capture ensued. Moreover, when the present drainage started, the Cretaceous rocks were probably covered, as they continue to be in Virginia. McGee[2] interpreted the inner lowland from the Hudson to the Potomac as due to downfaulting of the inner edge of the Coastal Plain. The rapidity of this faulting is assumed to have been so great that transverse streams could not maintain their courses. Why they resumed their transverse character after following the fault trough and why all are offset in the same direction are questions not answered. The faulting itself is not now generally believed.

Advancing on the hypothesis that the late Pliocene gravels, once called Lafayette, are of marine origin, Darton[3] accounted for the initial southwestward deflection of streams by assuming that the marginal sea bottom in Pliocene time had offshore bars, such as exist now at various places, parallel to the coast. On emergence these would turn the streams parallel to the coast. He adds to these conditions a preponderant uplift at the north, a factor adopted by later students. Over against this conception may be set that of Campbell, who regards the Sunderland formation south of Washington as an alluvial fan, in the growth of which the river was shifted westward to the edge of

---

[1] VEATCH, A. C., U. S. Geol. Survey, *Prof. Paper* 44, Pl. 6, 1906.

[2] McGEE, W J, Geology of the Head of Chesapeake Bay, U. S. Geol. Survey, *7th Ann. Rept.*, pp. 545–646, 1886.

[3] DARTON, N. H., Outline of Cenozoic History of the Middle Atlantic Slope, *Jour. Geol.*, vol. 2, p. 581, 1894.

the higher land.[1]   The same conception is applied to the James River.

The quantitative sufficiency of sand bars for the work proposed is questioned by Veatch[2] who, so far as New Jersey is concerned, substitutes for the sand bars the central cuesta which was never covered by Pliocene sediments. If the valley by which the previously transverse Delaware crossed that upland was filled during the Pliocene submergence, then on emergence with southward tilting, the stream would take its present course. He assumes the Pliocene gravel to be marine, but his conception may be adapted to a fluvial origin. In any case, southward tilting and a barrier to seaward are accepted parts of the picture. The rectangular turns of the streams and the longitudinal segments on soft rocks suggest capture. This hypothesis has received but little consideration, perhaps because it would be necessary to assume that large streams, with relatively great downcutting power, were captured by tributaries of very small streams. The difference in cutting power would seem to have been too great to be counterbalanced by the southwestward tilting.

Dismal Swamp.—Although an initial basin is not necessary to the development of a swamp,[3] the great swamps of our coastal plain occur where the surface was a few feet below the general level. Most of the newly emerged sea bottoms lack a little of perfect flatness. Swamps characterize the lower terraces in proportion to their youth and nearness to sea level.

Dismal Swamp south of Chesapeake Bay lies on a terrace to which it gives its name. Most of the dry land east of it is lower, and that to the north is no higher than the swamp.[4] Dry land on the west begins with the Suffolk escarpment at the edge of the Wicomico terrace. If all vegetable accumulation were cleared away a shallow basin would appear where the swamp is now, but the thickness of these accumulations is such that the swamp

[1] Campbell, *loc. cit.*

[2] Veatch, A. C., U. S. Geol Survey, *Prof. Paper* 44, p. 31, 1906.

[3] The conditions for the maintenance of swamps on our Atlantic Plain are discussed by N. S. Shaler in his General Account of Fresh Water Morasses of the United States. See U. S. Geol. Survey, 10*th Ann. Rept.*, pt. 1, pp. 261–339, 1890. He gives much information concerning different kinds of swamps and different plants that favor them.

[4] Darton, N. H., Norfolk folio (No. 80), U. S. Geol. Survey, 1902.

surface slopes away from its center in all directions, at places more than a foot to the mile. Lake Drummond at the center, 2 to 3 miles in diameter, is (or was in 1902) 22.2 feet above sea level. The tendency, aside from artificial drainage, is for the swamp surface to rise, and the radial slope to steepen, until the capillary lifting power of the material is no longer able to maintain the water table at its surface. With a steeper slope the destructional effect of outward drainage would exceed the constructional power of growing vegetation. Then channels would form and the water table would be lowered. To some extent this has been brought about artificially by ditching. Before the basin was filled, the dry land on the east was a faint swell of the same kind as those revealed by soundings in the adjacent sea floor.[1]

Summary History of the Embayed Section.—Geological evidence indicates that the dominant topographical features of this section, the long lowland and the main cuesta, were well begun before the Miocene. In that period they were largely obliterated by the thick smooth sheet of sediment.[2] Being renewed and brought almost to their present form by post-Miocene erosion they were again in large part hidden by the "Lafayette" mantle, but the dominant cuesta was not covered. When erosion began again on the Pliocene surface the main transverse rivers were following their present courses, offset to the southwest at the Fall Line.

In the relatively long epoch of erosion thus initiated (long as compared with the succeeding stages) the Pliocene surface was carved almost to maturity in the region between the Delaware and the Potomac, and much beyond that stage in adjacent districts. This was the chief epoch in the making of the great marginal valleys that now constitute the estuaries from North Carolina to Long Island Sound. The history of the Maryland coastal plain is thus summarized by Davis in the language of 30 years ago:[3]

[1] Note submarine contours on the U. S. topographic map of the Norfolk quadrangle.

[2] SALISBURY, R. D., Physical Geography of New Jersey, *Geol. Survey N. J.*, vol. 4, p. 92, 1895; VEATCH, A. C., *op. cit.*, p. 28.

[3] DAVIS, W. M., The Terraces of the Maryland Coastal Plain, *Science*, vol. 25, p. 701, 1907, a review of the work of George B. Shattuck on the Pliocene-Pleistocene Deposits of Maryland.

It is a coastal plain which, having been uplifted and effectually base-leveled, was renovated with a widespread cover of Lafayette sediment and then uplifted again as good as new. In this condition it was dissected to well-advanced maturity, then strongly submerged preparatory to an oscillating emergence which allowed the rapid carving of four scarps and the deposition of four terraces (the last being those of today) on its maturely dissected slopes.

SEA ISLAND SECTION OF THE COASTAL PLAIN

Distinctive Features.—Except near the coast no abrupt change would be noted in passing southward from the embayed section into the Sea Island section. Yet several significant differences require that general statements made about the former be altered for the latter. Both sections take their names from features of the coast, in which a strong contrast appears. Extensive drowning disappears, as do also the great barrier beaches. Rows of islands of a different origin take their places. The inner limit of terracing which, farther north, almost agrees with the Fall Line, falls back farther and farther. Swamps and a general appearance of youth rise here to higher terraces which, farther north, are sub-maturely dissected. The terrace-free inner zone is free from distinct cuestas and low belts which characterize the province north of the Potomac and west of middle Georgia.

Added to these differences (or underlying them) are significant differences in the geological formations or in their distribution. At the southern limit of the embayed section the almost uniform Miocene cover which, down to that line, lies over all older coastal plain formations south of the Potomac, disappears, exposing Cretaceous and early Tertiary rocks. These outcrop in narrow zones to the limit of the Sea Island section in central Georgia, where the plan is again altered by a great spread of the outcrops.

With a very large amount of generalization a topographic cross section of the Sea Island section in Georgia and at least a part of the Carolinas would show: (1) A belt of hills due to mature or submature dissection of the oldest coastal plain formations; (2) a belt of upland or submaturely dissected plain above the highest of the terraces; (3) a terrace belt moderately eroded; (4) a belt of uneroded terraces with many swamps. The last (5) is a zone of sea islands and salt marsh. In North Carolina the first is in part covered by the Brandywine terrace. The second disappears, and the sea islands cease before the northern limit of the section is reached.

Fall Line.—The province boundary in this section is not an obvious topographic feature. It is a transition zone 5 to 10 miles wide, within which hills and valleys have much the same appearance, whether carved from the deeply decayed granitic rocks of the Piedmont province or from the arkosic Cretaceous sandstone made from the waste of the former. As the dip is slight, the relief several hundred feet, and the granite base itself not flat, the actual limit of the sedimentary rocks is a very ragged line. Yet, despite this vagueness of boundary, the "Fall Line," between the "Central Upland" and the "Fall Line Hills" (coastal plain), was recognized by the people long before it was studied by geologists.

Fall Line Hills.—The terms Fall Line Hills and Sand Hills (used in this connection) are almost limited to the Sea Island section. The Cretaceous formations which outcrop at the inner edge of the province and appear in these hills are, unlike those of New Jersey, mainly sand (occasionally cemented) with only minor beds of clay. They are not even overlain by a clay formation as in central Alabama. There are therefore no lowlands in this section at the inner edge of the province. The relief of this inner margin reaches a maximum of 350 feet near the largest streams and 150 feet on smaller streams. Among "forest-covered tracts of dissected upland of unbelievable wildness" Stephenson names two counties in southern North Carolina and three in northern South Carolina, all in the Cretaceous Sand-hills.[1] This belt is more eroded than the plain farther out for the double reason that it is higher (crests 500 to 600 ft.) and has been longer exposed to erosion. Even here the cycle of erosion has not advanced so far as to destroy the horizontality of the sky line.[2]

The entire belt variously styled "Fall Line Hills," "Sand Hills," and "Red Hills" is 20 to 40 miles wide. The half (more or less) next to the Piedmont is largely on the Cretaceous outcrop. It has a barren yellow sandy soil and has little or no flat land remaining at the summit level. The other half (more or less),

---

[1] STEPHENSON, L. W., Major Features in the Geology of the Atlantic and Gulf Coastal Plains, *Jour. Wash. Acad. Sci.*, vol. 16, pp. 460–480, 1926.

[2] VEATCH, OTTO, Geology of the Coastal Plain of Georgia, Ga. Geol. Survey, *Bull.* 26, p. 27, 1911.

underlain by Eocene rocks, is covered with a bright red residual
sand or loam, very fertile.[1] The name Fall Line Hills is often
restricted to the former belt. The name Red Hills designates
only the latter. The equivalent of these Red Hills in Georgia
is the Louisville Plateau which, as its name indicates, is tabular
in form and not completely dissected. The Red Hills are sparse
north of the Santee River (middle of South Carolina).

The belt of light-colored sand hills next to the Fall Line is
continuous except for some transverse divides still capped by
the red Eocene. In northern North Carolina this belt is shut out
by the overlapping Tertiary deposits, most of the area being
occupied by Pleistocene terraces. Southward from that latitude
the inner boundary of the Brandywine terrace falls back farther
and farther from the Fall Line, so that in Georgia it not only
leaves the Cretaceous and Eocene outcrops untouched but is
separated from them by many miles.

Tifton Upland.—With altitude decreasing seaward from the
belt of Sand Hills and Red Hills, dissection by streams becomes
less deep and less complete. In North Carolina this younger
topography is explained by successive Pleistocene submergences
which renovated the surface. Farther south, with increasing
width of the Coastal Plain, a strip 30 to 50 miles wide intervenes
between the Red Hills and the oldest (Hazlehurst or Brandywine) terrace. In Georgia this intervening strip is called the
Tifton Upland.[2] Geologically it is distinguished from the Red
Hills (Louisville Plateau) by a Miocene cover (Altamaha grit),[3]
the weathering of which has produced a gray or yellowish sandy
soil clearly distinguished from the red soil on the Eocene. Topographically the Tifton Upland grades into the Red Hills with
respect to advancement in the erosion cycle as well as altitude.
By reason of weak rocks and submature dissection it is a district
of gently rolling hills with broad rounded summits, having
generally less than 50 feet relief and never more than 100 feet
except near the larger streams which cross in wide, flat-bottomed

[1] The belts of "Sand hills" and "Red hills" do not coincide accurately
with the outcrops of Cretaceous and Eocene rocks but it is the weathering
of the latter that is responsible for the red color.

[2] COOKE, Physical Geography of Georgia, Ga. Geol. Survey, *Bull.* 42, p. 37,
1925.

[3] VEATCH, O., and L.W. STEPHENSON, Ga. Geol. Survey, *Bull.* 26, p. 407,
1911 .

valleys several hundred feet deep. In southwestern Georgia it becomes a distinct cuesta with an escarpment nearly 150 feet high overlooking the Flint River, but this is outside of the section here considered (see page 79). There are no distinct cuestas in the Sea Island section.

Brandywine and Coharie Terraces.—The outer boundary of the Tifton Upland is fairly definite. Erosion near the large transverse streams has dimmed all boundaries, but between these the limit of the Brandywine (Hazlehurst) terrace is marked by an "abrupt transition to the rolling hills of the Tifton Upland."[1] After a similar low scarp at its outer edge the Brandywine terrace is succeeded by the Coharie (Claxton). Both of these plains are somewhat eroded. The few topographic maps available represent areas near the larger streams. From these maps it would be difficult to distinguish the two terraces from the Tifton Upland except in elevation. It is known, however, that large flat expanses exist in the unmapped area. The Coharie even bears some extensive swamps or "bays" (probably so-called from the bay tree). Despite erosion of the higher terraces near streams, the seaward edge of the Tifton Upland is an important line, separating contrasted topographies, the upland on the landward side being uniformly rolling and well drained, the lowland on the seaward side being flat, except near streams, and often swampy. Other similarities, such as a covering of sandy soil with longleaf pine and wire grass,[2] should not obscure the topographic distinction.

Sunderland Terrace.—In descending from the Coharie terrace to the Sunderland (Okefenokee), erosion topography is almost left behind. The boundary is like those already mentioned, an escarpment in places, elsewhere unmarked. As the Sunderland is the flattest terrace in Georgia, the boundary between it and the next higher or Coharie terrace is also a rather noteworthy line. If this same line be traced into Florida and westward, it merges with the edge of the Tifton Upland and becomes the landward edge of a narrow coastal lowland, rather clearly distinguished from the adjacent eroded "uplands" (Fig. 15).

The contrast of any one terrace in Georgia with the same in Maryland is marked. The Sunderland north of the Potomac

---

[1] COOKE, *op. cit.*, p. 29.
[2] VEATCH, OTTO, *op. cit.*, pp. 31*ff.*

River is probably more eroded than any terrace in the south. Yet in Georgia it is noted for its flatness and takes its name, Okefenokee, from the second largest swamp north of the Everglades. Each terrace, as traced southward, becomes progressively younger in its topographic cycle, partly because of greater width and distance from the sea, partly because important

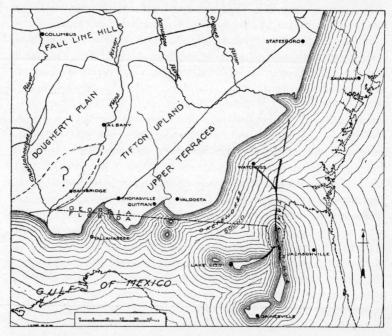

Fig. 15.—Land and sea in Georgia and Florida before emergence of the Sunderland terrace. Trail Ridge is being built by sediment derived from islands in northern Florida and carried northward by a marine current. (*Altered from Ga. Geol. Survey, Bull.* 42, *pl.* 10B.)

drainage lines are fewer. That some terraces younger and nearer to the sea should have more relief than the Sunderland is due not so much to more erosion as to sand ridges made by the waves.

Trail Ridge and Okefenokee Swamp.—With the emergence of the Coharie terrace the Sunderland became shallow marginal sea bottom. The land stood only 160 feet lower (or the sea that much higher) than at present and no part of this terrace was covered by much more than 40 feet of water. The highest spots in Florida already stood out as islands near the 82d meridian and 30 to 50 miles south of the Georgia state line. Currents in the shallow sea built a bar from these islands (probably of shore drift cut from their cliffs) almost due north on a line tangent to the shore of that time, *i.e.*, the edge of the present Coharie terrace (Fig. 15). Most of the southern half of the bar was above water, now 240 feet, but even the submerged northern half was a massive structure many feet above the sea bottom.[1]

When the land rose again, and the Sunderland terrace was added to the Coastal Plain, the lowest part of the new land lay just west of the former bar now known as Trail Ridge, and across the present state boundary. The depression became Okefenokee Swamp, whose level is about 120 feet. It could not drain eastward across the ridge, but exit was found to the southwest by the Suwanee River except for the deepest part of the basin. Along the line of the Georgia Southern railroad, near the state line, the ridge crest is 55 feet above the swamp on the west and 95 feet above the lower terrace on the east. Its width from plain to plain is 2 to 4 miles.

Wicomico Terrace.—The next terrace, the Wicomico, abuts at a maximum altitude of about 95 feet against the seaward slope of Trail Ridge. Its surface is very swampy. It is ribbed by low longitudinal sand ridges of faint slope, like Trail Ridge but lower. Between them are swales, some of them 20 feet deep. In one such swale, behind the outermost ridge, the Satilla River flows 30 miles to the south before finding a break. In a similar way the St. Marys River flows north almost to the Satilla (Pl. 3). Such streams recall Darton's hypothesis to explain the deflection of rivers at the Fall Line (page 35).

Lower Terraces.—Until more accurate maps are available little can be said of the terraces below the Wicomico except to list their names and heights (see table, page 27). Where the Talbot is absent, as it seems to be south of the Altamaha River, the rise from the Pamlico (Satilla) at 16 or 18 feet to the Penholoway at 60 or 70 feet is generally effected within half a mile. The most distinctive feature of the Pamlico terrace is found in the Sea Islands which front the shore of South Carolina and Georgia.

[1] Data concerning Trail Ridge and Okefenokee Swamp are taken from Cooke, *op. cit.*, pp. 28–31.

The Sea Islands.—The area of swamp land increases toward the coast. Correspondingly, the dry land ceases to be continuous and is segmented into "necks" and islands, separated partly by fresh-water swamp, partly by salt marsh, and partly by salt water. Many of the islands, including all of the larger ones, rise to the level of the Pamlico terrace, *i.e.*, 15 or 20 feet above tide. Greater altitudes are due chiefly to dunes which, though not very abundant, may reach heights of 50 feet. The islands are parts of the Pamlico terrace, isolated by a slight submergence which drowned the passage ways.[1] Such a fringe of islands is common enough on coasts of strong relief. Its exceptional character on our coastal plain calls for an explanation of the drowned passage ways and of the local absence of a barrier beach.

In explanation of the low levels between the islands the following factors enter: (1) The original unevenness of the sea bottom;[2] (2) normal stream erosion when the Pamlico terrace stood slightly higher; (3) the development of tidal canals following submergence.

Tides on the coast of South Carolina and Georgia have more than twice the height of those farther north or south, being apparently concentrated in the re-entrant curve. This favors salt marshes through which tidal currents make their own channels. In addition, tidal currents scour and deepen channels already made, in this case the slightly submerged valleys. Moreover, strong ebb and flow interfere with the work of continuous barrier building even if shore currents were as strong and continuous in a broad re-entrant curve as elsewhere. Beaches do indeed front the islands on the seaward side, but they follow the island contours and are quite as apt to present a convex curvature toward the sea as to be concave like the great arcuate barriers of the Carolina coast. Beaches and sand spits may follow the larger channels inward for some distance, but protected shores are generally bordered by salt marsh.[3]

The lower passes are filled with salt water or salt marsh, but the effect of the tide is not limited to salt water. The rise of the

[1] VEATCH, OTTO, *op. cit.*, pp. 37–38.

[2] See charts of the U. S. Coast and Geodetic Survey.

[3] The "Marshes of Glynn," celebrated by Sidney Lanier's well-known poem, are in this zone in Glynn County, Georgia, the second county from Florida.

sea surface dams the streams, it may be for 10 to 20 miles beyond the reach of salt water. By their overflow they cause the zone of fresh water swamps to be greatly expanded. This method of flooding, modified by artificial control, was a great economic factor when the Sea Islands and the adjacent mainland were the leading rice fields of the United States.

This discussion of the Sea Islands suggests that the conditions suitable to their development differ in some significant way from those that favor massive and continuous beach ridges. Yet at a former time Trail Ridge was just that kind of a ridge. However, at the time of its construction, most of Florida was probably under water. Tides went freely in and out of the Gulf of Mexico and the coast did not, as now, present a great concave curve toward the Atlantic, the effect of which is to raise the tides and to increase their scour.

Summary of History of the Sea Island Section.—From the almost uniform decrease of topographic age from the Fall Line to the coast it might be inferred that the entire physiographic history of the Sea Island Section falls within a single erosion cycle which has just now reached maturity at the inner edge and becomes progressively less advanced toward the present coast. This is a common conception and sufficiently accurate in a casual statement. It would necessarily be correct if the uplift of the plain had been by one continuous movement, which, however, is known not to have been the case.[1] During the deposition of the Miocene marine formations, which come in almost to the Red Hills, the outcropping Cretaceous and Eocene formations farther inland were cut down and may have been peneplaned. After Miocene deposition there was uplift and further erosion, whose effects may have been largely, if not wholly, undone throughout this section by a later fluvial covering in the Pliocene.

Probably there is no great error in thinking that a new erosion cycle began near the close of the Pliocene on a surface that was nearly or quite flat. If this be true, and if the formation was subaerial, erosion began simultaneously throughout its extent. Except for parts submerged later in the making of Pleistocene terraces, topographic differences between places near the Fall

---

[1] STEPHENSON, L. W., Major Marine Transgressions and Regressions and Structural Features of the Gulf Coastal Plain, *Amer. Jour. Sci.*, vol. 16, pp. 281–298, 1928.

Line and those farther out should depend merely on elevation and character of rocks.

With the first Pleistocene submergence this partly dissected surface was planed by waves and veneered with new sediment as far inland as the sand-hill belt in central North Carolina and about half as far in Georgia. The land then rose intermittently (with intervening subsidence) a total of more than 200 feet in five acts, each rise laying bare a new terrace. While such an oscillating movement has not been demonstrated for all of the terraces, it is obvious that the last or Pamlico terrace, after slight erosion, was again depressed to make the sea islands.

THE FLORIDIAN SECTION

Relation to Coastal Plain Province.—The Florida peninsula is due to the partial emergence of an extensive flat-topped plateau which rises abruptly from the deep-sea floor.[1] The center of emergence is not the adjacent continent but an independent land surface in the peninsula itself, which merged with the continental land surface by further uplift. The first center of peninsular uplift was in the northern half, on the west side. Later movements have added land on the east and south. The main axis of uplift is at right angles to the contour of the continent. Being thus merged with the Coastal Plain by the emergence of a broad intervening sag, it is not to be expected that the peninsula should be separable from the adjacent coastal plain by a definite line. A boundary, if drawn at all, must cut arbitrarily across terraces or other surfaces which extend from Georgia southward.

The primary factors which determine the character of the landscape in peninsular Florida and differentiate one part from another are: (1) Pleistocene terracing; (2) the presence or absence of soluble rocks; (3) the thickness of sand or other covering of a buried soluble stratum; (4) elevation above sea level sufficient to permit surface waters to descend and thus make solution possible; (5) stream erosion.

NORTHERN HALF OF THE FLORIDA PENINSULA

Pensacola Terrace and East Coast.—The lower terraces extend from Georgia into Florida without change of character. The

[1] This remarkable plateau is vividly described, with speculation concerning its origin, by N. S. Shaler, The Topography of Florida, *Bull. Mus. Comp. Zool.*, vol. 16 (geol. ser., vol. 2), pp. 139–158, 1890.

Pensacola terrace on the east coast, equivalent to the Talbot and Pamlico and extending inland to an altitude of 45 feet, has a fairly uniform width, rarely over 20 miles, down to the latitude of Lake Okeechobee, beyond which it constitutes the entire surface of southern Florida (Figs. 16 and 19).   It is also con-

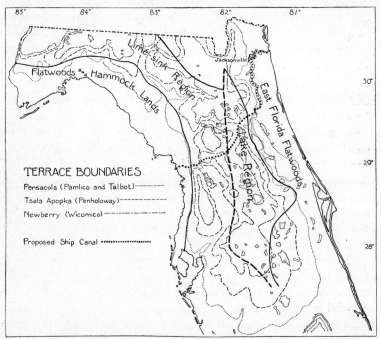

FIG. 16.—Sketch map of northern Florida.   Dotted lines show the boundaries of three Pleistocene terraces, the Pensacola (Pamlico and Talbot, limited by the 40- to 45-foot contour), the Tsala Apopka (Penholoway, limited by the 65- to 70-foot contour), and the Newberry (Wicomico, limited by the 95- to 100-foot contour.)   (*After G. C. Matson and others, U. S. Geol. Survey, Bull.* 319.) Heavy lines outline the main types of landscape.   The broken line between the Lime-sink region and the Lake Region indicates that no exact boundary can be drawn between the two.   District boundaries are highly generalized from maps by R. M. Harper in the sixth and thirteenth annual reports of the Florida Geological Survey.

tinuous on the west coast, having a width of 5 to 20 miles.[1]   With respect to swamps and shallow lakes its character is the same as in Georgia.   This belt merges, as to both topography and material,

[1] MATSON, G. C., Geology and Ground Waters of Florida, U. S. Geol. Survey, *Water Supply Paper* 319, p. 34, 1913.   Pl. V, map, shows the extent of the several terraces.

with shore features of recent origin.   Much of it is ribbed with
broad sand ridges, a very few feet high, representing successive
positions of the beach.   In the latitude of Jacksonville, 12 to 15
of these ridges with intervening swampy swales may be counted
in a width of 10 miles.[1]

Almost everywhere the surface of the Pensacola terrace is of
sand, but southward along the coast from St. Augustine (lat. 30°)
for a distance of 250 miles, coquina is quite commonly found
beneath the sand.   The coquina, though cemented, is of recent
origin and, near the coast, probably accumulated as a series of
beach ridges.   For much of the distance the coquina and the
sand above it form a low swell between the shore and the line
of swamps traversed by the St. Johns River.

A vigorous shore current from the north sweeps the eastern
coast.   In conjunction with the waves it has built an outlying
barrier stretching from the Sea Islands to the latitude of Lake
Okeechobee, and is rapidly extending the coast seaward.[2]   The
broad bars or sand islands behind Cape Canaveral, which is
20 miles from the coast proper, are an expression of this constant
growth.   A continuous lagoon enclosed by a barrier beach 130
miles long is known as Indian River.   The barrier is complete
except for artificial openings.   Because of the constant supply
of water from the land, the "river" has been to a large extent
freshened.   It is now only mildly brackish, except near the
artificial openings which admit sea water.   Such openings shift
southward with the shore current by elongation of the bar on the
north side and removal of sand on the south side.

West Coast.—On the west coast the Pensacola terrace surrounds Tampa Bay, a 20-mile indentation due to drowning by
westward tilting.[3]   From Tampa Bay north and west along the
coast, the forested and nearly flat surface of the Pensacola terrace
is underlain by limestone at such small depth that numerous
outcrops appear, rising a few inches above the surface of sediment.[4]   Some streams have rocky rapids near the shore.   Water

[1] See U. S. Geol. Survey topographic maps, Jacksonville and Mayport
quadrangles.

[2] MATSON, *op. cit.*, p. 36.

[3] MATSON, *op. cit.*, p. 36.

[4] HARPER, R. M., Geography and Vegetation of Northern Florida, Fla.
Geol. Survey, 6th *Ann. Rept.*, p. 302, 1914.

Fig. 17.—Airplane view of Daytona Beach, looking north. The city is on the barrier beach; lagoon and mainland in the background. (Photograph by R. H. LeSesne. Courtesy of the Daytona Beach Chamber of Commerce.)

power is developed on the Withlacoochee. The same rock surface extends out beneath the Gulf and makes rocky shoals.

Previous to receiving its Pleistocene coating, this rock, like other limestones in Florida, was pitted with sinkholes and probably honeycombed with caves. The old solution topography is imperfectly obliterated, and this, with the small beginning of renewed solution, accounts for most of the relief that now exists. Generally, this terrace lies too low and too near the water table to admit of active downward percolation. These solution features differentiate the lowest terrace along the Gulf Coast from the same terrace along the Atlantic. Most of the shore north of Tampa Bay is without a beach.[1] Fresh-water swamp gives way to salt marsh, often in a ragged fringe.

Higher Terraces.—As in Georgia and farther north, the higher terraces are limited by escarpments, not everywhere, but at intervals sufficiently frequent to establish their identity. The equivalent of the Penholoway terrace is here called Tsala Apopka, rising to 65 or 70 feet A.T., and that of the Wicomico is here the Newberry terrace, rising to 95 or 100 feet.[2] A broken and irregular strip of considerable extent along the axis of the peninsula (generally 100 to 200 feet high) is higher than the Newberry terrace and is designated by Matson as higher than the earliest Pleistocene sea level.[3] It is, however, continuous with the Okefenokee (Sunderland) terrace of Georgia and, if not wholly covered by the sea at that stage, should at least have been covered at one of the preceding higher Pleistocene stages.[4] In the description of higher terraces, this area is here included.

The topography of the higher terraces differs chiefly in degree from that of the Pensacola on the Gulf Coast. Swamps in original faint depressions of the sea bottom have been to some extent encroached upon by natural drainage, but they are still extensive, especially in the interior of the peninsula northeast of

[1] MARTENS, J. H. C., Beaches of Florida, Fla. Geol. Survey, 21*st*–22*d* *Ann. Repts.*, 1931.

[2] COOKE, C. W., Physical Geography of Georgia, Ga. Geol. Survey, *Bull.* 42, p. 35, 1925; also Correlation of Coastal Terraces, *Jour. Geol.*, vol. 38, pp. 577–589, 1930. See his table, p. 588.

[3] MATSON, G. C., Generalized Map of Pleistocene Terraces of Florida, *op. cit.*, Pl. 5.

[4] COOKE, C. W., "Physical Geography of Georgia," p. 31.

Tampa and also near the Georgia boundary. Relief is due more largely to solution than to any other agency. Some scattered hills of gentle slope seem to represent the failure of Pleistocene sediments to obscure older inequalities.[1] Steeper slopes, the ones that attract attention, are generally related to depressions made by solution, either sinkholes or lake basins, or, less often, to recent stream valleys. Most of the solution in these higher terraces is more recent than the Pleistocene submergence. It is favored by the porous sandy mantle, which prevents rain water from running off, retaining it for the slower processes of percolation, descent, and solution. As might be expected, streams are relatively few.

The area thus described occupies the middle of the peninsula in its northern half between the low coastal belts already described. Boundary lines, if interpreted strictly, could only be confusing, since the solution features also invade the lowest terrace along the Gulf Coast, and they are distributed with great irregularity in the higher parts.

Influence of Underlying Rocks.—In a very general way it may be said that the chief formation accountable for a solution topography is the Ocala (Eocene) limestone, which immediately underlies the mantle rock in the northern third of the peninsula west of its median line, the 82d meridian. East of that line[2] this limestone is overlain by the less soluble Hawthorne (Miocene) formation. Much of the Hawthorne, especially near the line of contact, is so thin that solution in the underlying Ocala dominates the topography. While the two terranes thus defined have much in common, there are also noteworthy differences. The western is in the main a lime-sink district and the eastern a lake district (Fig. 16). The distinction is not sharp, for a number of lakes are found in the western part and some sinks in the eastern, but the lakes in the western part are in all cases obviously expanded or coalescing sinks. This applies even to

[1] See U. S. Geological Survey topographic sheets of Ocala, Dunnelon, Citra, Tsala Apopka, and Williston quadrangles. Apparently some hills 50 feet or more above wide valley floors must be accounted for either in this way or by assuming a very large amount of post-Pleistocene erosion, which is improbable.

[2] For more exact location see Geologic Map of Florida, 1929, or Geologic Map of the United States, 1932.

the northern end of the lime-sink district, where Miocene beds overlie the Eocene.[1] The southern end of the district is similarly overlain by the Tampa (Miocene) limestone. In the main the lime-sink and Lake districts occupy the higher terraces or uplands, but their very indefinite boundaries can not be drawn by following those of terraces or of formations.

Lime-sink District.—The features of the lime-sink district are those that might be expected on a plain underlain by porous limestone in a humid country where vegetation and decay are abundant and where the soluble stratum is covered by a mantle of sand. No great area is without sinkholes but their distribution is very irregular. In exceptional places half of the surface is occupied by depressions. Some of them (not many) are of the familiar funnel form made by enlarging a crack which leads down to a subterranean passage. Others, probably most numerous, are small, dry, sandy basins with rounded bottoms and no visible outlets. Still others show by their vertical walls that the roof of a cavern has fallen in. Some large sinks of this kind have been formed suddenly in recent years. Others have begun suddenly to fill with water or to lose their water, all of which facts indicate connection with caves or underground passages.[2]

Associated with subsurface solution are natural bridges and giant springs, the latter being merely the emergence of streams, parts of whose courses are underground. Despite its moderate altitude, this district is noteworthy for features of this kind, especially near its eastern margin where it merges into the Lake district. Silver Spring near Ocala is well known as the source of a stream 50 feet wide and more than 9 feet in minimum depth. All these great springs represent passageways in the Ocala or other limestones though they are widely scattered, some of them occurring in the Lake district where the Ocala limestone is over-. lain by Miocene formations.

Even aside from sinks, this district has its relief, either older than the Pleistocene mantle or due to recent erosion. In its

[1] Some of these lakes are described in detail by E. H. Sellards, Some Florida Lakes and Lake Basins, Fla. State Geol. Survey, 6th Ann. Rept., pp. 115–159, 1914. His descriptions include at least one which falls in the eastern district as here outlined.

[2] MATSON (op. cit., p. 28) gives interesting illustrations of sinks, natural bridges, and great springs, mentioned below.

higher and hillier parts local relief of 50 feet is common, but some parts are flat, and all slopes are gentle except to the sinks or to the comparatively few recent stream valleys. The district is known economically as the source of hard-rock phosphate, the chief phosphate supply of the United States.

At the south, somewhere in the latitude of Tampa Bay, the characteristic features of this district cease and give way to the low swampy plain of southern Florida. At the north the lime-sink district of Florida merges into the Sunderland and higher terraces and uplands of Georgia. In a belt of considerable width on both sides of the Georgia-Florida boundary, all distinctions among terraces become subordinate to the general prevalence of solution features, including some lakes of considerable size. This belt is known in Georgia as the "Southern Lime-sink Region."[1] It belongs entirely to the East Gulf Coastal Plain and not to the Sea Island section.

Lake District.—Although the Lake district is believed to owe its basins to solution of the same limestone which carries the sinks farther west, it has large areas differing in important ways from the lime-sink district just described. West of the common boundary, rock outcrops are common; east of it, they are rare. Lime sinks, caves, and natural bridges are almost unknown in the Lake district[2] except in its western margin (Fig. 18). An occasional great spring in the Lake district is known to come from the Ocala limestone beneath the Miocene. Instead of sinks, and basins which obviously originated as sinks, this district is characterized by larger lake basins enclosed primarily by sand. If the landscape is to be compared with the lime-sink district, its features are at least on a much larger scale.

From the size of the basins, the forms of their slopes, and the general absence of outcrops, it is not obvious that solution is their cause. The landscape is not of the ordinary solution type and as good an observer as Shaler assigned to it another explanation.[3] The solution hypothesis is now favored by geologists,

[1] VEATCH, OTTO, Geology of the Coastal Plain of Georgia, Ga. Geol. Survey, *Bull.* 26, p. 28, Fig. 1, 1911.

[2] HARPER, R. M., Geography and Vegetation of Northern Florida, Fla. Geol. Survey, *6th Ann. Rept.*, p. 320, 1914.

[3] SHALER, N. S., The Topography of Florida, *Bull. Mus. Comp. Zool.*, vol. 16, p. 153, 1890. Shaler observed some sinks but regarded them as concomitants rather than causes of the basins. He was more impressed

partly because no other is defensible, but partly also because of more positive evidence.   That it has not always been accepted is mentioned here to make clear the fact that this district is unlike the country west of it.

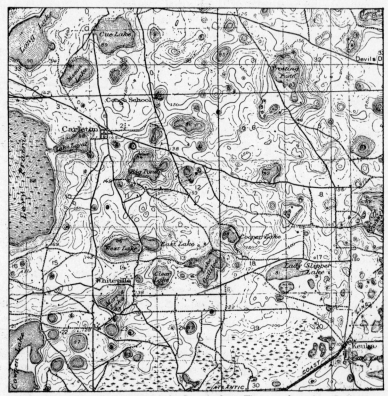

Fig. 18.—Map of a portion of the Interlachen, Fla., quadrangle.   It lies just east of the 82d meridian and north of the parallel of 29° 30′.   This is near the western edge of the Lake district, and the basins are of the lime-sink type. The underlying rock is the Hawthorne (Miocene) limestone, thinly covered by the porous Citronelle (Pliocene) formation.   The water level in all the basins is between 81 and 92 feet A. T. (*U. S. Geol. Survey.*)

The Lake district here described, and as the term is commonly used, does not include Lake Okeechobee and others on the flat lower terraces which occupy original depressions in the sea floor,

with the fact that all relief seemed to be molded in recent sands.   He adopted the view that the sands were tossed into this form by a marine current answering to the Gulf stream during a recent submergence.

as it was left when the Pleistocene sea retired. Nor does it include the lakes strung along the sluggish St. Johns River, which appear to be remnants of coastal lagoons like Indian River.[1]

Southern Florida

General Description.—South of the latitude of Tampa Bay, there is very little land that would be called high, even in Florida. On the axis of the peninsula the relatively high Lime-sink and Lake regions taper off in the next 50 miles, sloping east, west, and south as indicated by the drainage. The rest has an average elevation of less than 20 feet and is in large part swampy. It is an extensive, almost flat, marl and limestone shelf generally covered with a few feet of muck and a little sand. Add to these conditions a humid climate (rainfall 60 to 70 inches in the south), a warm sea, and prevailing east winds, and we have the known factors of southern Florida physiography. Its features may be listed as follows; vast swamps (perhaps five sixths of the area), a strip of dry land along the nearly straight east shore, a low, ragged and island-fringed west shore, local barrier beaches and lagoons, and finally coral reefs and other outlying "Keys." The explanation of some details may be facilitated by assuming very gentle warping on north-south axes, but this is not apparent to the eye.

The most obvious primary division of the land surface in southern Florida is into swamp and dry land, the former embracing about 6000 out of 7300 square miles.[2] Most of the remaining 1300 square miles of dry land is "pine land," but the term is used loosely and may include some small patches of hardwood and also some prairies.

Dry Land on the East.—The most commanding topographic feature of southern Florida, as also the best known part, is the strip of dry land along the east coast. It is often called a ridge, but for most of its length that word, unless explained, would leave

[1] Cooke, C. W., and S. Mossom, Geology of Florida, Fla. Geol. Survey, *20th Ann. Rept.*, pp. 42–43, 1929

[2] This 7300 square miles is the arbitrarily chosen area described by Samuel Sanford under the head of Geography of Southern Florida in U. S. Geol. Survey, *Water Supply Paper* 319, pp. 42–64. It is roughly limited by the Caloosahatchee River west of Lake Okeechobee and an eastward extension of the same line to the Atlantic Ocean.

a false impression. There is no crest, and generally no visible slope except the gentle rise from the shore. The most ridgelike part is south of Miami along Biscayne Bay, where the surface rises 22 feet from the water in ½ mile. The so-called ridge is generally a flat expanse less than 20 feet high, and a few miles in width. A gradual westward decline is made known by the character of the vegetation rather than by a visible slope (Fig. 19, page 58). The highest land is pine-covered. With diminishing altitude toward the west, wet prairie and cypress swamp may take the place of pine forest and give way in turn to the sawgrass of the permanent swamp, *i.e.*, the Everglades. Elsewhere the transitional prairie may be wanting. Such marginal prairies may be dry enough to cultivate in the dry season (winter) and be covered by 2 feet of water in the rainy season (summer). South of latitude 27° the width of the strip which is dry enough to maintain pines is generally 2 to 8 miles. Fifteen miles north of that latitude it is 20 miles, but that is unusual.

Although the strip of dry land as a whole has very gentle or imperceptible slopes, its surface is to some extent variegated with steeper forms. North of latitude 26° some of these are old dunes, in rare cases 50 feet high, covered with pines or scrub growth and not subject to migration even when cleared, hence obviously produced when the land and sea stood in a different relation.

Other features of relief are old beach ridges roughly parallel to the coast. They are low sandy swells alternating with swales which may contain lagoons, wet prairies, or cypress swamps. Swells and swales together form what are called "rolling sand plains," a fairly continuous belt which includes the dunes and extends from Indian River south almost to the Miami River with a maximum width of 6 miles. This belt is included in the eastern belt of pinelands, constituting at places its entire width.

The assemblage of features described above as constituting the eastern pineland ends a few miles north of Miami. Farther south, in general west of Biscayne Bay, outcrops and even wide expanses of bare limestone characterize the surface for a distance of at least 30 miles from the sea, and over an area which may be 200 square miles. Near Miami this "Biscayne Pineland" borders the bay and has its maximum height, 30 feet at one place, but the area above 22 feet is small. Farther south it passes behind a zone of salt marsh and mangrove swamp and, curving westward, dies out in disconnected fragments in the Everglades. Its surface is remarkably roughened by solution, which leaves jagged projections a foot or so in height. Sometimes these are broken off and the surface is strewn with sharp stones. Small streams (called rivers) leading from the Everglades cross this rocky zone in rapids.

Origin of Dry Land on the East.—The descriptions given here indicate that the dry land north of Biscayne Bay owes its relative altitude in large part, if not wholly, to winds and waves. Sandy beach ridges form a substantial part of its volume. The limestone surface under these is probably higher than it is farther inland, but the rock itself is largely coquina (a cemented mass of shells) and represents beach ridges of an earlier date. Southern Florida is in the zone of trade winds, and beach action has probably always been vigorous on the eastern coast.

Around Miami and farther south there are no dunes, and the rocky upland owes nothing of its height to modern beach deposits. The rock is oolitic limestone, *i.e.*, composed of material which often constitutes shoals and beaches. Hence a part or all of its relative altitude may be ascribed to surficial work on a Pleistocene shore. It is not even necessary to assume a shore. When southern Florida was a vast shoal, waves driven by the trade winds might break on its eastern margin and build a barrier, as off the Carolina coast, with or without land to leeward.

Some students of Florida do not believe that the relative heights of east coast and west coast are to be explained without crustal movement. A post-Pleistocene westward tilt is affirmed by Vaughan who concludes that from its early history the Florida plateau has been subject to very mild warping on north-south axes, the dry land being enlarged from time to time by the addition of successive low swells, always on the east side.[1] Only the latest increments reached the southern end of the peninsula.

Eastern Shore Line.—Barrier beaches and lagoons fringe most of the eastern shore of Florida but there are stretches in which the lagoon narrows to a marshy swale. It is in the quiet water (or marsh) inside of the barrier beach that the intracoastal

[1] Vaughan, T. W., A Contribution to the Geological History of Florida, *Carnegie Inst. Wash. Pub.*, vol. 133, p. 184, 1910.

waterway from Jacksonville to Miami has been constructed.
Shore currents driven by the prevailing northeast winds move
southward. Spits grow in that direction and artificial cuts
through the barrier also migrate southward. Biscayne Bay is a
shallow indentation shut off from the open ocean partly by a

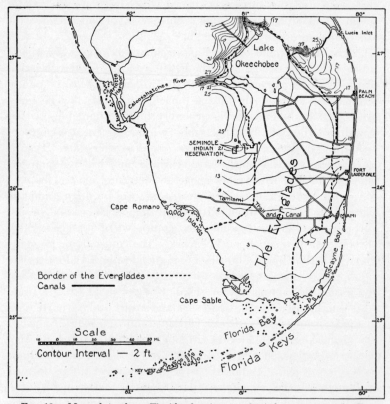

Fig. 19.—Map of southern Florida showing canals and contours in the Everglades. The contours indicate only the leval of the swamp surface and do not
show the full height west of Biscayne Bay. (*Everglades Drainage Commission,
Florida.*)

southward growing barrier terminating in Cape Florida, and
partly by an old coral reef farther south. On the mainland south
of Cape Florida the limestone upland is separated from the
shore by coastal marsh, much of it sawgrass and cypress but
overgrown by mangrove on the seaward side. It gradually
broadens from zero opposite Cape Florida to 12 or 15 miles on

the shore of Florida Bay. In the quiet waters of this bay, protected by the long line of Keys, the mangrove swamp of the mainland gives way to the salt water of the island-dotted bay with no very definite shore line. The mangrove forest of the so-called land invades the shallow water, which is thereupon shallowed still more by the settling of limy mud.

Dry Land on the West.—The amount of dry ground west of the Everglades is perhaps equal to that on the east, but it is scattered in patches and strips which have never been mapped. There is none south of latitude 25°30′ and none along the coast south of 26°10′. Some dry ground is found 50 miles inland, as around Old Fort Shackleford and the Seminole Indian Reservation (Fig. 19). The whole area west of the Everglades is even more monotonously flat than the dry land on the east. Its dry parts are all classed as "flat lands," a term which here includes the pinelands or "pine islands," prairies, and "cypress strands." The last-named type grades into cypress swamp which, with other types of swamp, occupies most of the area, surrounding or alternating with the drier parts.

Outcrops of dense, fine-grained limestone are widely scattered through the timbered parts but, though quite bare, they rise at most a few inches above the general level. Even where the limestone forms the surface for several miles it does not affect the flatness of the plain.

These slightly higher lands on the west owe little of their elevation to beach processes. There are no sand dunes south of the Caloosahatchee River and the only "rolling sand plain" is a succession of beach ridges back of Cape Sable at the southwest extremity of the mainland. On the west coast in this latitude the trade winds blow offshore, hence shore processes are feeble. Farther north toward Tampa are good modern beach ridges extending as far south as the mouth of the Caloosahatchee.

Character of the West Coast.—Evidence of drowning on the west coast is widespread, though the vertical movement involved is not great. Only a few feet of change in the level of land or water were required to drown the small streams south of latitude 26° and to isolate the Ten Thousand Islands. This part of the coast is very low and swampy. In its southern half the Everglades reach the mangrove swamp along the shore, and in its northern half the strip of fresh-water swamp between pineland

and sea is 5 to 15 miles wide. The shore is a maze of islands, tongues of land, and intricate passages, in which the dominance of sea or land can best be determined by vegetation. Salt water is indicated by mangrove forests, which are peculiarly luxuriant in the southern part of this strip. Salt water invades the drowned valley of Lostman's River to a distance varying from 5 to 17 miles according to the stage of the river and the tide.

The topography indicates that a moderate amount of erosion was accomplished when base level was a little lower. Larger indentations farther north, Charlotte Harbor, Tampa Bay, and others, are deeper and older and indicate greater relative change of land and sea levels. Here, too, the influence of westerly winds is felt, and beaches and bars are better developed. Such features stop at Cape Romano near the 26th parallel.

The Everglades.[1]—As distinguished from other kinds of swamp and marsh in Florida, the Everglades are characterized by sawgrass, which is not a grass but a sedge (*Cladium effusum*). In an area of about 5000 square miles (Fig. 19) this so-called grass is omnipresent, generally excluding everything else from view except the muck or water from which it rises and, if the observer can see over the sawgrass, an occasional clump of hardwood trees or "hammock" (Fig. 20). Defined in this way, the Everglades border Lake Okeechobee on the south but do not surround it, though they merge with the cypress swamps which rim the lake on the north and northeast. They form a broad belt (maximum 60 miles) from the lake to the southern extremity of the peninsula, except for a margin of mangrove swamps and other types. They are commonly said to reach the sea between Cape Sable and the Ten Thousand Islands but a strip of salt-tolerant mangrove forest intervenes. The Everglades belong to the domain of fresh water.

In the rainy season (June to October) the water level is about 2 feet higher than in the dry season (November to May). At such time the Everglades may be traversed by canoe, as was often done by the Seminole Indians and also by white troops in the Seminole wars in Andrew Jackson's time.

[1] SANFORD, S., U. S. Geol. Survey, *Water Supply Paper* 319, pp. 53–58. ELLIOT, F. C., "Biennial Report to the Board of Commissioners of the Everglades Drainage District," 1925–1926 and 1927–1928.

At places the Everglades extend east almost to the Atlantic, ending at a fairly definite line against the strip of dry land described above. In the northern part they yield in an irregular and patchy way to wet prairies (true grasses), cypress swamps, and occasional hammocks. This transitional zone between Everglade and pineland is specially characterized by prairies which are under water in the wet season and may to some extent be farmed in the dry season. The western boundary is similar but even more vague, since the surface on that side is even flatter

Fig. 20.—View in the Everglades. The vegetation is mainly sawgrass (sedge). The dark spots in the background are "hammocks." (*O. P. Phillips, Jour. Geogr., vol. 2.*)

than on the east. With the customary seasonal change of about 2 feet in the level of the water, the change from land surface to lake or to reverse is even more widespread on the west side than on the east. Except for the occasional hammock, slopes are not visible to the eye, and differences of elevation are revealed only by the spread of the water. The limit of the Everglades proper is where cypress takes the place of sawgrass, and the higher tracts begin to be covered by true grass. Most of the pine-covered flatlands or "pine islands" are a little farther west.

Lake Okeechobee.—Lake Okeechobee covers a shallow basin whose deepest part is about at sea level. In ordinary years previous to any drainage its surface was 19 to 21 feet above the sea according to season. The average was given as 20.5 feet and the extreme of variation as 4 feet. Its area at a 20-foot stage is 730 square miles. Most of the lake is open water, too deep for sawgrass. Its shore on the north, and to some extent on the east, is a wall of fine cypress. Elsewhere it is the indefinite edge of the Everglades, the water level being continuous from one to the other. The rainfall of 50 to 60 inches per year over the area of the lake itself is approximately balanced by evaporation (more than balanced in the dry season) and the same is true of the Everglades as a whole, but the lake receives the Kissimmee River beside smaller streams and must therefore overflow. Yet there is no natural stream leading from the lake to the sea. The Caloosahatchee on the west heads in a shallow depression called Lake Hicpochee 3 miles from Okeechobee with which it is now connected by a canal. The main outlet of Lake Okeechobee is now the St. Lucie canal on the east, but in the natural state the lake overflowed into the Everglades along the entire southern shore. The natural outlet of Lake Okeechobee is therefore the whole broad southward-sloping belt of Everglades, at least as broad as the lake itself. There are some open sloughs which show a tendency of the outgoing water to concentrate in streams when the water is low, but these soon lose themselves in the broad expanse.

Gradient of the Water Surface in the Everglades.—Were it not for the impeding effect of vegetation, the water surface would necessarily be horizontal. As it is, a low gradient is maintained, the level declining from 18 or 19 feet at the north to 3 or 4 feet at the south, or about 2 inches to the mile (Fig. 19). The surface also declines toward the barrier on the east, behind which it is (or was before the canals were dug) 18 feet high at the north and falls progressively toward the south. Where small streams escape through the barrier on the east the gradient of the adjacent swamp surface is steeper. Thus the level of the Everglades at the point nearest to Miami is given as 6.2 feet. Thirty miles away it is 13 feet (ignoring the effect of the canal). The gradient near Fort Lauderdale is much steeper.

Origin of the Everglades.—The thickness of the peat and muck which underlie the Everglades is fairly uniform, being 8 feet near Lake Okeechobee and decreasing toward the south. Under it is a floor of limestone believed to be nearly level. Rarely if ever does it fall below sea level, and nowhere, in the Everglades proper, does it reach the surface. The fact that it reaches the surface on all margins, except along the shore at the southwest, suggests that the Everglades may owe their existence to an original rock basin. The rock floor is slightly more uneven in the north than in the south, and various explanations have been offered, based on erosion, solution, and deformation. But no such basin is necessary to explain the swamp. The tendency of accumulating vegetation to build up and that of moving water to cut down are necessarily in opposition. In Dismal Swamp moving water is helpless on a gradient much steeper than any in the Everglades. Vegetation has not yet shown what it can do in southern Florida. If given a free field and no interference it would build much higher in the interior before the steepening slope would serve as a check. Meantime the vegetation would change, though slowly. The tree-clad hammocks would become steadily larger and more numerous and should ultimately be dominant.[1]

Reclamation.—Projects to drain and reclaim the Everglades were begun many years ago and much is already accomplished.[2] Most of the overflow of Lake Okeechobee now goes east through the St. Lucie canal to Indian River and thus to the Atlantic. Some goes west by the short canal leading to the Caloosachatchee. The shore on the southwest, south and southeast is diked to stop the overflow in those directions and to protect the reclaimed land from floods raised by hurricanes blowing over Lake Okeechobee. Four great canals lead south and southeast from the lake. These are to drain the swamp rather than the lake. The average level of the latter was already reduced a foot or more by 1927 and will be held at a maximum of 18 feet and a minimum of 15 feet, though in dry seasons the level will be still further lowered by evaporation. Irrigation and at least one 6-foot navigable waterway across the peninsula (Fig. 19) are included in the plans.

[1] COWLES, H. C., Address before the Association of American Geographers, 1911.

[2] A report by the Chief of Engineers, U. S. Army, on this subject dated April, 1928, embodying reports of others on the same subject is published as House Document No. 215 of the 70th Congress, 1st session. Cost estimates given below are taken from this document. See also references on p. 60.

It is officially estimated that an expenditure of 40 million dollars (including that already spent) will complete the public work necessary to reclaim 2 million acres, or somewhat more than half of the Everglades.   When this expense has been supplemented by that of private owners to supply the smaller ditches, there will have been spent on each acre of reclaimed ground (according to official estimate) $34.70.   The price paid for some reclaimed land already sold is several times that amount, but a long period of years must be allowed for complete settlement.

The Florida Keys.[1]—The word *key* is used in southern Florida for an island of any kind.   Most noteworthy among the Keys is a curved line of islands extending from Biscayne Bay to Key West and on to the Marquesas and Dry Tortugas (Pl. 3).   Northeast of Big Pine Key (long. 81°20′ W.) this line of islands is a broken coral reef which began to be made near the edge of the Florida plateau when the warm sea covered this belt to a depth of perhaps 10 to 20 fathoms.   Its rise above water was partly by the natural upward growth of coral, partly by the work of breakers which built the coral into a beach ridge, and partly, no doubt because of relative change in the sea level.   Its division into separate islands is largely the work of tidal currents.

Three to seven miles seaward from the line of keys is a living reef growing upward through 10 fathoms of water, though most of it remains submerged.   At places it reaches to the level of low tide, and Fowey Rocks at its northern end supports a lighthouse.   The 200-mile arc from this place to the Dry Tortugas supports the only living coral in the United States proper.

Like other coral reefs, the keys embody some coral in place as it grew, and much that was ground up by the waves and built into beach ridges.   Sand may mingle with this material in any proportion.   Thus a true coral reef may grade into a typical sand reef, spit, or barrier beach.   The islands north of Cape Florida belong to the class of barrier beach, even though they may contain small quantities of coral.   Key Largo, south of Biscayne Bay, is 27 miles long and at one place 3½ miles wide, but most of these coral keys are a fraction of a mile wide and less than half a dozen miles in length.   The coral limestone of their substructure generally rises less than 10 feet above the sea. Beach ridges or blown sand may be piled up a few feet higher.

[1] See VAUGHAN, *op. cit.*, pp. 95–185.

The tidal passes between keys are shallow enough to permit the construction of trestles to support the Florida East Coast Railroad[1] from Key Largo to Key West. Keys of solid rock may support scrubby hardwoods, palms and even pines.

The keys from Big Pine to Key West resemble those just described only in their low altitude, limestone foundation, and vegetation. They are not made of coral. If elongated, their trend is at right angles to the arc. They are in no sense a reef, but a remote outcropping of the same limestone that makes the Biscayne pinelands and the ridge at Miami. The northwest-southeast passage ways between them have a tidal origin like the passes between the coral keys. Twenty miles farther west is the Marquesas group, coral again, but in this case a broken atoll.

Between the mainland and this long sickle-shaped line of keys lies Florida Bay, a shallow flat-bottomed pan, deepening slightly toward the west but not reaching a depth of 12 feet east of Cape Sable. Like the rest of the shallow sea west of Florida, and like the peninsula itself most of the time before emergence, this flat expanse is accumulating limy mud. Numerous mud banks and shoals rise to the surface, some of them at low tide only. The higher ones are covered with mangrove. These also are called keys and constitute the most numerous class, though at present they are least significant.

EAST GULF COASTAL PLAIN

Distinctive Features.—Notable changes are observed in the Coastal Plain in passing westward from the Sea Island section. The transition, while not abrupt, is effected within a short distance, mainly between the Ocmulgee and Flint rivers, *i.e.*, near the line that divides the drainage to the Atlantic from that to the Gulf. The Alapaha, longest and most direct headwater of the Suwanee River, is in the zone of transition.

Among the changes noted, a fundamental one is seen on the geologic map in the great widening and spread of lines of outcrop (Fig. 21). Cretaceous and Eocene series, which in Eastern Georgia come to the surface in a narrow belt near the Fall Line, spread out from the Piedmont almost to the Gulf, and from the Tennessee River to the delta of the Mississippi. This spread is due partly to greater thickness of the several formations and

[1] Abandoned since this writing.

partly to a larger number. Along with these variations comes more diversification in character, notably in resistance to erosion. The conditions are thus afforded for a broad belted coastal plain. Both eastern and western sections of the Gulf Coastal Plain are thus characterized.

The description of the Sea Island section might almost be written without references to differences in underlying rocks except for their influence on soils. There are no lowlands of erosion and no in-facing escarpments. The primary factors there are elevation, distance from the sea, and advancement in the erosion cycle. In contrast, the Gulf Coastal Plain must be described largely in terms of its underlying rocks. Among other stratigraphic facts, account must be taken of the great development of Early Tertiary limestones. Solution features, negligible in southeastern Georgia, at once become prominent in southwestern Georgia, and their importance continues southward through Florida and westward through Alabama at least to the Tombigbee River. At the same time the belt of Pleistocene terraces decreases to a narrow margin.

Landward Boundary.—The inner boundary of the east Gulf Coastal Plain is commonly called the Fall Line, but the term is borrowed from the Embayed section and has little appropriateness here. The Coosa and the Tallapoosa rivers in eastern Alabama and the Chattahoochee on the Georgia border have distinct rapids but most of the streams have not, and between streams no continuous line can be drawn that separates contrasted landscapes. In Alabama there is a belt 10 to 30 miles wide within which streams cut down into the floor of Paleozoic rocks and the divides are capped by Cretaceous sediments. There is a corresponding mingling of coastal plain and plateau topographies and soils. From northern Alabama to southern Illinois, the limit of the coastal plain is approximately at the Tennessee River, which has cut a trench 150 to 300 feet deep in the Paleozoic rocks. Coastal plain sediments are absent from a strip on the west side between the river and the top of the steep valley slope. They are present on the east side in southern Tennessee, covering more than half the surface throughout an area of about 500 square miles. However, the topography of this area is dominated by the underlying Paleozoic rocks in which the streams are incised for several hundred feet. The significant features and topographic history of this area are those of the plateau to the east, not of the Coastal Plain to the west.[1]

Belts of the East Gulf Coastal Plain

Fall Line Hills.—Seaward from the transitional zone is a broad belt corresponding to, and continuous with, the yellow Cretaceous sand hills farther east. Its maximum width in western Alabama and eastern Mississippi is 50 miles. As shown on the map (Fig. 21), this belt lies entirely south and west of the Tennessee River. This is only a rough generalization, for, as stated above, the ragged remains of Cretaceous sands cap the divides for some distance on the other side. West of the river in Tennessee they make a highly irregular belt nowhere more than 8 miles wide, and insignificant north of latitude 36°.

Altitudes in this belt reach more than 700 feet in northern Alabama, but the level declines toward the Black Belt on the south and west. This is sometimes called the Central Pine Belt of Alabama,[2] a dissected upland with a few broad or flat divides. Much of the area is carved to maturity by valleys 100 to 200 feet deep.[3] An exceptional cuesta near the middle of the belt in Alabama contains some areas of rugged wilderness. Relief near the larger streams may reach 250 feet within a half mile. Such areas, while belonging properly in the Coastal Plain *province*, are not "coastal plain" as that term is commonly used by residents.

The underlying rock formations of this zone are the Tuscaloosa next to the Fall Line and the Eutaw farther out. Both are sandy and poorly consolidated but support steep slopes.[4] Except for some fair red soils on the Eutaw the district is unproductive. Two thirds of it remained wooded in 1913.[5]

The Black Belt.—The poorly favored belt of sandy hills just described is succeeded by the richest and best known lowland

[1] For description see W. B. Jewell, Geology and Mineral Resources of Hardin County, Tennessee, Tenn. Geol. Survey, *Bull.* 37, pp. 15–16, 1931.

[2] Harper, R. M., Geol. Survey Ala., *Mon.* 8, p. 78, 1913.

[3] The province boundary as drawn at present is only tentative. Where the country is characterized by narrow valleys cut in the underlying strong Paleozoic rocks it has a typical plateau topography like that of the province on the north.

[4] Smith, E. A., The Coastal Plain of Alabama, *Ala. Geol. Survey*, p. 362, 1894. Lowe, E. N., Soils and Mineral Resources of Mississippi, Miss. Geol. Survey, *Bull.* 12, p. 29, 1915.

[5] Harper, *op. cit.*, p. 84.

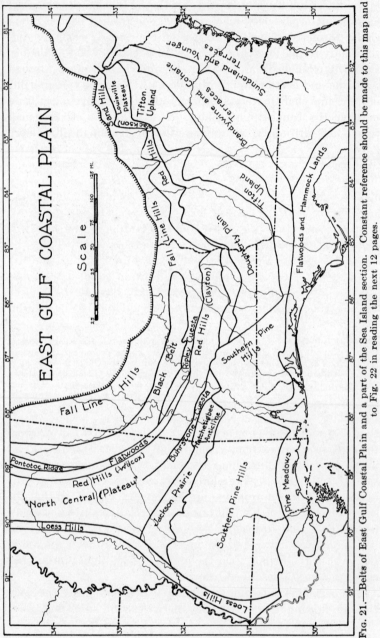

FIG. 21.—Belts of East Gulf Coastal Plain and a part of the Sea Island section. Constant reference should be made to this map and to Fig. 22 in reading the next 12 pages.

in the East Gulf Coastal Plain. This is the Black Belt, so named on account of the deep black residual soil formed on the Selma chalk (formerly known as the Rotten Limestone) which overlies the sandy formations (Fig. 22). With a width of 20 to 25 miles, this belt extends from near the Georgia border west through Alabama and north through Mississippi. With the thinning out of the Selma chalk in that direction the Black Belt gives out a little north of the Tennessee boundary. It is a lowland of very small relief. Its altitude in central and western Alabama is little more

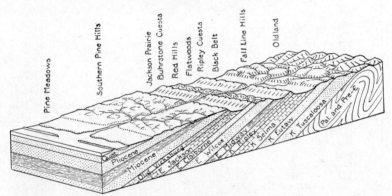

Fig. 22.—Relation of structure and topography in the East Gulf Coastal Plain. Not all of the cuestas shown in the section are prominent throughout the area. The Ripley is locally absent. The Buhrstone is most prominent in western Alabama. Formations from the Vicksburg to the Citronelle are shown as outcropping in a single escarpment, as they do in Mississippi. The corresponding formations in Georgia make two widely separated escarpments. Vertical scale 80 times the horizontal.

than 200 feet between streams, but it rises to 260 feet or more toward its eastern extremity, and to 400 feet near its northern end in Mississippi. Throughout its length, it is bordered on both sides by hills that rise several hundred feet above the plain. The underlying Eutaw formation dips 46 feet to the mile,[1] so that the sand hills on the north might attain their relative altitude within a few miles if that formation were not eroded. It has, however, been much cut down, and the margin of the Eutaw is almost at the level of the Selma. On the opposite side, higher formations cause the cuesta described below.

The permanent streams of the Black Belt are chiefly the large through-flowing rivers, Alabama, Black Warrior, and Tombigbee,

[1] SMITH, *op. cit.*, p. 362.

which have incised their valleys beneath the plain to a maximum depth of 60 feet and have at places prominent chalk bluffs.[1] Smaller streams are not numerous and many of them are intermittent.[2] A lack of surface water has been the chief deficiency of this district. Fortunately the underlying Eutaw carries water, and the Selma chalk contains enough clay beds to keep it under pressure so that parts of the Black Belt, especially the western part, have artesian wells.[3]

The Tombigbee River is closely related to this belt, flowing for 100 miles near its eastern edge in Mississippi and western Alabama, but for most of this distance the river's bed is on the Eutaw sands where it has a flood plain 3 to 7 miles wide, far below the level of the Black Belt.   The situation suggests that the Tombigbee may once have flowed on the Selma chalk when its surface was several hundred feet higher and its edge much farther inland. The stream may then have maintained its course during the erosion cycle that lowered the surface of the chalk and reduced its extent. The Alabama and Tallapoosa rivers show similar relations.

The soil on the Selma chalk is a very calcareous and sticky clay with abundant organic matter, though not the same everywhere.[4] This land has always been prairie. Scattered through the whole belt are patches of sandy soil with a mildly rolling surface, rising perhaps 10, rarely 15, feet above the prairie. These are the remains of a formation believed to have covered the entire area in Pliocene time and commonly ascribed to the "Lafayette." Such patches are, in their natural state, covered with a growth of post oak. Though less fertile than the black prairie, they are most desirable for homes, and until late in the nineteenth century most of the cotton was grown here, the black soils being planted to corn. With the depletion of the black soils and the consequent

[1] An excellent geographic description of the Black Belt is given by H. F. Cleland.   See *Geog. Rev.*, vol. 10, pp. 375–387, 1920.

[2] STEPHENSON, L. W., LOGAN, W. N., and WARING, G. A., U. S. Geol. Survey, *Water Supply Paper 576*, p. 4, 1928.

[3] SMITH, E. A., Underground Water Resources of Alabama, *Ala. Geol. Survey*, p. 21 and Pl. 13, 1907. CRIDER, A. F., Geology and Mineral Resources of Mississippi, U. S. Geol. Survey, *Bull.* 283, p. 16, 1906.

[4] SMITH, E. A., Underground Water Resources of Alabama, p. 13. LOWE, *op. cit.*, p. 29.

introduction of commercial fertilizers, these black lands became the home of cotton.[1]

The Black Belt is obviously a peneplain and probably developed in Pleistocene time or at least since Pliocene deposition.[2] Later uplift accounts for the entrenchment of streams. Probably this rise of the land was the same as that which occasioned the Pleistocene terraces along the coast. Probably also, it was indirectly responsible for the phenomenal gullying near the Fall Line in Georgia, described by Lyell[3] in 1846 when the gullies were less than 20 years old. Following the uplift, steep valleys were cut but the surface remained forested until after 1826. Being then deforested, gullies of great size quickly developed on the steep slopes.

Ripley Cuesta.—The seaward dip of the coastal plain sediments carries the Selma chalk beneath the more resistant Ripley sand and clay, some of whose beds are indurated. This formation, with the Clayton limestone at the base of the Eocene, makes a cuesta in northern Mississippi whose height is 200 to 300 feet above the Black Belt. This cuesta is known as Pontotoc Ridge, a wedge-shaped upland 12 miles wide at the Tennessee line. It has a very hilly scarp slope toward the Black Prairie on the east and a longer, less sharply dissected dip slope to the Flatwoods on the west. In Tennessee this ridge loses its prominence because the adjacent lowlands are poorly developed. Ninety miles farther south it narrows to a point and disappears. For 100 miles

[1] HARPER, R. M., *op. cit.*, p. 89. As pointed out by Harper, the introduction of commercial fertilizer made agriculture much less dependent on native fertility. For crops of high value it may almost be said that the chief merit of a soil is its ability to serve as a base or carrier for fertilizers regardless of whether it has or has not any fertility in its natural state. By the aid of artificial fertilization cotton culture has spread widely over the Coastal Plain. Unless the facts concerning each soil are stated exactly, there is much confusion as to what is meant by a "good soil." This is particularly true in the culture of fruits and other high-priced products.

[2] CLELAND, *op. cit.*, p. 381.

[3] LYELL, SIR CHARLES, "Principles of Geology," vol. 1, 12th ed., 1875, p. 338, also Fig. 23. Also Lyell's "Second Visit to the United States," 1846, vol. 2, p. 25. The gullies described by Lyell are $3\frac{1}{3}$ miles west of Milledgeville in residual clay from the underlying granite, but a more famous and extensive group, known as the Providence gullies, is carved in the Eocene rocks south of Columbus.

south of this point the stronger rocks are either absent or too thin to have much effect on the general level. Here the two low-lands, Black Belt and Flatwoods (see below), are contiguous and distinguished more by soils than by altitude.

East of the Tombigbee River, in Alabama, the Ripley forma-tion resumes its resistant character and its topographic effect, making a belt of hills known as the Hill Prairies. As on the Pontotoc Ridge in Mississippi, summit levels here are often accordant and there are some broad, flat remnants formerly ascribed to the leveling effect of the "Lafayette formation." Whether formed by deposition or by erosion, they represent a general level which antedates the lowlands on both sides. A rugged scarp slope toward the north is marked by deep gullies, and many hillsides bare of vegetation.

East of the median line of Alabama the outcrop of the Ripley widens greatly. Concurrently, the soft beds, which farther west occasion a lowland (the Flatwoods) on the outer slope of the Ripley cuesta, disappear. These changes do not affect the north-ward scarp, which continues under the name of Chunnenugga Ridge, rising 100 to 200 feet above the Black Prairie. The topog-raphy on the dip slope of the Ripley is, however, affected by the absence of a lowland on the south. So it is not surprising that, back from the rough Chunnenugga escarpment, the relief of this belt is small. Bluish sandy clays which could not long remain exposed on the narrow hilly belts farther west, make the surface of what is here called the Blue Marl Lands. Much of the surface is covered by the sandy mantle formerly known as Lafayette.

East of where the Black Belt ends, the sandy rocks of the Ripley are in contact with those of the lower formations. Hence the Blue Marl belt merges with, and is included in, the Fall Line Hills. The entire width is deeply trenched by the Chattahoochee River and dissected by its tributaries. Farther east the com-bined belt narrows and becomes the Sand Hills of the Sea Island section.

The Flatwoods.—Following the Ripley cuesta comes another lowland, the Flatwoods, stretching from near the Tennessee-Mississippi boundary to and beyond the Alabama River. Its low level and relatively smooth surface are due to the easy degradation of a clay formation of the Midway (lowest Eocene) group. Except near its ends, the width of this belt is 5 to 8 miles and its altitude nearly the same as that of the Black Belt. Occasional patches of low sandy hills bearing scrub oak indicate that this lowland, like its larger neighbor, was once covered with a stratum of sand. The surface on the clay is a less perfect peneplain than that of the Black Belt and, unlike that area, was, in its natural state, covered with a fine growth of pine and hardwood. Probably 80 per cent of the area has never been cultivated.[1] Flood plains a few feet below the general level and a fraction of a mile wide afford the only good farms. The cold, gray, stiff clay elsewhere is sticky when wet and hard and cracked when dry and generally poorly drained. Wells in such material yield little water, even were the quality good. Fortunately, as in the Black Belt, artesian water is obtainable from the underlying sands, in this case the Ripley, though deeper wells may go down to the Eutaw.

Red Hills Belt.—The low narrow belt of Flatwoods is bordered on its outer side by the hilly margin of a higher and stronger formation in which sand is much more abundant. This is the local representative of the Wilcox group (Eocene) once designated as "Lignitic." Like other sandy formations already mentioned, this is not generally hard or strong in the sense of being hard to break, but erosion is hindered by the fact that rain is absorbed instead of running off and washing the surface.

The belt of hills, rising 200 to 400 feet above the Flatwoods, is continued eastward with a smaller relative height beyond that lowland, making a very small jog in central Alabama by which the escarpment is transferred to a lower formation, the Clayton limestone at the base of the Eocene. In eastern Alabama and western Georgia the Clayton escarpment overlooks the Blue Marl plain described above.

The escarpment here described, stretching from Georgia to Tennessee, is the inner margin of a dissected upland belt variously designated. In Georgia where it is narrow it is commonly thrown in the Fall Line Hills (Fig. 21). In Alabama it is sometimes called Southern Red Hills.[2] It broadens greatly in Mississippi where it constitutes the "North Central Plateau" or "North Central Hills."[3] As indicated by these names, the surface is

---

[1] Stated in 1913 by Harper, *op. cit.*, p. 96.

[2] HARPER, *op. cit.*, pp. 97*ff.*

[3] U. S. Geol. Survey, *Water Supply Paper* 576, p. 3, Fig. 1, 1928.

dissected.   Bright colored soils, red, yellow, orange, or chocolate, are sufficiently abundant to justify the popular designation "red."   In part these colors belong to the sediments themselves. In part they are the result of weathering; hence very red soils may appear on rocks of neutral tints.   In part the redness belongs to the "Lafayette" mantle, which is poorly discriminated from the residues of weathering in place.

The most essential feature of the Red Hills belt is a nearly plane horizon whose slope, agreeing with the dip of the rocks toward the south and west, is too faint to be perceived.   The altitude of the inner edge throughout its length differs little from 600 feet.   The plain is therefore high enough above adjacent lowlands and large transverse streams to admit of erosion several hundred feet deep.   As a result, some parts are decidedly rough. Generally speaking, erosion in the present cycle has not yet reached maturity, at least not everywhere.   Considerable patches of undissected upland remain in northern Mississippi.   Also in Alabama there remain some "red levels," especially near the outer or lower edge of the belt.   The broad fertile valley floors are quite consistent with this immaturity where the altitude is only 400 to 600 feet and the sediments are poorly consolidated.

In western Tennessee and Kentucky the belt of Red Hills is poorly distinguished from similar upland belts adjacent to them on the east, because the intervening lowlands are not developed. The location of the two great rivers, Mississippi and Tennessee, has been the main factor in determining a broad irregular line of upland on the main divide which is much nearer to the Tennessee than to the Mississippi.[1]

In the North Central Plateau of Mississippi the stage reached in the erosion cycle is indicated by the fact that in most of the area (not all) more and better highways are found on the divides than in the valleys.[2]   Toward the west the dissected upland changes character by reason of a thick deposit of loess (page 80).   On

---

[1] GLENN, L. C., Underground Waters of Tennessee and Kentucky West of the Tennessee River, U. S. Geol. Survey, *Water Supply Paper* 164, 1906. Glenn's geologic map, Pl. 1, with contours at 50-ft. intervals, shows very little control of elevation by geological formations.   See also Francis G. Wells, Ground Water Resources of Western Tennessee, U. S. Geol. Survey, *Water Supply Paper* 656, pp. 6–7, 1933.

[2] SHAW, E. W., The Pliocene History of Northern and Central Mississippi, U. S. Geol. Survey, *Prof. Paper* 108, p. 150, 1918.

the south it falls off with the gentle dip slope to the lowland of the Jackson Prairie.

Buhrstone Cuesta.—The belt of so-called Red Hills has thus far been spoken of as fairly homogeneous in its topography, and so it is, north of central Mississippi. In western Alabama there rises within this belt a line of hills, the ruggedest in the entire Coastal Plain province. This is due to the outcropping of the Tallahatta sandstone formation, familiarly called the Buhrstone, which has been indurated to a degree that is exceptional for the Coastal Plain province. There is locally a bed of white quartzite 20 feet thick.[1] Some hills rise 300 to 400 feet above nearby streams.[2]

The belt of Buhrstone hills, 10 or more miles wide, extends into Mississippi past Meridian[3] at least to the Pearl River where it embraces a wild, picturesque, and thinly populated district.[4] Farther northwest the peculiar character and effect of the formation are lost. Likewise, east of the median line of Alabama its topographic effect is less marked, though not wholly lost, west of the Chattahoochee. In southeastern Alabama the remaining beds which underlie the surface between the Buhrstone and the limestone escarpment on the south are soft and their surface is characteristically flat.[5]

Jackson Prairie.—Within the state of Mississippi the belted character of the Coastal Plain continues to be clear. The North Central Plateau declines gradually to the Jackson Prairie, a gently rolling lowland developed on nonresistant clays, mainly of the Jackson formation (Uppermost Eocene). Many small, rich, black prairies characterize the surface. It is limited on the south by the escarpment of the Southern Pine Hills, described below. Outcropping at the foot of this escarpment is a group of limestones called Vicksburg (Oligocene) whose surface is less smooth than that of the clay belt, though in part included with the latter in the Jackson Prairie. The entire prairie belt, 40 miles wide at

---

[1] Lowe, E. N., Soils and Mineral Resources of Mississippi, Miss. Geol. Survey, *Bull.* 12, p. 73, 1915.

[2] Smith, E. A., Coastal Plain of Alabama, *Ala. Geol. Survey*, p. 396, 1894.

[3] See topographic map of the Meridian quadrangle, U. S. Geological Survey.

[4] Crider, *op. cit.*, p. 28.

[5] Lawson, D. W., Jr., The Coastal Plain of Alabama, Sec. II, *Ala. Geol. Survey*, p. 359, 1894.

the west, narrows toward the east and loses its distinctive character near the Alabama boundary.

Hatchetigbee Anticline.—The low smooth Jackson Prairie of Mississippi gives way in western Alabama to a decidedly rough country. This is partly due to a change in the character of the Jackson formation from calcareous clay to limestone, and partly to the rise in the Hatchetigbee anticline, a flexure of exceptional magnitude for the Coastal Plain. It affects an area at least 50 by 20 miles in extent and represents an uplift of 600 to 700 feet.[1] It brings to the surface formations whose southward dip carries them beneath the surface 10 to 20 miles farther north, among them the strong buhrstone. The rougher parts of this truncated dome are thus accounted for. Much of the rock, especially on the less raised flanks of the dome, is limestone, the equivalent of the Jackson as explained above, together with some overlying Vicksburg. An area of indefinite extent, including that described here, is sometimes called the Lime Hills.[2] As a whole the area is hilly, some parts of it rivaling the rugged hills of the Buhrstone cuesta. It remains two thirds wooded despite the good qualities of the limestone soil.

Dougherty Plain.—In the southeastern corner of Alabama, reaching into Florida and spreading widely in Georgia, these same limestones form an upland of different character. Here it is a plain, in large part nearly flat, its most noticeable features being shallow flat-bottomed or rounded depressions made by solution.[3] These are of all sizes up to several hundred acres and may in some cases represent the collapse of cavern roofs.[4] The name Dougherty Plain is applied only in Georgia, but there is no essential difference between the limestone areas east and west of the Chattahoochee River. The lime-sink district of Florida has the same character.

From the Conecuh River in Alabama (long. 86°30′) to the Flint in Georgia, this limestone plain has the form of a low cuesta,

---

[1] STEPHENSON, L. W., Major Features of the Geology of the Atlantic and Gulf Coastal Plains, *Jour. Wash. Acad. Sci.*, vol. 16, p. 472, 1926.

[2] HARPER, *op. cit.*, pp. 104–106.

[3] COOKE, C. W., Physical Geography of Georgia, *Ga. Geol. Survey*, p. 41 1925. A similar description for the Florida portion is given by Lawson, *op. cit.*, p. 383.

[4] This is a common statement about sinks, generally a gratuitous assumption. Descriptions of sinks in this district do not make such an assumption necessary in most cases.

though its infacing escarpment is not everywhere well defined and is everywhere deeply notched by the valleys of transverse streams. Generally the inner edge is 400 to 500 feet above the sea. West of the Chattahoochee the plain slopes southward into western Florida, to the edge of the Southern Pine Hills. East of the Chattahoochee, the slope is southeastward to the Flint River, beyond which a retreating escarpment of overlying beds marks the edge of the Tifton Upland (see below).

Active solution in the Dougherty Plain has transferred most of the drainage from the surface to underground channels though, as elsewhere, the larger streams run in terraced valleys, each stream terrace probably corresponding to one of the Pleistocene shore terraces.

Southern Pine Hills.—The state of Mississippi was treated by McGee as comprising two great sloping uplands with relief of 200 feet or more, separated by the Jackson Prairie lowland with local relief of less than 50 feet.[1] The southern upland is the Southern Pine Hills. Like the North Central Plateau it is cuesta-like. Its north-facing scarp, beginning near Vicksburg, passes south of Jackson to the south side of the Hatchetigbee anticline. It is held up mainly by the sandy or gravelly, porous, and therefore not easily erodible, Citronelle (Pliocene) formation.[2] Generally this rests on the Catahoula sandstone[3] (Miocene) whose importance as a scarp maker increases westward and decreases eastward as its character gradually changes and it becomes the Tampa limestone. Resistance to erosion is, in this case, aided by actual induration, some of the sandstone being quartzitic,[4] though it is still due mainly to the porous character of most of the beds. The belt of Southern Pine Hills in Mississippi, Alabama, and western Florida is underlain by the Citronelle formation[5] as the corresponding Tifton Upland in Georgia is underlain by the similar but slightly older Alum Bluff (Miocene) formation.

[1] McGee, W J, The Lafayette Formation, U. S. Geol. Survey, 12*th Ann. Rept.*, p. 366, 1901.

[2] For the extent of the Citronelle formation see U. S. Geol. Survey, *Water Supply Paper* 576, geologic map, Pl. 2.

[3] Matson, G. C., The Catahoula Sandstone, U. S. Geol. Survey, *Prof. Paper* 98, pp. 216–217, 1917.

[4] Lowe, *op. cit.*, p. 89. The Catahoula sandstone is here designated as the Grand Gulf formation.

[5] Matson, G. C., The Pliocene Citronelle Formation of the Gulf Coastal Plain, U. S. Geol. Survey, *Prof. Paper* 98L, pp. 167–192, 1917.

Near Jackson on the Pearl River the underlying Vicksburg limestone is worn down to the level of the lowland. Farther east it participates in the escarpment. Still farther, in eastern Alabama and western Georgia, it makes its independent scarp at the edge of the lime sink district and Dougherty Plain. Here the higher scarp-making formations[1] fall back to the south. East of the Chattahoochee they make the Tifton Upland. West of it they persist only in a narrow strip of typical Southern Pine Hills between the Dougherty Plain and the young Pleistocene plain along the coast.

The Southern Pine Hills belt slopes southward from an altitude of 400 or 500 feet to the limit of the Pleistocene coastal terraces, 170 feet A.T. in Mississippi,[2] though altitudes of 300 feet are found a few miles back from this line. Dissection at the north is generally mature or nearly so. Uncut uplands become broader toward the southern margin, but even here the surface is so much dissected that the limit of the young Pleistocene formations might be drawn fairly well by the contrast in topography.[3] The larger streams cross the belt in wide flat-bottomed, steep-sided valleys, 100 to 300 feet deep. The red, orange, or yellow residual loam, which covers the Southern Pine Hills belt, is characteristic of the Citronelle formation (once called Lafayette).

Tifton Upland.—The Tifton Upland has already been described (page 40) in connection with the Sea Island section, in which its eastern half belongs. It is the eastward continuation of the Southern Pine Hills, being the same physiographically, although its surface beds are not quite the same geologically. This belt is continuous across northern Florida, extending east into the Carolinas and west into Texas where it is known as the Kisatchie cuesta. Throughout its extent it has the same sandy soil and the same abundance of long-leaf pine.

[1] In this connection as in many others, it is necessary to warn the reader against taking the word "scarp" too literally. It is used by geologists merely for want of a better word to designate a somewhat steeper slope, generally rougher, which interrupts a plain or a gentler slope, generally in the opposite direction.

[2] MATSON, The Pliocene Citronelle Formation, *op. cit.*, p. 179. This paper discusses the topography on the Citronelle formation, describing its terraces (mainly fluvial) in detail.

[3] *Ibid.*, p. 179.

The inner scarp of the Tifton Upland overlooks the Flint River Valley. At places south of the 32d parallel it is nearly 150 feet high. The topography of the upland is closely similar to that of the Southern Pine Hills in Mississippi and to the Kisatchie cuesta farther west (page 110). Its higher margin shows some solution features. Toward the south these become so abundant that a broad east-west strip along the Georgia-Florida boundary has sometimes received special treatment as a Lime-sink district.[1] It embraces parts of various coastal belts and is continuous with the Lime-sink district of northern Florida.

Transverse Valleys.—Major streams all cross the coastal plain in broad terraced valleys, shallow in the lowlands and at places 300 feet deep in the upland belts. In many places the bluffs are steep and the valleys are wide, flat-bottomed trenches. Extreme widths reach to 7 or 8 miles, and the number of terraces may be three or more. Some of the lower terraces have been definitely correlated with Pleistocene shore terraces. Higher ones are correlated with the Citronelle formation which is in large part a fluvial deposit but to some extent rehandled and redeposited by waves.[2] In general the terraces have a distinctly steeper gradient than the present flood plains, indicating seaward tilt.[3]

Pleistocene Terraces.—Between the Southern Pine Hills and the sea is a narrow strip of coastal lowland generally less than 20 miles wide, narrowing almost to zero near Mobile Bay and broadening somewhat near the Chattahoochee. Generally this lowland, called "Pine Meadows," gives way to the southern Pine Hills, at a height of not over 100 feet.[4] It is known to consist of terraces, which are no doubt continuations of those described farther east. The landscape everywhere is one of faint relief, but low seaward-facing scarps are discernible, and the belt is crossed by shallow swales bordered by slightly higher ground, suggesting natural levees.[5] The last-named features suggest that in a relatively recent stage the coastal belt consisted of delta plains rather than of sea bottom (*cf.* page 113). The presence of the sea at

[1] VEATCH, OTTO, *op. cit.*, p. 34, also Fig. 1, p. 28.

[2] MATSON, *op. cit.*, p. 168.

[3] SMITH, *op. cit.*, p. 54.

[4] McGEE, *op. cit.*, p. 368, gives a good description of the meeting of these two contrasted landscapes.

[5] MATSON, *op. cit.*, p. 190.

various stages is, however, attested not only by the low scarps but by low sand ridges, perhaps 15 feet high, parallel to the shore, evidently dune ridges.[1]

Near the Apalachicola River, the belt widens to 50 miles. The thin covering of Pleistocene sediments is insufficient to obscure completely the older sinkholes or to prevent new ones from forming, and the landscape begins to resemble that of the low west coast of Florida (page 48).

Loess Hills.—All the belts described above, from the North Central Hills of Mississippi to the Gulf, extend to the broad alluvial plain of the Mississippi, by which they are interrupted, and beyond which some of them appear in the West Gulf Coastal Plain. However, the east bluff of the Mississippi is mantled with loess to a great depth, at places 100 feet. All distinctive features of the several belts are thus obscured. The form of the loess body and the characteristic erosion forms within it completely dominate the landscape. On this account separate description is necessary for a strip from 5 to 15 miles wide extending from the Ohio River to the Gulf.

The bluff rises 125 to 250 feet above the flood plain except at the southern end, where it declines. The altitude generally decreases southward from nearly 500 feet at the north. From 30 to 100 feet of its height is accounted for by the thickness of the loess formation. As the thickness decreases rapidly toward the east there is in some parts of the belt a distinct eastward slope (*cf.* Fig. 141, page 509). With the thinning in that direction there is also a change in the character of the material. Its distinctly calcareous character and its great thickness are alike confined to a belt which rarely exceeds 15 miles and may be as narrow as 5 miles. Somewhat farther east the term *loess* becomes inappropriate and the formation is known as brown (or yellow) loam. Though it coats the surface to a maximum distance of 100 miles from the bluffs, its effect on the topography is too small to require mention in the discussion.

In the narrow belt where the loess is thick and slopes are steep the topography is peculiarly rugged. A characteristic property of loess is that, although mealy and easily washed away by a current, it retains very steep slopes where water does not actually move over its surface. Direct runoff is largely forestalled by per-

---

[1] U. S. Geol. Survey, *Water Supply Paper* 576, p. 8, 1928.

colation. The anomaly of almost vertical cliffs 50 feet high in incoherent material is not uncommon. With a fall of 125 to 250 feet from the nearby uplands, the valleys of small streams are narrow, deep, and numerous.

Despite steep slopes the fertility is such that this belt ranks well in agriculture and in density of population. The location of its chief cities, Memphis, Vicksburg, Natches, and Baton Rouge, is due to the fact that the Mississippi at these points is at the immediate foot of the bluff, so that river and railroads meet without an intervening link on land subject to flooding.

HISTORY OF THE EAST GULF COASTAL PLAIN

A long and eventful history is more plainly indicated in this section than in other parts of the Coastal Plain province. The belt of pine meadows along the shore is obviously in its first erosion cycle. Presumably the Southern Pine Hills belt is in its first cycle, now in its maturity near the inner edge, and dating from the deposition of the Citronelle formation. Farther inland no surface except alluvial plains is definitely known to be in its first cycle. The Dougherty Plain is a cuesta lying between two scarps, by whose retreat the plain is constantly narrowed at the inner edge and broadened at the outer. The nearly flat surface which constitutes most of its area bevels the beds. It is the result partly of stripping and partly of peneplanation.

The Black Belt is obviously a peneplain made in a late cycle and now trenched by rejuvenated streams, but it is certain that this was not the first peneplain developed on the landward half of this section. In Mississippi, Shaw finds strong suggestion of four cycles, several of which may have resulted, at least locally, in peneplains.[1] One of these, already suggested, is the plane now reached by most of the higher divides in north central Mississippi. It is essentially the present horizon if isolated hills and ridges be disregarded. Shaw correlated this surface tentatively with the Coosa peneplain of East Tennessee and the Nashville Basin[2]

[1] SHAW, E. W., Pliocene History of Northern and Central Mississippi, U. S. Geol. Survey, *Prof. Paper* 108, p. 151, 1918. The following statements about Appalachian and Coastal Plain cycles are based largely on this paper. Because of the lack of topographic maps Shaw's conclusions (or inferences) are not put forward by him as final.

[2] SHAW, *op. cit.*, p. 153.

(page 434).   It is not improbable that in some such late cycle a peneplain was widely developed on the soft rocks of the Coastal Plain and that all lower land forms are carved from it.

Many divides now rise to the full height of the former peneplain, but by studying and plotting divides in large numbers Shaw found many of them, near major streams, at accordant heights below that of the old plains.   These he interpreted as indicating the beginning of at least one newer peneplain.[1]   Successive rejuvenations resulted in the present terraced valleys.   Presumably it was during the course of these partial cycles in the sandy formations of the upland belts that the newer and lower peneplain was extensively developed on the clays of the Black Belt and the Flatwoods.

The summits of isolated hills rising above the general horizon may reach approximately to an older and higher level which was degraded to make the Coosa.   If a plane be laid down on the tops of the highest hills in northern Mississippi (600 feet in the middle, 700 feet on Pontotoc Ridge, and 800 feet in the northeastern corner) it will rise toward the northeast and coincide essentially with the Highland Rim peneplain in Tennessee.[2]   As that peneplain was widely developed over the stronger Paleozoic rocks at a time when the Cretaceous and early Tertiary rocks of the Coastal Plain were dry land, it no doubt covered a large part of the present Coastal Plain.   If this reasoning is correct, there have been at least two cycles of general, and one of local, peneplanation (Black Belt, etc.) since the inner Coastal Plain became dry land. There is nothing improbable in this outline of events, but the favor with which it is regarded is based quite as much on deductive reasoning as on inferences from the altitudes of divides and isolated remnants.

Back of the history here summarized lies the making of the surface on which all the coastal plain sediments rest.   The structure of the latter is favorable to artesian water, and information gained by drilling is sufficiently abundant to justify the statement that the basal Cretaceous sediments were laid down on a peneplain,

---

[1] Such incipient peneplains developed only near streams have come to be known as *straths* or *strath terraces* (see page 181).

[2] HAYES, C. W., Physiography of the Chattanooga District, U. S. Geol. Survey, 19*th Ann. Rept.*, pt. 2, Pl. 2, 1899.

cut on folded Paleozoic rocks.[1] This peneplain was made, or at least finished, in Early Cretaceous time.

In this section the buried peneplain slopes about 30 feet per mile. Plainly it has been tilted seaward, since no peneplain could be developed on such a slope. If projected inland with the same gradient, it would pass high over all peneplain remnants in the Appalachian Highland. The Cumberland peneplain in East Tennessee slopes about 10 feet per mile. These two surfaces were formerly regarded as being a single continuous surface bent at the Fall Line, but this is no longer generally believed.

With the cutting down of the Cretaceous rocks and the retreat of their inner edge, the buried Cretaceous peneplain is constantly being exhumed and dissected. As denudation and dissection take time, and must be well advanced before the level of the hilltops is affected, it is to be expected that a margin of the denuded old land will represent the resurrected peneplain. In agreement with this assumption it is found that in northeastern Mississippi the gently sloping Coosa (?) peneplain on the coastal plain sediments gives way at their edge to a much steeper peneplain on Pre-Cretaceous rocks.

MISSISSIPPI ALLUVIAL PLAIN

General Relations

The section here considered embraces the delta of the Mississippi and its bottom lands within the limits of the Coastal Plain, also those of its tributaries in so far as they merge with those of the main stream and can be included within a generalized boundary. In some ways this great area of alluvial plain is like that of all other streams which cross this province to the Gulf of Mexico. Separate treatment as a section is desirable partly because of mere size. The aggregate area below flood level alone is 30,000 square miles and the entire section is larger, perhaps 35,000 square miles. The area actually flooded in 1927 was about 20,000 square miles.[2]

The Mississippi Embayment.—This vast low plain owes its existence in part to a structural trough. In part it is erosional.

---

[1] Stephenson, L. W., Major Marine Transgressions and Regressions and Structural Features of the Gulf Coastal Plain, *Amer. Jour. Sci.*, vol. 16, p. 281, 1928.

[2] At the request of J. H. Wheat the following estimates were made from

The most important factor in its present topography is aggradation.   Casual inspection of the geologic map shows a broad structural trough between the Appalachian uplift on the east and the
Ozark and Ouachita highlands on the west.   This part of the
province is familiarly known as the Mississippi embayment.
Within the embayment the outcrops of successive coastal plain
formations trend north and south.   Features encountered in
traveling west from northern Alabama and central Tennessee
toward the axis of the trough are similar to those seen elsewhere in
traveling toward the Gulf Coast.   For a large part of its history
this structural trough was submerged, and when it emerged the
Mississippi followed its axis to the sea.   Probably depression has
recurred from time to time and is still recurring, as evidenced by
the New Madrid Earthquake (page 85).

In the later epochs of coastal plain deposition the embayment
practically ceased to exist.   The rocks which now form the
Kisatchie cuesta (Miocene) were laid down near a shore which
stretched nearly east and west.   As these sediments formed rock
which is exceptionally strong for the Coastal Plain, a later rise
of the continent gave to this formation the effect of a transverse
barrier.   In crossing the barrier the alluvial plain of the Mississippi is narrower than at any other point between Illinois and the
Gulf (Pl. 3).   Its greater breadth farther north is favored in
various ways: (1) Sinking no doubt continues; (2) streams, being
longitudinal, are free to follow the outcrops of weaker rocks;
(3) the main stream receives important tributaries whose flood
plains coalesce; (4) the rivers have expended their energy in widening their valleys here while cutting through the Kisatchie barrier;
(5) the northern part of the plain is older than the southern part.

The Erosional Factor.—Despite the omnipresence of aggradation in this section at present, the trough between the bluffs
is to be credited largely to excess of erosion.   Subsidence of the
axis, more than of the adjacent uplands, has no doubt lowered the
plain somewhat near the northern end and has made possible
the great thickness of the delta deposits.   A former Mississippi
no doubt flowed from Illinois to the Gulf on a surface which was

---

data on hand in the Office of the Chief of Engineers, U. S. Army: Land
subject to overflow 19,200,000 acres; overflowed in 1927, 12,500,000 acres
(19,531 square miles); to be left to overflow (spillways) under the new plan
of the Mississippi River Commission, 6,048,000 acres.

almost even with that of the adjacent uplands. Such a condition probably existed in late Tertiary time not long before the Glacial Epoch, when the "Lafayette" gravel was laid down by overloaded streams over large areas. It survives on some of the present Mississippi bluffs and some residual plateau surfaces within the alluvial plain (page 87).

From the standpoint of present-day physiography the story of the Mississippi trough below Cairo previous to the late Tertiary plain, just described, may be regarded as ancient history. It may be thought of as embracing repeated epochs of marine sedimentation alternating with land conditions in each of which the river reappeared, either cutting down or filling up its valley. Even since the cutting of the present trough began, conditions have not been uniform. It is fairly certain that the present trough was once deeper than it is now and that filling is now in progress, or at least that such is the latest record. This is inferred from the depth of alluvium below the channel. From Cairo to Memphis its depth below low water is 150 to 200 feet.[1] As the river is not known to scour its channel to depths greater than 100 feet, it appears that downcutting has ceased and deposition has occurred.

It thus appears that the total amount of downcutting has been somewhat greater than the present height of the bluffs. These are 150 to 250 feet high on the east side, except in the coastal lowland of southern Louisiana. Bluffs on the west side are lower except from Little Rock to Cape Girardeau where the boundary is against the Interior Highland.

New Madrid Earthquake.—The earthquakes of 1811 and 1813 deserve mention because of their manifest association with crustal movements in the Mississippi embayment, and also because of their direct topographic effects.[2] These latter are by no means negligible. The most easily demonstrable features are lake basins made by sudden subsidence. Reelfoot Lake in the northwest corner of Tennessee, partly or wholly of this origin, is 20 miles long and at least 20 feet deep in places. Many smaller lakes were formed, some of them deep, and much larger tracts are known to have sunk while others rose above the flood level. Several of the

[1] Mississippi River Commission, Progress Report for 1881, Appendix *J*. Pl. 12.

[2] FULLER, M. L., The New Madrid Earthquake, U. S. Geol. Survey, *Bull.* 494, 1912, an excellent compend which reviews historical accounts, describes features produced, discusses causes, and gives bibliography.

upheaved areas are many miles in length but relatively narrow, alternating with swales of similar origin.   Since they are elongated in the direction of the valley and of the prevailing drainage,

Fig. 23.—Stumps of timber killed by submergence during the New Madrid earthquake, Reelfoot Lake, Tenn.   (*Fuller, U. S. Geol. Survey, Bull.* 494.)

it is not always easy to decide whether the origin of a given swell was tectonic or erosional.   Other features make it fairly certain that the New Madrid earthquake was not the first in this region and there is no reason to conclude that it is to be the last.

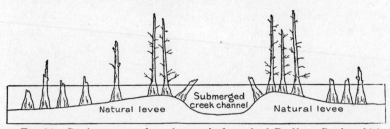

Fig. 24.—Section across the submerged channel of Reelfoot Creek, which may still be traced on the bottom of the lake shown in Fig. 23.   On the slopes of the natural levees, trees were killed by submergence and only stumps remain. On top of the natural levees the water was not deep enough to kill the cypress trees.   (*Fuller, U. S. Geol. Survey Bull.* 494.)

Less important in topography, but very significant as records, are fault scarps, landslides, cracks made by soil waves, and great quantities of ejected sand.   There can be no doubt of the magnitude of the disturbance.   It is almost equally certain that it represents a continuation of the process by which the Mississippi embayment came into being, namely a subsidence of the hard rock floor, probably with incidental deep-seated faulting. The effect of such dislocation would be to shake down the loose alluvium, causing movement from the sides toward the axis of depression, resulting in faint corrugation and expelling sand with the ground water.

It is interesting to note that the profile of the Mississippi shows some distinct deviations from the uniform gradient which might be expected.[1] In an exceptionally steep descent just below New Madrid there is a fall of 4 feet in about as many miles, and from 37 to 44 miles above Memphis the fall is approximately 1 foot per mile. It is followed by a similar steep slope after an interval of 11 miles. The proximity of the first of these exceptional slopes to New Madrid suggests a relation to faulting but this is not proved.[2]

Older Divides

Crowley's Ridge.—A noteworthy feature in Arkansas and Missouri is Crowley's Ridge (Pl. 3 and Fig. 25)[3] a maturely dissected remnant of the higher, nearly level plain in which the present alluvial trough was carved. Extending from Thebes, Ill., to Helena, Ark., it is 200 miles long and clearly defined by steep lateral slopes which are remarkably parallel. Its width averages about 3 miles in the southern half where the height is 100 to 150 feet, and 12 miles in the northern half where the maximum height above the plain is 250 feet. The ridge trends north and south and approximately bisects the alluvial plain, the Missis-

[1] Report by a Special Board of Engineers on Survey of Mississippi River, House Document, vol. 1, Sixty-first Congress, 1st session, 1909, p. 136, Profile of Mississippi River. See also, Annual Report of the Chief of Engineers, U. S. Army, 1909, pt. 3, Appendix *PPP*; Report of the Mississippi River Commission, p. 2706, Table 2, Low Water Slope, Mississippi River, Cairo to Memphis, 1908.

[2] C. Wythe Cooke (personal communication) suggests that this represents the limit of Pleistocene submergence at the Brandywine stage and that the second steep slope bears the same relation to the Coharie submergence. The altitudes at the foot of each slope (266.5 and 211.4 ft., respectively) differ little from those of the inner edges of the several terraces. The third steep slope (altitude 200 ft.) is not correlated with any terrace.

[3] A proper reading of these paragraphs requires reference to the geologic map of the United States or of the states concerned.

sippi in this part of its course being at or near the foot of the east
bluff.   The sedimentary rocks which compose the ridge are of the
same age as those in the Bluffs on the east, even to the late
Tertiary surficial gravel which covered the plain before
entrenchment.

The position of the ridge, its topography, and its constituent
rocks all indicate that it was an important divide.[1]   The making

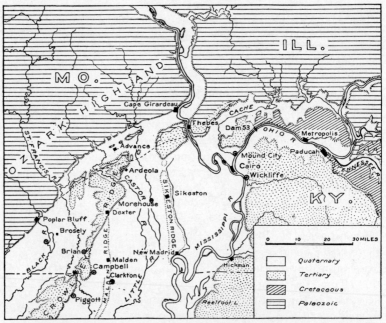

Fig. 25.—Geologic map of head of Mississippi embayment showing the
northern end of Crowley's Ridge. (*Matthes, Amer. Assoc. Pet. Geologists,
vol.* 17.)

of the wide alluvial plain in its northern part was the work of two
great rivers, not of one.   It is equally true that more than one
stream contributed to the making of the plain farther south where
lateral planation has consumed the former divides.

The form and trend of Crowley's Ridge in northern Arkansas
suggest that it may have originated as a cuesta,[2] but this explana-

[1] BRANNER, J. C., Preface to Ark. Geol. Survey, *Ann. Rept. for* 1889, p. xiii.
[2] MARBUT, C. F., The Geographic Development of Crowley's Ridge,
Proc. Boston Soc. Nat. Hist., vol. 26, pp. 481–488, 1895.   Marbut at that
time favored the hypothesis that the ridge is analogous to the cuestas of

tion fails to account for the ridge as a whole. Its surface was planed (probably peneplaned) before the spreading of the late Tertiary gravel. Later streams took their courses on this smooth, gravel-covered surface without regard to any diversity in strength of the underlying rocks. They crossed the outcrops at a low angle, leaving the divide (now Crowley's Ridge) composed of older rocks at the north and successively younger rocks toward the south.[1] The position of the ridge is therefore independent of geologic structure.

Junction of the Mississippi and Ohio Rivers.—As the valley west of the ridge is essentially as large as that on the east, it is generally agreed that the only river capable of cutting it was the Mississippi. It is accordingly assumed that during the last great excavation the Mississippi and the Ohio flowed on opposite sides of Crowley's Ridge, uniting at some point below Helena, Ark., a city on the Mississippi at the extremity of the ridge.[2]

It was presumably late in the Pleistocene Epoch that the Mississippi left its westerly course and broke through the ridge to join the Ohio higher up. Its present course from Cape Girardeau to Cairo carries it through a gap in a ridge of strong Paleozoic rocks. In the same ridge 15 miles farther west is a gap 9 miles wide. There is also a narrow passage at the southern boundary of Missouri where the St. Francis River now goes through. Both of these latter openings are believed to have been occupied by the Mississippi during the progress of its change. The manner of this change has been variously conceived, but in any case it is necessary to think of the stream on the west as being so raised as to spill over the divide at its lowest points. The upper Mississippi basin was glaciated at least five times, in each of which it may be assumed that the river received an excessive load of sediment and aggraded a part or all of its course. This is known to have occurred at the place here considered, at least during the Illinoian and later glacial stages. It was believed by Branner that

---

Mississippi, bearing the same relation to the west side of the embayment as those do to the east side.

[1] The geological map of Arkansas (1929) shows Wilcox beds at the north, giving way to Claiborne, and finally to Jackson at the south. Still older beds may compose the ridge at the north end in Missouri but the Tertiary is not subdivided on the geological map of that state.

[2] BRANNER, *loc. cit.*

the several gaps were used by the river in succession, beginning at the south. Matthes[1] puts forward the hypothesis that all the gaps were occupied simultaneously as spillways for the swollen and aggrading Mississippi as the Illinoian glacial stage drew to a close. Neither hypothesis is without its difficulties. If the river took one of these courses and held it until the channel was cut deep in the limestone barrier, it is not clear why that course should be abandoned and another begun at the top of the limestone. On the other hand, to cut all these limestone trenches simultaneously would require an abundance of water and a nice balance. It is reasonable to assume that during the wasting of the Illinoian ice sheet, and before eastward drainage began in the region of the Great Lakes, the Mississippi carried a very large volume of water. It is not impossible that three or four separate channels of the river might continue during pronounced downcutting if the stream was at no time very much above grade.

Ohio-Tennessee Divide.—The course of the Ohio at the time referred to above was not that of the present Mississippi below Cairo but at the east foot of Crowley's Ridge along the line now followed (in part) by the St. Francis. At the same time the Tennessee farther east was following the same course that its waters do today, *i.e.*, from its present mouth down the Ohio and the present Mississippi.[2] The Ohio was then flowing across southern Illinois from 5 to 15 miles farther north than at present. Its old course is marked by a prominent trough, the Cache River sag. It is clearly shown on the topographic sheets of the U. S. Geological Survey and appears on the geologic map of Illinois as a band of alluvium separated from the present Ohio channel by hard rocks. It is fair to assume that the Ohio changed its course to join the Tennessee for the same reason that the Mississippi joined the Ohio, namely, to find a lower channel. Presumably, too, the shift of the Ohio occurred later, after its valley was aggraded by the sediment-laden waters of the Mississippi. The exact reason for breaking over at the place where it did has not been investigated.

---

[1] MATTHES, F. E., Mississippi Valley Studies, Report of Committee on Sedimentation, Nat. Res. Council Reprint and Cir. Ser., No. 98, pp. 87–88, 1931. The low passes in the ridge are accounted for in this paper by the fact that the Ohio River flowed at its eastern edge, undercutting its bluff and thus cutting away the heads of small streams which then, as now, flowed northwest.

[2] MATTHES, *loc. cit.*

Flood Basins

Yazoo Basin.—Peculiarities in the drainage of this section are accounted for mainly by the fact that the flood plain of an aggrading stream slopes from, instead of toward, the stream.   The higher edge near the stream is the so-called natural levee.   The lowest line on such a plain is often at or near the foot of the bluff.   The course of the Yazoo in Mississippi is thus determined.   It gathers its waters from the very banks of the great river and would run as an independent stream to the sea if not intercepted by the Mississippi which swings over to the foot of the bluff at Vicksburg. The sloping alluvial plain thus drained by the Yazoo from Memphis to Vicksburg, at both of which points the Mississippi washes the foot of the bluff,[1] is known as the Yazoo Basin or sometimes inaccurately, as the "Yazoo delta."[2]   Its southward slope of $7\frac{1}{2}$ inches per mile is about twice the gradient of the Mississippi River (on account of meanders) and exceeds the eastward slope toward the Yazoo.   Subordinate streams flow down the slope in courses almost parallel to the Mississippi, but tortuous and often interlacing, the gradient being much too small to support a system of dendritic drainage.   The entire Yazoo Basin was subject to overflow until the levee system was completed in 1886.   It was then thickly forested but is now a leading cotton district.[3]

Basins on the West Side.—The St. Francis River at the east foot of Crowleys Ridge is almost the counterpart of the Yazoo. It is enabled to enter the Mississippi only because the river and the ridge come together at Helena.

The White and the Arkansas from the Interior Highlands manage after a fashion to keep open a passage through the aggrading banks of the Mississippi, but only by wandering through a web of tortuous channels, themselves raised above the plain.   For much of the distance below Little Rock the Arkansas is paralleled by

[1] See p. 81 on the location of these and other cities.

[2] The St. Francis, Yazoo, Tensas, and Atchafalaya basins are shown on Fig. 26, p. 92.   If attention be centered on the natural levees of the Mississippi, Arkansas, Ouachita, and Red Rivers, it will be seen that each of the basins named is almost surrounded by higher land.

[3] The floods of 1927 covered the southern half of the Yazoo basin.   See map in the Report of Chief of Engineers, U. S. Army, Document No. 90, 70th Congress, 1st session.

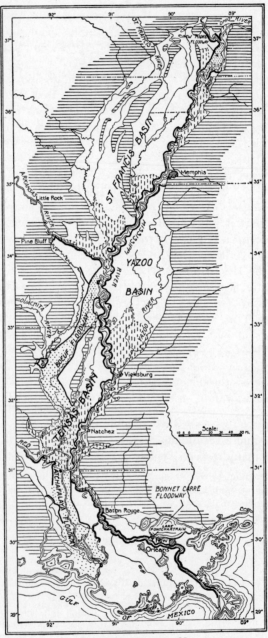

For caption see page 93.

streams of the Yazoo type. Bartholomew Bayou, which almost touches the Arkansas at Pine Bluff 30 miles below Little Rock, fails to reach either that stream or the Mississippi, but wanders for 100 miles (probably 200 along its crooked way) to reach the remote Ouachita, which after another 100 miles joins the Tensas (also of the Yazoo type) and ultimately the Red River. Even the Red River can only be said with reservations to enter the Mississippi, for before reaching the main stream it mingles its waters with the Atchafalaya, a distributary on the west side of the great delta.[1]

The Tensas basin comprises the flood plain on the west side of the Mississippi from the Arkansas to the Red River. It is in all essential respects like the Yazoo basin though less simple. In its southern part it merges with the basin of the Ouachita which, farther north, is separated from the Tensas by a low swell not subject to overflow. At the Arkansas-Louisiana boundary the banks of the Mississippi are 112 feet above the sea, while those of the Ouachita, 50 miles away, are 49 feet lower. The latter locality is believed by Veatch to be on the downthrown (north) side of a fault (page 119), along which a recent movement of 25 feet has occurred,[2] but with all possible allowance for this fact, a difference of at least 24 feet must be ascribed to the normal slope of the flood plain away from the Mississippi. The last movement on the fault across the Ouachita is credited by Veatch with producing the extensive swamps on the north side near the state line.

The Mississippi Delta

Typical and Exceptional Features.—The delta of the Mississippi is in many respects typical. It has a web of distributaries,

---

[1] No description of this drainage pattern can be of much value without examination of maps. The streams named are shown on Pl. 3. An excellent general map, entitled The Alluvial Valley of the Mississippi, is issued by the Mississippi River Commission, scale 1 inch to 5 miles, 1921. Another, entitled Mississippi River Flood of 1927, is referred to above.

[2] VEATCH, A. C., U. S. Geol. Survey, *Prof. Paper*, 46, p. 55.

Fig. 26.—Map of the Mississippi Alluvial Plain, showing plans for protection from floods. Areas above flood level are ruled horizontally. Artificial levees designed to protect from the highest flood are shown by heavy lines. Stippled areas are to be protected from minor floods by lower levees with "fuse plugs," not shown. In times of major floods these areas constitute the "floodways." Areas ruled vertically may be covered by backwater from the main streams. The several "basins," St. Francis, Yazoo, and Tensas, are outlined by natural and artificial levees and land above flood level. (*Report of Chief of Engineers, U. S. Army, Document No.* 90, *70th Congress, 1st Session.*)

each of the larger ones having its own natural levees.   The surface, while characteristically flat, has been unequally aggraded. Some parts approaching flood level are dry most of the time. Large areas are covered by even minor floods.   Spots of considerable size like lakes Pontchartrain, Salvador, and others, remain below the water table.   They are covered by salt or fresh water essentially at sea level.   The whole has long been sinking, probably, in part, because of accumulating load, in part for other reasons.[1]   Beds deposited when the delta was young are now several thousand feet below the surface.

In some other features the Mississippi delta is less typical, and in some it is apparently unique.   The form of its seaward margin is determined more by the river and less by the waves than that of most great deltas.   West of the main channel the waters of the Gulf have made a beginning toward straightening the ragged edge by cutting back projections and building bars and barriers, but the eastern margin is a maze of indefinite banks, mud flats, marshes, islands and forelands with no definite boundary. Most of the water is carried by the main stream which flows past New Orleans and preserves its unity to the "Head of the Passes" where the final branching of distributaries begins (Pl. 3).   These form the "bird-foot," whose several claws or fingers are 20 to 25 miles long.   Each pass is bordered by natural levees which lie above water for a width of one or several miles. Between these fingers are the waters of the Gulf.   The rate at which the margin of the bird-foot advances seaward is 300 to 340 feet per year, or roughly 1 mile in 16 years.

Permanence of Channels.—The extent to which the main channel and the several passes have been able to maintain their form and individuality is remarkable.[2]   Silt-laden water flows through the lengthening passes almost without gradient.   A channel for ships is kept open only by constant dredging.   Overflow of banks is common.   Yet permanent openings through these banks seem to be forestalled by the river's own preference

[1] SHAW, E. W., Mud Lumps at the Mouth of the Mississippi, U. S. Geol. Survey, *Prof. Paper* 85, p. 18, 1914.   Shaw minimizes the effect of isostasy and points out other reasons for sinking.

[2] HILGARD, E. W., The Exceptional Nature and Genesis of the Mississippi Delta, *Science*, vol. 24, pp. 861–866, 1906; abst. in *Bull. Geol. Soc. Amer.*, vol. 17, p. 731, 1907; also, A New Development in the Mississippi Delta, *Pop. Sci. Monthly*, March, 1912.

for its present channels. Twenty-five miles above its mouth it might reach the sea by a ¼-mile cut through its bank, which it sometimes overflows. One hundred miles from its mouth (*i.e.*, near New Orleans) it might reach the sea in 10 miles except for the artificial levee built a few decades ago. All elementary treatises on deltas prescribe just such changes, yet the Mississippi does not make them. Hilgard ascribes this permanence of channels to the exceptionally tough clay shown in the mud lumps. For various reasons this explanation is not convincing.[1] It is not yet clear just how the river is adjusted to its present course, or why it meanders so little in the last 200 miles, or why it requires a channel 100 to 200 feet deep from Baton Rouge to the Gulf, or why low water at New Orleans should be lower than mean tide level at the mouth,[2] or just how the great burden of silt is carried to the sea.

Mud Lumps.—A unique feature of the Mississippi delta is its mud lumps. These are domes of fine, tough, structureless clay rising 2 to 10 feet (rarely more) above the shallow water, generally within a mile or two of the ends of the passes. They may reach an acre in extent, or several may coalesce to form a larger island. The period of rise may be a matter of hours, or of days, or of months. One such island has survived 100 years; others may collapse and subside. Gas issues, often in typical mud volcanoes. Mud lumps constitute one of the most serious problems in the navigation of the Mississippi. They are too rare to be of great importance physiographically, but they are of great interest from the standpoint of geophysics. Investigation of them has gone sufficiently far to give high probability to the theory that thin layers of highly mobile clay under pressure of accumulating sediments on the delta are caused to flow laterally and break through to the surface at favorable points.[3]

The Five Salt Islands.—Near the shore in the western part of the delta, ranged in a northwest-southeast line, are five so-called islands, the smallest having an area of less than half a

[1] *Cf.* SHAW, *op. cit.*, p. 19.

[2] HAAS, W. H., The Mississippi Problem, *Ann. Assoc. Amer. Geog.*, vol. 19, p. 6, 1929.

[3] Shaw's work, already cited, contains the best available descriptions and the fullest discussion of the problem. It includes also an excellent description of the lower delta.

square mile and the largest a diameter of 2 miles.[1]   All but one lie within the salt marsh, Cote Carline (Jefferson's Island) at the northwest end of the line being surrounded by prairie.   All are conspicuous as dry ground, rolling if not hilly, the highest point rising 150 feet above the marsh.   All have been known as valuable land since colonial times, but it was not until the eager search for salt during the Civil War that these domes came to be known as the surface expression of buried masses of rock salt. It is now known that these and other similar eminences in Louisiana and Texas (page 114) correspond to structural domes beneath.   Other similar structural domes have no topographic expression.   These structures contain not only salt but often sulphur, petroleum, anhydrite, and limestone (or dolomite). The great salt mines, sulphur mines (wells), and some of the great oil fields of the western Gulf Coastal Plain are in structures of this character.   Salt, being a weak rock and easily deformed, is believed to have flowed under pressure, rising in domes where the pressure was less.[2]   (*Cf.* mud lumps, above.)   The structures are, however, older than the present topography.   They have been subject to considerable erosion, perhaps in more than one cycle.

History of the Mississippi Alluvial Plain

The early history of this section has much in common with that of its neighbors.   It is intimately connected with the subsidence of the great structural trough between the Appalachian and Interior Highlands.   The effect of this continues.   Without the Mississippi embayment, with its relatively young and weak rocks, the alluvial plain below Cairo would be much the same as that above Cairo, perhaps equal in width to the Ohio and Mississippi flood plains combined.

It is not often that one erosion cycle is brought to completion over a large area before another begins.   But probably no serious error is involved in thinking of this part of the Coastal Plain province as essentially leveled up, or leveled down (partly one, partly the other) for a new start in erosion, late in Tertiary

[1] Veatch, A. C., The Five Islands, State Expt. Sta. La., *Spec. Rept.*, no. 3, pp. 209–262, 1899.

[2] DeGolyer, E., Origin of North American Salt Domes, *Bull. Amer. Assoc. Petroleum Geol.*, vol. 9, pp. 831–874, 1925.

time.[1] Existing remnants of the resulting surface are, in many cases, covered with gravel, but it is not necessary to assume that the whole surface was thus covered, or to adopt any theory as to the origin of this gravel.[2]

It was in this surface, after uplift, that the Mississippi and its tributaries sunk their lower courses in early Pleistocene time, meandering widely, planing away what lay above the new grade except for one prominent divide left standing as Crowley's Ridge, and another in southern Illinois between the former Ohio and its present course. Stream channels were sunk at this time below their present levels, probably because the land stood higher after the late Pliocene uplift. Later the continent stood lower than at present (Port Hudson submergence) and flood plains were built up, of which only fragments now remain in the terraces of the Port Hudson formation (*cf.* Red River, page 115). This shift from deep valley cutting to deep valley filling on account of crustal movements was no doubt complicated with similar effects due to excessive stream load during glacial stages, alternating with cutting power in interglacial stages, unless counteracted by changes in the level of the sea (page 34). Incidental to unequal filling by different streams came the change of the Mississippi's course by which it joined the Ohio farther north.

It was during an epoch of aggradation that the great accumulation of loess occurred on the adjacent uplands. Essentially, this was the work of winds which gathered the dust from the flood plains, presumably subject to greater alternation of flooding and desiccation than at present.[3]

The phenomenal delta-building habit of the Mississippi belongs to its modern history. It is noteworthy that down to

[1] *Cf.* DANE, C. H., Upper Cretaceous Formations of Southwestern Arkansas, Ark. Geol. Survey, *Bull.* 1, p. 169, 1929.

[2] This is the old question of the Lafayette formation (McGee, W J, U. S. Geol. Survey, *12th Ann. Rept.*, 1891) which was once believed to represent extensive submergence of the low margin of the continent and later explained (Chamberlin and Salisbury, *Geology*, vol. 3, p. 305) as a deposit from overloaded streams. In both cases a topography of small relief is assumed. It is known now that many of the deposits once called Lafayette are of other ages and diverse origins, but the fact still remains that there is much late Tertiary gravel and sand associated with a surface of very small relief.

[3] CHAMBERLIN, T. C., Supplementary Hypothesis Respecting the Origin of the Loess of the Mississippi Valley, *Jour. Geol.*, vol. 5, pp. 785–802, 1897.

Pleistocene time the waves and currents of the Gulf succeeded fairly well in distributing the sediments brought down by the river, so that the deposits near its mouth were not much thicker than contemporary deposits to the east and west.   On the other hand, Pleistocene and Recent sediments, generally measured in hundreds of feet, are thousands of feet thick in the present delta. This may be partly because the stream's load is much greater since the advent of glacial drift in its upper basin.   It is conceivable that local subsidence permits sediments to accumulate which would otherwise have been distributed along the shore. Again, it may be that shore currents are less strong than formerly. One of the reasons why currents in the Gulf are now so feeble is that Florida stands in the way.   Through most of Tertiary time this barrier was submerged.   Only recently has it had its present length.   Hence, so far as currents are concerned, the conditions for delta building are probably at their best.

THE FLOOD PROBLEM

Rivers were the first highways in the interior of the continent. The oldest settlements are on their banks, often on sites liable to floods.   Cultivation of the natural levees dates from the earliest times.   The occupation of the alluvial plains has been limited mainly by floods.   With the completion of a levee system in the 1880's, much of the Mississippi flood plain was quickly occupied though great areas of wooded swamp still remain, especially on the west side.   The river was supposed to be walled in, and the United States Army was supposed to be powerful enough to tell it where not to go.   A long series of floods, culminating in the disaster of 1927, brought about a different temper.   The present disposition is to ascertain what the river's will is, and then to make the best compromise possible.   It is conceded that a great aggrading stream must have the right of occasional use of some land outside its banks.   Such use is normal, not abnormal, and within limits the choice of such lands is to be made by the river, not by man.[1]

[1] An excellent symposium on Flood Control with special reference to the Mississippi River is published by the American Society of Civil Engineers as *Paper* 1709, reprinted from the *Transactions* of that society, vol. 93, pp. 655–969, 1929.   See especially the paper by N. C. Grover on Run-off Characteristics of the Mississippi Drainage Basin, pp. 690–696.

The Mississippi River drains 1,250,000 square miles and has an average discharge of 700,000 cubic feet per second. But this varies from a minimum of 100,000 to 4,000,000 second-feet.[1] The flood in 1927 was not only 55 feet deeper than average low water[2] but many times broader and swifter. It is obviously out of the question that one and the same channel should be adjusted to all the varying needs of so changeable a stream. Ideally a channel might exist, large enough to carry the greatest flood and idle most of the time. But this is not in accord with Nature's economics as applied to graded or aggrading streams. Her plan is to keep open a channel of moderate size and use other ways to dispose of extraordinary floods.

The relinquishment of certain lands to the river (some of which may be farmed when not needed by the river) may diminish flood height elsewhere in more than one way. It may form a broad collateral passage to the sea. Such "spillways" are now contemplated by the Mississippi River Commission.[3] It has also been proposed that broad low-lying or swampy areas be abandoned to flood waters without regard to their removal by current, partly to afford opportunity for evaporation, partly for mere storage of excess water in order to relieve the channel downstream.[4] Large areas of such low-lying back swamps are still very sparsely occupied and can be used as here suggested (Fig. 26). Evaporation will no doubt be an important factor.

Both plans here described are in harmony with Nature's way. The efficiency of either, or the sufficiency of both, is an engineering problem.

[1] This is the rate at which water from all sources is estimated by N. C. Grover (personal communication) to have entered the Lower Mississippi basin in 1927. In the paper cited above, Grover uses the conservative estimate of $3\frac{1}{2}$ million second-feet. In that paper he also uses the official estimate of the capacity of the Mississippi River channel at New Orleans, namely, $1\frac{1}{2}$ million second-feet. He believes that it cannot be counted on to carry more than $1\frac{1}{4}$ million second-feet.

[2] More exact figures are given by W. H. Haas, The Mississippi Problem, *Ann. Assoc. Amer. Geog.*, vol. 19, pp. 1–7, 1929.

[3] The Mississippi River Commission issues maps of the Alluvial Plain, scale 1 inch = 4 mile, with overprint showing the plan of works to regulate the river.

[4] MORGAN, ARTHUR E., The Mississippi, *Atlantic Monthly*, November, 1927, pp. 663–668. See also pp. 737–754 in the symposium cited on page 98.

WEST GULF COASTAL PLAIN

GENERAL DESCRIPTION

The alluvial plain of the lower Mississippi divides the Gulf Coastal Plain into two sections which are much alike in general plan. Some of the individual belts and escarpments may be traced most of the way from Georgia to the Rio Grande. The western section, like the eastern, ends at the Mississippi bluff, but the western bluff is lower than the eastern and less deeply covered with loess. The Coastal Plain ends at the north against the Ouachita Mountain province in Arkansas and Oklahoma at the line of contact between Cretaceous and Paleozoic rocks.

Western Boundary.—In undertaking to delimit the Coastal Plain province in Texas we are face to face with the fact that geology is not one of the exact sciences. The relation of a particular area to several provinces may be such as to leave optional its inclusion in one province or another. Boundary lines drawn to show certain relations may obscure others.

The question at issue here is how much of the area of Lower Cretaceous terrane should be included in the Coastal Plain province. South of the Colorado River it is definitely excluded by its pronounced uplift and its separation from the Coastal Plain by the Balcones fault. The fault scarp, although highest in southern Texas and diminishing toward the east and north, is still 400 feet high at Austin on the Colorado, north of which it falls off and is not noticeable beyond latitude 31°. The area whose classification is most in question is that between the Colorado and Brazos rivers. North of the Brazos River, in the district called the Grand Prairie, the inclusion of the Lower Cretaceous in the Coastal Plain need not be questioned. Its rocks constituted part of the continental shelf and all were raised above the sea without substantial deformation (see definition of coastal plain, page 1 and Fig. 28, page 103).

It is equally true that the Lower Cretaceous terrane between the Brazos and Colorado rivers (Hill's Lampasas Cut Plain) is genetically a part of the Coastal Plain. Its southern part was faulted up with reference to the plain on the east, but aside from that, nothing has happened in its history that does not happen to coastal plains. However, its history has been a long one and is shared quite as much by the Great Plains province as by the

Coastal Plain.   Its rocks are hard and, while there is nothing in the essence of the Coastal Plain to exclude resistant rocks, they are exceptional in that province and common in the Great Plains. The same may be said of the deeply dissected plateau surface. On the whole it seems best to assign this district to the province which it most resembles surficially, *i.e.*, to the highlands on the west rather than to the lowlands on the east.   Nevertheless on account of its relation to the Grand Prairie (a part of the Coastal Plain) a description of the district in question is given below.[1]

Throughout much of this section the province boundary is not strongly marked topographically.   In Arkansas and Oklahoma it lies at the foot of the Ouachita and Arbuckle Mountains. Here the boundary is at the inner (landward) edge of a mildly rolling, forested belt of sand, nowhere more than 10 miles wide, the outcrop of the Trinity formation at the base of the Lower Cretaceous.   As a north-facing escarpment lies a few miles to the south, the Trinity terrane is relatively a lowland.   It is one of the belts of so-called Cross Timbers, narrow belts of remarkable continuity in Texas, marking the outcrops of certain sands, and significant as border features of physiographic units.

Turning south into Texas, this belt, under the name of Western Cross Timbers, follows an irregular course, south by west, to the Colorado River west of Austin.   It is commonly spoken of as a valley, but it is not a stream valley.   The regional slope rises westward from it at the rate of 40 feet per mile and escarpments overlook it from the east.   It is here treated as belonging to the Coastal Plain province as far south as the Brazos River.

Where the Brazos River crosses the Lower Cretaceous terrane (approximately lat. 31°30′ to 32°30′) it is taken as the province boundary.   The difference in topography between the two sides does not appear in a single view, but within a few miles of the river the smooth expanses of the Grand Prairie on the east contrast strongly with the dissected plateau on the west.   South of Waco on the Brazos, the higher and rougher topography on the

---

[1] In the author's companion volume ("Physiography of Western United States," McGraw-Hill Book Company, Inc., New York, 1931) the surface of the Lower Cretaceous south of the Red River, including the Grand Prairie north of the Brazos, is all assigned to the Great Plains province. Neither the Great Plains on the west nor the Coastal Plain on the east can be adequately treated without mention of this area, but the relations of the Grand Prairie to the Coastal Plain are now treated as primary.

Comanchean rocks begins a few miles west of the Eagle Ford
Prairie, which is near the western edge of the Upper Cretaceous.

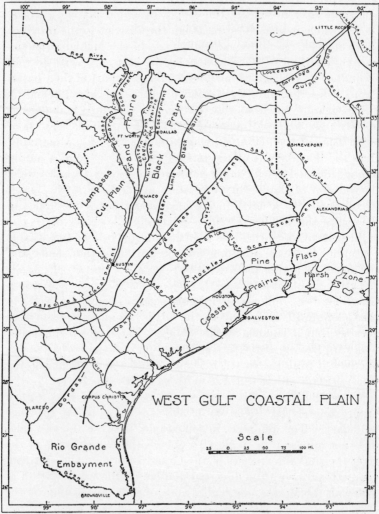

Fig. 27.—Sketch map showing the principal escarpments and belts in the West
Gulf Coastal Plain.

At the parallel of 31° the Balcones fault scarp appears, and
from that point southward and westward it marks the province
boundary.

Subdivisions.—Physiographic treatment of this part of Texas has been largely in terms of the underlying rocks.[1] Thus the Grand Prairie covers all Lower Cretaceous rocks except the basal (Trinity) sands which underlie the narrow belt of Western Cross Timbers. The Black Prairie covers the Upper Cretaceous with a like exclusion of basal (Woodbine) sands bearing the Eastern Cross Timbers, while the East Texas Timber Belt is on the Tertiary. The names of these districts are in familiar local usage and also in the literature. Moreover, they correspond to important distinctions in soil, vegetation, and conditions of life, but they are not based on the most outstanding features of topography, nor are the areas thus indicated bounded by the main escarpments.

A different plan of subdivision is based on the more prominent infacing escarpments, of which there are four in northern Texas[2] (Figs. 27 and 28). Their relations to geologic formations are indicated in the table at the top of page 104.

[1] HILL, R. T., Geography and Geology of the Black and Grand Prairies, Texas, U. S. Geol. Survey, 21st Ann. Rept., pt. 7, 1901; also Physical Geography of the Texas Region, U. S. Geol. Survey, "Topographic Atlas of the United States," folio No. 3, 1900.

[2] DEUSSEN, ALEXANDER, Geology and Underground Waters of the Southeastern Part of Texas, U. S. Geol. Survey, Water Supply Paper 335, 1914.

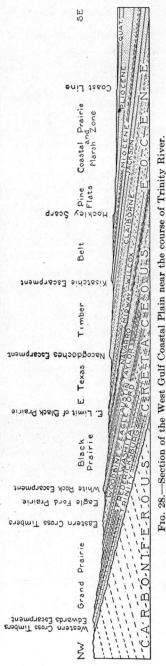

FIG. 28.—Section of the West Gulf Coastal Plain near the course of Trinity River.

FORMATIONS OF THE TEXAS COASTAL PLAIN AND THEIR TOPOGRAPHIC
RELATIONS

Formation	Belts
Pleistocene	
Beaumont clay ⎫	
Lissie gravel ⎭ .... Pleistocene terraces	
Pliocene	
Reynosa formation ⎫	
Lagarto clay	
Miocene	
Fleming clay ⎬ ..... Kisatchie cuesta	
Oakville sandstone	
Catahoula sandstone ⎭	
Oligocene	
Frio clay................... Lowland	
Eocene	
Jackson................... Lowland	
Claiborne................. Nacogdoches cuesta	
Wilcox................... Margin of E. Tex. Timber Belt	
Midway................. Black Prairie (less typical)	
Cretaceous	
Navarro.................. Black Prairie (less typical)	
Taylor marl............... Black Prairie (typical)	
Austin chalk.............. White Rock escarpment and Black Prairie	
Eagle Ford clay........... Eagle Ford Black Prairie	
Woodbine sand........... Eastern Cross Timbers	
Washita limestone ⎫	
Fredericksburg limestone ⎭ .. Grand Prairie and Edwards escarpment	
Trinity sand.............. Western Cross Timbers	

The first or Edwards escarpment bounds the Grand Prairie on
the west and overlooks the Western Cross Timbers.   The second,
or White Rock escarpment, lies well within the Black Prairie at
the outcropping edge of the Austin chalk.[1]   It overlooks a belt of
black soil (the Eagle Ford Prairie) and beyond it to the west, the
Eastern Cross Timbers.   The third escarpment, the Nacogdoches, is on the iron-encrusted Claiborne group in the East
Texas Timber belt.   The fourth, or Kisatchie, also in the timber
belt, is on the Catahoula sandstone.   The dip slope from the
top of each escarpment to the foot of the next is in some cases
interrupted by minor scarps and cuestas.   All dip slopes are
gentle, being progressively more so as the coast is approached.
None are obvious.

[1] The limits of the "Black Prairie" are variously assigned.   See footnote
1, p. 108.

As the several types of topography are disposed in belts depending on lines of outcrop, it is essential to notice that such lines are most widely spaced along the Red River. By reason of a former embayment in that valley, caused by a syncline similar to that of the great Mississippi Embayment, lines of outcrop which elsewhere parallel the coast are directed up the valley, making a sharp angle in its axis. It comes about thus that north-south outcrops in northern Texas have an east-west trend in the Red River Valley. In speaking of these belts it is necessary to distinguish an east-west or Red River segment from the main north-south portion.

First Major Cuesta

The Grand Prairie.—The Grand Prairie lies between the Western Cross Timbers and the similar narrow belt of Eastern Cross Timbers. The substratum of rock between these two is mainly firm limestone dipping gently seaward, always having a main scarp overlooking the Western Cross Timbers, and at places minor scarps. It is characteristic of the whole area that the several limestone formations have suffered stripping, thus giving rise to plains determined by the bedding. Such plains are nearly level. The imperceptible dip slopes contrast strongly with the steep slopes of erosion valleys cutting into or through the beds. Together these features give an angular aspect to the landscape where valleys are in view, quite different from that of the rolling hills farther east on the younger and softer rocks. In local speech the Grand Prairie is often called the "hard-lime rock region."

The east-west (Red River) segment of this prairie belt in Oklahoma is only 5 or 6 miles wide and its north-facing scarp nowhere rises more than 100 feet above the sandy lowland on the Trinity formation. It is transected at short intervals by wide valleys on whose flat floors the forest is continuous with those on the sandy belts to the north and south. The prairie is thus isolated in patches on the flat divides, the product of stripping or peneplanation in one or more cycles.

In Texas the Grand Prairie is rarely more than 25 miles wide. The landscape is dominated by the nearly flat stratum plains, broken here and there by relatively steep-sided valleys which disappear in a general view. It is a grassy country suggesting the Great Plains, the uplands being given largely to grazing, the valleys being important agriculturally. The surface takes on more relief toward the west near the Edwards escarpment whose height does not exceed 100 feet in this district.

The Lampasas Cut Plain.—As stated above the Lower Cretaceous terrane between the Brazos and Colorado rivers is here assigned to the Great Plains province. It is described briefly here, mainly for the purpose of justifying its exclusion from the Coastal Plain province. The relatively unbroken stratum plains of the Grand Prairie become very narrow at the Brazos River, south of which they are represented only on the eastern margin, and they narrow to a point before the Colorado is reached. West of this narrow strip is the greatly broadened outcrop of the strong limestones. This broad and relatively elevated district is Hill's Lampasas Cut Plain. Its western margin is 1500 to 1800 feet high and 300 to 400 feet above the valleys at the foot of the escarpment. Erosion here has gone much further than in the Grand Prairie. Flat lying remnants of the Edwards limestone form buttes and mesas with a few rather extensive uplands on the main divides. It is this limestone that makes the "top of the country" and determines the horizon of view. The whole district is dissected to a stage of advanced youth with local relief reaching as high as 400 feet. Its character is that of the margin of the Edwards Plateau in the Great Plains province.

Eastern Cross Timbers.—The narrow band of Eastern Cross Timbers, on the outcrop of the sandy Woodbine formation, extends from Arkansas west and then south almost to the Brazos River. It is a zone of no great relief, sloping seaward with the dip. Its inner edge is higher and more sharply rolling and is seen from the Grand Prairie as a line of low, rounded, wooded hills. In the Red River Valley it broadens to 20 miles or more and is followed by the river, meandering over its broad flood plain. As the narrow east-west Grand Prairie comes to an end in Texas the two bands of cross timbers are contiguous in southwestern Arkansas. Here the Woodbine sand formation is overlain and protected by the gravelly Tokio formation, the two together forming a ragged cuesta about 100 feet higher than the rolling surface of the inner Cross Timbers to the north. These latter lie in a "broad groove" or "vale" or "inner lowland" followed by an old military road running from Little Rock to Fort Towson, Okla., and used for conducting the Choctaw Indians to their new home in the west.[1] The bordering belt of low sand and gravel hills and uplands (500 to 700 feet A.T.) is the innermost of a series of cuestas in Arkansas and Louisiana and was called by Veatch the Lockesburg Wold.[2]

Eagle Ford Prairie.—Between the Eastern Cross Timbers and the White Rock escarpment, at the foot of the first long seaward slope, is the first of the famous black prairies, a strip averaging no more than 10 miles in width but 150 miles long from the Red River Valley to the Brazos, and continuing farther south as a very narrow and interrupted trough, and also eastward in the Red River Valley. In topography, soil, and culture this prairie is the counterpart of the larger Taylor Prairie farther east.

SECOND MAJOR CUESTA

White Rock Escarpment and Prairie.—The White Rock escarpment is rarely more than 100 feet high except near rivers but is continuous for 250 miles, becoming intermittent toward the south and disappearing near Austin. This feature is practically absent in the Red River Valley, but in southwestern Arkansas beds of a little younger age make Veatch's Saratoga Wold,[3] a cuesta ranked by Hill with the Pontotoc ridge of Mississippi.[4] The scarp slope in Texas is hilly and at places rough. Streams descending it have cut backward and eroded the dip slope for a few miles. The Austin chalk, which makes the escarpment, underlies the gentle eastward slope for 10 miles or more and forms the soil. This zone of White Rock Prairie is not only higher but has more local relief than the typical black

[1] HILL, R. T., Neozoic Geology of Southwestern Arkansas, *Ark. Geol. Survey*, vol. 2, p. 12, 1888. MISER, H. D., and A. H. PURDUE, Geology of the DeQueen and Caddo Gap Quadrangles, Arkansas, U. S. Geol. Survey, *Bull.* 808, p. 17, 1929.

[2] VEATCH, A. C., Geology and Underground Water Resources of Northern Louisiana and Southern Arkansas, U. S. Geol. Survey, *Prof. Paper* 46, p. 15, 1906; DANE, CARL H., Upper Cretaceous Formations of Southwestern Arkansas, Ark. Geol. Survey, *Bull.* 1, 1929. Dane describes the Lockesburg Cuesta more in detail, separating it into two ridges.

[3] VEATCH, A. C., *op. cit.*, p. 15.

[4] HILL, R. T., Neozoic Geology of Southwestern Arkansas, *Ark. Geol. Survey*, vol. 2, pp. 14 and 46, 1888; DANE, *op. cit.*, p. 142.

prairies on either side.[1] It is found intermittently south and
west of Austin where it constitutes the innermost zone of the
Coastal Plain and lies at the foot of the Balcones escarpment.[2]

Taylor Prairie.—Taylor Prairie, contiguous with the White
Rock Prairie and not sharply distinguished from it, is the most
extensive and typical zone of the Black Prairie district, though in
most respects, except for extent, it is equaled by the Eagle Ford
zone. It is developed on the Taylor marl, a very stiff calcareous
clay, the soil on which is called "black waxy." This marl
overlies the Austin chalk, the highest of the indurated Cretaceous
formations. The surface on the soft Taylor marl is nowhere
more than mildly rolling, while some of the interstream surfaces
are broad flats whose only relief is "hog wallows."[3] The width
of the zone is locally 20 miles. Its eastward extent in the Red
River division is less than 30 miles. South of Austin it extends
in less typical development to San Antonio. This is the foremost agricultural district of Texas. Its one great problem is
water supply for domestic use and stock. The heavy clay yields
no water to shallow wells. As may be inferred from the structure
of the Coastal Plain, it is underlain by sandy strata mentioned
above which bear artesian water, but this is deep and expensive.
The main dependence is on cisterns and reservoirs. (Compare
the Black Belt of Alabama, page 70).

Marginal (Elgin) Prairies and Wilcox Forest Belt.—Seaward
from the typical black prairies of the Taylor zone with its "black
waxy" soil, the underlying rocks as well as the soils become more
sandy though the latter retain their black color and calcareous
character. Even the topography does not change much, though
relief increases slightly. Trees appear sparingly and the zone is
classed as marginal prairie. This zone is on uppermost Cretaceous and Midway (Eocene) beds.[4] In passing from one to
the other there is no significant physiographic change but forests
become more prevalent as the sea is approached. Neither is any

[1] Confusion may be avoided by remembering that Hill uses the proper
name Black Prairie to include the Eagle Ford Prairie and that Deussen
limits the Black Prairie to that which lies east of the White Rock escarpment.

[2] DEUSSEN, A., Geology of the Coastal Plain of Texas West of Brazos
River, U. S. Geol. Survey, *Prof. Paper*, 126, p. 12, 1924.

[3] Hill (*op. cit.*, p. 67) states that these shallow basins are due to unequal
drying and shrinkage of the calcareous clays.

[4] DEUSSEN, *op. cit.*, p. 11.

considerable change in topography noted in passing on over the Wilcox series of Eocene sediments to the base of the Nacogdoches cuesta (Claiborne series), though the sandy soils lose their calcareous character and black color, becoming yellow or red. The last-named zone forms part of the East Texas Timber Belt.

In southwestern Arkansas the zone of sandy Wilcox beds forms a distinct though much broken cuesta, Veatch's Sulphur Wold.[1] The cuesta extends but a short distance into Texas but the same Wilcox sands extend south and west beyond the Colorado River. Here the zone is a little higher than the country on either side, faintly suggesting the Sulphur cuesta in Arkansas. Relief increases somewhat toward the southwest and, with increasing aridity, the forest of post oak and blackjack gives way to mesquite, chaparral, and cactus.

The outcrop of the sandy Wilcox series, which rarely exceeds 10 miles in width south of the Brazos, broadens greatly in northeastern Texas and northwestern Louisiana and is an important element in making the extensive sandy rolling forested surface of that district.

NACOGDOCHES CUESTA

The Nacogdoches cuesta (on the Claiborne series of the Eocene) presents the third major infacing escarpment encountered in going seaward from the Central Lowland in northern Texas and the first in going east from the Edwards Plateau (Balcones fault) in the south. North of the Colorado it is a well-developed cuesta, although both slopes are carved by streams, the scarp slope and broad summit being decidedly hilly, the dip slope only rolling. The lower part of the dip slope covers 10 to 25 miles of clays (Yegua) worn down to a gently undulating surface whose fertile soil contrasts with that of the higher zone. This broad ridge owes its existence mainly to the iron content of the underlying sediments which are largely marl and greensand. Concentration of iron in certain beds which now cap the hills (some of them called mountains) explains their

[1] VEATCH, A. C., op. cit., p. 15. Cf. MARBUT, C. F., The Geographic Development of Crowleys Ridge, Proc. Boston Soc. Nat. Hist., vol. 26, p. 482, 1895. Marbut's Malvern Ridge extending from Little Rock to Arkadelphia is apparently a continuation of the same feature on rocks of the same age. It borders a continuous lowland followed by the St. Louis, Iron Mountain, and Southern Railroad.

resistance to erosion. Some of the iron is sufficiently concentrated to be used as ore. Iron in the soils also explains the prevalent bright colors, yellow, red, and orange.

The entire cuesta north of the Brazos River has a maximum width of fully 75 miles. South of the Brazos both the rougher marl zone and the smoother clay zone continue, the former less prominent than farther north. The total width here is 15 to 25 miles with a great expansion in the Rio Grande embayment. The rocks that make the Nacogdoches Cuesta are widely exposed in northern Louisiana and southern Arkansas but the distinctive form is lost in a broad expanse of low rolling hills.

KISATCHIE CUESTA

The fourth major escarpment is a clearly marked feature from the Rio Grande to the Mississippi flood plain. Beyond that it has already been described as the outcrop of the Catahoula and Citronelle formations at the northern limit of the Southern Pine Hills belt. This is the most prominent relief feature in Louisiana, where it reaches its maximum development. It is described as a "high, rugged line of hills" and a "very abrupt declivity" bordering the "somewhat level Jackson plain" to the north[1] though the extreme elevation above sea level in Louisiana is but little more than 400 feet.

The Kisatchie escarpment is at the edge of the Catahoula formation which is mainly sandstone.[2] Toward the southwest, beyond the Brazos River, the Catahoula gives out and the escarpment is carried by the overlying Oakville formation.[3] Still farther south it merges with the Bordas escarpment (outcrop of the Reynosa sandy limestone) which follows a nearly parallel course, being 15 to 20 miles farther east at the Colorado River but converging toward the south.

[1] HARRIS, G. D., and A. C. VEATCH, The Geology of Louisiana, Rept. State *Expt. Sta. La.*, pt. 5, p. 96, 1899.

[2] In Louisiana, certain lower formations, the Vicksburg limestone in the east and the Fayette sandstone in the west, participate in the escarpment. As most of this area has not been mapped topographically, these features can be located best by reference to the geologic maps in the papers referred to, *i.e.*, U. S. Geol. Survey, *Water Supply Paper* 335, and *Prof. Papers* 46 and 126.

[3] DEUSSEN, ALEX., U. S. Geol. Survey, *Prof. Paper* 126, p. 9, 1924.

The summit of the Catahoula-Oakville-Bordas escarpment is the line at which the final descent to the sea begins. An exception must be made for that part of its length where the Reynosa outcrop makes an independent escarpment, mainly between the Guadaloupe and Nueces rivers. The relief of this Catahoula-Oakville-Reynosa cuesta, as of others, is conspicuous near its higher margin and decreases as the dip slope is descended. After a descent for 30 to 50 miles the slope is suddenly steepened by a noteworthy drop of 25 to 50 feet, called in northern Texas the Hockley scarp.

Remnants of a Gravel Plain.—In all of the belts mentioned between the Balcones and Hockley scarps, some of the broad divides between the major streams are gravel-covered flats 600 to nearly 1000 feet high. Such a flat near Austin is 275 feet above the Colorado River. Some of the tracts extend 20 to 30 miles, though not without dissection. These must be taken into account as a minor element modifying the preceding descriptions. They represent a once extensive (perhaps continuous) alluvial cover, made by overloaded streams whose flood plains or alluvial fans in many cases coalesced. They are mentioned at this point because they were once continuous with the Reynosa formation which underlies the outer zone of the last cuesta described, just within the Hockley scarp. They were made as stream deposits while the rocks of the Reynosa formation were being deposited either in the same manner or under the marginal sea.[1] (*Cf.* the Citronelle formation, page 77, and the "Lafayette.")

The Hockley Scarp.—In East Texas the seaward-facing Hockley scarp is a prominent feature, separating a flat, almost featureless plain on the south from a faintly rolling upland, now being rejuvenated, on the north.[2] The upland itself is almost flat near the edge but the relief increases northward with increasing altitude and steepening slope which averages 9 to 15 feet per mile. Before the crest of the Kisatchie cuesta is reached the

---

[1] DEUSSEN, *op. cit.*, p. 105.

[2] BARTON, DONALD C., Surface Geology of Coastal Southeast Texas, *Bull. Amer. Assn. Petroleum Geol.*, vol. 14, p. 1302, 1930. In this paper Barton speaks of this upper plain as in "early youth of a second cycle." He interprets its faintly rolling character as due to erosion carried to maturity when the surface stood only a few feet above its base level. Sharp incision is taking place as the result of uplift.

work of the newer cycle merges with that of the old in a "robust maturity."

The margin of the upland above the Hockley scarp is 200 to 210 feet high. The description of this upper surface might be applied without change to the Brandywine terrace at many places on the eastern coast, as the description of the lower surface fits the Sunderland where least eroded. The altitudes also agree.[1] The general slope of the lower plain is 3 to 5 feet per mile; much less near the coast, and more near the scarp where its altitude is 160 to 175 feet.

The Hockley scarp seems to find its continuation south of the Colorado River in the drop already mentioned as interrupting the Kisatchie cuesta.[2] It separates the somewhat dissected Pliocene plain from the oldest, nearly level, Pleistocene terrace. If the line of the Hockley terrace be continued eastward into Louisiana it agrees essentially with the southern edge of what Harris calls the "hill land"[3] which is the same as the Southern Pine Hills belt in Mississippi, and apparently the same as the Pliocene strip in southern Texas. Provisionally this line may be taken as the limit of Pleistocene terracing. Older terracing seems to be recognized in the Pliocene of southern Texas[4] as already noted in Mississippi (footnote 2, page 78).

Pleistocene Terraces

Coastal Lowland.—A belt of coastal lowland 50 to 75 miles wide is generally believed to represent submergence at one or more times during the Glacial Epoch. Its inner edge is generally 100 to 175 feet high but rises to more than 300 feet near the Rio

[1] No attempt is made here to reconcile the conclusions of the different workers in these widely separated regions, namely, that the Brandywine surface in the East is a Pleistocene terrace and that the Hockley scarp represents the limit of Pleistocene terracing in Texas.

[2] This scarp south of the Colorado River is at the landward edge of the Pleistocene Lissie gravel as mapped by A. Deussen (U. S. Geol. Survey, *Prof. Paper* 126, map, Pl. 8). In East Texas it traverses the area of Lissie gravel as mapped by Deussen (U. S. Geol. Survey, *Water Supply Paper* 335, map, Pl. 1). It is just here, however, that the Hockley scarp is best known (see Barton, *loc. cit.*).

[3] Harris, G. D., U. S. Geol. Survey, *Water Supply Paper* 101, p. 15, Fig. 1, 1904; see also Matson, Geo. R., Louisiana Clays, U. S. Geol. Survey, *Bull.* 660, map, Pl. 5, opp. p. 148, 1917.

[4] Deussen, A., U. S. Geol. Survey, *Prof. Paper* 126, pp. 5–6, 1924.

Grande.   Most of the slope is in the inner third, the outer two thirds being very flat and, near the coast, often marshy.   An outer zone (generally more than half except in Louisiana) is called Coastal Prairie (and marshes), though it is not all treeless, especially near streams.   In Louisiana it is the "swamp-lake" or "coastal-marsh" zone.   It is a clay plain almost untouched by erosion except for the steep-sided channels of transverse streams whose bottoms may be 30 to 40 feet below sea level.[1] Near the shore are some remnants of massive beach ridges or lines of dunes.   One such ridge in southwestern Louisiana is 25 feet high and possibly due to crustal deformation.[2]   The inner zone of the Coastal Lowland is sandy and almost as flat as the outer, though its seaward slope is steeper.   South of the Brazos it is the Lissie Prairie, or Alice Terrace,[3] generally separated by a faint scarp from the Coastal Prairie, or Beaumont Terrace.   With increasing rainfall toward the east the Lissie Prairie has more and more trees.   In Louisiana it becomes the "Pine Flats" or "Pine Meadows."[4]   The faint scarp at its seaward edge is not everywhere present and the line between clay and sand can not everywhere be adhered to as a boundary.[5]

Hypothesis of a Deltaic Plain.—All the above statements concerning coastal terraces are consistent with the common supposition that they are emerged sea bottoms.   Some features of these lowlands in eastern Texas suggest that the flats in that locality are the surfaces of old deltas of the Brazos and Trinity rivers.[6]   Foremost among these features are broad faint ridges or swells, not detected by the unaided eye but sandier than the intervening flats, irregular in form and often fragmentary. These have long been known and variously explained.   By careful plotting, Barton finds that they suggest the pattern of

[1] HARRIS, G. D., U. S. Geol. Survey, *Water Supply Paper* 101, p. 16, 1904.

[2] BARTON, DONALD C., Surface Geology of the Coastal Plain of Southeast Texas, *Bull. Am. Ass. Petroleum Geol.*, vol. 14, p. 1314, 1930.

[3] DEUSSEN, A., U. S. Geol. Survey, *Prof. Paper* 126, p. 5, 1924.

[4] HARRIS, G. D., and A. C. VEATCH, The Geology of Louisiana, Rept. State *Expt. Sta. La.*, pt. 5, p. 113, 1899.

[5] Attempts to divide this coastal lowland into consistently marked belts are not very successful in east Texas.   Donald C. Barton proposed such a division but abandoned it later (*Bull. Geol. Soc. Amer.*, vol. 41, p. 361, 1930).

[6] BARTON, DONALD C., Deltaic Coastal Plain of Southeastern Texas, *Bull. Geol. Soc. Amer.*, vol. 41, pp. 359–382, 1930.

distributaries on a delta and interprets them as natural levees. Attention is also called to the fact that the Trinity and Brazos rivers are almost without tributaries below the Hockley scarp. Galveston Bay, commonly thought to be a drowned valley, is interpreted, on this hypothesis, as an unfilled sector between two deltas. These inferences are emphasized by comparison with the Mississippi delta on which the pattern of drainage ways is similar, and whose margin is indented by inlets which, if isolated on a map, might be mistaken for drowned valleys. Accordingly, the Coastal Plain of east Texas is interpreted by Barton as the slightly upraised deltaic plain of the Trinity and Brazos rivers at a time of greater volume in the late Pleistocene or early Recent time, and having essentially the same features that the Mississippi Delta would have if growth were checked and the plain slightly raised (*cf.* Pleistocene terraces in Mississippi, page 79).

Mounds and Pimpled Plains.—A feature that is very characteristic of the flat Pleistocene terraces, and widely prevalent over the lower and flatter parts of the West Gulf Coastal Plain, consists of nearly circular mounds from 1 or 2 feet to 5 feet high and 30 to 50 (rarely 100) feet in diameter. Their origin has been much discussed and at least a dozen hypotheses have been offered.[1] No explanation yet proposed is conclusive in this region, though apparently satisfactory explanations have been found for superficially similar mounds in other parts of the United States.[2]

Occasional larger domes are related to geologic structures generally containing salt and oil.[3] The largest have diameters of 1 or 2 miles. Damon Mound, west of the Brazos River, has the

---

[1] VEATCH, A. C., U. S. Geol. Survey, *Prof. Paper* 46, p. 56, 1906. This paper gives twelve hypotheses proposed by different investigators. WATERS, A. C., and C. W. FLAGLER, Origin of the Small Mounds on the Columbia River Plateau, *Amer. Jour. Sci.*, vol. 18, p. 212, 1929. This paper sets forth thirteen theories. RICH, J. L., Soil Mottlings and Mounds in Northeastern Texas as Seen from the Air, *Geo. Rev.*, vol. 24, pp. 576–583, 1934.

[2] See the author's companion volume, "Physiography of Western United States," p. 271, McGraw-Hill Book Company, Inc., New York, 1931.

[3] STEPHENSON, L. W., Structural Features of the Atlantic and Gulf Coastal Plain, *Bull. Geol. Soc. Amer.*, vol. 39, p. 897, 1928. See also footnote 2, p. 96.

greatest height, 83 feet. Spindletop Mound near Beaumont, Texas, is best known on account of its sensational oil production. Its greatest diameter is less than a mile and its height about 10 feet above the plain. The highest of these mounds show young erosion valleys. (See also description of the Salt Islands in the Mississippi Alluvial Plain, page 95.)

DRAINAGE

The main drainage lines in this section have conspicuously parallel southeasterly courses. There is a strong suggestion that these courses were first taken on a former nearly plane surface, a surface which must have been well above the present level near the Fall Line, where erosion has been continuous, but repeatedly raised by deposition near the coast. The upper courses of these streams, in the province to the west, have held their own during one or more cycles of base leveling and have since been entrenched.[1] Their lower courses near the sea are cutting their first valleys in the new plain. Gradients of transverse streams are decidedly less steep than the seaward slope of the land.

Alluvial plains on the main streams range in width from 2 or 3 miles up to 10 or 15 miles. Generally these valleys are terraced, the several terraces corresponding to and merging with the coastal terraces (*cf.* page 79). They differ somewhat from place to place in constituent materials or in vegetal cover, but the continuity of aspect noted in following a forested transverse valley is in marked contrast with the diversity of the belts traversed. This produces a crisscross pattern in which the interstream belts greatly predominate in most of Texas but the transverse alluvial bands broaden toward the north and east. The alluvial plain (including Pleistocene terraces) of the Red River is 10 to 15 miles wide and that of the Mississippi must be treated as a separate section.

The Red River has certain peculiarities. It follows the axis of a structural depression analogous to that of the Mississippi but less marked. It is more comparable with that of the Rio Grande. The effect of this depression on the trends of outcrops, and thereby of topographic zones, has already been pointed out. Another effect is seen in the low gradient of the stream. From

[1] See companion volume, "Physiography of Western United States," p. 59.

the nature of its upper basin in the Interior Lowland province the load is large.   Features due to fluvial deposition are therefore to be expected.   These include a very wide (though terraced) alluvial plain and intricate meanders.

The Red River differs from those farther southwest in the greater rainfall and more luxuriant and extensive forests of its

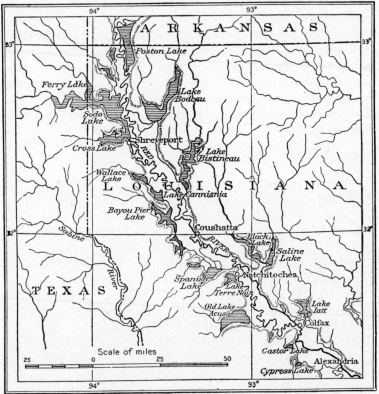

Fig. 29.—Lakes in tributary valleys of the Red River before the removal of the Great Raft.   (*A. C. Veatch, U. S. Geol. Survey.*)

basin.   This condition, taken in connection with its low gradient and abundant sediment, has made it peculiarly subject to clogging by driftwood.   The "rafts" of this river have long made it famous.   These were masses of driftwood which, for long stretches in Louisiana, completely filled the channel, retarding the current, inducing deposit of mud and sand, and growing constantly upstream.   The Great Raft is believed to have begun in the fifteenth century. Before its removal in 1873 it attained a length of 160 miles, reaching almost to the Arkansas boundary, its rate of growth upstream being $\frac{4}{5}$ mile per year.

The immediate effect of this obstruction was the deposition of mud and sand and the aggradation of the flood plain until new courses were adopted at various places, notably below Alexandria at the center of the state where the sluggish Bayou Boeuf now marks the old abandoned channel.[1] Another effect of aggradation was the ponding of tributary valleys. Lakes 5 to 25 miles in length, formed in these valleys, ranged on either side like leaves on a twig (Fig. 29). When, in 1873, after various unsuccessful attempts, the rafts were finally removed, all channels at once began to degrade and the lakes began to shrink and disappear. In 20 years the channel was lowered 15 feet near Shreveport.

SUMMARY

General Features.—In summary, the major features of the West Gulf Coastal Plain are as follows: The first (mainly Lower Cretaceous) cuesta in northern Texas scarps to the west, overlooking the narrow strip of Western Cross Timbers. Its eastern or dip slope includes (1) the relatively smooth uplands of the Grand Prairie north of the Brazos, (2) the narrow strip of Eastern Cross Timbers (which makes the first of three cuestas in Arkansas), (3) the narrow Eagle Ford Black Prairie, (4) the corresponding zones (less uniform in width and less continuous) with an east-west trend in the Red River Valley.

The second (mainly upper Cretaceous) cuesta begins with the White Rock escarpment (generally absent in the Red River Valley but not very different geologically from the second cuesta in Arkansas). The seaward slope from this escarpment embraces (1) the rolling White Rock Prairie continuous with (2) the nearly level Taylor Black Prairie, and beyond that with (3) the gently rolling Elgin Prairie on the uppermost Cretaceous and Midway formations, (4) the more strongly rolling timber zone on the sandy Wilcox series, which makes the third cuesta in Arkansas. South and west of the Colorado, the combined and fairly uniform

---

[1] Details of such changes are interestingly described and well figured by VEATCH, A. C., U. S. Geol. Survey, *Prof. Paper* 46, pp. 62–64, 1906.

width of all belts between the Balcones scarp and the Nacogdoches cuesta is not over 30 miles.   The zones are not marked
off by escarpments and may be disregarded except in detailed
studies.

The third (Nacogdoches) cuesta is best developed in East
Texas as a nearly simple monoclinal ridge in which the hilly
character of its inner margin is much more noticeable than any
scarp slope.   Its forested rolling hills of iron-cemented rocks,
covered by iron-stained sandy soil, give way on its lower seaward
slope to fertile clays and low relief.   These features are preserved in its narrow southwest extension but its broad and
irregular expanse in Louisiana and Arkansas is less sharply
differentiated from adjacent belts.

The fourth (Kisatchie) cuesta is the most continuous belt
in the Gulf Coastal Plain.   Generally it has a distinct infacing
scarp, and its dissected surface falls off, in the Hockley scarp,
somewhat abruptly to the flat Pleistocene coastal lowland.   It
corresponds to the southern Pine Hills of Mississippi and the
Tifton Upland of Georgia (page 40).   The coastal lowland is at
places divisible into two zones separated by a faint scarp.   A
fairly distinct lower zone of marshes may also be outlined at
places.   Elsewhere attempts at subdivision are unsatisfactory.

History of the West Gulf Coastal Plain.—The conception
of a coastal plain as a former continental shelf which has suffered
no substantial change except erosion needs some qualification, or
at least interpretation, in this section.   The fault at the western
boundary (Balcones fault, page 100) is not the only deformation
known to geologists.   Other faults, located well within the
province, probably had at one time great topographic significance.
In an important fault zone 10 to 15 miles east of the Balcones
there are displacements as great as 600 feet, generally with
downthrow on the west.   When these faults were in their
youth a considerable trough may have existed along the western
margin.[1]   In the very axis of the Red River embayment, in the
angle where the north-south outcrops meet the east-west out-

---

[1] STEPHENSON, L. W., Major Features in the Geology of the Atlantic
and Gulf Coastal Plains, *Jour., Wash. Acad. Sci.*, vol. 16, p. 473.   If one
were disposed to be captious he might ask whether these faults in their
youth limited the extent of the Coastal Plain, and if so, at what stage the
inner margin of the Coastal Plain was again added to the province.

crops, the Preston anticline lifts the beds 800 feet.[1] It is a fold comparable in size with the Hatchetigbee anticline in Alabama.

Topographically, these faults and folds have disappeared, but a recent displacement of 25 feet is believed to have deformed the profile of the Ouachita River, causing extensive swamps on its upstream side (page 93). The fact that such faults and folds have been made and their original relief destroyed, when the Coastal Plain had already passed through the greater part of its history, indicates that the topography of the older part of the province is the product of at least several, if not of many, cycles. The lowlands of the Black Prairie may be thought of as local peneplains like the Black Belt of Alabama though less sharply bounded. The chief part of this section that is clearly in its first cycle lies seaward from the crest of the Kisatchie Cuesta, *i.e.*, on formations not older than Pliocene. With this zone are associated, both geologically and topographically, the terraced alluvial plains, also the high patches of gravel plain covering broad divides in the older belts.

The gravel plain surviving in interstream fragments probably indicates that not long previous to the making of the coastal lowlands (the glacial epoch elsewhere) most of the western Coastal Plain was essentially flat, the result partly of peneplanation, partly of stream planation and alluviation. The present relief of the section was developed since that time. The Balcones fault seems to have been made (or renewed) either before the alluviation or, perhaps, before the extensive downcutting that preceded it, at all events in Pliocene time.[2] The faults whose scarps have wholly disappeared are older, unless their disappearance is accounted for by the weaker rocks traversed.

The nearly level Pliocene surface mentioned above stood well above the present level, except near the coast, and was dissected into hills and valleys differing from those of the present only in respect of age and in the greater depth of the main valleys. There followed depression, during which the surface of the coastal lowlands was constructed, probably in the main under water.

[1] STEPHENSON, L. W., A Contribution to the Geology of Northeastern Texas and Southern Oklahoma, U. S. Geol. Survey, *Prof. Paper* 120*H*, pp. 129–154, 1918.

[2] STEPHENSON, L. W., Major Features in the Geology of the Atlantic and Gulf Coastal Plain, *op. cit.*, p. 472.

The same constructional surface extended far up the main valleys, notably those of the Red and of the Mississippi.   As the result of later elevation this surface has been in large part destroyed in the Mississippi Valley and trenched by the Red River, along which it survives as a high terrace or "upland flats," more than 20 miles wide in northern Louisiana and Arkansas.[1]

[1] This interpretation follows A. C. Veatch, U. S. Geol. Survey, *Prof. Paper* 46, p. 53 and map, Pl. 3.   Matson's map, U. S. Geol. Survey, *Bull.* 660, Pl. 5, makes all the alluvium in the Red River Valley in northern Louisiana Recent instead of Pleistocene.

CHAPTER II

PIEDMONT PROVINCE

GENERAL RELATIONS

The Appalachian Highland.—The Appalachian Highland is the second of eight major divisions of the United States. It embraces six provinces and stretches from the Gulf Coastal Plain to the St. Lawrence and from the Atlantic Coastal Plain to the Central Lowland. These limits are at best approximate. Like other physiographic divisions, this one takes its name from its most prominent features; it is therefore designated as a highland, but it is by no means all high. A literal application of the term "highland" would not only exclude parts of the Piedmont, New England, and Ridge and Valley provinces, but would include a part of the Interior Low Plateau province west of the Cumberland Plateau in Kentucky and Tennessee. "Appalachian Highland" is a convenient and useful geographical term, but the area to which it is applied cannot be determined by a literal use of the words.

So far as this extensive region has unity, it is found in the results of repeated uplifts, involving for the most part greater altitude and stronger relief than that of adjacent regions. In some parts an earlier uplift was of the mountain-making type, tilting and deforming the rocks as in central Pennsylvania. Elsewhere, as in western Pennsylvania, the horizontal position of the beds has been preserved through all changes. The most pronounced differences in present topography are due to differences in rocks, either in their material constitution or in structural features made during older uplifts. Most of the province boundaries may be defined in terms of rocks and structure as well as in terms of topography.

Subdivisions of the Highland.—South of New England and the Adirondacks, the provinces of the Appalachian Highland are longitudinal belts roughly parallel to the edge of the continent. The Piedmont and Blue Ridge provinces on the east have long been known as the "Older Appalachians" in contrast with the two provinces on the west which constitute the "Newer Appalachians." These two terms, like "Appalachian Highland," while reflecting a general truth, are used as proper names, not as literal descriptions.[1] As pointed out below, the one area is not all "older" and the other not all "younger." However, omitting exceptional features for the present, the rocks of the former pair are igneous or metamorphic, very old, much deformed, and resistant. This belt had a complicated history of mountain making and erosion before the Newer Appalachian belt emerged from the sea. At a much later time the older belt became two physiographic provinces by the reduction of its seaward side of a relatively late peneplain (Piedmont province), while the higher belt on its western side (Blue Ridge province) was not destroyed.

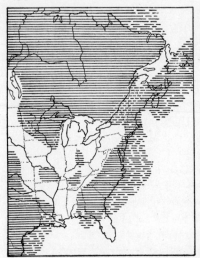

FIG. 30.—Sketch map of North America in mid-Paleozoic time, showing land (shaded) east and north of the interior sea. The outline is not strictly correct for any one time but shows areas that were dry land most of the time and areas covered by sea most of the time in the middle and later Paleozoic.

On emerging from the sea, the newer surface on the west was divided into two physiographic provinces by the crumpling of its eastern margin while the beds farther west and north were upraised in almost horizontal position. The eastern margin became the Folded Appalachians[2] or Ridge and Valley province.

[1] Some geologists strongly oppose the use of these terms. As noted later, a margin of the Blue Ridge province is not older than the "newer" provinces, and some parts of the northern Piedmont are geologically younger. The distinction between the two parts is useful, and no other short names, free from objections, have yet been proposed.

[2] The term Folded Appalachians is used synonomously with Ridge and Valley province and is understood to designate the belt in which structures due to folding dominate the topography. While folding is abundant in the Older Appalachians, its topographic effect is not dominant for reasons to be stated later.

The remainder is the Appalachian Plateau province. The familiar name Great Valley applies to only a part of the Ridge and Valley province (page 200).

In the latitude of New England the terms Older and Newer Appalachians are less appropriate and are not here employed. The Hudson-Champlain Valley is treated as an extension of the Ridge and Valley province but the whole of New England is best treated as a single province. This is a matter of convenience rather than of logic, for the Blue Ridge and Piedmont provinces do have their northward extensions, more or less distinguishable, in New England. However, to treat New England in these terms would be to emphasize distinctions which are of small importance in that region and to ignore others that are more significant. Moreover, the New England province is almost severed from the others in the latitude of New York and is further distinguished by having been glaciated. (For fuller statement see page 343). The Adirondack province is much like parts of New England and might be combined with that province were it not for the desirability of recognizing the continuity of the Ridge and Valley province which separates them.[1]

STRUCTURE AND BOUNDARIES

Influence of Rocks and Structure.—As distinguished above, the Piedmont province is the nonmountainous portion of the Older Appalachians. Its plain or plateau surface is necessarily the result of degradation, since the underlying rocks are everywhere deformed (Fig. 31). Rarely is the surface parallel to beds of rock, and nowhere is the original surface preserved. The general slope is from the mountains toward the Coastal Plain.

Considered as a whole, the rocks of the Piedmont are strong. The most marked exception is found in the Triassic rocks, treated separately below (page 145). Metamorphism has tended to equalize the strength of the older rocks. Any marked differences in resistance should be reflected in the drainage pattern. Structural control of drainage does appear in some places, but its general absence is much more striking. The rivers of the

[1] J. W. Powell, in the first attempt to discuss the United States in terms of physiographic provinces, treated these two as one. See National Geographic Monograph No. 3, published as "Physiography of the United States," American Book Company, New York, 1895.

Carolinas cross belts of granite, gneiss, schist, and slate without change of pattern.   However much the profiles are affected,[1] the map shows no difference.   No doubt the straight south-westward course of the upper Chattahoochee River in Georgia has a structural cause.   So also has Pine Mountain, northeast of Columbus in Georgia, a linear monadnock of quartzite 60 miles

Fig. 31.—Deformed rocks of the Piedmont province truncated by a peneplain. View of an iron mine near Milnerville, Pa.   (*Courtesy of the Geography Supply Bureau.*)

long (map, Pl. 3).   There is a very prominent structural line in Virginia which causes the James River to parallel the Blue Ridge for 40 miles.   Still, viewed in a large way, the drainage of this province falls into patterns in which resemblance to those on the Coastal Plain is more remarkable than any difference.   Either the diversity in hardness of the Piedmont rocks is not generally significant, or the structure is too complex to be followed, or the events of morphologic history have caused the streams to dis-

[1] For descriptions see J. A. Holmes, Physiographic Features of North Carolina, Chap. I in Papers on Water Power in North Carolina, N. C. Geol. Survey, *Bull.* 8, 1899.

regard it. It is noteworthy that at a number of places small
subsequent tributaries, developed under conditions not unlike
those of the present day, are guided by structures which the older
and larger streams ignore.

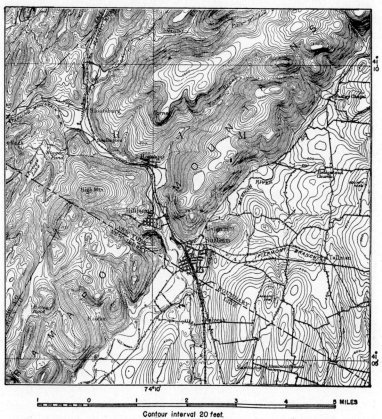

Contour interval 20 feet.

Fig. 32.—Topographic map showing the contrast between the Triassic Lowland of the Piedmont province and the Reading Prong of the New England
province near the New York-New Jersey boundary. (*U. S. Geol. Survey.*)

Inner Boundary.—The northwestern or inner boundary of
the Piedmont is by definition at the foot of the mountains, but
allowance must be made for a short stretch east of the Susquehanna River, where there are no mountains between the Piedmont
and the Ridge and Valley provinces (page 153).   Otherwise,
in the northern and less typical part, this boundary line is
determined by the contact of the relatively soft rocks of the

Piedmont with the resistant rocks of the mountains. The boundary in New Jersey is at an altitude of 200 to 300 feet (Fig. 32). Its altitude in Pennsylvania is 350 to 700 feet, varying with rock character and distance from the main drainage lines. Its lowest altitude in Maryland is 500 feet. Farther south there is little or no difference in the strength of rocks on opposite sides of the line. There the province boundary must be described simply as the limit of peneplaning in the later cycles (See History, page 158). As the boundary south of the Potomac is farther from the sea, and the rocks are strong on both sides, the altitude of the line soon rises to 700 or 800 feet in northern Virginia and increases to 1500 feet near the Carolina boundary. It falls but little lower at any point in the Carolinas and reaches 1800 feet in the Dahlonega Plateau of Georgia.

Outer Boundary: the Fall Line.—At its seaward edge the hard rocks of the Piedmont pass beneath the sediments of the Coastal Plain. It was formerly assumed that the buried surface was a continuation of the exposed surface of the Piedmont, the two being parts of the same peneplain. From wells drilled in the Coastal Plain it is now known that the hard-rock floor beneath the younger sediments has a steeper slope than that of the Piedmont. The inference is generally accepted that this sub-coastal plain floor is an older peneplain tilted seaward from time to time[1] (Fig. 33). No doubt it extended far inland and, if now preserved, would rise not only far above the Piedmont but probably above the mountains. Where not buried it was destroyed in the making of the present surface. This buried surface, named by Johnson the Fall Zone peneplain, intersects the present surface at a very small angle, the former sloping 20 to 100 feet, the latter 5 to 15 feet per mile.

The Fall Zone peneplain might be identified with the one on the Piedmont or on the mountains by assuming that it has been bent downward, perhaps by the weight of the sediments. But in that case the bending should be by a continuous curve, not by a definite angle. Even if bending could make such a clearly localized break in an otherwise straight slope it is beyond belief that the line of this break should so neatly coincide for a thousand

[1] Shaw, E. W., Ages of Peneplains of the Appalachian Province, *Bull. Geol. Soc. Amer.*, vol. 29, p. 582, 1918. See also Johnson, Douglas, "Stream Sculpture on the Atlantic Slope," pp. 9–10, 1931.

miles with the edge of the sediments, when it is remembered that the heavy mass is wedge-shaped, extending inward to a very thin edge, and especially when it is remembered that this thin edge has at times stood many miles farther seaward, and at other times landward from its present position.

Some of the coastal plain sediments, which antedate the wearing down of the Piedmont, once extended farther inland than at present. In the development of the present surface, such overlapping formations were cut down and trimmed back to the line at which the newer peneplain and the older buried peneplain intersect. With subsequent elevation of the land,

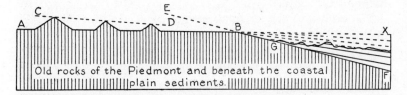

Fig. 33.—Diagram showing the interpretation of the Fall Line as the intersection of two peneplains. (*Altered from Renner, Geogr. Rev.*)
AB is the Piedmont peneplain which once extended to *X* over the coastal plain sediments; *CD*, an older peneplain indicated by remnants only; *EF*, a much older peneplain preserved by burial. Erosion of the Coastal Plain has exposed this surface between *B* and *G*, causing rapids in transverse streams.

resulting in further wasting of the thin edge of the coastal plain sediments, the older and steeper peneplain was exposed along a narrow zone (Fig. 33). This relatively steep zone, intervening between two gentler slopes, is now much eroded but is still detectable in carefully generalized profiles.[1]

Rapids and Falls.—This distribution of slopes is much more obvious in stream channels than between streams. All streams are relatively swift in crossing the denuded edge of the older and steeper peneplain. Some have pronounced rapids or falls. The popular use of the term "Fall Line," long before geologists explained the cause, indicates the prevalence of falls (or rapids) in this zone. Originally rapids should have begun where the two peneplains intersect, and ended where the channel passed to the coastal plain sediments. As seen at present this steeper

[1] RENNER, GEO. T., JR., The Physiographic Interpretation of the Fall Line, *Geog. Rev.*, vol. 17, pp. 276–286, 1927; Figs. 4–8, p. 283, are profiles constructed from the U. S. Geol. Survey topographic sheets.

element of the stream profile has receded upstream from a few hundred feet in some streams to a few miles in others.   Thus the powerful Susquehanna which falls 80 feet in 12 miles, reaches tide water at Port Deposit, Md., 3 miles back from the edge of the Piedmont.   The Potomac falls 40 feet in 3 miles, beginning at a point about 10 miles above Washington.   Falls south of the Potomac have receded but little from the edge of the crystalline rocks.   The Rappahannock drops its last 40 or 50 feet in 2 miles, reaching tidewater at Fredericksburg, at which point the crystalline rocks are exposed in the channel.   The James descends to tidewater with a fall of 84 feet in 3 miles ending at Richmond.[1]

The width of the original steeper zone at the edge of the Piedmont, caused by the stripping of the older peneplain and some times called the "fall zone," is generally but a few miles. South of the Potomac it would be two and a half to three miles if merely stripped and not otherwise eroded.[2]   Between the Potomac and the Hudson it is locally a little more, but it increases to 14 miles in western Connecticut.   Divergent statements about the width of the "fall zone" result from two ways of defining and delimiting it.   These limits should not be confused. There is, first, the actual zone of exhumed older peneplain, as it would be without erosion, ascertained only by careful plotting of surviving surfaces.   This is the narrow zone described above. Second, there is a zone of considerably greater width, outlined by drawing the inner boundary around the upper limits of all falls and the outer boundary around the lowest points at which crystalline rocks are exposed in stream channels.

Originally the rapids should have had the same gradient as that of the buried peneplain.   Actually, it is found that differences in hardness among the Piedmont rocks themselves are such that differential erosion has localized the fall in some cases.   No doubt this is true of the Potomac, though the case of that stream may be complicated, and its falls emphasized, by later deforma-

---

[1] McGEE, W J, The Geology of the Head of Chesapeake Bay, U. S. Geol. Survey, *7th Ann. Rept.*, pp. 537–656, 1886.   Valuable descriptions of the Fall Line are included in this paper, though not all of its conclusions are here adopted.

[2] Figures given here are taken from Renner, *op. cit.*, p. 282.

tion, the Westminster anticline, described by Campbell as younger than the prevailing peneplain.[1]

Local Description of the Fall Line.—As a topographic feature the Fall Line varies in clearness with the slope of the old buried peneplain and the extent of its erosion where exhumed. Throughout most of the boundary this slope does not exceed 30 feet per mile, but locally, as in the District of Columbia, it exceeds 100 feet per mile. For most of the distance south of the Potomac the edge of the Piedmont province is not a strongly marked topographic feature between streams. It is only here and there that a casual view reveals a marked seaward slope within the belt, a few miles wide, in which the sharper hills and finer textured drainage of the Piedmont give way to the gentler slopes and less closely spaced streams of the Coastal Plain. The transition from one province to the other is specially confused in North Carolina south of the Neuse River, where a belt of soft Triassic sandstone about 10 miles wide underlies the margin of the Piedmont province. Locally this has been eroded even more rapidly than the sandhills of the Coastal Plain.[2] The location of the Fall Line is further confused in the Carolinas by the fact that many streams, the Roanoke, Tar, Neuse, Cape Fear, Peedee, and others, have their channels on crystalline rock and interspersed with rapids for 20 miles after entering the Coastal Plain.[3] This is made possible by a relatively gentle seaward slope of the crystalline floor; also by the fact that streams here do not drop to sea level at the Fall Line as they do north of the Roanoke, but still retain their cutting power.

It is mainly between the Potomac and the Delaware that the Fall Line is marked by a conspicuous rise on the Piedmont side. "About the head of Chesapeake Bay, and indeed commonly in the north, the boundary is distinctly marked by a prominent line of wooded hills forming the irregular, stream-notched

---

[1] CAMPBELL, M. R., Chambersburg (Harrisburg) Peneplain in the Piedmont of Maryland and Pennsylvania, *Bull. Geol. Soc. Amer.*, vol. 44, pp. 553–573, 1933; ref. to p. 562.

[2] HOLMES, *op. cit.*, p. 23.

[3] *Ibid.* p. 77. On p. 21 Holmes gives a table showing the altitude of the Fall Line on all streams from the Appomattox, on which it is zero, to the Ocmulgee on which it is 250 feet.

escarpment of an undulating plateau 250 to 350 feet high."[1]
The drop of 100 to 300 feet to the Coastal Plain is accomplished
within a zone 2 to 4 miles wide (Fig. 34).   The prominence of
this slope and the fact that the main valleys of the Coastal
Plain follow its foot led McGee, on physiographic evidence

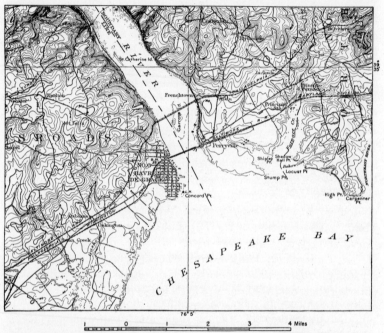

Fig. 34.—Topographic map showing the Fall Line at the mouth of the Susquehanna River.   The Pennsylvania Railroad and the Baltimore and Ohio are
approximately at the foot of the slope.   Most of the Coastal Plain lies southeast
of Chesapeake Bay.   The heavy contour lines are at intervals of 100 feet.
(*U. S. Geol. Survey, Havre de Grace quadrangle.*)

alone, to postulate a fault or sharp monocline along this line.[2]
Subsequent geologic work has failed to verify the existence of
this fault or monocline, and indeed such a structure is not
necessary in order to explain the physiography.   The slope of
the buried crystalline surface is here unusually steep, rising
locally to 100 feet per mile, which is steeper than the escarpment

[1] McGEE, W J, U. S. Geol. Survey, 7*th Ann. Rept.*, p. 549.

[2] *Cf.* DARTON, N. H., Mesozoic and Cenozoic Formations of Eastern
Virginia and Maryland, *Bull. Geol. Soc. Amer.*, vol. 2, pp. 431–450, 1891.

at most places. The courses of streams at its foot are discussed on page 35.[1]

THE PIEDMONT UPLAND

Use of Terms.—As used here, the term Piedmont Upland designates much the larger part of the province. Usage excludes only the Piedmont Lowlands, which are plains developed at a lower level on Triassic and other weak rocks in the northern part of the province. The distinction in level is generally clear where the two sections meet, but the names by which they are called must not be taken as universal descriptions. There are some rough tracts in the lowlands, and there are minor lowlands within the upland. As here defined "upland" is a geographic rather than a descriptive term, though it is often necessary to use the word in a local or topographic sense in contrast with valleys.

Topography in General.—The Piedmont Upland is a peneplain (one or more) in various stages of development and various stages of destruction. Its most typical parts are found in the interior, not near the mountains where development was incomplete and monadnocks are abundant, nor near its seaward edge where erosion in a newer cycle has made most headway in its destruction. The typical landscape is a rolling[2] surface of gentle slopes and no great relief, say, 50 feet, more or less, cut by or bounded by valleys of steeper slope and greater depth, often several hundred feet. Near the larger streams, tributaries also are in deep and steep valleys, but these same tributary valleys when traced headward are found to be wide, shallow, and of gentle gradient. The deeper valleys are those of rejuvenated streams.

---

[1] Although McGee's fault or monocline is both unverified and unessential, it is still worth remembering that the Coastal Plain is here much depressed, and that the explanations of why rivers follow the Fall Line (p. 35) are plausible or unobjectionable rather than convincing or conclusive.

[2] The much abused term *rolling* is very useful when employed in its proper specific sense. It is the opposite of *angular*. There must be no break between hillside and hilltop or valley bottom. Practically the surface is all hillside and also all valley side. Hilltops and valley bottoms have no definite limits. Peneplains, excluding their flood plains, are typically rolling. So also are till plains when not too flat.

The rolling areas between rejuvenated streams are largest in the South, especially in Georgia, where, as in the Atlanta plateau, such topography is dominant and deep valleys are few.[1] Toward the north such areas become smaller. Over large areas even small valleys are rejuvenated, though rarely does it occur that all of the gentler slopes of the older cycle have disappeared from the divides except near the Fall Line. From Pennsylvania to Alabama there are few extensive areas in which the features of an old, now dissecting or dissected, peneplain are not apparent. Surfaces that are level enough to favor agriculture are much more extensive on the uplands than in valley bottoms. Accordingly most of the roads and other cultural features are on the former.

Almost everywhere as the Fall Line is approached, valleys become sharper and deeper, and dissection is more complete, that is to say, the current erosion cycle is more advanced. This feature is most marked where the Fall Line slope is steepest, *i.e.*, north of the Potomac, but it is noted throughout the entire length of the province. It is a common observation that in going upstream from the Fall Line, the smaller tributaries in the upland are found in old valleys of gentle slope, not yet trenched.

Even in the well-peneplaned area remote from the mountains, occasional monadnocks are found, generally so isolated as to be conspicuous even when small. Stone Mountain near Atlanta is a dome of light-gray granite, almost free from joints. To this structure it owes its exceptional abruptness, being but 1½ miles long, yet 650 feet high and remarkably steep (Fig. 35). Pine Mountain in western Georgia is a broken and complex ridge near the Fall Line, parallel to it and stretching for 60 miles eastward from the Alabama boundary. In a few places it rises 300 to 500 feet above the Piedmont where the general surface is 800 feet high and exceptionally smooth. Flat Swamp Mountain in North Carolina is a low ridge on intrusive rock crossed by the Peedee River 30 miles from the Fall Line. In crossing it the river falls 100 feet in 5 miles.[2]

[1] LaForge, L., The Physical Geography of Georgia, Geol. Survey Ga., *Bull.* 42, pp. 55–92. In this chapter La Forge describes the Piedmont province in Georgia, dividing and subdividing it for description and explanation.

[2] Holmes, *op. cit.*, p. 71.

Fig. 35.—Airplane view of Stone Mountain and the Atlanta Plateau, looking southwest. (Photograph by U. S. Army Air Service. Reproduced by courtesy of the Georgia Geol. Survey.)

The Southern Piedmont.—The several parts of the upland in Georgia and Alabama differ somewhat in altitude, extent of erosion, and the relative abundance of monadnocks. Much of this variety is explained by the generalizations already stated, the dominant seaward slope, and the decreasing perfection of the peneplain as the mountains are approached. Another locally important factor is the contiguity of the Great Appalachian Valley, whose depth makes it possible for streams draining the adjacent Piedmont to cut deep valleys. Still another factor is the longitudinal drainage of that part that is called the Atlanta Plateau. By this plan the upper Chattahoochee basin is farther hydrographically from the sea than the basins of other streams to the southeast. All of these factors are seen to be connected with streams and their work. Together they would seem to account for most of the differences among the districts. Contrasts in the underlying rocks are not a major factor except in explaining some monadnocks.

For the explanation of these differences in Georgia, LaForge has introduced four (possibly five) cycles of erosion.[1] The evidence for these cycles consists mainly in differences of level amounting in some cases to several hundred feet, but largely explained by the regional slope. The districts so distinguished merge, one into another, by slopes which are not much steeper (except in one locality) than those within the districts themselves. A series of successive cycles lacks proof, though there is nothing improbable in the assumption that the total rise was accomplished by more than one uplift. In the series assumed by LaForge, remnants of the oldest peneplains are found farthest inland and the youngest near the Fall Line. This assumption differs materially from another mentioned below under History (page 158).

The Dahlonega Plateau.—The high inner edge of the Piedmont in Georgia is known by a distinctive name, the Dahlonega Plateau. Much of it is crowded with monadnocks, between which the peneplain came to various degrees of perfection, generally sufficient to justify the name "plateau" and to exclude this margin from the Blue Ridge province. Some parts show an ideal peneplain surface (Fig. 36). Its general level rises to almost 1800 feet near the mountains, and falls, generally in 10

[1] LaForge, *op. cit.*, p. 91.

or 15 miles, to 1400 feet where it merges with that of the smoother Atlanta Plateau.   There is no reason here to treat the Dahlonega Plateau as a distinct unit.   Only at the east, near the Savannah River, is the slope from one to the other at all abrupt.   It is only in this locality that a distinctive name is justified.   This steep slope, local as it is, constitutes the chief evidence on which the Dahlonega Plateau has been assumed by some to be the remains of an older peneplain.

Fig. 36.—Surface of the Piedmont in northeastern Georgia, 5 miles southwest of Tallulah Falls.   This noteworthy flat at an altitude of 1500 feet represents the Dahlonega Plateau where it is best developed and least eroded.   The locality is near the headwaters of the Chattahoochee River which barely incise the surface.   Six miles to the east, the Tugaloo River, having a much shorter course to the sea, has cut its channel 700 feet lower.   (*Photograph by Wright.   Reproduced by courtesy of the Denison University Bulletin.*)

There is, however, another explanation of this difference in height and the relatively abrupt offset in level.[1]   Previous to the capture of the Chattooga and Tallulah rivers (see below) the Dahlonega plateau was drained by the headwaters of the Chattahoochee whose southwestward course to the sea is much longer than those of the southeast-flowing streams.   This requires that its local base level be higher.   In South Carolina and northeastern Georgia the Piedmont streams flowing directly to the ocean are shorter, and developed their peneplain 500 feet lower, but as the divide is followed southwestward, the difference in the distance of its opposite sides from the sea grows less and the

[1] Wright, Frank J., The Older Appalachians of the South, *Jour. Sci. Lab., Denison Univ.*, vol. 26, p. 217, 1931.

difference in altitude disappears.   This hypothesis involves some difficulties of a minor sort but none so grave as those which it escapes.   The principle involved is a familiar one and must be invoked repeatedly to explain differences of level between surfaces of the same age (*cf.* page 249).   No doubt, also, the inner margin of the province was raised more than the outer margin since peneplaning.

As might be expected from the greater altitude of the Dahlonega Plateau, dissection is deep and in many places thorough, so that, between monadnocks on the one hand and sharp valleys, some of them 400 feet deep, on the other, much of the surface is very rough though the general level of the hilltops still gives evidence of a peneplain.   At the western end, tributaries of the Coosawattee River, which flows directly from this plateau into the low Appalachian Valley, are so active in dissecting the surface that the entire landscape is one of steep forested hillsides with little agriculture.[1]

The eastern end of the Dahlonega Plateau, being drained by the headwaters of the Chattahoochee, which has still a long distance to flow over the hard Piedmont rocks, is less sharply dissected.   Some valleys here are favored agriculturally and the country was well settled more than 100 years ago when Dahlonega was the gold mining center of the United States and had a mint.

The Tallulah Gorge.—A detail of this district is the gorge of the Tallulah River where it descends 360 feet in 4 miles by a series of falls to join the deeply entrenched Chattooga and thus to form the Tugaloo which is the upper Savannah.[2]   Such deep entrenchment is not characteristic of the eastern Dahlonega Plateau.   Taken in connection with the drainage pattern, it has given rise to the hypothesis of recent capture by which these waters found a shorter, steeper, and easier course to the sea.[3]   The southwest-flowing Chattooga joins the southeast-flowing

[1] See, for example, the Talking Rock topographic sheet of the U. S. Geological Survey.

[2] JONES, S. P., The Geology of the Tallulah Gorge, Georgia, *Amer. Geologist,* vol. 27, pp. 67–75, 1901.

[3] HAYES, C. W., The Southern Appalachians, *Nat. Geog. Mon.,* 1896; Campbell, M. R., Drainage Modifications and their Interpretation, *Jour. Geol.,* vol. 4, pp. 657–678, 1896; JOHNSON, D. W., River Capture in the Tallulah District, Georgia, *Science,* vol. 25, pp. 428–432, 1907.   The last-mentioned paper contains other references.

Tallulah, forming the Tugaloo-Savannah which continues the course of the Tallulah (Fig. 37). In line with the Chattooga a few miles from the junction is Deep Creek, one of the head-

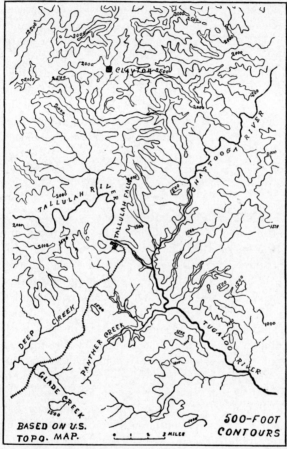

FIG. 37.—Sketch map showing former headwaters of the Chattahoochee River. The Chattooga River seems to have been continuous with Deep Creek (head of the Chattahoochee) perhaps by way of Glade Creek and Panther Creek (reversed). The southwest-flowing stream was captured by the Tugaloo (Savannah) River which, being thus reenforced, has since cut down its channel 400 feet deeper. (*Altered from U. S. Geol. Survey.*)

waters of the southwest-flowing Chattahoochee. The Chattooga was the upper course of the Chattahoochee and was captured by the headward-growing Savannah. After the capture the reinforced Savannah (which had a moderate advantage even before) was able to cut down rapidly at least 400 feet deeper than before into the Dahlonega Plateau, while the beheaded stream continued its southwestward course at the old high level. The deep and quick entrenchment at the elbow of capture developed falls or rapids in the captured streams. As the Tallulah at this point has just crossed a belt of resistant quartzite its falls have not yet been graded out, though their recession has made the famous gorge. Upstream from the falls and the quartzite barrier, the stream flows with moderate gradient in a wide-open valley. Meantime the Chattooga, on a belt of weaker mica schist, has regraded its course at a lower level and, though its valley is deep, it is not a gorge.[1]

The significance of the Tallulah Gorge and its history lie in the fact that the divide which separates the southeast-flowing streams of the Carolina Piedmont from those of the highlands to the northwest, where the drainage is in other directions, is constantly being pushed to the northwest. Most of this change is accomplished by slow shifting of the divide but in an occasional case the head of a Piedmont stream taps and captures a competitor. There are other examples of this process farther north, but in localities less well known.

The Inner Piedmont in the Carolinas.—From Pennsylvania to Georgia, monadnocks are more abundant near the mountains. At places they are so closely set that, although separated by strips of peneplain, the view in all directions is intercepted by monadnocks, some of which are as high as the spurs on the adjacent Blue Ridge. It was suggested above that this prevalence of monadnocks near the mountains is due to the fact that erosion cycles are always further advanced in the lower part of a river basin than near its headwaters. This principle is sufficient to account for the semimountainous character of the inner Piedmont in the Carolinas[2] where the drainage is directly from the mountains to the sea and there is no noteworthy contrast in the strength of the rocks. Brushy Mountain (2600 ft.), South Mountain (3000 ft.), and others 10 to 20 miles from the inner

---

[1] As the hypothesis of capture is generally accepted, other considerations pro and con are omitted. References given above are sufficient.

[2] M. R. Campbell is convinced by his recent work, not yet published, that the isolated mountains in North Carolina belong to the Blue Ridge province and are faulted up with respect to the Piedmont (personal communication).

boundary are extensive masses, comparable with the spurs of the Blue Ridge. Such mountains are distinctly separated from each other and from the Blue Ridge by peneplaned valleys. Large areas even near the mountains are without monadnocks, and no simple line can be drawn between that part of the Piedmont characterized by these residuals and that part which is relatively free from them.

The Inner Piedmont in Virginia.—In Virginia abundant monadnocks are confined to a fairly definite belt, generally 15 to 20 miles wide, at the foot of the Blue Ridge.[1] This belt differs geologically from the smoother lands to the east. It is underlain by strong schists and gneisses. Its eastern limit is an important zone of faulting.[2] For a large part of its total length the fault zone is followed by streams on its eastern side. These streams have carved their valleys from strips of younger and weaker rocks brought to their present position by downthrow on the eastern side of the faults. The most northerly of these weak strips is an extensive Triassic terrane extending from Pennsylvania across Maryland and 60 miles into Virginia. It is described below as one of the Piedmont Lowlands. West of it in Maryland is Catoctin Mountain, included in the Blue Ridge province. The same strong schist which makes this mountain extends far south in Virginia, but, since it there constitutes only isolated mountains standing on the Upland, it is allotted to the Piedmont province.

For 50 miles south of the Triassic lowland, downthrow on the eastern side of the fault has preserved a strip of limestone only 2 to 4 miles wide, in which some smaller streams have cut longitudinal valleys. Then follows another narrow strip of Triassic rocks, succeeded by a 50-mile stretch in which Pre-Cambrian rocks contain many narrow strips of marble. The James River follows this weak belt for more than 40 miles after making a sharp turn at the fault line near Lynchburg (see map, Pl. 2). Farther south the Roanoke River makes a similar turn and flows parallel to the fault line for 15 miles. South of the Roanoke the close

[1] Strikingly shown on the Buckingham topographic sheet of the U. S. Geological Survey.

[2] This fault is delineated on the U. S. geological map (1932) which is presumably more accurate than the geological map of Virginia (1928). See also A. S. Furcron, James River Iron and Marble Belt, Va. Geol. Survey, *Bull.* 39, 1935.

relation between the monadnock belt and the gneissic terrane disappears. At the Carolina boundary the fault line approaches the boundary of the Blue Ridge province. A possible genetic relation between these two lines deserves attention.[1]

Between the Blue Ridge on the west and the fault line here described (mainly north of the Roanoke) monadnocks are not only abundant but, in many cases, of mountainous dimensions. It was this imperfectly peneplaned belt which first bore the name Piedmont, the literal significance of which (foot of the mountain) is more applicable here than elsewhere. However, an attempt to restrict the use of the term to this area now could only result in confusion.[2]

There is much to be said for classifying the monadnock belt in Virginia with the mountains on the west instead of the Piedmont plateau on the east. Its geologic continuations both north and south are so classed. The fault zone that limits the belt runs tangent to the mountain front at both ends. So far as Virginia alone is concerned, this reclassification would be satisfactory,[3] but the Piedmont province would still have many monadnocks near its inner edge in other states where no workable plan could throw them into the mountain province.

The Upland North of the Potomac.—The landscape on the upland in Maryland and Pennsylvania is fairly described in the general statements made earlier (page 131), but altitudes and slopes in this part need special mention. Lowlands here intervene between the upland and the mountains. The upland has its maximum elevation along a median axis known in Maryland as Parrs Ridge.[4] Near the Pennsylvania-Maryland line the top

[1] This question has recently been studied in the field by M. R. Campbell, who states in a personal communication his belief (to be published in the near future) that the Blue Ridge Front and the mountains east of it in North Carolina are due primarily to faulting and only modified by recent erosion.

[2] Theoretically, the Piedmont may be one thing and the Piedmont *province* something much larger but as popular usage of this term can not now be changed, an effort to establish a different usage in science would be of doubtful wisdom.

[3] Here, as in many other cases, smaller divisions having a considerable degree of homogeneity lend themselves to regrouping according to the purpose of the discussion in hand.

[4] CLARK, WM. B., The Geography of Maryland, *Md. Geol. Survey*, vol. 10, p. 82, 1918.

of this swell is at 1000 to 1100 feet. Its topography is typical
Piedmont peneplain except that valleys of a later cycle are cut
somewhat more sharply than elsewhere to a depth of 300 feet.
In this rejuvenation the structure is rather prominently revealed
at some places by selective erosion of the metamorphic rocks,
causing northeast-southwest ridges. At a few places wide valleys
or limited lowlands are developed on marble or other weak rock.

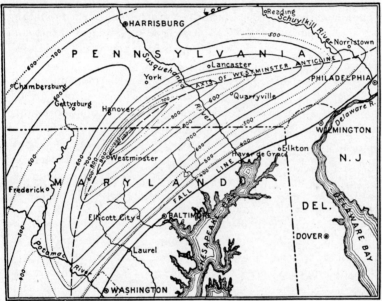

Fig. 38.—Map of eastern Maryland and Pennsylvania showing Campbell's
hypothesis of surface deformation since deposition of the Bryn Mawr (Pliocene)
gravel. Dotted contour lines at intervals of 100 feet show the present altitude
of the Bryn Mawr gravel above the sea. Solid contour lines show the level of
the prevailing peneplain. Parrs Ridge is on the axis of the Westminster anticline. (*M. R. Campbell in Bull. Geol. Soc. Amer., vol. 44.*)

In areas of such erosion outstanding ridges are seen. Such are
Dug Hill Ridge (Westminster quadrangle) and Parrs Ridge
strictly so-called. As the latter name is used in geologic work,
it generally indicates the broader swell from which such ridges
have been carved.

Southwestward toward the Potomac the broad swell declines,
and it dies out a few miles south of the river.[1] It also becomes

---

[1] M. R. Campbell, who has traced this southward extension, makes Parrs
Ridge a postpeneplain anticline and accountable for the Great Falls of the
Potomac, at least for their height.

lower and less defined toward the northeast. East of the Susquehanna and approximately in line with this axis is Mine Ridge on the southern border of the Lancaster Lowland (page 152).   In the main, Mine Ridge is the relatively high northern edge of the south-sloping upland, but its height is locally increased several hundred feet by residual hills.

East of the 76th meridian the Lancaster Lowland is not developed and the Piedmont Upland on the Susquehanna-Schuylkill divide extends north to the limit of the province. Some of the area here referred to (mainly Honeybrook and Phoenixville quadrangles) is typical Piedmont Upland but residual masses rise 300 to 400 feet above it, Welsh Mountain (1000 to 1100 ft.) being the highest and most abrupt.   Relatively level areas on the summits and shoulders of these masses have been interpreted by E. B. Knopf[1] as the beginnings of peneplains in four or more interrupted cycles, all of them younger and lower than the summit peneplain in the mountain provinces.   These levels are represented as appearing in stairlike succession in approaching not only Mine Ridge and Welsh Mountain, but the Reading Prong, South Mountain and Parrs Ridge in Maryland (Fig. 39).   Not all geologists recognize so large a number of cycles, and among those who do, the application of names has not been consistent in all cases.   If the name "Harrisburg" be used for that peneplain which is here 500 to 600 feet high near the mountains and declines seaward, it designates the dominant horizon of the Piedmont Upland in this part of the province and, for aught that is known, from Pennsylvania to Alabama, though its present altitude varies from place to place.

The exact nature and history of the Parrs-Mine ridge chain is not beyond dispute.   Throughout its length the summit of the swell agrees with the present divide.   This suggests that the ridge is residual.   There can be no question of the residual nature of the masses mentioned in Pennsylvania, which are quite distinctly above the prevailing upland level, but farther south, where the feature to be explained is a broad swell whose summit and sides have a peneplain character, its explanation as a residual

[1] KNOPF, E. B., Correlation of Residual Erosion Surfaces in the Eastern Appalachian Highlands, *Bull. Geol. Soc. Amer.*, vol. 35, pp. 633–668, 1924. See also an earlier paper by F. Bascom, Cycles of Erosion in the Piedmont Province of Pennsylvania, *Jour. Geol.*, vol. 29, pp. 540–559, 1921.

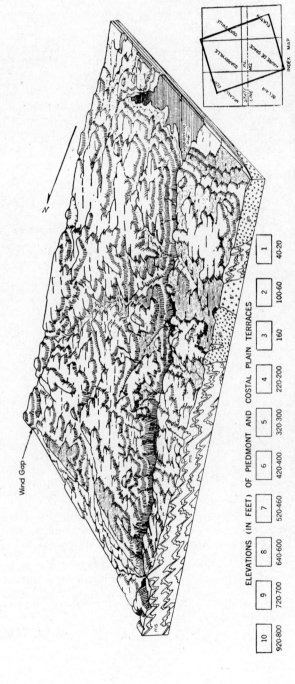

ELEVATIONS (IN FEET) OF PIEDMONT AND COSTAL PLAIN TERRACES

10	9	8	7	6	5	4	3	2	1
920-800	720-700	640-600	520-460	420-400	320-300	220-200	160	100-60	40-20

Fig. 39.—Block diagram of a part of southern Pennsylvania and northern Maryland showing areas whose summit levels indicate a succession of ten piedmont terraces as interpreted by E. B. Knopf. (*Maryland Geological Survey Report on Baltimore County*, 58–93, 1929.)

of erosion has caused more question.   Erosion in a single cycle could scarcely have reduced the divide to a peneplain while leaving lateral slopes of 50 feet to the mile.   It was suggested long ago[1] that the summit of Parrs Ridge is a remnant of an older peneplain partly destroyed in later cycles.   More recent and detailed study of its slopes by E. B. Knopf[2] has resulted in the delineation of eight eroded terraces, assumed to have been developed during interrupted uplift of the land mass, each terrace representing the beginning of a new peneplain on the seaward margin of an emerging surface.

Over against the hypothesis of a terraced dome, in which the development of the present surface followed intermittent uplift step by step, is set the hypothesis that only one peneplain is essential and that Parrs Ridge is the result of late Tertiary deformation of a single surface.   Evidence that this ridge is due, at least in part, to Late Tertiary uplift is believed to be found[3] in gravel deposited mainly by the Susquehanna and the Potomac before their valleys were cut to the present depth. The profile of the late Tertiary Susquehanna, as reconstructed by Campbell, is now arched upward 200 feet where it crosses the axis of the supposed uplift.   This arching, with its supposed southward continuation in Parrs Ridge, has been called by Campbell the Westminster anticline (Fig. 38).   While this restoration of the Susquehanna profile is disputed,[4] there is nothing improbable about such warping in a region where oscillation has long been habitual and folding has repeatedly occurred along northeast-southwest axes.   In other provinces a few miles to the northwest all peneplains show warping.   This explanation of Parrs Ridge does not require, though it does not deny, the existence of more than one Piedmont peneplain.   The probability of postpeneplain deformation in the Piedmont province

[1] CLARK, MATTHEWS, and others, The Physical Features of Maryland, *Md. Geol. Survey*, p. 75, 1906.

[2] KNOPF, E. B., The Physiography of Baltimore County, *Md. Geol. Survey*, pp. 58–96, 1929.   On pp. 88–89 is a table correlating all terraces in Pennsylvania, Maryland, and Virginia.

[3] CAMPBELL, M. R., Geomorphic Value of River Gravel, *Bull. Geol. Society Amer.*, vol. 40, p. 529, 1929; also Chambersburg (Harrisburg) Peneplain in the Piedmont of Maryland and Pennsylvania, *Bull. Geol. Soc. Amer.*, vol. 44, 553–573, 1933.

[4] STOSE, G. W., Is the Bryn Mawr Peneplain a Warped Surface? *Amer. Jour. Sci.*, vol. 19, pp. 178–184, 1930.

should be considered in connection with the profile of the Susquehanna River whose fall from Harrisburg to the sea is 4.5 feet
per mile, or more than twice that of its middle course in the
Ridge and Valley province.

NORTHERN PIEDMONT LOWLAND

Two extensive lowlands in the northern part of the Piedmont
province are mainly, but not wholly, on soft Triassic rocks.   At
most places where these areas are in contact with the Piedmont
upland on the crystalline rocks, the former are distinctly lower.
There are also important differences within the lowlands themselves.   Probably it is true at most places, but not everywhere,
that these lowlands are one cycle younger than the upland.

Boundaries.—The northern one of these two subdivisions
extends to the Hudson River in New Jersey and southeastern
New York.   From this place to Reading, Pa., it abuts against
the Reading Prong of the New England Upland, the equivalent
of the Blue Ridge.   On its seaward side in New Jersey it reaches
the Coastal Plain, but in Pennsylvania it is separated from the
latter province by a narrow tongue of the crystalline upland which
parallels the Delaware River (Pl. 1).   The lowland extends
westward to include the valley of the Schuylkill, beyond which
for a short distance the upland occupies the entire width of the
province.[1]

Despite the small elevation and relief of the Piedmont lowland
in New Jersey it is separated from the Coastal Plain by a more
or less distinct rise.   In the Princeton quadrangle, where the
edge of the Triassic lowland is about 200 feet high, the rise
amounts to 100 feet or more in one or two miles.   Toward the
northeast, as the sea is approached and all altitudes decline, the
difference is less.   North of the latitude of Perth Amboy, glacial
drift obscures the boundary.   In southeastern Pennsylvania
there is no contrast in altitude between the broadly rolling surface
of the Triassic and that of the crystalline belt northeast of Philadelphia.   Farther west, as the Schuylkill is approached, the
stronger rocks south of the river rise to levels above 500 feet
and are outlined by a north-facing escarpment about 200 feet

[1] On the map of Physical Divisions of the United States issued by the U. S.
Geol. Survey in 1930, this transverse band of upland is unfortunately made
to coincide with the Schuylkill Valley instead of lying west of it.

high. This escarpment, marking the edge of the upland, continues northwestward across the province to the mountains, being nowhere more than 6 miles west of the Schuylkill River.

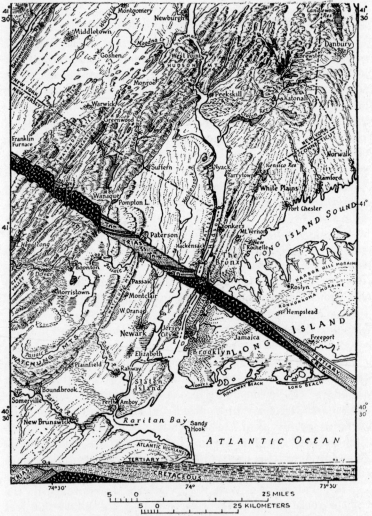

Fig. 40.—Block diagram, vicinity of New York. (*Raisz*, XVI *Internat. Geol. Congress, Guidebook* 9.)

Influence of Underlying Rocks.—Within the boundaries here traced, both the altitude and the topography of the lowland vary considerably. Part of the variation is plainly referable to rock character. The Triassic itself (Newark group) contains three formations, of which the Lockatong in the middle, consisting largely of hard dark shale, is more resistant than the others and underlies belts distinctly higher than the rest of the lowland. The softer Brunswick shale above and Stockton formation below, mainly soft sandstone, form the more typical rolling lowlands. A typical Lockatong swell rising to 480 feet is seen north of Norriston, Pa., flanked on either side by rolling plains 100 to 150 feet lower.[1] Another, the Hunterdon Plateau, west of the Raritan River in New Jersey, 10 to 15 miles east of Easton, Pa., is an upland which slopes southwestward from an altitude of over 500 feet with hills rising above it to 700 feet. To the east, and adjacent to its highest part, is a rolling plain not much more than 200 feet high.[2]

Trap Ridges.—A much greater contrast in resistance is found between the Triassic sediments on the one hand and the igneous rocks on the other. The latter, both extrusive and intrusive (both commonly known here as trap rock), occur in sheets parallel to and included between the Triassic beds. Along with the sediments they were tilted by faulting before the erosion which produced the present features. The igneous rocks were base-leveled along with the rest in one or more of the earlier cycles. All of their summit surfaces show the remains of peneplains and there is probably no case in this part of the province in which the adjacent sediments were not peneplaned in one or more later cycles unless it be the Hunterdon Plateau. The Schooley peneplain, preserved on the summit of the Watchung Mountains, is identified with the surface to which most of the Appalachian Highland was reduced, and which is now represented by the crests of typical Appalachian ridges.

The typical trap ridge is exemplified by the Watchung Mountains, two ridges 40 miles long, parallel to each other and to the axis of the lowland in northern New Jersey. From their

---

[1] Philadelphia folio (No. 162), p. 24, U. S. Geol. Survey, 1909. A brief but satisfactory statement of the physical properties of the Piedmont rocks is given by F. Bascom in U. S. Geol. Survey, *Bull.* 828, p. 7, 1931.

[2] Raritan folio (No. 191), U. S. Geol. Survey, 1914. The authors of this folio treat the Hunterton Plateau as a remnant of the peneplain which appears in the even crests of the mountain province and on the trap ridges.

smooth, almost horizontal crests 500 to 550 feet high, steep scarp slopes descend to the southeast and gentle dip slopes to the northwest. The escarpment of First Watchung Mountain, *i.e.*, the one overlooking the plain to the southeast, is 400 feet or more in height. The breadth of each mountain is 1 to 2 miles. Both ranges, and also the parallel Long and Hook mountains farther west, are made by intercalated basalt flows which dip with the sediments 8 to 10 degrees toward the northwest.[1] Except for details of size, etc., this same description would apply to the Palisades of the Hudson. In this case the igneous sheet is intrusive. Many of the trap ridges are curved in plan because of warping along transverse axes. It is noteworthy that, except for such details, all the dips of this district are toward the mountains on the northwest. The clear reflection of monoclinal structure in topography, with contrasted dip and scarp slopes, is much more marked in New Jersey than in Pennsylvania. Some of the ridges in the latter state rise to 800 or 900 feet but are less simply outlined both in plan and in profile.

Different Base Levels.—Differences in level between adjacent areas seem in some cases to be quite independent of underlying rocks. For example in the Somerville, N. J., quadrangle, 12 to 15 miles north of Princeton, there seem to be two distinct levels in adjacent areas on the Brunswick shale. South of the Raritan River and the town of Somerville is a very mildly rolling landscape 100 to 120 feet high. Immediately west of this the horizon is at 175 to 200 feet, and the relief reaches 100 feet in a mile. The relations suggest that a new local peneplain is being developed at the expense of an older one, though both surfaces have been included under the name Somerville peneplain.[2]

The extent to which each of the factors indicated above is responsible for the diverse altitudes within this district is undetermined. Plainly the igneous rocks stand higher because they have worn better. It is equally true, though less obvious, that the several formations of the Triassic have been unequally

[1] Passaic folio (No. 157), p. 21, and also structural sections, U. S. Geol. Survey, 1908.

[2] *Cf.* KNOPF, E. B., Correlation of Residual Erosion Surfaces in the Eastern Appalachian Highlands, *Bull. Geol. Soc. Amer.*, vol. 35, pp. 633–668, 1924; ref. to p. 662. The opinion is here expressed that the so-called Somerville peneplain embraces remnants of several peneplains.

worn down, also that the downcutting of some areas on softer rocks has been retarded by the proximity of harder rocks which maintained local and temporary base levels. That some summits which have held their height better than others on similar rock represent slightly older peneplains seems probable. It is also apparent that surfaces of small relief rise upstream from the Fall Line, or with increasing distance from the main drainage lines. This area, being near the sea and therefore quickly responsive in its topography to small changes of level, may well

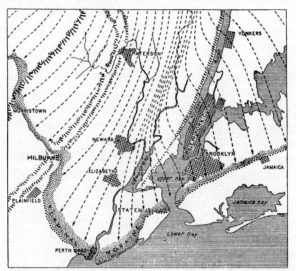

Fig. 41.—Sketch map showing the direction of ice movement in the vicinity of New York City. (*Passaic folio, U. S. Geol. Survey.*)

be expected to record diversities of base level, even within a small range and within a short time. The preservation of these subordinate features is favored by their recency. All distinctions are both small and local. Events and features of the small order drop out of the picture in the study of more general peneplains of greater age and farther from the sea (see page 156).

Glaciation.—The northern part of this lowland is surfaced with deposits from the last continental ice sheet. The thickness of these deposits, averaging perhaps 20 feet, is not great enough to affect the general aspect of a lowland, but the rearrangement of streams, their relative paucity, and the frequency of swamps in the glaciated area are noteworthy. A well-developed terminal

FIG. 42.—Topographic map of an area southeast of Plainfield, N. J. The central belt of hills and hollows is terminal moraine. On the west is a part of the outwash plain, sloping west and beginning to be eroded. On the east is ground moraine, in part swampy. The entire section is approximately 3 miles long. Contour interval 5 feet. Maximum height above the swamp about 150 feet; above the outwash plain about 60 feet. (*Passaic folio, U. S. Geol. Survey.*)

moraine, 200 feet thick at places and very hummocky, extends northwestward from the mouth of the Raritan to Morristown, crossing the Watchung Mountains (Figs. 41 and 42). Stratified drift laid down by glacial waters is at places very thick and very important topographically, though inconspicuous because of its flat surface. West of the Palisade ridge it fills a deep depression and makes the Hackensack Meadows (marsh) where otherwise would be an arm of the sea 100 feet deep.[1]

Drainage.—In an area of weak rocks traversed or barred from the sea by bands of strong rock and in part glaciated, peculiarities of drainage may well be expected. An area of more than 300 square miles between the Highlands and the Watchung Mountains must drain across the latter. At present its surface water is all gathered into the Passaic River, which leaves the basin by a notch at Paterson (see map, Pl. 1). Near Millburn, 15 miles to the south, is another notch equally large but clogged with glacial deposits and not now in use. It has been common to assume that both of these great gaps were the work of east-flowing streams whose waters were united later either by capture[2] or as an incident to glacial deposition.[3] More recently Johnson has put forward the hypothesis that the two great gaps, or rather pairs of gaps (because the Watchung Range is double), were made by the Hudson River, flowing into the basin at Paterson, out at Millburn, and probably to the sea by way of the present Raritan.[4] The Hudson seems to have followed its present course to a point near the New York-New Jersey line and there crossed the Palisade ridge through a gap similar to the others mentioned.

Burial of the Piedmont and the base-leveled Watchung Mountains by Cretaceous sediments have long been invoked in order to explain the gorges by superposed drainage. Johnson has applied it in a different manner. He assumes that the Hudson (in its

[1] Passaic folio (No. 157), p. 14, U. S. Geol. Survey, 1908.

[2] DAVIS, W. M., The Rivers of Northern New Jersey, *Nat. Geog. Mag.* vol. 2, 1890.

[3] SALISBURY, R. D., Passaic folio (No. 157), p. 19, U. S. Geol. Survey, 1908.

[4] JOHNSON, DOUGLAS, "Stream Sculpture on the Atlantic Slope," Chap. VII, Columbia University Press, 1931. The argument involves the local drainage to an extent that is too detailed for this treatise but it is of much interest scientifically, especially because of the proximity of this district to a large population and to many universities and colleges.

former course as described above), instead of being consequent on the Cretaceous cover, developed as a subsequent stream on the outcrop of weak beds at the base of the series. The position it occupied was like that of the present Delaware between Trenton and Philadelphia, being on the same formations, whose outcrops at that time were necessarily farther west. The Hudson Valley was then bordered on the east by a cuesta just as, after much erosion and shifting of outcrops to the southeast, the same cuesta now borders the low strip from Raritan Bay to Philadelphia. These conditions began in the Schooley cycle but may have continued much longer. With the seaward retreat of the cuesta the Hudson may have been captured near the state line by a stream east of the Palisades (its present course) or it may have followed its old course until displaced by glacial ice.[1]

When both the Paterson and the Millburn gaps were closed by the ice sheet from the north, the southern or ice-free part of the Watchung basin became a lake, known now as *Glacial Lake Passaic*. It overflowed to the southwest through Moggy Hollow north of Somerville. When the ice melted back, the Millburn gap continued to be obstructed by drift and the lake did not again drain eastward until the notches near Paterson were uncovered. The glacial lake then disappeared, but much of its basin is still swampy.[2]

LANCASTER-FREDERICK LOWLAND

The more southerly of the two Piedmont lowlands stretches from the Schuylkill-Susquehanna divide west and south across Maryland into Virginia, a total of 180 miles, with a width ranging from 10 to 40 miles. Like its eastern correlative, it is far from being a simple unit. Within and around the lowlands are patches of highland, odds and ends that do not fit well into any system of homogeneous provinces and sections.

The Lowland in Pennsylvania.—Diversities begin at once to appear in an examination of the form and boundaries of the area. Its wide expanse east of the Susquehanna is largely on

---

[1] Note that the axis of the later glacial lobe (and probably of earlier ones also) was west of the Palisade ridge. See New York folio (No. 83), U. S. Geol. Survey, 1902.

[2] For a detailed history and description of Glacial Lake Passaic, see R. D. Salisbury, Glacial Geology, *N. J. Geol. Survey*, vol. 5, Pls. 36 to 42 and accompanying discussion; also Passaic folio, p. 19.

Ordovician limestone worn down to small relief. Its present altitude there is not far from 400 feet, less near the Susquehanna and more toward the headwaters of smaller streams near the border. The surface of the crystalline rocks on the south rises to 900 feet in Mine Ridge. Along the eastern edge of the lowland, about on the 76th meridian, broad limestone bays at an elevation of 500 feet or more indent the edge of the crystalline upland, here 700 to 900 feet high. The northern part of the lowland is partly on Paleozoic limestone, partly on Triassic sandstone and shale, but the surface of the Triassic, even where level, rarely fails to rise 100 or 150 feet above the limestone surface.[1]

At the northern margin of the province the Triassic rocks rise in a rough belt called South Mountain, extending west from the Schuylkill River almost to the Susquehanna. On the map (Pl. 1) the eastern and higher part of this belt is included in the Piedmont Upland which here crosses the province and separates the two lowlands. It is a belt of knobs and short ridges, many of them from 900 to 1200 feet high. The belt is sharply outlined on the north against the Lebanon Valley (page 234) and for much of its length is almost equally clear from the south. This linear highland is topographically continuous with the Reading Prong of the New England province, being interrupted only by the narrow transverse valley of the Schuylkill. It serves to connect that range with the greater South Mountain west of Harrisburg. However, as its rocks and much of its history are those of the Piedmont Lowland, it is included here in the Piedmont province. Moreover, other and smaller districts like it are completely surrounded by the lowlands. The rest of the Triassic rocks between this high belt and the broad limestone lowland centering at Lancaster have been worn down to a peneplain, now dissected and lying 100 to 150 feet higher than the smoother surface on the limestone.

West and south of the Susquehanna the limestone is limited to a narrow strip on the southeast side, bordering the crystalline upland where the latter is 700 to 800 feet high. The Triassic belt, 15 or more miles in width between the limestone and the abrupt rise of South Mountain on the west, is higher and has more relief

[1] Compare the Lancaster sheet of the U. S. Geol. Survey with the same area on the geologic map of Pennsylvania.

but is still properly classed as a lowland.   The horizon is 500 to 600 feet high on the divide between the Susquehanna and the Potomac basins.   The rolling surface, studded with knobs of trap rock, some of them rising 500 feet above the plain, is typically shown around Gettysburg.

Just as the lowland is itself elongated in line with the province, so also are most of the highlands that rise like islands from its floor.   Tongues of the upland extending into the lowland, or *vice versa*, have the same linear character and direction, indicating corrugation of the old structure before any existing surfaces were made.   Many of the islands of upland within the lowland are geologically like the trap ridges of New Jersey.

Chester Valley.—A remarkable limestone valley having the structural relations just described serves in a way to connect the Northern with the Lancaster-Frederick Lowland, but is more closely connected with the former.   This is the Chester Valley which begins at Quarryville, south of Mine Ridge, and extends 55 miles east-northeast in a strikingly straight course to a point north of Philadelphia (Pl. 1).   Throughout its length it constitutes a trench 1 to 3 miles wide, and several hundred feet below the nearby uplands.   As this area has been repeatedly peneplaned, the synclinal structure of this valley can only affect its form indirectly, by causing a zone of soluble limestone to be preserved between slates, quartzites, and schists on either side.   Its present surface is part of the youngest peneplain. There is no evidence that this valley was ever followed by a stream.[1]   Not only the Schuylkill River but smaller creeks cross its course with no regard for its presence, their courses conforming to the general slope of the province and perhaps determined by superposition (page 258).   Inspection of a railroad map will show the marked geographical significance of this narrow lowland.   The York Valley west of the Susquehanna is similar.

The Lowland in Maryland and Virginia.—Near the Potomac in Maryland is a small but significant limestone area in the valley of the Monocacy River.   This is a smooth plain about 350 feet high at Frederick but sloping gently southward.   East of it is the crystalline upland, 500 to 600 feet high, probably the main late Tertiary (Harrisburg) peneplain.   West of the limestone plain, and 100 feet higher, is another plain mainly on the very narrow

[1] BASCOM, F., Philadelphia folio, p. 18.

belt of Triassic rocks at the foot of Catoctin Mountain, on whose crest are remnants of a higher peneplain.

It would seem only natural to correlate the peneplain on limestone in the Monocacy Valley at Frederick with the similar one (50 feet higher and a little farther from the sea) on the same limestone in the Conestoga Valley at Lancaster, Pa. The latter is E. B. Knopf's Lancaster peneplain, assumed to be next younger than the Harrisburg. In both cases the adjacent surface on Triassic sandstone and shale is higher than that of the limestone and lower than that of the nearest crystalline rocks. Probably there was some difference in altitude at all stages of erosion but minor changes in base level are also possible. Among levels that are so young and so local and so little differentiated in altitude, long distance correlations are uncertain. The two levels in Maryland are here treated as the work of a (perhaps) composite cycle which is roughly equivalent to the Somerville in New Jersey.

South of the Potomac there is no limestone, yet the same low level, 300 to 350 feet, prevails over most of the lowland, which is here separated from the Blue Ridge province by a strip of Piedmont Upland. The whole province is lower here than in Maryland, but the Piedmont Upland on the west is generally not below 500 feet, and on the east not below 400 feet. Many of the trap rock intrusions in the Potomac basin do not rise perceptibly above the surrounding surface of Triassic sandstone and shale.

HISTORICAL INTERPRETATION OF THE PIEDMONT PROVINCE

Questions Involved.—It is generally agreed that this province has been peneplaned since the tilting and burial of the older peneplain on its seaward side. Obviously the highest peneplain, partially preserved on the mountains to the west, is also older than the Piedmont surface. Whether these two older peneplains, one on either side, are the same is a question probably to be settled in the negative.[1] The question is also raised whether the entire Piedmont Upland is to be regarded as a single peneplain or whether the reduction was accomplished in two or more cycles in such a manner that the work of the younger cycles only

[1] The history of the Piedmont province cannot be fully discussed except in connection with the mountain provinces. See pp. 186 and 255.

partially destroyed the older records. In either case there is the further question whether, or to what extent, the surface may have been altered by invasion of the sea, the deposits of which have since vanished.

Before proceeding with the events of physiographic history, two general principles of interpretation need mention. First, a multiplicity of uncompleted cycles is more apt to leave its record near the sea than farther inland. Peneplains begin near streams in their lower courses where they reach base level. The incipient peneplains slowly widen and extend upstream. The land may go

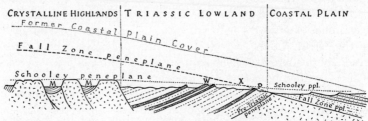

Fig. 43.—Cross section of northern New Jersey showing the geomorphic evolution as interpreted by Douglas Johnson "Stream Sculpture on the Atlantic Slope." Trap ridges are indicated by *W*, Watchung Mountains, and *P*, Palisades of the Hudson. The Schooley peneplain intersected the Fall Zone peneplain at *X*.

up and down uneasily and a half dozen new beginnings may be recorded in the land forms near the sea before the first of the changes has been propagated inland very far. The record farther inland is like that of a tidal gauge which ignores passing waves and records only the more long continued changes of level. Davis recognized this principle many years ago when he wrote, with reference to this same region, "The cutting and filling resulting from comparatively brief and trivial elevations and depressions make a record so complete and so complicated that its details encumber the problem and place its solution out of reach for the present."[1]

Second, it happens sometimes both here and elsewhere that two peneplains are recognized, the higher being uniformly on

[1] DAVIS, W. M., Geological Dates of Origin of Certain Topographic Forms on the Atlantic Slope of the United States, *Bull. Geol. Soc. Amer.*, vol. 2, p. 577, 1891. See also Barrell, The Piedmont Terraces of the Northern Appalachians, *Amer. Jour. Sci.*, 4th ser., vol. 49, pp. 328 and 348, 1920. Barrell argues here that numerous records in the form of incipient peneplains, etc., should, *a priori*, be expected to appear on the margin of the continent.

harder rocks and the lower on softer rocks. It is objected by
some that the two are products of the same cycle, the difference in
altitude being sufficiently accounted for by the difference in rocks.
They would regard the higher level on harder rocks as representing an unfinished stage of the same cycle which was carried to
completion on the softer rocks. But in that case the surface on
the harder rocks would not be a plain or even a dissected plain.
It should not be difficult to distinguish this case from that of two
peneplains. The true explanation is not always the same, but
under perfectly normal and not uncommon conditions the remains
of the older peneplain may be confined to hard rocks and the
beginnings of a newer one to soft rocks. This may be exemplified
in the Great Valley east of Harrisburg (page 234) where three
grades of rock preserve peneplain surfaces at three different levels.
This is commonly accepted as evidence of three cycles.

The relations just described may also be conceived in another
way. An even-topped ridge or a maturely dissected plateau
may be reduced in altitude by unconcentrated wash without
losing its even-topped profile. The lowered surface can not
be said to have passed through a new cycle. Rather frequently
an even skyline is spoken of as "representing" an old peneplain
though acknowledged to have been lowered by such uniform
erosion.[1] Thus a peneplain, spreading impartially over strong
and weak rocks, may be lowered a little on the former and much
on the latter. Two surfaces result, which are not satisfactorily distinguished in current physiographic terminology. As
language is now used, two plane surfaces, believed to have
acquired their form in the same erosion cycle, are given the same
designation regardless of differential lowering, *provided* they are
not contiguous. If contiguous, they would be called by different
names, with the implication that two cycles are indicated.
Where the difference in rock resistance is great and the difference
in altitude is small, surfaces at different levels are quite as apt
to have resulted from one cycle as from two. The limits of the
application of this principle are hard to define. Taken with
other complications just described, it goes far to justify the
treatment of erosional history in terms of a few major cycles in

[1] See references on pp. 199 and 250. The author has treated this subject
at length in a paper on Cyclic and Non-Cyclic Aspects of Erosion, *Bull.
Geol. Soc. Amer.*, vol. 47, pp. 173–186, 1936.

which minor events or changes may find their setting when it is necessary to mention them.

Cycles in the Southern Piedmont.—Plain records of physiographic history in Georgia begin with an older peneplain, evident at places among the mountains of the Blue Ridge province at a height of 3000 feet or more (page 175), probably the same as the highest summit peneplain farther north, the Schooley or Kittatinny. This surface was arched by uplift, first to a height of 1500 feet or more in the mountain province. Presumably the Coastal Plain was depressed at the same time, the hinge being not very far from the present fall line. In the erosion cycle thus inaugurated, a wedge-shaped mass was removed, approximately 1500 feet thick near the mountains and thinning to zero at the coast line of that time. At the base of this mass was the newer peneplain. If the line of zero uplift was outside the present province boundary, the new peneplain covered the entire Piedmont. If inside, then a margin of the Piedmont would preserve the older peneplain. In any case a zone of considerable width would have been uplifted so little and so slowly that its topography would never have been rejuvenated, even though slightly and slowly lowered. Such a condition would be most certain to prevail on a terrain like the Piedmont,[1] where rocks are deeply decomposed (at places more than 100 feet). It is not strange that such a zone should sometimes be classed with the older peneplain and sometimes with the newer. Preference is here given to the latter.

Inequalities among the several parts of the southern Piedmont may reflect only differences in rocks (believed to be very small) and direction of drainage. If accounted for by successive small uplifts and subcycles of erosion (see page 156), each lower surface in turn spread inland from the coast or back from the main rivers. This hypothesis is apparently unnecessary and not very strongly supported. At a relatively late time the entire region was raised to its present height. All of the deeper valleys and

---

[1] HAYES, C. W., and CAMPBELL, M. R., Geomorphology of the Southern Appalachians, *Nat. Geog. Mag.*, vol. 6, 1894. This pioneer paper continues to merit attention, despite its preliminary character and despite the fact that some of its statements require careful reading in order to see their consistency. The paper gives an excellent description of the effect of slight uplift on a peneplain cut on deeply weathered rocks.

nearly all steep slopes are due to revived erosion since the uplift of the Piedmont peneplain.

History of the Upland in the North.—In the North, as in the South, uplift has been mainly in the mountain province, uplifted peneplains slope seaward, those of different cycles converge, and the same problem arises with respect to the assignment of uplands near the Fall Line to this or that erosion cycle. The older custom was to allot a considerable belt west of the fall line to the peneplain which makes the floor beneath the coastal plain sediments, and to identify both with the summit peneplain in the mountains.[1] The strip adjacent to the Fall Line was assumed to owe its preservation to the combined effects of low altitude and temporary burial. This conception is now abandoned. That the subcoastal plain floor is an older peneplain, truncated along a line not far west of the edge of the sediments, need not now be questioned. Whether the surface that cuts it off at that line should be called Schooley or Harrisburg[2] or something else may still be open to question.[3]

The larger part of the Piedmont Upland in the north as well as in the south may well be a peneplain of a single cycle, commonly called the Harrisburg. Geologists would differ as to the extent of surface to be excluded from this statement. They would disagree on (1) the degree of uniformity in altitude

[1] CLARK, WM. B., E. B. MATTHEWS, and others, The Physical Features of Maryland, *Md. Geol. Survey*, vol. 6, pp. 27–92, 1906, ref. to p. 75.

[2] CAMPBELL, M. R., Geographic Development of Northern Pennsylvania and Southern New York, *Bull. Geol. Soc. Amer.*, vol. 14, p. 283, 1903. In this same paper Campbell names and defines the Harrisburg peneplain. He has since proposed the name Chambersburg as a substitute for Harrisburg. (*Bull. Geol. Soc. Amer.*, vol. 44, pp. 553–573, 1933.)

[3] The Maryland geologists (Clark and others, *op. cit.*, p. 77) do not recognize peneplains younger than the Weverton east of Parrs Ridge. Barrell finds outside of Parrs Ridge a definite set of terraces, marine at least to 745 feet A.T. The outermost terrace, 520 to 540 feet high, he correlates with the "Lafayette" formation. Both in elevation and in its relation to the "Lafayette" gravels this would agree with Keith's "Tertiary" (Harrisburg?) peneplain. (See Barrell, *op. cit.*, p. 426, also Pl. VI). E. B. Knopf (Physiography of Baltimore County, *loc. cit.*) also finds a series of terraces decreasing in age toward the sea. See also Wm. O. Hickok, Erosion Surfaces in South Central Pennsylvania, *Amer. Jour. Sci.*, vol. 25, pp. 101–122, 1933. This paper, involving also other provinces, treats the area as composed of a large number of nearly, if not quite, horizontal surfaces, each of which appears as a stream terrace in valleys farther from the sea.

required of a surface to be called a peneplain. (2) The importance attached to approximate agreements in altitude, some treating as fortuitous what others ascribe to systematic control. (3) The allowance to be made for unequal lowering of a noncyclic character, *i.e.*, by rain wash, without rejuvenation. Pauses in uplift, and incipient local peneplanation during and following the long Harrisburg cycle are inherently probable. If the Weverton or other intervening peneplains were ever extensive they were wholly or largely destroyed in the making of the Harrisburg surface. The two hypotheses for explaining Parrs Ridge are sufficiently stated on page 144.

History of the Lowlands.—Following the cycle or cycles in which the hard rocks of the province were reduced to low relief and low altitude, came minor uplifts, followed by erosion which made lowlands at more than one level. On the basis of altitude the limestone lowland about Lancaster, Pa., about 400 feet high. would seem to be the oldest of this series. The younger the surfaces considered, the more are they confined to separate drainage basins, and the greater is the uncertainty in their correlation. Surfaces later than the Harrisburg were long grouped together as the work of the Somerville cycle.[1]

More elaborate studies in more recent years in the basin of the Delaware have broken up the lowland in New Jersey into different levels, tentatively correlating the original Somerville with the Sunderland terrace of the Coastal Plain (page 29) and making it younger than the Lancaster peneplain.[2] There is no inherent improbability in a multiplicity of incipient peneplains at the edge of the continent, but the acceptance of any one series

[1] In New Jersey the Harrisburg peneplain has been recognized very sparingly. *Cf.* U. S. Geol. Survey, New York folio (No. 83), 1902, Passaic folio (No. 157), 1908, Philadelphia folio (No. 162), 1909, Trenton folio (No. 167), 1909. In the last two folios named, F. Bascom implies that three post-Jurassic peneplains recognized farther west may merge as they approach the sea, being represented here by the single upland peneplain. In the Raritan folio (No. 191), 1914, R. D. Salisbury described two peneplains younger than the one on the uplands (Schooley), but only the younger of these (Somerville) is known to be present in the Raritan quadrangle.

[2] BASCOM, F., Cycles of Erosion in the Piedmont Province of Pennsylvania, *Jour. Geol.*, vol. 29, p. 556, 1921. E. B. Knopf (*Bull. Geol. Soc. Amer.*, vol. 35, p. 662) also regards the Lancaster as older than the Somerville.

is, for the present, tentative rather than final. What is true of the Delaware basin applies equally to the basins of the Susquehanna and the Potomac.

The latest peneplains, confined to soft rocks and of limited area, needed only a short time for their making and may all be Pleistocene. Keith computes that the cycle in which the "Tertiary" (Harrisburg?) peneplain was produced in the Potomac basin was 134 times as long as either of the two following subcycles.[1]

As measured by their enduring results, the great erosional events thus far mentioned have been (1) the making of the "Fall Zone peneplain," now largely buried by coastal plain sediments, (2) after uplift, the development of the Schooley peneplain indicated by many mountain tops, (3) after further uplift (probably intermittent) the development of the main Piedmont (presumably Harrisburg) peneplain, (4) following still further intermittent uplift, the development in favored situations of lower peneplains collectively known as the Somerville.

RESOURCES OF THE PIEDMONT PROVINCE

Mineral Resources.—Many of the resources of this province are so related to its geology and physiography as to deserve mention by way of illustration. Its igneous rocks furnish some of the granite used as building stone in eastern cities. Its metamorphic rocks furnish the serpentine, much used in Philadelphia and some other Piedmont and Fall Line cities. More widely known is the reddish-brown Triassic sandstone obtained from this province and New England and made famous by the once fashionable "brownstone fronts" of New York and other cities. The gold of Georgia and adjacent states (page 136) was the most important in the United States until the discovery of gold in California in 1849. The first coal mined in this country came from Triassic rocks near Richmond, Va. The Piedmont shares with the mountain province on the west in the production of a number of relatively rare but important mineral substances, also in the production of gems, some of which are characteristic of metamorphic rocks. Many of the older

---

[1] KEITH, ARTHUR, Geology of the Catoctin Belt, U. S. Geol. Survey. *14th Ann. Rept.*, pt. 2, p. 383, 1893.

Appalachian rocks are rich in feldspar, the deep decay of which has left stores of high-grade clay.

Soils.—The Piedmont province as a whole is not noteworthy for fertility of soil. The smooth limestone peneplain around Lancaster, Pa., is exceptional, being one of the great tobacco districts of the country. Geologically it has little in common with the Carolina Piedmont, one of the most famous tobacco regions of the world. Speaking generally, the productive soils of the Piedmont are those which are favored topographically. This means, first of all, those of the lowlands. Alluvial plains are very limited in extent but they afford the best soils of the province aside from the limestone soil of the Lancaster-Frederick lowland. In the upland of Maryland and Virginia the broader divides were early seized upon for estates of the wealthy when settlement had once transcended the Coastal Plain.

Soil erosion on the Piedmont has long been a source of loss. Though widespread in the United States[1] such erosion is most serious here because of the small amount of level land. It is also favored by the character of the clay soils derived from highly feldspathic rocks decayed to great depths.[2] Large areas are cut to pieces by gullies but the loss of soil by denudation without gullies is believed to be still more serious. The statement is made that 65 per cent of the piedmont area from New York to Central Alabama has lost its top soil and that present farming is on the subsoil with vastly increased requirement for fertilizers. Of this area more than 10 per cent has also lost its subsoil.[3]

---

[1] Bennett, H. H., *Science*, vol. 81, pp. 321–326, 1935. The statement is here made that more than 50 million acres in the United States have been made "physically unfit for cultivation" by gullying and that another 50 million are about as bad; beside which 125 million acres have lost all or the greater part of their top soil.

[2] Ashe, W. W., Terracing of Farm Lands in North Carolina, N. C. Geol. Econ. Survey, *Bull.* 17, p. 12, 1908.

[3] Bennett, H. H., *Science*, vol. 69, p. XLVIII, 1929.

CHAPTER III

BLUE RIDGE PROVINCE

General Relations.—The Blue Ridge province is the belt of mountains west of the Piedmont province. The mountains are remnants of a former highland which antedated the lower peneplains on either side. The northern half of the province is a narrow belt, rarely 14 miles wide. The southern half broadens to a maximum of 70 miles. The boundaries on both sides, though not straight in detail, are notably straight when considered in their entirety. At some places the mountains are separated from the Piedmont by a single abrupt slope. At others the high relief of the Blue Ridge province falls off gradually, or residual masses make the exact boundary indefinite. These are features to be expected at the borders of residual ranges. In this case the boundary, taken as a whole, is clear, and at many places strikingly so (Fig. 49 page 178).

Necessarily the Piedmont peneplain began to develop on its seaward side and spread westward. That it should have reached its limit along a line that is so nearly straight, leaving so narrow and linear a mountain mass unconsumed, indicates some element of control. North of the Potomac River no other explanation is necessary than the presence of resistant crystalline rocks in the mountains and relatively soft Triassic sediments beneath the Piedmont. Throughout the rest of the boundary all rocks are hard.

Since the highland was uplifted with an eastward tilt, the mass of rock removed in making the Piedmont peneplain was wedge-shaped, being thicker near the mountains. Inland expansion of the peneplain therefore proceeded with increasing difficulty and at a decreasing rate. This tended to straighten the edge of the spreading peneplain. It is not improbable that the uplift was mainly within the present mountain province. In that case the "wedge" thickened abruptly near the present mountain front and the relative straightness of the boundary is thus in part accounted for.

163

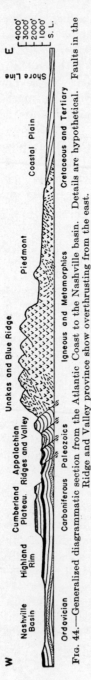

FIG. 44.—Generalized diagrammatic section from the Atlantic Coast to the Nashville basin. Details are hypothetical. Faults in the Ridge and Valley province show overthrusting from the east.

As stated earlier, most of the rocks of this province are old, strong, and of highly complex structure. They represent an ancient land mass repeatedly raised into mountains and continuously eroded while the interior sea washed its western coast throughout most of Paleozoic time and the newer Appalachians were unborn. This picture needs one important modification. The western front of the range, practically everywhere from Georgia to Pennsylvania, is on Lower Cambrian quartzites which were raised into mountains in the Appalachian revolution when the mountains and plateaus farther west were made.[1] The mountains on the very resistant Lower Cambrian rocks are allied in origin to the Folded Appalachians, but geographically they belong in the Blue Ridge province, not only because of contiguity, but because in all their later morphologic history they have behaved more like the rocks to the east than like those to the west. They are topographically inseparable from the Blue Ridge province.

Sections of the Blue Ridge Province.—It is convenient to treat the major part of this mountain province in two sections separated by the Roanoke River. The most obvious distinction is between the linear form of the northern section and the broad expanse of the southern section in which transverse divides are important. The southern section is also higher. Its more prominent summits do not fall into a plane, whereas long stretches of the northern section, when seen against the sky, present a horizon of small relief. There are corresponding differences in their histories.

The mountains end at the south in northern Georgia, beyond which for 200 miles the

[1] KEITH, A., The Great Smoky Overthrust, *Bull. Geol. Soc. Amer.*, vol. 38, p. 154, 1927; also Nantahala folio (No. 143) and others of the U. S. Geol. Survey.

Piedmont province borders the Great Appalachian Valley. However, on the western edge of the Piedmont rise the Talladega and other low mountains or hills, together constituting a low monadnock range 50 miles long, in line with the Great Smoky Mountains though many miles removed. These low ridges represent what would have been a continuation of the mountain range had the uplift there been greater and the expansion of the newer peneplain less easy.[1]

As shown on the generally accepted map,[2] the Blue Ridge province ends at the north near the Susquehanna River. Nevertheless, mountains border the Piedmont on its inner side throughout its length except for a gap of a few miles near the Susquehanna. From the Schuylkill to the Hudson the range, called here the Reading Prong of the New England province, is quite as massive as any part of the northern section of the Blue Ridge province. By every criterion this range belongs to the Older Appalachians. Conventionally it is assigned to the New England province rather than to the Blue Ridge because of its contiguity with the former and the interruption near the Susquehanna River. This assignment is purely a matter of convenience, and sometimes convenience is served by considering this district in the other connection. Such is the case in considering the erosional history of the Blue Ridge. The Reading Prong in New Jersey, where it is called the Highlands, is 20 miles wide and affords a more extensive nearly level horizon than can be seen anywhere in the Blue Ridge province north of the Roanoke River.

NORTHERN BLUE RIDGE SECTION

Description.—The character of the Appalachian structure is responsible for some very narrow strips which are none the less strongly individualized and continuous for long distances. The Blue Ridge is one of these. From the Susquehanna to the Roanoke its width nowhere exceeds 12 to 14 miles and at places it is only half of that. In large part the range is a belt of rounded

[1] *Cf.* HAYES, C. W., The Southern Appalachians, *Nat. Geog. Soc. Mon.*, vol. 1, No. 10, p. 326, 1895.

[2] Physical Divisions of the United States, scale 1:7,000,000, U. S. Geol. Survey, 1930.

and not very steep knobs of diverse altitude. Generally there is no well-defined axial crest except near the Potomac where the belt consists of three definite and parallel ridges of unequal height.[1] Altitudes given in this general description are those of the highest ridge.

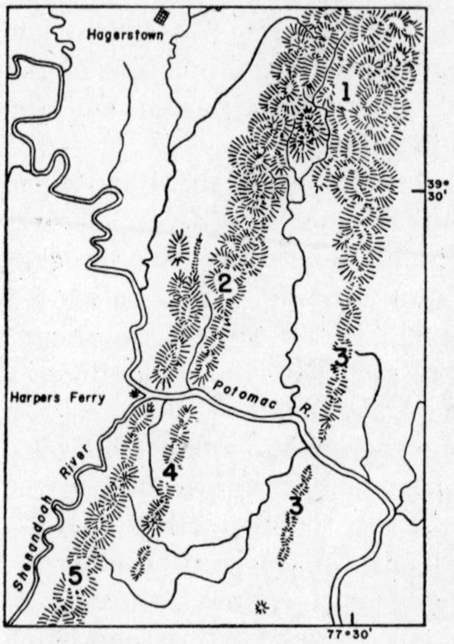

Throughout the section, soil covers all the slopes, as forests formerly did and for the most part do now. Bare-rock ledges and cliffs are rare. As seen in silhouette, the summit level shows moderate undulations alternating with considerable horizontal stretches (Fig. 46).

In southern Pennsylvania the sky line as seen from a distance is fairly level, undulating a little above and below 2000 feet, but only a few small flats, or approximate flats, lie at or above that level. There is no uniformity in the height of the knobs and swells, but enough of them rise to similar heights to make a fairly level horizon. The altitude declines to 1700 feet in Maryland, and to 1200 to 1300 feet before the Potomac is reached. Immediately south of that river the crest is uneven and all the mountains are lower. After 7 miles the altitude again rises to 1500 feet and increases slowly and irregularly for many miles. At intervals are deep sags or

FIG. 45.—The Blue Ridge province near the Potomac River. In northern Maryland the province is a 10-mile belt of rounded mountains with no single linear crest. Near the Potomac this belt bifurcates, forming the linear Catoctin Ridge on the east and the so-called Blue Ridge on the west. The Blue Ridge of Maryland extends south of the Potomac 12 miles under the name of Short Hills. West of this is the Blue Ridge proper of Virginia. It extends 10 miles north of the Potomac under the name of Elk Ridge. The ends of the two main ridges crossing the Potomac overlap and the name is shifted from one ridge to the other. (1) Blue Ridge province without continuous linear ridges; (2) Blue Ridge in Maryland; (3) Catoctin Ridge and isolated hills; (4) Short Hills; and (5) Blue Ridge in Virginia. Length of area, 45 miles. (*After Arthur Keith, U. S. Geol. Survey.*)

narrow notches, called wind gaps, between which the ridge

[1] For a general map see A. Keith, Geology of the Catoctin Belt, U. S. Geol. Survey, 14*th Ann. Rept.*, pt. 2, Pl. 37, 1893. Frequent reference must be made to this paper.

profile, though not flat, as some other Appalachian profiles are, generally undulates but mildly. The highest points are well removed from the gaps. For long stretches the horizon is above 2000 feet and it rises in occasional swells to 3000 and even 4000 feet.

North of the Potomac, and for 40 miles south of it, horizontality of sky line, though not perfect, is more striking than is any diversity. As the range is seen from a distance, one would scarcely think of giving names to the low swells that appear against the sky. The crest obviously indicates an old peneplain. Farther south the crest is generally higher and more broken, and many of the high points have names. Stony Man (4031 ft.) and Hawks Bill (4066 ft.) east of Luray and 65 miles from the Potomac are the culminating points of this section. They occur in a stretch of rather strongly waving crest 3000 to 3500 feet high. From that locality southward, despite the unevenness of the crest, most of the summits or swells show a fair agreement in height to beyond Turk Mountain in the Harrisonburg quadrangle, 40 miles south of Luray and 85 miles from the Roanoke. (Locations shown on Pl. 2.) The last 8 miles, from Black Rock to Turk Mountain, have an almost unbroken horizon 3000 feet high on Catoctin schist. Thirty miles further on, Elk Pond Mountain and Rocky Mountain in the Lexington quadrangle have a 4-mile granite[1]

[1] Strictly speaking this is the hypersthene granodiorite shown on the Virginia geological map, one of the most resistant formations in the Blue Ridge province.

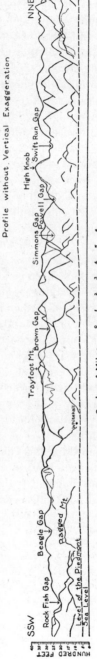

Fig. 46.—Longitudinal profile of the Blue Ridge in the Harrisonburg quadrangle, Virginia. Vertical scale 5 times the horizontal. The northern end is 70 miles south of the Potomac River. (*Diagram by L. H. Desjardins.*)

crest at about 4000 feet.   With less perfect horizontality this altitude is maintained for 10 miles.   North of this tract for 25 miles and south of it for 30 miles, the sky line is highly irregular. Then in the Bedford quadrangle, not far from the Roanoke, is a 10-mile stretch of crest on steeply dipping Cambrian quartzite whose altitude varies little from 2500 feet.   In front of this, 20 miles north of the Roanoke, stand the detached Peaks of Otter, 4000 feet high.

The forms and altitudes mentioned here find their significance in the search for some prominent level or levels which may be interpreted as indicating former peneplanation.   No one doubts that such a surface or surfaces once existed, though imperfections are assumed, and any such surface has surely been warped as well as eroded since uplift.   North of the Potomac an old peneplain (Schooley) is clear, as also on the Reading Prong and over large areas in the Ridge and Valley province to the west and north. Considerable stretches on the Blue Ridge in Virginia seem almost sure to have been peneplaned, but as these have different heights, much uncertainty remains as to the elevation of the old base level, the extent of former peneplaning, the amount of later warping, and even of the number of base levels represented.[1]

For 5 or 6 miles north of the Potomac, a summit level at 1200 to 1300 feet is striking.   This gives way so abruptly to higher levels as to suggest a distinct base level.[2]   Some geologists have referred to the surface at this level as the "Weverton peneplain" (page 160).   At least the immediate valley of the Potomac seems to have been reduced to near base level at an intermediate stage of uplift.

Wind Gaps and Their Significance.—The wind gap is an important feature both in description and in explanation of the Appalachian ranges.   It differs from the water gap in being less deep and in not being occupied by a stream.   The kind of wind gap referred to here (and generally in scientific discussions) is the former water gap.[3]   As some geologists[4] have drawn important

---

[1] *Cf.* HAYES, C. W., and M. R. CAMPBELL, Geomorphology of the Southern Appalachians, *Nat. Geog. Mag.*, vol. 6, p. 75, 1894.

[2] KEITH, ARTHUR, Geology of the Catoctin Belt, p. 385, 390.

[3] For other origins of wind gaps see Arthur M. Miller, *Science*, vol. 42, pp. 571–573, 1915.

[4] BARRELL, J., The Piedmont Terraces of the Northern Appalachians,

inferences from the depth and distribution of such gaps, it is important to note their significance in erosional history. One type of relationship is well illustrated in that part of the Blue Ridge which lies east of the Shenandoah River. Sixteen miles

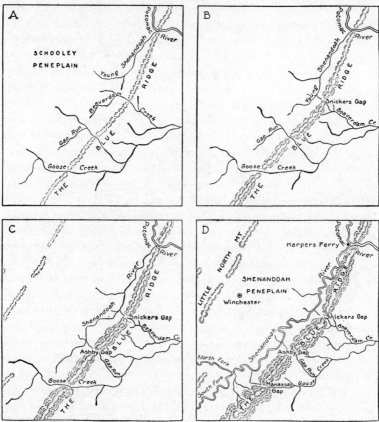

Fig. 47.—Diagrams illustrating the origin of a series of wind gaps. The four figures represent successive stages of drainage adjustment, beginning with streams on the Schooley peneplain. As the result of three captures, three water gaps are converted into wind gaps.

south of the Potomac is Snickers Gap, a notch 2 miles wide, cutting down to an altitude between 1100 and 1200 feet where the ridge is 1500 feet high on one side and 1800 feet on the other. The notch originated as a water gap, made by a stream from the

Amer. Jour. Sci., 4th ser., pp. 338*ff*., 1920. See also references to E. B. Knopf and to Meyerhoff and Hubbell.

west (the ancestral Beaverdam), whose headwaters drained a part of what is now the Shenandoah Valley. The Shenandoah River was then a short stream pushing its head southwestward along the limestone belt (Fig. 47*A*). In the limestone belt the gradients of both streams were held up by the hard Blue Ridge barrier but the advantage was with the Shenandoah because its master stream, the powerful Potomac, cut down its gap faster than did the small Beaverdam. The elongating Shenandoah not only captured and diverted its competitor but lowered the limestone belt so that the Blue Ridge became a divide with small streams flowing both ways from the gap, the one flowing eastward being the beheaded Beaverdam.[1]

The original Beaverdam may have pursued its eastward course before the completion of the Schooley peneplain. No doubt the Blue Ridge in this latitude appeared on that peneplain, if at all, merely as a low, probably discontinuous, line of swells or knobs. Streams may have crossed it on broad sheets of alluvium, or it may have been buried later by coastal plain sediments and streams thus superposed. As the deepening of the gap practically ceased at the time of the capture, its present depth shows approximately the level of the streams when capture occurred. This much is agreed upon.

The picture may now be varied by assuming either (1) that the present elevation of the Blue Ridge above the Shenandoah Valley and Piedmont represents a single uplift, and that the reduction of those adjacent surfaces was accomplished in a single cycle, or (2) that the uplift took place in two stages and that an intermediate peneplain, perhaps the Weverton, was developed at the level of the notch, and later destroyed. In the former case the capture occurred in the midst of the cycle, perhaps soon after maturity. In the latter case it occurred after the close of the first cycle and early in the second. If, after the second uplift, transverse streams cut down very slowly, or the head of the longitudinal stream was extended very rapidly, the gap would indicate approximately the level of the vanished peneplain. On

---

[1] This is probably the best known case of stream capture in the United States, being described by Bailey Willis in his admirable paper on the Northern Appalachians (*Nat. Geog. Soc. Mon.*, 1895) written at a time when such knowledge was not general. This case represents a typical capture and a typical wind gap.

this supposition a series of gaps at nearly the same elevation might constitute evidence of an erosion cycle not otherwise demonstrable. The two possible assumptions are here stated explicitly because the choice between them becomes important in determining the evidential value of wind gaps and in interpreting the history of the Ridge and Valley province.

Nine miles south of Snickers Gap is Ashby Gap, having a similar form and history. Ten miles farther on is Manassas Gap (altitude 914.4 ft.), a little wider but otherwise comparable. The altitudes of the three gaps, taken from north to south, are somewhat above 1100, 1000, and 900 feet, respectively. All represent captures by the Shenandoah. Barring crustal warping, and assuming the three transverse streams to have worked under similar conditions, it is fair to infer that the stream through Ashby Gap entrenched itself an additional 100 feet while the Shenandoah was crowding its divide southward to make the next capture. Similarly the stream through Manassas Gap was allowed still more time and opportunity to deepen its gap before capture.

These three gaps south of the Potomac illustrate the relations in which wind gaps may afford corroborative evidence of a former local peneplain. The relations here indicated are consistent with the hypothesis that there was an intermediate peneplain. In that case the similarity of altitudes of gaps is no accident. However, this approximate agreement of levels merely creates a presumption, it does not amount to proof that there was such an intermediate peneplain. Moreover, it is not to be assumed that wind gaps in the Appalachians always, or even usually, show this consistency as to depth. Geologists differ greatly in the importance attached to them (see page 261). In using the accordance of wind gaps to prove the former presence of a peneplain, very little weight has been attached to the principle, illustrated above, that the gaps related to a single peneplain should not have the same height, but should vary with distance from the master transverse stream.

SOUTHERN SECTION

Geography and Structure.—Southwestward from Roanoke Gap the Blue Ridge province increases in breadth to a maximum of 70 miles. It also increases in height. There are said to be 46 peaks and 41 miles of divide above the level of 6000 feet; also 288

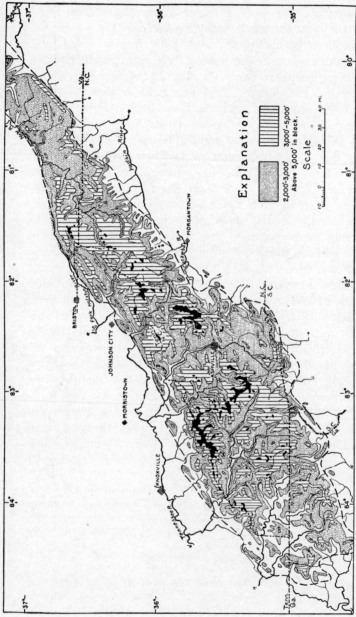

FIG. 48.—Map of the Southern Blue Ridge province. The vertically ruled area is above 3000 feet and embraces most of the higher mountains never reduced to the Schooley peneplain, also most of the area in which the Schooley level is apparent. Areas above 5000 feet are shown in black. The dotted area is between 2000 and 3000 feet high. It embraces most of the later local peneplains, but much of it at the northeast, is at the Schooley level. The unshaded area, below 2000 feet, is largely comprised in valleys incised below the Asheville level, but at the southwest it includes the Ducktown basin. All areas are very much generalized. (From U. S. Geol. Survey by L. H. Desjardins.)

more peaks and 300 more miles of divide above 5000 feet.[1]
Many of the most extensive high levels are near the margins on
the southeast and northwest sides, both fronts being steep.
Most of the boundary is also fairly simple, but it is complicated
by a few large outliers in North Carolina and somewhat obscured
by smaller ones in Georgia. The main divide is near the southeastern margin and bears the name Blue Ridge. From this the
main streams flow northwest to the Great Valley. While this
divide is almost continuously high, it bears few of the highest
peaks and domes, and its general level is lower than that of some
of the secondary divides west of it. Moreover, it is rarely a well-
defined ridge. Its subordinate ridges trend in all directions.

The direction of the Blue Ridge as a whole, and of minor divides
within it, is generally independent of structure, all of the rocks
being highly metamorphosed and without great differences in
hardness.[2] Linear ridges of continuous trend are almost confined
to the belt of metamorphosed Cambrian rocks on the west, strong
conglomerate, quartzite, slate, and schist, with some less-altered
beds. These rocks are closely folded and faulted on lines agreeing
in direction with the trend of the province. To a remarkable
extent the western boundary of this province is determined by the
limit of overthrust of the strong metamorphosed rocks on the
unaltered limestone of the Great Valley.[3] In large parts of this
western belt, differences in resistance afford the conditions for
distinct subsequent ranges, though without broad valleys as in
the next province to the west. On this margin of the province are
high ranges, notched 2000 to 4000 feet deep by streams flowing
northwestward from the Blue Ridge. Collectively, all these
ranges on the west are called the Unakas.[4] Their best known

[1] Message of the President of the United States transmitting a report of
the Secretary of Agriculture in Relation to Forests, Rivers, and Mountains
of the Southern Appalachian Region, 57th Congress, 1st session, Senate
Document 84, 1902. Descriptions of geology and geography written by
Arthur Keith.

[2] KEITH, A., Pisgah folio (No. 147), Cranberry folio (No. 90), U. S. Geol.
Survey.

[3] KEITH, A., The Great Smoky Overthrust, *Bull. Geol. Soc. Amer.*, vol.
38, p. 154, 1927.

[4] This name Unaka is one of indefinite application. C. W. Hayes ("The
Southern Appalachians," 1895) applies it to the ranges on the northwest
side which he regards as converging and uniting with the Blue Ridge at

member is the Great Smoky Mountain south of the latitude of Asheville. The Chilhowee, Stone, Bald, Holston, Iron, and many small ranges farther north belong to the same belt of Cambrian rocks and to the Unaka group, having similar structures and topography.

Between the Unakas and the Blue Ridge the only semblance of linear arrangement is that of the divides between northwest-flowing streams, and this semblance is not striking. There is little control by structure. Lines of structural deformation cross the larger divides more often than they follow them. The appearance is that of a mountain upland on which the streams have been flowing in the same direction for at least several partial cycles without the need of effecting very much adjustment because the differences in resistance are not such as to require it.

Description of Topography.—In general the mountains of this section may be classed as "subdued," that word being used technically to designate a stage in the cycle when height and steepness are so far lost that a mantle of decayed rock is general. (For views of subdued mountains, see pages 348 and 399.) Crags, bare cliffs, and talus slopes are correspondingly rare. Precipitous slopes on bare rock, if found at all, are not generally in combs and crags of sharp divides but in recently deepened gorges. Summits are commonly rounded, and higher slopes are less steep than valley sides. Domes abound, but mountains which could properly be called peaks are few. Forests were once all but universal. They cover the highest mountains, but in a few districts there are rounded, grassy summits called "balds." The reason for the absence of trees on these summits is not mere altitude, since the very highest summits are forested. Nor can it be found in the character of the rocks.

Localities where the mountains are less typically subdued may be found on the northwestern margin where the rocks in the mountains are very strong and the presence of soluble limestones in the valley province has resulted in a marked lowering of the local base level and a corresponding sharp dissection of the

---

Grandfather Mountain. In the report of the Secretary of Agriculture, cited above, the Unakas, on the authority of Arthur Keith, are defined as including all the minor ranges named below and merging with the Blue Ridge in southern Virginia. This virtually identifies the Unaka Mountains with the belt of Cambrian rocks and is the usage here followed.

mountains. The statement has been made that less than 10 per
cent of the surface in the southern Appalachian Mountains has a
slope of less than 10 degrees.[1] The texture of the drainage pattern is generally coarse, *i.e.*, tributaries are not closely spaced.
In this respect the topography of the long-forested mountains
contrasts strikingly with that of deforested areas, which are in
some cases minutely gullied.

Coves.—A feature of distinct interest in geomorphology is
found in the "coves" on the northwest slope of the Great Smoky
Mountains, especially in Cades, Tuckaleechee, and Wear Coves
southeast of Knoxville.[2] These are isolated, flat-floored mountain valleys, oval in shape, each covering 5 to 10 square miles.
The valley floors range from 1200 to 1800 feet in altitude among
mountains several thousand feet higher. The mountains at this
place are carved in the great slab of metamorphosed Cambrian or
Pre-Cambrian conglomerate, etc., overthrust upon the limestone
which floors the adjacent valley province. The thrust plane is so
nearly horizontal that the overthrust block or slab is worn through
in spots, known geologically as "windows," in which the limestone
forms the surface.[3] Each fertile limestone valley is culturally
and economically, as well as geologically, an "inlier" of the Great
Appalachian Valley.

The Subsummit Peneplain.—It remains to inquire whether
the mountains fall into groups with respect to altitude. Are
there any levels more conspicuous than others which may serve as
planes of reference? Abundant evidence that the mountains to
the west and north were carved from an upraised plane (or
warped) surface has led to the assumption that a similar surface
may have existed here. The existence of a subsummit peneplain
in this section is now established, but its recognition requires
some imagination except in favored localities. The beginnings of
peneplanation in a later cycle, as around Asheville, are more
obvious and were recognized earlier.[4] In distinction from this

[1] Message of the President of the United States, etc., *op. cit.*, p. 21.

[2] Knoxville folio, U. S. Geol. Survey, 1895.

[3] KEITH, A., "The Great Smoky Overthrust."

[4] The Asheville peneplain was first described by Bailey Willis (Round
about Asheville, *Nat. Geog. Mag.*, vol. 1, pp. 291–300, 1889). For some
years it was assumed to be the local representative of the "Cretaceous"
(Schooley) peneplain. In his search for a higher peneplain, Willis made the
suggestion that such a former surface might be represented by the "balds,"

newer surface, the older and higher surface is often referred to as the upland or subsummit peneplain.

The best exemplifications of the higher peneplain are in southern Virginia (Hillsville quadrangle) and near the boundary of South Carolina (Pisgah quadrangle), both localities being on the margin of the section. It is also well exemplified in a smaller area on the Blue Ridge east of Grandfather Mountain. In the development of the peneplain these localities were favored by rocks rich in feldspar, hence a little less resistant than some others; and in the preservation from later erosion the same districts have been favored by their situation near the main divide. Assuming the peneplain to have spread over all the area that lies lower than its present remnants (a generous assumption), it may have covered something like half of the entire surface of the section (*cf.* Fig. 48). There are therefore abundant monadnocks and subdued ranges which rise above the old base level and obscure the imperfect peneplain. Moreover, large areas in which the upland peneplain was well developed have since been cut to lower levels, with or without the development of newer peneplains. Nevertheless, an old surface of low relief (even though now dissected by younger valleys), distinguished from the monadnocks on the one hand and from the broad valleys or incipient newer peneplains on the other, can be seen at intervals throughout the Blue Ridge, especially on headwaters which flow more or less parallel to the main divide and therefore have less fall and less entrenchment. The upper basins of the New and French Broad rivers are typical in this respect.[1]

Hillsville District.—Near the Virginia-North Carolina boundary (Hillsville quadrangle) the upland peneplain is distinctly plateaulike with few monadnocks. It forms the summit of the

---

but this has not been verified. Hayes and Campbell (Geomorphology of the Southern Appalachians, *Nat. Geog. Mag.*, vol. 6, 1894) and again Hayes (The Southern Appalachians, Nat. Geog. Soc., *Mon.*, vol. 1, no. 10, 1895) give a history involving two peneplains, but the older and higher is identified with the Asheville peneplain, not with what is now known as the upland or subsummit peneplain. The latter (presumably Schooley) was affirmed by Arthur Keith in 1896 (Some Stages of Appalachian Erosion, *Bull. Geol. Soc. Amer.*, vol. 7, pp. 519–529) and described later (1903–1907) by him in various folios of the U. S. Geol. Survey.

[1] *Cf.* WRIGHT, FRANK J., The Erosional History of the Blue Ridge, *Jour. Sci. Lab. Denison Univ.*, vol. 23, p. 335, 1928.

Blue Ridge, which is here a plateau of small relief sloping gently to the northwest from an altitude of 3000 to 3100 feet and cut off on the southeast by an abrupt escarpment which descends in 1 or 2 miles to the gently rolling Piedmont surface 1500 feet high. The upland peneplain is represented by only a narrow strip of plateau at the top of the escarpment and the equally narrow strips a few miles long on the summits of some divides between the northwest-flowing streams.[1] These divides determine a nearly flat horizon. The rest of the surface (described on page 174) slopes northwestward to and beyond the limit of the province. On the northwestern border of the province rises an even-crested mountain range of the Unaka group, having the same height as the Blue Ridge and probably representing the same peneplain.

The Blue Ridge escarpment on the southeast is, of course, retreating. Indentations and outliers might be expected but the narrowness of the zone thus characterized is remarkable.

Just south of the Virginia-Carolina boundary, monadnocks begin to rise above the peneplain to 3500 feet. Residuals increase in number and height, and at no great distance south of the state boundary the peneplain is seen with difficulty among mountains which rise from a few hundred feet to 2000 feet above it. Its level near the Watauga and New Rivers is 3400 to 3700 feet.[2]

Subsummit Peneplain among the High Mountains.—In the vicinity of Grandfather Mountain (near the 36th parallel), the highest peneplain level is 3800 to 4000 feet, *i.e.*, 2500 feet above the Piedmont plain. The surface here is on a fault block of Cambrian quartzite which makes Grandfather Mountain (5964 feet) the highest point in the Blue Ridge. Present drainage radiates from this locality, and that of former cycles may have done the same, hence it is not surprising to find former erosion surfaces high, even if not locally raised by later deformation. Here, where the peneplain was less developed, and where the headwaters of Piedmont streams have been encroaching, the mountain front is less like a simple wall than it is farther north or farther south. For most of its length in North Carolina the front overlooking the Piedmont is a belt 10 to 15 miles wide, lying at places behind massive but isolated outliers on the Piedmont.

[1] For a description of this locality see Frank J. Wright, The Older Appalachians of the South, *Bull. Sci. Lab. Denison Univ.*, vol. 26, p. 201, 1931.

[2] KEITH, A., Cranberry folio (No. 90), p. 1.

Fig. 49.—Escarpment of the Blue Ridge, seen from Caesar's Head, South Carolina, looking west-southwest.   The higher level is the summit of the Blue Ridge, here reduced to the Schooley peneplain whose present altitude at this place is a little more than 3,000 feet. The plain at the left is the Piedmont, here about 1,200 feet high.   (*In U. S. Geol. Survey folio No. 147, from which this view is taken, the picture is extended both right and left.*)

In the latitude of Asheville, especially among the high mountains east of it and north of the Swannanoa, one of which, Mt. Mitchell (6711 ft.), is the highest point in the Eastern States, the upland peneplain is poorly exemplified. Between the mountains that rise higher and the broad valleys which approach a later and lower base level, it is difficult to detect levels which represent the upland peneplain. South of the Swannanoa (the west-flowing river which joins the French Broad at Asheville), residual mountains decrease in height and breadth, giving way to the broad plateaulike expanse described below.

Pisgah District.—Farther south, on the northwestern border of South Carolina and the adjacent part of North Carolina, the upland peneplain is remarkably developed.[1] Its restored surface is 3200 feet or more in height. It declines a little toward the French Broad on the northwest, and at Caesar's Head on the southeast is cut off sharply by descent in a single mile to the Piedmont at 1300 feet (Fig. 49). As in southern Virginia, the Blue Ridge here is not a ridge, but merely a divide at the edge of a faintly sloping plateau. The narrowness, steepness, and simplicity of the escarpment at places where the peneplain is best developed is noteworthy.

The deformation of the rocks, here as elsewhere, was along northeast-southwest axes, but within the range of the good peneplain small heed is paid to differences in rocks. Structural lines are not followed either by the Blue Ridge or by the province boundary. Farther west the French Broad River flows parallel to the eastern edge of the Carolina gneiss and probably reflects the greater hardness of that rock.

Uplands Farther West.—It is not to be understood that all the evidences of an upland peneplain are on or near the Blue Ridge. Suggestions are found on a number of divides between northwest-flowing streams, but more abundantly near their headwaters than farther down toward the Unakas. Where peneplaning is at best local, it should scarcely be expected on the Cambrian quartzites and their strong associates in the Unakas. Moreover the streams flow northwest, and the chances of preservation of an old peneplain grow less with distance from the main divide.

---

[1] KEITH, A., Pisgah folio (No. 147), U. S. Geol. Survey, 1907.

The Unaka ranges have few plateaulike summits, but the crests of some narrow ridges on steeply dipping strata are horizontal for some miles.   In the Roan Mountain quadrangle, Iron Mountain has a long horizontal crest at about 3000 feet.   Some of the Unaka ridges resemble those of the Folded Appalachians to the west but are unlike them in not being separated by broad valleys.

The Asheville Peneplain.—Within this vast expanse of subdued or once worn-down mountains and redissected surface, are

Fig. 50.—Gorge of the Nolichucky River, 300 to 400 feet deep, incising its strath, here about 2400 feet high, east of the Unaka Mountains.   The strath is developed on granite, which is more easily eroded than the quartzite that makes the mountains.   (*Photograph by Arthur Keith, U. S. Geol. Survey, Prof. Pap.* 72.)

strips and patches of lower and smoother surface.   For the most part they border the headwaters of the large streams near the Blue Ridge.   Much the best known of these is the gently rolling floor of the French Broad Valley traversed by the Southern Railroad running through Asheville.[1]   At places it is 10 to 12 miles wide but of extremely irregular shape, having branches several miles wide in tributary valleys and a broad extension around Hendersonville, 20 miles southeast of Asheville, where there is no important stream.   Its average elevation of 2100 to 2200 feet changes little in an airline distance of 30 miles southward from

[1] WILLIS, BAILEY, Round about Asheville, *Nat. Geog. Mag.*, vol. 1, pp. 291–300, 1889.

Asheville, but it rises slowly upstream even in the main valley, and more rapidly along tributaries. Altitudes of 2400 feet are thus reached. At Asheville the river is incised 200 feet. Near the upstream end of the plain, incision is insignificant. Ten miles downsteam from Asheville the stream has a new valley 400 feet deep and the remnants of the higher valley floor appear as terrace remnants against the mountain slopes (*cf.* Fig. 50). As the valley deepens and widens downstream, this terrace is cut to pieces or washed away entirely. All evidence of its former existence are lost in the gorges of the Great Smoky Mountains.

The surface here described is not one of planation, *i.e.*, it is not a former flood plain over which a stream meandered, though flood plains may be included in it. It is strictly an incipient peneplain, a surface whose interstream areas have been worn down, not planed off.[1] A new peneplain began here, as elsewhere, near the main river when that stream could no longer cut down, primarily because of its approach to sea level, but no doubt also held up somewhat by resistant rocks. Such an incipient peneplain is a strath[2] in the true sense of that term. The present entrenchment of the stream is due to renewed uplift. For most of its length the

---

[1] These two essentially different processes are not always properly distinguished. C. W. Hayes, in his monograph on the Southern Appalachians, already referred to, speaks of new peneplains produced by lateral corrasion (p. 330).

[2] For the use of the term "strath" see Archibald Geikie, "The Scenery of Scotland," p. 175, London, 1901; also Walter H. Bucher, *Science*, vol. 75, p. 130, 1932. This paper is an attempt to alter the various American uses of the term so as to conform to usage in Scotland. The word there designates "broad expanses of low ground between bounding hills," apparently without reference to origin but "usually traversed by one main stream and its tributaries." It is also applied to "wide tracts of lowland which embrace portions of several valleys." Plains made by stream planation and veneered with alluvium (flood plains) are often embraced in such lowlands but they are incidental, not essential. The idea expressed by Geikie (from whom the above quotations are taken) would be expressed in America by "incipient peneplain" or some indefinite expression such as "broad valley," "trough," or "intermontane valley." The word strath has been somewhat used in America for exactly the feature here described, but trenched by a rejuvenated stream. In that case it should be called a "strath terrace" as suggested by Bucher. W. H. Hobbs ("Earth Features and Their Meaning") uses the term for valley floors formed by aggradation. This feature is indeed prominent in some of the straths of Scotland, but to limit the term to this feature is not warranted.

newer peneplain is now a "strath terrace," but the rejuvenation of the stream has not yet reached the upper limit of the plain.

For 20 miles south from Asheville (upstream) the plain is broad. Thence it extends another 20 miles (airline distance) up the French Broad to the southwest. This latter part is only a valley floor a mile or two in width and constricted by local narrows; it is mainly or wholly an alluvial plain. Its increase in elevation is remarkably small, perhaps 4 feet to the mile as the crow flies, and but half of that as the small stream winds. So low a gradient is wholly out of keeping with the drainage of the mountains in the present cycle.

A more remarkable expansion of the local peneplain extends southeastward past Hendersonville where only the headwaters of creeks are found flowing west from the Blue Ridge. Yet the peneplain stretches for miles at an elevation barely above that of Asheville. Five miles east of Hendersonville is the main divide of the Blue Ridge, marked by no feature except the abrupt beginning of sharp and deep dissection by the heads of Piedmont streams.[1] Here the same nearly flat horizon marks the level of the fields on the peneplain draining to the French Broad and the tops of the sharp forested ridges carved by the Piedmont streams, though among these ridges are some higher knobs which may indicate a former position of the main divide. Plainly the dissection is new and proceeding rapidly, and the divide is shifting westward. Certainly it has already shifted at least 10 miles. The relation between the peneplain in the mountains and the present surface of the Piedmont is discussed further on page 191.

Other Post-Schooley Straths.—Similar incipient peneplains on other northwest-flowing streams are at different altitudes, depending in each case on the former local base level and the amount of later uplift. The coves described on page 175 belong to the same class. All such incipient peneplains slope down stream. Small streams need more fall and higher headwaters than larger ones. Those crossing hard barriers have the same requirements. On rocks which furnish an insoluble load, streams need higher gradients than on limestone. The head of a stream that reaches its goal by a short course can cut lower than that of a long circuitous stream reaching the same goal. For one or more of these reasons

_____
[1] See topographic map of the Saluda quadrangle.

the narrow strath of the Pigeon River is 500 feet higher than that of the French Broad 15 miles to the east.[1] A section across other streams southwest of the French Broad, and crossing them at similar distances from their heads, would show a strath on the Tuckaseegee (a smaller stream) at about the same height, on the

Fig. 51.—Strath at the head of the Little Tennessee River, looking northeast (down stream) from Keener Gap in northern Georgia. Altitude, 2000 to 2100 feet. The mountains in the distance are 3500 to 4000 feet high. The river at this place is at the level of the strath. Farther down stream it is deeply entrenched. (*Photograph by C. W. Hayes; reproduced from Bull. 42, Ga. Geol. Survey.*)

Little Tennessee at 2000 to 2100 feet, on the Hiwassee at about 1800 feet, and on the Ocoee at 1600 to 1700 feet, and so on to the Piedmont valleys at 1000 feet or less. A comparison among parallel valleys shows a progressive decline.[2] The question whether all of these incipient peneplains were made at the same time is raised on page 191.

[1] For past and future captures on this account see Frank J. Wright, Stream Piracy near Asheville, N. C., *Jour. Sci. Lab. Denison Univ.*, vol. 24, pp. 401–406, 1929; also The Older Appalachians of the South, already cited.

[2] *Cf.* Hayes, C. W., The Southern Appalachians (cited on p. 176). Such statements are qualitatively correct. To make them quantitatively accurate it would be necessary to name the locality referred to in each valley, since these straths slope down stream. Moreover, two levels may be distinguished in some localities.

At the very head of the Little Tennessee River, at Rabun Gap in northern Georgia, the incipient peneplain of the newer cycle (Fig. 51) forms the summit of the Blue Ridge escarpment.[1] Its height is here 2100 feet and it is separated by an escarpment of 400 or 500 feet from the plain on the south.   This is the Dahlonega Plateau, 1600 to 1700 feet high, developed along the tributaries of the Chattahoochee (page 134).

The Ducktown Plateau on the Ocoee River is a remarkable basin floor, 10 miles wide and 20 miles long, mainly in Georgia. It is 1600 feet high in Tennessee but rises upstream and toward

Fig. 52.—Ducktown Plateau, a local peneplain on the Ocoee River, almost surrounded by mountain slopes.   Dissected by valleys 200 feet deep.   Level of hill tops, 1600–1800 feet.   Looking northwest to the Big Frog Mountains in the southeastern corner of Tennessee.   (*Photograph by C. W. Hayes; reproduced from Bull. 42, Ga. Geol. Survey.*)

the margins.   Similar straths or strath terraces are found on other streams from the Ocoee northeast to the Nolichucky, at least on the upstream side of the Great Smoky Mountains.   All rise to greater altitudes upstream, and because of the difference in length and gradient of streams the altitudes of these straths along different streams and at different places differ by almost 2000 feet, the highest being about 3800 feet near Grandfather Mountain.

The several branches of the Toe River (headwaters of the Nolichucky) northeast of the French Broad have straths at 2600 feet, while that of the New River rises upstream from 2400 feet at

---

[1] KEITH, A., The Highland, Physical Geography of Georgia, Ga. Geol. Survey, *Bull.* 42, p. 118, 1925.

the edge of the province to 2800 feet at the junction of its north and south forks. A similar surface borders the south fork up to an altitude of nearly 3500 feet near Grandfather Mountain and is treated by Wright as a continuous strath of the same cycle.[1] Keith regards the upper portion as older.[2] In any case it would be misleading to speak of all these graded surfaces as parts of one peneplain, even if all are of the same age. Graded valley floors or straths are indeed incipient peneplains but their relation to a general base level is remote. If all can be shown to represent the same cycle, that fact is significant, but otherwise there is little or no physical unity in such a system of straths.

The New River, which is farthest north of the rivers concerned, flows north to the Great Valley and ultimately to the Ohio. Remnants of its old valley floor, appearing to represent a once continuous strath, merge with the peneplain in the Great Valley at about 2400 feet A.T. In this part of the mountain province (Hillsville quadrangle) the level of valley floors rises toward the southeast along the minor streams heading at the Blue Ridge divide, reaching altitudes of 2700 feet where the nearby remnants of the upland peneplain are a little above 3000 feet (page 177).

All of the rivers south and west of the New flow into the Tennessee, and on none of them is there a continuous strath terrace connecting the high level valleys at the headwaters with the floor of the Great Valley. Fragmentary benches appear, suggesting possible former continuous terraces along the French Broad and Nolichucky,[3] but they are not indicated on topographic maps and they lack the convincing character of the old valley along the New River. If a correlation of peneplains on opposite sides of the Unakas is to be made on the basis of continuity, such correlation must rest mainly or wholly on the case of the New River strath terrace (see History, page 190).

While these broad valleys of the later cycle (or cycles) are not coextensive with rocks of certain ages or formations, it is well

[1] WRIGHT, FRANK J., The Erosional History of the Blue Ridge, *op. cit.*, pp. 340 and 342, 1928. On p. 337 of this paper a number of altitudes are given along several of the streams here named, indicating the downstream slope of the plains. Other altitudes given here are taken from Keith's U. S. Geol. Survey folios or his paper already referred to in the *Bull. Geol. Soc. Amer.*, vol. 7.

[2] KEITH, ARTHUR, personal communication.

[3] WRIGHT, FRANK J., "Older Appalachians of the South," pp. 165 and 194.

known that the feldspathic rocks are more easily wasted than the more quartzose rocks, and it is almost true to say that the beginnings of peneplanation in cycles later than the Schooley are confined to the former.[1] But not all of the feldspathic rocks were thus reduced. Even within broad areas of granite there are unaccountable expansions of the plains at some places and restrictions at others on the same formation, which seems to indicate that the streams detected differences in rock character that do not appear on the geologic map.

HISTORY OF THE BLUE RIDGE PROVINCE

Summary of Summit Levels.—It is evident that most of the mountains of this province have been carved from an upraised lowland or peneplain (one or more) surmounted by isolated monadnocks and massive residual ranges. The altitude of the ancient peneplain on the main divide is about 3100 feet in northern Georgia, 3200 feet on the border of South Carolina, 3800 to 4000 feet in latitude 36° (near Grandfather Mountain) and 3100 feet in Southern Virginia. From the Roanoke to the latitude of Washington, a distance of 150 miles, altitudes are too irregular for generalization. Levels of 2500, 3000, 3500, and 4000 feet are all seen to be represented by stretches 8 to 15 miles long in which the sky line either is fairly flat or shows accordant summits. In northern Virginia and southern Pennsylvania the summit peneplain is at about 2000 feet for many miles, but there is a broad sag near the Potomac. In the study of history it is convenient to consider the Reading Prong of the New England province in connection with the Blue Ridge. The maximum altitude of the well-developed old lowland at its summit is about 1300 feet in New Jersey, where it was first noted and named the Schooley peneplain.

The Upland Cycle.—This ancient lowland (now upland) is treated here as a single peneplain developed in the Schooley cycle, though its unity can not be affirmed with finality. It is conceivable that some of its lower levels represent the Schooley peneplain in basins draining toward the Atlantic while other parts were draining toward the Ohio and the Gulf of Mexico, and therefore had a higher local base level. Thus plains at different levels

---

[1] Hayes, C. W., Physiography of the Chattanooga District, U. S. Geol. Survey, 19*th Ann. Rept.*, pt. 2, p. 19, 1899.

might be correlated in time. Provisionally, the Schooley is treated as the oldest surviving peneplain not preserved by burial. It was probably more perfect, and certainly more extensive, than any later peneplain has been. It covered the Appalachian Highland except for relatively small areas, the largest being in the southern part of this province. No later peneplain has had more than local development on hard rocks. This one appears on rocks of all grades. Above this surface before uplift, there remained only knobs and swells up to 1000 feet or more in Virginia, and subdued mountains to several times that height in North Carolina and Tennessee.

At the time of its greatest perfection the northern part of this peneplain sloped gently toward the Atlantic. The courses of the larger streams differed little from those of the present. South of the Roanoke, then as now, most of the drainage was probably toward the interior, perhaps by more direct courses than at present. The main divide in the south was, so far as known, near its present position on the Blue Ridge, but probably farther east, as conditions at present necessitate a westward shifting.

Post-Schooley Uplift in the North.—The uplift that followed peneplaning seems not to have changed the direction of drainage in this province. Maximum uplift in the north was northwest of it, perhaps near the old divide. In the south the greatest rise was probably on the southeastern side. In both cases uplift seems to have steepened the gradients of streams.[1]

With regard to the form of the uplift in the north, some geologists have emphasized a distinct arching in order to explain present altitudes; others incline more to favor successive broad elevations of a previously submerged surface, each elevation followed by incipient peneplaning along the coastal margin. In the latter case a seaward slope is, very roughly speaking, a succession of peneplain remnants at decreasing levels,[2] the name *Kittatinny* being applied to the highest, and *Schooley* to the second in the series. The older supposition[3] identifies the summit

---

[1] HAYES and CAMPBELL, *op. cit.*, p. 79 and Pl. 5; WRIGHT, F. J., "The Older Appalachians," p. 230.

[2] Papers already cited by Bascom and Knopf are written largely from this standpoint. But none of the important papers wholly ignore either warping or intermittent uplift.

[3] DAVIS, W. M., Geological Dates of Origin of Certain Topographic Forms

peneplain which is 2000 feet high on Kittatinny Mountain in western New Jersey (page 210) with the Schooley peneplain at 1300 feet in the Highlands of the Reading Prong, and with successively lower levels on the Watchung Mountains and the Palisades of the Hudson. Approximately two thirds of the elevation is credited to uplift before the Harrisburg cycle.

A partial substitute for warping is found by Stose in faulting.[1] He pictures a longitudinal fault in New Jersey whereby the Folded Appalachian belt on the west is raised above the Reading Prong; also a similar fault of 600 feet throw in southern Pennsylvania between the Blue Ridge province and the Piedmont, the former being 2000 feet high and the latter having monadnocks of hard rock 1000 to 1100 feet high which are interpreted as representing the same surface before faulting.

On the hypothesis of broader uplifts and successive erosion cycles, only isolated mountains resting on the Schooley surface are conceded to belong to the highest peneplain. The view here favored is that the Kittatinny and Schooley peneplains are the same, and that all evidences of extensive peneplains in the entire Appalachian Highland may best be referred to a very few major cycles. There must be ample allowance for local peneplains or straths, the work of minor episodes. In all cases allowance must be made for residual relief and for later warping and also for lowering by rain wash without dissection.

Peneplanation in central Virginia may well have been less perfect than farther north, but a part of the greater altitude there is due to warping. The highest peneplain has been destroyed for some miles near the Potomac, but even where preserved it sags to 1700 or 1800 feet. It has been assumed that this represents a downwarp (or smaller uplift) which was followed by the river.[2] But the view here favored is that the main streams followed essentially their present courses during the Schooley cycle (page 199). The level rises toward the south from the Potomac and reaches 2800 feet in the latitude of Massanutten Mountain and no doubt higher altitudes farther south. For the next 150

---

on the Atlantic Slope of the United States, *Bull. Geol. Soc. Amer.*, vol. 2, p. 554, 1891. Also, Rivers of Northern New Jersey, *Nat. Geog. Mag.*, vol. 2, 1890.

[1] STOSE, GEO. W., Possible Post-Cretaceous Faulting in the Appalachians, *Bull. Geol. Soc. Amer.*, vol. 38, pp. 493–504, 1927.

[2] KEITH, A., The Catoctin Belt, *op. cit.*, p. 392, 1893.

miles, residual relief and postpeneplain warping are not yet satisfactorily distinguished.

Post-Schooley Uplift in the South.—The greater altitude of the Schooley peneplain in the south than in the north probably indicates some excess of uplift. However, it may never have been so near sea level in the south. Even by the shortest route to the sea this part of the province is farther inland, and if drainage was toward the interior, the local base level was hundreds of feet above sea level. In that case the Schooley peneplain over the Piedmont province would have been distinctly lower. However, this difference of local base level on the two sides of an asymmetric divide should have been distinctly less at the end of so long a cycle as the Schooley than in any succeeding cycle. Both primary and secondary divides in the Blue Ridge province continued to be marked by hills or mountains. Probably the main divide, even where most reduced, still rose above the peneplain level. If so, it was east of its present position and has vanished from those parts of the present Blue Ridge where the old peneplain now overlooks the Piedmont.

Opinions regarding the exact nature of the uplift in the south, as in the north, are at variance. At least it was greatest where the mountains now remain. The bold mountain front in the Carolinas has suggested faulting but that question is still in dispute.[1] Ignoring possible faulting, it suffices to assume that, when uplift followed the Schooley cycle, the advantage possessed by the short and direct streams on the Piedmont over their roundabout competitors was greatly enhanced. Rejuvenation reached their headwaters much sooner, and they were able to cut down some hundreds of feet lower than the long streams on the northwestern side.[2] On other margins than the eastern and southeastern, the upland peneplain is so poorly preserved that few data are obtainable as to the character of its deformation.

When it is remembered that, aside from the Piedmont province, the Harrisburg peneplain is generally restricted to relatively weak

[1] Frank J. Wright's paper on The Blue Ridge of Southern Virginia and Western North Carolina (*Jour. Sci. Lab. Denison Univ.*, vol. 22, pp. 116–132, 1927) discusses the criteria by which faulting should be tested. M. R. Campbell, on the basis of recent and as yet unpublished work, makes faulting very important (personal communication).

[2] DAVIS, W. M., The Stream Contest along the Blue Ridge, *Bull. Phila. Geog. Soc.*, vol. 3, pp. 213–244, 4 Pls., 1903.

rocks, its extensive development on the crystalline rocks of the Piedmont seems anomalous.   The most natural explanation is that the uplift of the older surface was not great, perhaps little more, and at the outer edge less, than the depth of weathering beneath the older (Schooley) peneplain.   This supposition involves another, namely that the pronounced post-Schooley uplift of the Blue Ridge diminished rapidly toward the east and south.   The extent of considerable uplift might almost be limited to the zone 10 to 30 miles wide in which monadnocks abound. Such an assumption may also require that some of the higher monadnocks, like Stone and Pine Mountains on the Georgia piedmont, rose above the Schooley peneplain.

The Piedmont and the weaker rocks of the Folded Appalachians were cut down to a new base level.   More complete knowledge in the future may make it necessary to ascribe the surfaces of these provinces to two, three, or even four cycles (or subcycles),[1] one of which might well correspond to the Weverton stage mentioned on page 160.   Whatever question may be raised in respect to the unity of the Piedmont and Great Valley surfaces involves also the contemporaneity of the several straths.

Relation of the Straths to the Valley Peneplain.—The straths are now many hundreds of feet above the floor of the Great Valley.   This is partly because of later uplift.   Aside from that, their level may have been held up by the resistant rocks of the Unaka Mountains which the streams must cross.   It is not known that falls and rapids were graded out, or that they were not. If they were, then the narrow incipient peneplains in the mountains were mere arms or extensions of the Great Valley.   On the New River only is the strath continuous with the floor of the Great Valley.   However, that part of the Great Valley itself, now 2400 to 2500 feet high, may be thought of as having always had an exceptionally high local base level, partly because of the great distance to the sea by way of the Kanawha and the Ohio, and partly because of difficulty in cutting a long gorge through the strong sandstones of the Allegheny Plateau.   This part of the Great Valley must always have been relatively high and it cannot be safely assumed that it bore the same relation to straths in the

---

[1] KEITH, ARTHUR, Some Stages of Appalachian Erosion, *Bull. Geol. Soc. Amer.*, vol. 7, pp. 519–525, 1896.   See also reference to Lawrence LaForge, footnote, p. 132.

mountains as did the part farther south, which was longitudinally drained and lower.

In most of the preceding discussion it is tacitly assumed that the prominent straths are all products of the same cycle, and are of the same age as the dominant peneplains on the Piedmont and in the Great Valley. It is necessary, however, to face the possibility that the straths themselves represent a series of subcycles, the higher ones (or higher parts) being definitely older than the surface of the Piedmont and the Valley of East Tennessee. The floor of the Great Valley itself, declining as it does from an altitude of 2400 or 2500 feet in Virginia to 800 feet in Alabama, is described by Keith, not as a single sloping plain, but as a series of three nearly horizontal peneplains (see page 190). On this hypothesis the valley floor where crossed by the New River is relatively old. This assumption has important bearings not only on the interpretation of the Great Valley, but on that of the Allegheny Plateau (page 300), also on that of the Blue Ridge front, as noted below. Neither the hypothesis of a single cycle for all the local peneplains, nor that of multiple cycles or subcycles, can be demonstrated on the basis of published maps, and neither can yet be discarded. If the straths are here spoken of collectively as products of the Asheville cycle, it is with this reservation in mind.

Relation of the Straths to the Piedmont Peneplain.—At a few places the peneplains of the Asheville cycle extend across the present Blue Ridge divide and lie at the summit of the escarpment overlooking the Piedmont (pages 182 and 183.) Parts of them now drain to the east or south and are being deeply dissected. As it is impossible to think of them as being made by streams flowing in that direction it is plain that the divide has shifted since the Asheville cycle.

The surface of the Piedmont has been treated as Harrisburg peneplain. Presumably its age is the same as that of the dominant peneplain, 1000 to 1100 feet high, east of Chattanooga. If the Asheville peneplain be correlated with the latter, it is presumed to be correlated with the Piedmont. This means that the steep escarpment in the Saluda quadrangle east of Hendersonville, N.C., marks an 800-foot vertical interval between peneplains of the same age but drained by streams flowing in opposite directions, one to the nearby Atlantic, the other to the remote Mississippi and the Gulf of Mexico. The difference in distance to the sea was believed by Davis to afford sufficient explanation of the difference in altitude between the two surfaces. Both are assumed to represent the best that their respective streams could do toward leveling their basins with the sea, under the conditions imposed on each by distance and by rock resistance. That two parts of the same peneplain should thus "break joint"[1] and fail to match is no curiosity; it is a necessary consequence of an asymmetrically located divide. A necessary consequence is the shifting of the divide. Commonly, divides shift far enough in a single cycle to eliminate such inequalities of level on their two sides. The long endurance of the asymmetry in this case is noteworthy. Correlations given above suggest that it was present in both Schooley and Harrisburg cycles. This suggests that repeated uplifts along or near the line of the present front tended to undo the work of adjustment which the streams were constantly attempting.

It may be that the morphologic history as sketched here is too simple, and that additional events must be inserted. The need of such change may be exemplified in the vicinity of Blowing Rock east of Grandfather Mountain. For some distance here the Blue Ridge escarpment trends nearly east and west. On the north is the roughened upland peneplain at about 3800 feet. South of it for 12 to 20 miles are the remains of another level at 2500 to 2700 feet, deeply and sharply dissected by the headwaters of the Yadkin River. This gives way in turn, rather abruptly, to the rolling surface of the Piedmont, 1300 to 1400 feet high. The 2500-foot level is apparently a peneplain and younger than the one at the summit. Keith correlates it with the strath on the west-flowing Wautaga River 25 miles to the northwest.[2]

It is almost equally plain that this level is older than the Piedmont. If that is not the case, postpeneplain faulting must be invoked. In other places it has been shown that bits of peneplain of Asheville age, now drained seaward by Piedmont streams,

---

[1] The expression "break joint" was used by Davis in the paper already referred to, "Stream Contest along the Blue Ridge." It seems to have appealed to the imagination of physiographers. The principle is now generally recognized, but its application to this case is not universally conceded. Keith, who seems to have been first to announce the principle, makes the Piedmont at least one cycle younger than the Asheville peneplain.

[2] Cranberry folio (No. 90).

belonged originally to the basins of west-flowing streams, but in this case there seems to be no possibility of former westward drainage. The forms in this locality would suggest that a peneplain of Asheville age was developed east of the mountains and destroyed in a later cycle to make the present Piedmont surface.[1] The case of the Dahlonega Plateau, which is in some ways similar, has been fairly well explained by the history of the drainage (page 135). No similar explanation has yet been shown to be applicable to the high level on the Upper Yadkin.

Post-Asheville Uplift.—The cycle, or succession of cycles, just described was interrupted like the others by an uplift, mainly in the mountain province. No doubt the Piedmont was somewhat steepened, perhaps enough to stimulate cutting from source to mouth simultaneously in all southeast-flowing streams. The present slope of the Piedmont is probably greater than can be allowed during the development of so good a peneplain. On the other hand, streams on the insoluble rocks of the Piedmont could never have done their work on so small a gradient as those on the limestones to the west.[2] It is probably safe to assume that deformation during the post-Asheville uplift, as in the earlier case, was mainly in a rather narrow zone not far from the foot of the mountains. The nature of the last uplift on the western side of the province is subject to the same uncertainty that remains with regard to the number of erosion cycles and the correlation of their several peneplains. So far as the Asheville peneplain can be traced by remnants to the northwest, its decline in altitude is not greater than the gradient of the river should have been during its development. For aught that is known the deformation on this side also may have been confined to a narrow zone. Even the amount of uplift which it is necessary to assume can not be determined until the effect of the Great Smoky conglomerate and other strong rocks in holding up a local base level has been evaluated.

Among the striking effects of the last uplift was the revival of headwater erosion against the east side of the Blue Ridge and a

---

[1] This is Keith's view as expressed in the Mount Mitchell folio (No. 124) and elsewhere.

[2] There is need of quantitative studies to determine the degree of slope on which peneplains may develop. Account must necessarily be taken of the size of streams and the kind of load yielded by the underlying rocks.

correspondingly accelerated shifting of the divide. Occasional stream captures have been inevitable and there are more to follow.[1] Other effects are seen in the deep entrenchment of tortuous meanders in which some streams traversed their straths. Winding gorges 400 to 500 feet deep are not uncommon.

[1] These local problems are well discussed by F. J. Wright, The Older Appalachians of the South, *op. cit.*, pp. 234–246.

CHAPTER IV

THE RIDGE AND VALLEY PROVINCE

GENERAL STATEMENT

Position and Extent.—The long narrow belt mentioned on page 122 as the Folded Appalachians is here described as the Ridge and Valley province. It borders the Older Appalachians and the New England province on the west, reaching to the Coastal Plain at the south and the St. Lawrence Valley at the north. Its length is 1200 miles and its maximum width on a line drawn through Harrisburg and Williamsport, Pa., is 80 miles. The width is 14 miles on the New York-New Jersey boundary. It barely reaches 35 miles in New York and 65 in northern Virginia. The extreme width in East Tennessee is 40 miles, which is near the average of its southern half.

Geologic Relations.—Geologically this province represents the eastern margin of the Paleozoic interior sea (Fig. 30). Structurally it is part of an anticlinorium, the successor to a geosyncline which sank intermittently for ages, receiving sediments from the concurrently rising old land surface on the east. As indicated on page 122, this province does not comprise quite the full width of the belt that was folded and faulted in the Appalachian revolution. Through most of its length the oldest sandstones and shales in the geosyncline, coming to the surface on its eastern edge, were made so strong by metamorphism that in their erosional history and present topography they belong to the Older rather than the Newer Appalachians.

Among the 30,000 to 40,000 feet of stratified Paleozoic rocks involved in the folding, all outcropping at one place or another, there are great differences in hardness. In the humid climate of Eastern United States, limestone (unless cherty) is generally wasted away most rapidly. Shale is usually, not always, a little more resistant, but both are weak. Well-cemented siliceous sandstone and conglomerate are most resistant. As selective erosion is particularly conspicuous in this region, and as folding

195

may bring the same stratum to the surface repeatedly, a small number of strong formations suffices to make a great number of ridges. Three ridge makers are especially significant. The Medina sandstone at the base of the Silurian (called "Tuscarora" in Pennsylvania and "Clinch" in the south) probably makes as many mountain ridges as all others combined. Next in importance are the Pocono (Mississippian) and the Pottsville (Pennsylvanian), both consisting of sandstone and conglomerate. The Oriskany and Chemung sandstones (Devonian) also make some lower ridges. In central Pennsylvania the lower part of the great Silurian sandstone (Oswego or Oneida conglomerate) is separated from the upper part (Medina proper) by 500 to 800 feet of weak beds, thus adding an additional ridge maker.[1]

Viewed empirically, the Ridge and Valley province is a lowland (an assemblage of valley floors) surmounted by long, narrow, even-topped mountain ridges. Either of these elements may predominate, the mountains being widely spaced and isolated, or so closely ranged that the lowlands are disconnected or absent. The valley floor is again trenched by streams. Morphologically the province is one of folded mountains in their second (or later) cycle, in which resistant strata form ridges, and weaker rocks are worn down to lowlands, themselves more or less eroded in a still later cycle.

By a careful study of the strata, taking account of thickness and dip, the original folds may be hypothetically restored. An estimate of their height in Pennsylvania is 30,000 to 40,000 feet.[2] Erosion during the rise kept their actual heights below these figures but that fact does not affect the total amount of material removed above the present summits. The lateral compression that made the folds also caused thrust faults. Indeed, much of the eastern boundary is determined by thrust faults, along which the older and more resistant rocks were pushed westward over the younger and weaker rocks.[3] By these means a much

[1] EATON, HARRY N., Some Subordinate Ridges of Pennsylvania, *Jour. Geol.*, vol. 27, p. 121–127, 1919.

[2] ASHLEY, GEO. H., *Bull. Geol. Soc. Amer.*, vol. 41, p. 695, 1930. R. T. Chamberlin (*Jour. Geol.*, vol. 18, p. 243, 1910) computes the average height of the restored Pottsville surface above the present valleys to be 3 miles.

[3] KEITH, ARTHUR, The Great Smoky Overthrust, *Bull. Geol. Soc. Amer.*, vol. 38, p. 154, 1927; Recently Deformed Overthrusts in the Appalachians, *Bull. Geol. Soc. Amer.*, vol. 39, p. 178, 1928.

broader belt was reduced to one half, perhaps to one third, of its former width. It was from the extremely mountainous surface thus described that the present surface was produced. The larger steps in the process were: (1) General peneplaning, (2) upwarping, (3) reduction of the weaker rocks to plains at lower levels, (4) further uplift and dissection.

FEATURES OF THE TOPOGRAPHY

MOUNTAINS

Types of Ridges.—Ridges resulting from differential erosion of base-leveled folds may be anticlinal, synclinal, or monoclinal.

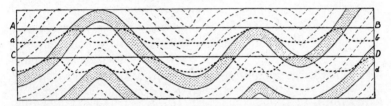

FIG. 53.—Diagram to illustrate the occurrence of anticlinal, synclinal, and monoclinal mountains and valleys. The shaded strata are resistant and therefore mountain makers. *AB* and *CD* represent perfect peneplains. The former is assumed to have been cut down later to *ab* and the latter to *cd*. Whether any particular fold, either anticline or syncline, shall produce a mountain or a valley is seen to depend on the level at which it is cut. All of the cases mentioned in the text are here illustrated. The diagram shows also that even though adjustment in one cycle be complete, readjustment is necessary in the next cycle.

All of these forms are found in the Appalachians, but monoclinal ridges are most numerous.[1] If a folded series be assumed in which the amplitude of the folds is large in proportion to the thickness of the strata, and the whole series be base-leveled, the chances that the new surface will cut a given strong stratum near a crest or a trough are less than the chances of intersection at some intermediate height. In the latter case renewed downcutting would leave the strong rock standing up as a monoclinal ridge (Fig. 53). If the peneplain is at or above the level of the anticlinal crest, erosion in a later cycle may strip the strong stratum, leaving an anticlinal mountain. With the plane

[1] Cross sections published in the folios of the U. S. Geol. Survey amply illustrate all of these types. See also the state geological maps of Virginia, Tennessee, and Alabama. Thrust faulting is noteworthy in most of the sections.

distinctly lower, or the fold higher, its axis would be cut through and an anticlinal valley developed.

If the peneplain passes just above a hard stratum in the trough of a syncline, the hard stratum thus preserved is apt to protect a synclinal mountain in the new erosion cycle. If the plain is more than a little higher than the hard bed in the axis of the trough, a synclinal valley will develop between monoclinal ridges whose escarpments face outward. Some dependence upon coincidence is thus seen in the development of both anticlinal and synclinal mountains. Monoclinal ridges sometimes, but not always, show a contrast between a steep scarp slope and a gentle dip slope. In some of the Appalachian ridges the rocks are vertical.

As an anticline terminates by the pitching of its axis, the second-generation anticlinal mountain here described tapers down and narrows to a point. It has been compared to a half cigar[1] (Fig. 54B). Traced in the other direction, the fold may rise until the top of the arch is cut off and the hard rock on its flanks forms two monoclinal ridges, their scarps facing each other across an anticlinal valley. In a similar way a strong stratum in a syncline may form the rim of a canoe-shaped valley (Fig. 54A). A contour line drawn around a number of pitching folds side by side must necessarily follow a zigzag course. Such a structure, subject to erosion in two cycles as above described, results in zigzag ridges. These are illustrated on a great scale in central Pennsylvania (Pl. 1) and on a smaller scale in the Ouachita Mountains in Arkansas (p. 679).

Mountain Profiles.—The crests of these mountains are moderately even or level, but rarely is the summit broad enough to afford a flat surface. A few synclinal mountains, like Broad Top in Pennsylvania, are tabular. Such forms must occur in synclines if at all, but the folding is generally too close. Evenness of crest for long distances is at places very striking and impressive. In a very general way it is most conspicuous in Pennsylvania and less marked in Virginia. But even where no deviation from the horizontal is detected by the eye, as on Kittatinny Mountain in New Jersey and its correlatives in Pennsylvania, topographic maps show a difference in altitude of several hundred feet

---

[1] WILLIS, BAILEY, "The Northern Appalachians," *Nat. Geog. Soc. Mon.* 6, 1896.

between parts near the great transverse streams and other parts midway between.[1] This is important, indicating (1) that the broad surface of which these ridges are remnants was a true peneplain, not a plain of marine degradation, and (2) that it was graded with reference to master streams which followed the courses of the present Delaware, Susquehanna, and Potomac.

Reduction of Summits by Erosion.—To say that these horizontal crests represent a peneplain means only that they acquired their horizontality in a certain manner. It does not preclude the

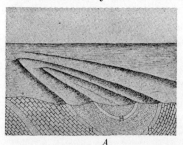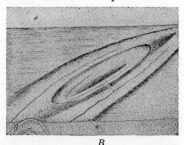

A *B*

Fig. 54.—Ridges and valleys made by erosion of pitching folds. *A*, syncline, *B*, anticline. (*Diagrams by Bailey Willis, Courtesy of Henry Holt & Company, Inc.*)

supposition that since uplift the entire surface has been lowered by erosion without losing its horizontality. It does not become a new peneplain when thus lowered. Without such latitude of language there would be an infinite number of peneplains and none could ever be identified. A bit of rock now at the surface may have been 100 feet, or 500 feet, below the surface when the peneplain was first made. There is such a thing as degradation without valley cutting and hence without loss of a plain's identity.[2] This principle is especially applicable to the narrow Appalachian ridges. Other things equal, the softer the rocks, and the thinner and more nearly vertical the ridge-making stratum (in other words, the narrower the outcrop) the more the level has been reduced.[3]

---

[1] VER STEEG, KARL, Wind Gaps and Water Gaps of the Northern Appalachians, *Ann. N. Y. Acad. Sci.*, vol. 32, pp. 87–220, 1930. Ref. to p. 104.

[2] FENNEMAN, NEVIN M., *Jour. Geol.*, vol. 16, pp. 746–754, 1908; *Bull. Geol. Soc. Amer.*, vol. 47, pp. 173–186, 1936.

[3] HAYES, C. W., Physiography of the Chattanooga District, U. S. Geol. Survey, 19th *Ann. Rep.*, pt. 2, p. 26, 1899. Hayes here argues this point at

Broad horizontal surfaces are narrowed rather than lowered. This generally results in the fact that the higher ridges are lower than the plateau to the west, which was in large part peneplaned at the same time.   There is also a difference in elevation among the ridges themselves.   In some cases opinion differs as to whether these unlike altitudes give evidence of several erosion cycles or of unequal reduction by uniform wasting.   The fact that canoe-shaped and cigar-shaped mountains are generally higher at their pitching ends, where the dip is least and the outcrop broadest, is an impressive illustration of unequal reduction.

The highest level crests in all parts of the province are treated here as products of the same erosion cycle.   Absolute certainty cannot be claimed for this generalization, but it is better to err on the side of simplicity than of complexity.

VALLEY FLOORS

Variation in Altitude and Relief.—A description would be misleading which left the impression that the entire area is neatly divided between clean-cut ridges and obvious valley floor. Much the greater part of it is easily seen to be one or the other, but there are places where the newer peneplain (valley floor) was poorly developed.   Where soft or soluble rocks underlie large continuous areas, the surface agencies did their best work and left little relief.   Generally speaking, this is true of the southern end of the province and of a broad strip of the middle portion next to the Blue Ridge province.   Together these areas constitute the Great Valley.   Elsewhere the plain is in narrower strips or smaller patches, some of them connected, others isolated.

The altitude of the valley floor ranges from less than 400 feet near the large rivers in the northern states to more than 2400 feet on divides in southern Virginia.   In the former localities the depth of the valley below the ridge tops is 1000 to 1500 feet, in the latter locality it is generally less.   In a very general way, broad extent of valley floors, low altitude, perfection of develop-

---

length and allows at least 300 feet of reduction, implying that it might be much more. WRIGHT, FRANK J., The Older Appalachians of the South, *Jour. Sci. Lab. Denison Univ.*, vol. 26, p. 156, 1931. Wright allows "at least several hundred feet," but hesitates to set a limit. ASHLEY, GEO. H., *Bull. Geol. Soc. Amer.*, vol. 46, p. 1403, 1935, suggests a minimum reduction of 100 feet in a million years.

ment, and freedom from later dissection go together. Unequal altitudes are partly residual and partly due to later warping (page 264). Probably most of this valley peneplain is the end product of the same erosion cycle. Exceptions will be mentioned later. Valleys, like ridges, may be synclinal, anticlinal, or monoclinal (Fig. 53).

Stream valleys, cut beneath the newer peneplain, vary in depth from a few feet to 500 or 600 feet, being deepest where later uplift was greatest. Parts of the plain are not yet reached

FIG. 55.—Ridges and water gaps seen in looking north from Reservoir Park (alt. 600 feet) Harrisburg, Pa. In the foreground is the Harrisburg peneplain at 520 feet. The ridges, with their altitudes west of the gaps, are Kittatinny Mountain 1140 feet, Second Mountain 1300 feet, and Peters Mountain 1420 feet. Their crests represent the Schooley peneplain. (*Ashley, Bull. Geol. Soc. Amer., vol.* 46.)

by the headwaters of streams of the present cycle. On the other hand, still newer peneplains are beginning to develop on the lower courses of some of the larger streams.

Drainage Patterns.—The physical characteristics of this province are intimately connected with its streams, which are primarily causes, not effects, of the present topography. Adjustment to structure brings about a condition in which streams follow the strike as much as possible, keeping on belts of soft rock. They cross the hard belts through "water gaps" as rarely as possible and then by the most direct route, *i.e.*, at right angles. The whole tendency is for drainage to become longitudinal, but this tendency stops when downcutting has reached a certain stage, *i.e.*, when every divide is being worn down equally on both sides.   This stage is now almost reached, but not quite.   A few noteworthy captures are still due to occur.

For reasons considered later (page 257) the drainage of this province at an earlier stage was mainly transverse.   Longitudinal streams were a subsequent development.   In the struggle of longitudinal subsequent streams with transverse consequent streams, the former often captured the latter, and with each capture one hard-rock crossing was eliminated, and the "water gap" became a "wind gap" (page 168).   The final result of a succession of such captures tends to show a "trel-

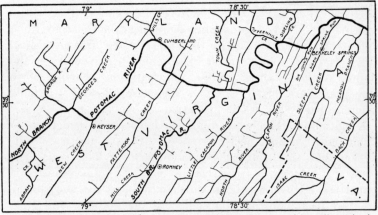

Fig. 56.—Trellised drainage pattern of the Potomac River and its tributaries in Western Maryland and West Virginia.

lised" pattern (Fig. 56).   The course of any larger stream is a series of rectangular jogs, well illustrated by the course of the Potomac.   An intelligent glance at the stream pattern of the Ridge and Valley province is sufficient to show the great extent to which its drainage has been revamped.   Most of the longitudinal streams have come by slow headward growth and most of the old transverse streams have vanished.   The many deserted wind gaps are impressive.

Sections.—For a less generalized treatment this province may be divided into three parts, designated respectively as the Hudson-Champlain (or Northern), Middle, and Southern sections. The boundary between the Northern and Middle sections is approximately at the Delaware River and that between the

Middle and Southern sections is at the divide between the New and Tennessee rivers.

HUDSON-CHAMPLAIN SECTION

GENERAL RELATIONS

Distinctive Features.—There can be no proper understanding of the Hudson Valley apart from its relations with the Ridge and Valley province of which it is a part topographically and geologically, structurally and historically. But the description and discussion of the Middle and Southern sections are inadequate for the Hudson Valley and in some respects inappropriate. The province, which is 80 miles wide in central Pennsylvania, with a multiplicity of folds, is suddenly reduced near the Delaware River to less than a fourth of its width, with only one large monoclinal range, the Kittatinny, called Shawangunk[1] in New York and ending at the southern limit of the Catskills. Farther north such ranges are all but absent. The valley floor also is quite different, partly because of glaciation.

Longitudinal drainage is prominent in the Northern (Hudson-Champlain) section, as transverse drainage is in the Middle section, but this contrast is more apparent than real. The Hudson itself escapes from the province as a transverse stream across the Highlands, above which it receives the longitudinal drainage from both directions, just as the Potomac and other transverse streams do in the Great Valley. The north-flowing waters in the Champlain Valley reach the sea without crossing the grain of the continental structure, only because the edge of the continent there is drowned.

Any boundary between the Northern and Middle sections must be arbitrary. It is largely a matter of convenience in discussion.[2] If located at the limit of glaciation, as is done here, there will be at least one element of topography and one important chapter in

[1] Pronounced Shongum.

[2] On the author's map of Physical Divisions of the United States, issued by the U. S. Geol. Survey, the boundary is essentially at the Hudson River and the 42d parallel. As the Wallkill Valley west of the river is like the valley to the east, and must be discussed in the same treatment, it is believed that both the topographic homogeneity of the section and the brevity of discussion will be favored by placing the boundary at the limit of glaciation, or approximately at the Delaware River where it forms the Pennsylvania-New Jersey boundary.

morphologic history belonging to the one section and not to the other. Moreover, this line, a few miles west of the Delaware River, marks the end of the broad, much folded belt in Pennsylvania, and the abrupt narrowing mentioned above.

Boundary on the West.—The western boundary in the southern part is a much eroded escarpment of Devonian shales and sandstones, of which the Catskill, not a very resistant stratum at this place, is uppermost. Under this, and protected by it, are shales of the Hamilton and Portage groups. Where the Delaware River follows the edge of the plateau on the New Jersey-Pennsylvania boundary, a steep slope at least 1000 feet high extends from the plateau surface across the underlying shales to the river at 300 to 400 feet A.T. The river is here some 400 feet below the prevailing valley level.

From Port Jervis, where the Delaware emerges from the plateau, and the states of New York, New Jersey, and Pennsylvania meet, the boundary line of the province is continued northeastward up the Neversink River and Basher Kill in the same geologic relations. Both streams follow the belt of narrow outcrops of the older Paleozoic rocks upturned at the edge of the plateau. The depression along this line, *i.e.*, the Port Jervis Trough between the plateau and Shawangunk Mountain, is continuous from Pennsylvania to the Hudson. In this trough the southwest-flowing Basher Kill is in headwater opposition with a tributary of Rondout Creek which flows northeast to the Hudson, both being in the same geologic relations as those of the Delaware described above. In latitude 41°45′ Shawangunk Mountain ends and the lowland along the Hudson spreads westward to the rugged escarpment of the Catskills.[1]

As far north as latitude 42°15′, the plateau surface on the west is definitely limited to the resistant Catskill formation. The underlying shales form the valley lowland, or the lower part of the escarpment where entrenched streams like the Delaware flow at its foot. The Helderberg limestone and Oriskany sandstone beneath the shales, and outcropping farther east, cause only minor embossments on the valley floor. North of latitude 42°15′ these simple relations are altered. The limestones are thicker and stronger and their outcrops rise to higher levels.

[1] The geologic map of the state of New York (1901) should, if possible, be followed in the reading of these paragraphs on boundaries.

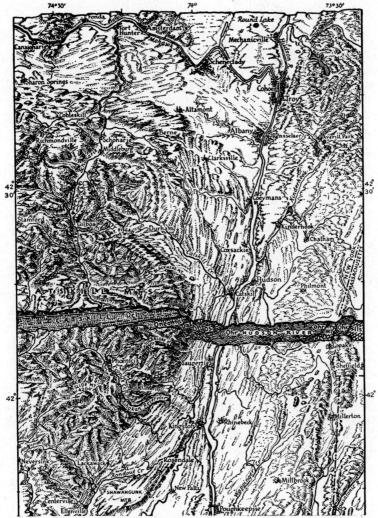

Fig. 57.—Diagram of Catskill and Helderberg Mountains. (*Raisz, XVI Internat. Geol. Congress Guidebook 9.*)

Concurrently the dip flattens and the outcrop becomes a northeast-facing escarpment.   West of Albany the Helderberg and Onondaga limestones outcrop in a great cuesta 1700 feet high, called Helderberg Mountains.   This is necessarily a part of the plateau province, particularly as its southwestward dip slope ends quickly against a higher cuesta which in turn gives way to a still higher. These outcrops are near the axis of a great scoop-shaped syncline which pitches to the southwest into the plateau.   Toward this axis the rocks dip southward from the Mohawk, westward from the Hudson, and northwestward from the Port Jervis Trough (Fig. 57).

Where the Helderberg and Onondaga are steeply tilted in the Hudson Valley and Port Jervis Trough, their combined outcrops are narrow and their topographic effect small.   With a rise and flattening toward the north they form a rock terrace or bench, the Helderberg Mountains.   This bench rises northward like a ramp, skirting the edge of the higher Catskill plateau.   In the Berne quadrangle west of Albany, it is definitely plateau. One quadrangle farther south it is part of the lowland.   Between the two there is uniform gradation.   It is the necessity of crossing this ramp from the Catskill front in the Durham quadrangle to the Helderberg front in the Albany quadrangle that makes the province boundary indefinite and arbitrary for a space of about 15 miles.   That it is not indefinite farther north may be seen by examining Fig. 76 on page 282.

In the latitude of Albany the Helderberg escarpment continues westward, overlooking the Mohawk Valley, but the valley of the Mohawk above Schenectady is not treated here with the Hudson Valley lowland.   The two are separated by a distinct east-facing escarpment on or near the 74th meridian, 15 to 20 miles west of the Hudson.[1]   From the Mohawk north to the Adirondacks this escarpment is due to a fault (page 324).   South of the river the cause is less clear.

From the 43d parallel northward the western boundary of the Hudson-Champlain Valley lowland is essentially at the edge of the crystalline rocks which make the Adirondack Highland. The rise from the valley floor, 300 to 400 feet high, to mountains

---

[1] Clearly shown on the Berne, Amsterdam, and Schenectady topographic sheets of the U. S. Geol Survey.

1500 to 2000 feet high, is generally abrupt and often picturesque. From Whitehall at the head (south end) of Lake Champlain, northward for 70 miles, the west shore may be taken as the boundary. Occasional patches of valley flat on the west side may be 3 miles wide. North of latitude 44°30' (Plattsburg quadrangle) a 10-mile strip of Cambrian sandstone and Ordovician limestone underlies a lowland between the lake and the mountains. The same lowland, a part of the St. Lawrence Valley, wraps around the Adirondack province on the north.

Boundary on the East.—For the 75 miles of its length west of the Hudson River the southeastern boundary of this section is determined by the Highlands or Reading Prong of the New England Upland. Its nearly flat horizon is 1100 feet high near the Delaware, or about 400 feet above the valley floor. Near the Hudson the highland is higher, the valley floor lower, and the difference almost 1000 feet. Everywhere the front is definite though not free from spurs. For another 20 miles east and north from the place where the Hudson enters the Highlands, the boundary is of the same nature, a definite escarpment of granitic rocks overlooking a lowland on shale, slate, or limestone.

Thus far the boundary of the lowland has been against a southwestward extension of the New England Upland. From this point northward it lies against the higher Taconic section which has sometimes been assigned to the Ridge and Valley province and sometimes (as is done here) to the New England province. In favor of the former is the fact that its eastern margin is a limestone valley, much like the Great Valley in the Middle section, clearly distinguished from the Green Mountains and the New England Upland. The western boundary of the Taconic section is less clear and less simply described. In the treatment of geologic history there are some advantages in linking the Taconic section with the Hudson-Champlain Trough. On the other hand, the morphologic character of the Taconic section allies it distinctly with the New England province. Its physical geography and all other kinds of geography favor its assignment to that province.

The distinction between Hudson Valley and Taconic Mountains arises chiefly from the fact that the sedimentary rocks in the latter, mainly Cambrian and Ordovician shales, have been metamorphosed and thus strengthened to resist erosion. This metamorphism increases gradually from the Hudson River eastward. Along a fairly definite line the rock changes from slate to schist.[1] For a part of its length, mainly in the northern half, the line thus described is determined by westward over-thrusting of schist on slate.[2] There is more than one such thrust, but the boundary of the province as here treated does not follow any one structural line throughout its length. The ultimate criterion is topography. In the slate hills west of this line there is an absence of alignment of ridges and valleys. The Taconic Mountains are cast into ranges having a definite trend and are, at most places, much higher. (*Cf.* Fig. 101, page 354.)

In the main the schists constitute the Taconic Mountain range, which rises well above the slate hills to the west, though occasional ones of those hills might be called mountains, especially north of latitude 43°. A fairly abrupt topographic break follows the line along which slate gives way to schist. This is the first noteworthy change in general slope or style of topography encountered in going east from the low hills of slate and shale which characterize the surface on both sides of the Hudson. An exception to the above statement must be made for a 20-mile stretch east of Albany and Cohoes, where the abrupt ascent is not on schist but on the folded Rensselaer quartzite of the Rensselaer Plateau,[3] which is also a part of the Taconic section (p. 353).

In latitude 43°45′ the Taconic Mountains come to an end. Thence to the St. Lawrence Valley the boundary of the Hudson-Champlain Lowland is at the foot of the Green Mountains. For about half the distance the mountain front is a nearly straight wall, rising from a valley about 500 feet high. In the last 40 miles to the Canadian border the mountain front is much frayed and at places no simple line can be drawn.

---

[1] DALE, T. NELSON, The Slate Belt of Eastern New York and Western Vermont, *U. S. Geol. Survey*, 19*th Ann. Rept.*, pt. 3, pp. 153–300, 1899. Plate 13 is a geologic map from latitude 43° to 43°45′, about the northern limit of the Taconic Mountains.

[2] *Cf.* Geol. map of United States, 1932.

[3] DALE, T. NELSON, Geology of the Hudson Valley between the Hoosic and the Kinderhook, U. S. Geol. Survey, *Bull.* 242, 1904. See Pl. 1, geologic and topographic map.

Topography of the Hudson-Champlain Valley[1]

The Hudson-Champlain lowland is a continuation of the middle section of the Ridge and Valley province. Differences of level arise from (1) the presence of more than one peneplain, (2) the imperfection of peneplains, especially where the rocks have been strengthened by metamorphism, (3) glaciation, (4) crustal movements associated with the Pleistocene ice. Among the planes of reference used in the following descriptions, the Harrisburg peneplain is fairly well established. Lower levels, for the most part close to the Hudson River and Lake Champlain, may be correlated with one or more of the later surfaces designated as Somerville peneplain in the Piedmont province.

Wallkill-Paulinskill Valley.—The interpretation of the present surface is least complicated between the Hudson and Delaware rivers. Here the valley floor is everywhere carved into hills which are mainly preglacial though modified by ice. The summit level reaches 900 to 1000 feet near the New York-New Jersey boundary on the divide between the southwest-flowing Paulinskill and the northeast-flowing Wallkill. Southwestward, toward the Delaware, the level merges with the Harrisburg peneplain which is 700 to 800 feet high in eastern Pennsylvania.[2] Northeastward from the divide toward the Hudson the elevation declines more rapidly, and the maturely dissected surface gives way to an older valley topography, perhaps to a post-Harrisburg peneplain, much of which in the Wallkill Valley is only 300 to 400 feet high. Most of the surface from the Delaware to the Hudson is on the Hudson River shale, but limestone is more abundant on the southeastern side. Generally its surface is a distinctly separate and lower plain less than 400 feet high. This is one of many localities in the Ridge and Valley province in which a surface on limestone and an adjacent surface on shale lie at different levels. Whether two cycles are indicated or whether the two surfaces represent a single peneplain unequally reduced by rain wash is a question considered more fully on page 157.

---

[1] Descriptions under this general heading will be made much clearer by constant reference to the map, Pl. 1.

[2] Stose, George W., The Delaware Water Gap, U. S. Geol. Survey topographic map.

For a dozen miles south of Newburg on the Hudson, the province boundary is approximately followed by the Newburg Shortline of the Erie Railroad. The Schunemunk Mountains west of the railroad, which rise above 1600 feet, are a small remnant of Devonian sandstone and are similar to other ridges of the Ridge and Valley province.

As the Hudson is approached, the effects of metamorphism begin to be seen. Marlboro Mountain, more than 1000 feet high, north of Newburg, is a strike ridge of metamorphic grit 3 to 4 miles west of the river.[1]   Generally the Hudson River shale is sufficiently homogeneous so that relief features are not conspicuously elongated with the strike, though most of the streams are longitudinal.   Both topographic form and drainage lines have been modified by glaciation, as shown by lakes and swamps.

Kittatinny-Shawangunk Mountain.—West of the Wallkill lowland is Shawangunk Mountain, known as Kittatinny in New Jersey and Blue in Pennsylvania. Except Schunemunk Mountain, which is only 6 miles long, this is the only one north and east of the Delaware that is typical of the province. It is a monoclinal ridge of Medina and Clinton conglomerate and sandstone which dip northwestward beneath the plateau, at places almost vertically, elsewhere at a lower angle. There are even subordinate parallel folds in the broad northern end.[2]   The crest ranges from 1400 to 2000 feet in height, with a few sags and higher swells.   Yet within a single view the level is remarkably uniform.   The New Jersey portion is the type locality of the Kittatinny peneplain, here identified with the Schooley.   Locally, as in the Newburg quadrangle, the eastern escarpment rises 1400 feet in a single mile.   As the crest of this mountain is from 600 to 1600 feet above the valley, and the strong stratum is only 250 to 300 feet thick, most of the eastern slope is on the underlying and protected Ordovician shales.   The broad, high northern part was overridden by the continental ice, which polished the rocks and left such well known lakes as Mohonk and Minnewaska.

---

[1] Holzwasser, F., Geology of the Newburg Quadrangle, *Bull. N. Y. State Museum*, 270, p. 20, 1926. See also Gordon, C. E., Geology of the Poughkeepsie Quadrangle, *Bull. N. Y. State Museum*, 148, 1911.

[2] Darton, N. H., Shawangunk Mountain, *Nat. Geog. Mag.*, vol. 6, pp. 23–34, 1894. The best general map of this part of the province is the geologic map of New York (including a part of New Jersey), published in 1901.

Lowlands at the Foot of the Plateau Escarpment.—Between the Kittatinny-Shawangunk Mountain and the plateau is the narrow but strikingly continuous Port Jervis Trough, cut out mainly on Devonian limestone (Helderberg and Onondaga). Its flat bottom is rarely a mile wide between the mountain on the east and the steep slope which leads up over Devonian shales to the hard cap of the Allegheny Plateau. Shawangunk Mountain ends 10 miles from Kingston on the Hudson, and the Port Jervis Trough, here the valley of Rondout Creek, merges with the broader lowland.

As the valley floor west of the Hudson is followed northward from Kingston to the Albany quadrangle, a division into two belts becomes more and more apparent. The low eastern belt on Hudson River shales is separated by an escarpment (Helderberg) from a higher belt of stronger relief on Devonian limestone and shale. In the main this latter surface is the eroded Harrisburg peneplain, but toward the north it rises gradually to the plateau level and becomes the Helderberg Plateau, or Mountains, as described above, making it necessary to swing the boundary line over to include it in the plateau province. The low eastern shale belt will be mentioned later.

The narrow western belt, not more than 6 to 8 miles wide south of Catskill Creek, deserves attention quite out of proportion to its extent. Here, Appalachian folding has made in miniature the same structures, both simple and complicated, which cause the major features in central Pennsylvania.[1] The resulting morphology is the same except in dimensions. Heights are measured in tens of feet instead of hundreds, and a single view may command the entire width of two or more pitching folds, eroded into ridges of all types described on page 197. Limestone beds make the ridges. There is this difference, that the large-scale features farther south were carved from the highest and oldest peneplain and these from the Harrisburg. A general scarcity of glacial drift makes this locality peculiarly favorable for a study of Appalachian structures and morphology.

Slate Hills East of the Hudson.—Immediately east of the low plain along the river the topography is not very different

---

[1] DAVIS, W. M., The Folded Helderberg Limestones East of the Catskills, *Bull. Museum Comp. Zool.*, vol. 7 (Geol. ser., vol. 1), pp. 311–330, 1884; also, The Little Mountains East of the Catskills, *Appalachia*, vol. 3, pp. 20–33, 1882 (not consulted).

from that on the west side, though it may be noted that the hills are almost all of the mammillary type, never ranged in strike ridges or cuestas as some are on the west side of the river. Many of the hills are of glacial drift. In so far as they are of rock their lack of linear form is due mainly to uniformity in hardness among the beds. To a distance varying from 12 to 18 miles east of the river the rocks are mainly slate,[1] folded and faulted, or at least tilted, the severity of such deformation and also of metamorphism increasing toward the east. Concurrently the altitude increases eastward. The altitude of hilltops nearest the clay belt along the Hudson may be 400 to 500 feet at one place, 500 to 700 feet at another, or in exceptional cases, 1000 to 1200 feet. These last-named altitudes are found only near the Hudson-Champlain divide and presumably well above the Harrisburg base level.

Collectively the slate hills form a landscape of knobs and domes with a relief of 100 to 400 or 500 feet. While lines of trend are not seen in the hills, some valleys follow the strike. Approximate uniformity in altitude along the western border (except near the Hudson-Champlain divide) suggests that these hills were carved from a surface of small relief, probably the Harrisburg peneplain, but farther east altitudes increase and become irregular, and the presence of a former peneplain is problematical. Neighboring hills have no accordance of altitude, and exceptional eminences occur throughout the area.

Lowlands Near the Hudson.—A strip embracing the river, generally 5 to 8 miles wide south of the Albany quadrangle and twice as wide farther north, is lower and flatter than what remains of the supposed peneplain on either side. It is interpreted as an incipient newer peneplain or strath developed near the main drainage line. Much of it is now covered by clay or sand and is quite flat. Most of the flats lie between 200 and 400 feet in altitude and are in process of dissection by small streams leading to the Hudson, whose surface is at sea level. The descent from the tabular clay surfaces to the Hudson is at places by steep bluffs, the river being in a narrow trench averaging perhaps a

---

[1] DALE, T. NELSON (cited above on p. 208). It should be noted that the term *Slate Belt* as used by Dale designates only the area in which the slate is suited to commercial use. The term *Slate Hills* as here used has no such restriction.

mile in width. Elsewhere the slope is terraced. From the place where the Hudson enters the Highlands, northward for 50 miles, *i.e.*, to the latitude of Catskill Creek, the clay and sand flats are surmounted by isolated rounded glacial hills 100 to 200

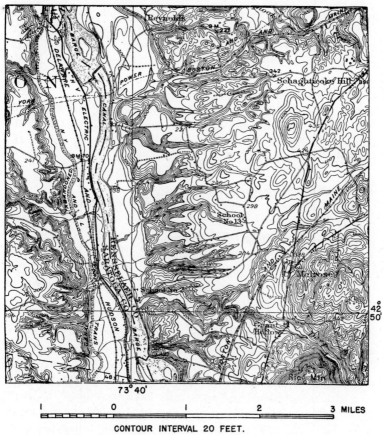

CONTOUR INTERVAL 20 FEET.

Fig. 58.—Topographic map of a part of the Hudson Valley north of Troy. The map shows (1) the recent valley bottom, (2) the clay terrace in which valleys are cut by young tributaries, (3) the western edge of the belt of slate hills. (*U. S. Geol. Survey.*)

feet high. It may be more accurate to say that the flats here were developed only between hills which they failed to cover. A few rock hills are monadnocks. Farther north hills are exceptional, but above Troy, where the maximum width is 15 to 18 miles, the

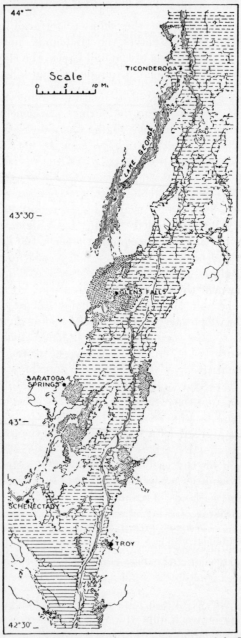

FIG. 59.—Approximate limit of standing water in a part of the Hudson-Champlain Trough. The lined area is largely underlain by clay with minor areas of
stratified drift. Knowledge is more certain where the lines are not broken.
Stippling indicates kame terraces, gravel outwash plains, other glacial deposits,
and deltas. Areas left blank are ground moraine. (*Charles Emerson Peet,
Jour. Geol., vol.* 12.)

flat is interrupted by large islands of ground moraine which lie a little higher (Fig. 59).

All of this flat surface is on sediments laid down as lake beds or deltas during the presence of glacial ice or in the standing water which accompanied or followed its melting. While much of the material is clay, the beds at the surface are generally sandy. Especially is this true near the edges, where deltas invaded the standing water. Characteristically, though not universally, this surface consists of two terraces.[1] Of these, the upper and outer member has the larger proportion of sand, or even gravel, as might be expected in the shallow water near shore, where deltas were common. The terrace nearer the river, and 60 feet lower, consists largely of the so-called "Albany brick clays." Into this surface the river has carved its present trench, 100 feet, more or less, in depth and rarely a mile and a half in width (Fig. 59).

Mohawk Delta.—North of the place where the Helderberg escarpment swings to the west, the preglacial lowland spread widely over the soft Hudson River shales. Here the body of standing water which succeeded the glacier had its greatest width, 15 to 18 miles. It is therefore known as Lake Albany,[2] though its exact nature, whether lake, estuary, or strait, has been a subject of controversy (page 225). Whatever its limits or connections, this body of water received the Mohawk River where it issues from the escarpment west of Schenectady. That river, reinforced by the waters of Lake Iroquois (page 495 and Fig. 91), built a great delta which constitutes the present sandy plain as far as the Helderberg Mountains on the south and the Hudson trench on the east. To the north it extends beyond Saratoga Lake and its outlet. In this direction it not only surrounds extensive islands of ground moraine[3] but borders on, or merges with, deltas of other streams. Farther north this strip of sediment-covered flats is essentially continuous with the similar flat in the Champlain basin.

The general aspect of the delta country north of the Helderberg Mountains as far as Glens Falls (where the Hudson enters the

---

[1] STOLLER, J. H., Glacial Geology of the Cohoes Quadrangle, *Bull. N. Y. State Museum* 215–216, p. 8, 1918.

[2] WOODWORTH, J. B., Ancient Water Levels in the Champlain and Hudson Valleys, *Bull. N. Y. State Museum*, 84, p. 175, 1905.

[3] PEET, C. E., Glacial and Post-glacial History of the Hudson and Champlain Valleys, *Jour. Geol.*, vol. 12, pp. 415–469, 1904; ref. to p. 437, Fig. 13.

valley from the west) is that of a sandy plain youthfully dissected. Dunes are rather plentiful. Lakes, Saratoga and others, are apparently limited to the several erosion valleys of the former Mohawk,[1] which may have been filled with residual ice blocks while the surrounding deposits were made. Huge deposits of water-laid drift, here as elsewhere, intervene locally between the valley flat and the neighboring highlands. These are mainly "kame terraces" deposited in the trough between the shrinking ice and the valley wall.[2] They therefore antedate the lake and the deltas.

Flats Bordering Lake Champlain.—The clay and sand flats in the Champlain Valley[3] are not essentially different from those of the Hudson, though perhaps less eroded. A strip 5 or 6 miles wide next to the lake consists largely of terraced clay plains less than 100 feet above the lake, or 200 feet above the sea. Farther from the lake are higher and sandier terraces up to altitudes of 500 feet or more. All sediments here are pierced by monadnocks and their surfaces have a faint southward slope varying according to their age (page 219). All the larger stream valleys are terraced. Sandy deltas occur at all levels, following the former lake in its subsidence. North of latitude 44°30′, where flats west of the lake become extensive, noteworthy features are the broad deltas of the AuSable and Saranac Rivers, the latter affording the military training ground near Plattsburg.

The low flat surface near the lake is connected with the corresponding flat along the Hudson by a narrow but uninterrupted sand plain followed by the Champlain Canal, whose summit level is 149 feet above the sea. This low passage follows and indents an older valley floor (the upper terrace) 300 feet or more in height and generally not less than 5 miles wide, except where crowded with monadnocks near the head of the lake.

[1] For the repeated shifting of the Mohawk River to a more southerly course see Stoller, J. H., Late Pleistocene History of the Lower Mohawk and Middle Hudson Region, *Bull. Geol. Soc. Amer.*, vol. 33, pp. 515–526, 1922; Fairchild, H. L., Post-glacial Features of the Upper Hudson Valley, *Bull. N. Y. State Museum*, 195, pp. 14–15, 1917.

[2] STOLLER, J. H., Glacial Geology of the Saratoga Quadrangle, *Bull. N. Y. State Museum*, 183, p. 21, 1916; see also PEET, *op. cit.*, p. 241.

[3] BALDWIN, S. P., Pleistocene History of the Champlain Valley, *Amer. Geologist*, vol. 13, p. 170–184, 1890.

Preglacial Rock Surface

The Rock Terrace.—The above-mentioned water-laid sediments cover a rock surface of low relief.[1] This surface was the floor of a wide preglacial valley, an incipient peneplain bounded by the dissected upland which has been tentatively correlated with the Harrisburg peneplain. The buried surface is now 200 feet above the sea, at a point 40 miles north of Albany, and has the same elevation in the northern part of New York City. The highest intermediate point (probably due to hard rock or to recent rise) is 350 feet and the lowest level 140 feet. There is no progressive rise in either direction. This preglacial valley floor was covered by the waters of Lake Albany to the present 360-foot

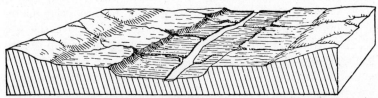

Fig. 60.—Diagram showing the preglacial form of the Hudson Valley north of Troy. The upland is represented on the edges. The intermediate level, 4 to 5 miles wide and 200 feet above the sea, is the rock terrace. The lowest level, averaging 2 miles in width, is the rock gorge. The river is slightly above sea level. (*Stoller, N. Y. State Museum Bull.* 215.)

contour in latitude 43°. The hypothetical strand line farther south is lower.[2]

The Rock Gorge.—The nearly level rock floor, some 200 feet above sea level (or above the Hudson south of Troy), is trenched by a younger valley averaging no more than 2 miles in width (Figs. 60 and 61). This is the rock gorge or "inner gorge." South of latitude 42° the rock terrace and the inner gorge are made evident by outcrops and by the present form of the valley. Farther north, terrace and gorge alike are obscured or wholly concealed by the "Albany clay" and other sediments which filled the gorge and covered the terrace. The river has, however, made considerable progress in cleaning out the rock gorge by cutting a new trench within the old valley. Generally this new gorge in the clay is narrower than the gorge in the rock so that its bluffs or

[1] Stoller, J. H., "Glacial Geology of the Cohoes Quadrangle," p. 8; Woodworth, *loc. cit.*

[2] Stoller, *op. cit.*, p. 43.

"banks" consist of clay (Fig. 61). North of Troy, where the channel of the Hudson is above sea level, the stream has cut its new postglacial valley down to or into the bottom of the old rock gorge and is now flowing in a rock channel at some places.

In its buried portion the presence of the rock gorge is made known at places by falls in tributary streams where they descend to the level of the Hudson. Thus the upper Hudson itself, coming from the west, enters the old gorge at Fort Edward, falling 100 feet at Bakers Falls, which have retreated several miles

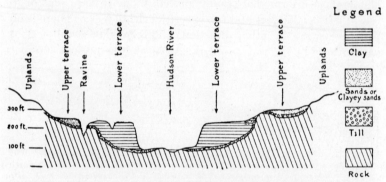

Fig. 61.—Section across the Hudson Valley showing present surface features and relations of Pleistocene deposits to the underlying rock surface. Width of valley 4 to 5 miles. (*Stoller, N. Y. State Museum Bull.* 215.)

upstream. The Mohawk drops into the old gorge at Cohoes Falls, 1 mile from its mouth. Ten miles below Poughkeepsie, Wappinger Creek drops 60 feet from the rock terrace into a tributary gorge 2 miles from the Hudson.

The width of the rock gorge is remarkably uniform, averaging about 2 miles. Its depth increases astonishingly toward the south. North of Troy (lat. 42°45′) it is little more than 100 feet below the rock terrace. South of Troy the gorge is cut below sea level and is filled with deposits of glacial age up to the bed of the river. The greatest known depth, 950 feet, is where the river enters the Highlands at Storm King[1] (Fig. 62, p. 219).

[1] Berkey, C. P., and Marion Rice, Geology of the West Point Quadrangle, *Bull. N. Y. State Museum*, 225–226, p. 11, 1919.

Knowledge of this deep and partly filled gorge of the lower Hudson was gained by exploratory borings made by the Board of Water Supply of the City of New York, preparatory to constructing the Catskill Aqueduct which must necessarily pass under the river. As the tunnel must be in solid rock,

Neither above nor below this place is the southward increase in depth regular, but the gorge continues through the Highlands and past the Palisades and New York harbor to the edge of the continental shelf, where its bottom is at least 2400 (probably 4000) feet below sea level.

That the gorge is primarily a river valley cut during an episode of continental elevation cannot be doubted, but its present depth

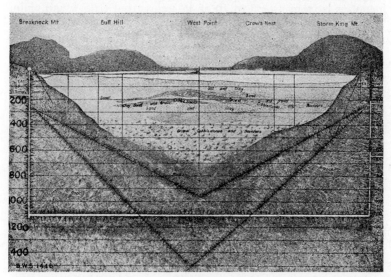

Fig. 62.—Diagrammatic cross section of the Hudson River channel, looking south where the Catskill aqueduct (New York City Water Supply) passes under the river at a depth of 1100 feet. The vertical lines beneath the river and the diagonal lines in the rock are exploratory borings. Solid rock was found about 700 feet below the water surface. (*N. Y. State Museum Bull.* 225-226.)

at different points may have been modified somewhat by crustal movement and also by glacial scour.[1]

Rock Surface in the Champlain Basin.—The sand and clay plains described on page 216 overlie a rock surface which is the same in origin, and probably in age, as the rock terrace in the Hudson Valley. Both are incipient peneplains, developed near streams when the drainage was in the main as at present. The

---

it was constructed 1100 feet below the surface of the river. For the first adequate discussion of the gorge discovered in this work see J. F. Kemp, Buried Channels beneath the Hudson and Its Tributaries, *Amer. Jour. Sci.*, 4th ser., vol. 26, pp. 301–323, 1908.

[1] BERKEY and RICE, *op. cit.*, p. 145.

divide between north-flowing and south-flowing streams was apparently near Fort Ann, where the present narrow strip of lowland is greatly constricted and choked by monadnocks.

The boundary of the low rock surface in the Champlain basin is irregular, for its margins were very imperfectly reduced to the newer base level, as is shown by the rock hills that rise above the flat surface of clay or sand. Generally the eastern edge of these deposits is from 4 or 5 to 10 or 12 miles from Lake Champlain. The limiting altitude at the north is above 500 feet, but it diminishes southward. Between the edge of the newer sediments and the Green Mountains are rock hills of irregular height up to 1200 or 1500 feet. The wide valleys of the Otter and Missisquoi rivers merge with the sediment-covered lowland which has a decided slope toward Lake Champlain. Near the Canadian boundary the preglacial Champlain Lowland widens greatly as it merges with that of the St. Lawrence.

The lake basin represents the inner gorge, modified by glaciation. The bottom reaches 300 feet below sea level but glacial scour may well account for part of this depth, as also for a part of the width. A filling of glacial drift and clay has made it impossible thus far to locate the northward course of the old channel to the St. Lawrence.[1] The latter has its own preglacial gorge similar to that of the Hudson and, like it, traceable across the continental shelf.

In so far as a well-defined rock channel crosses the Champlain-Hudson divide, it must differ in origin and age from the two gorges made by streams in headwater opposition. It could be made only by overflow from one basin to the other. Such a condition became inevitable when the north-flowing stream was dammed by continental ice.

SUMMARY OF PHYSIOGRAPHIC HISTORY

Structural Conditions.—While the present lowland is the result of erosion, the conditions which favored and localized erosion were determined by a long geologic history in which a belt of weaker rocks came to be bordered by stronger rocks on both sides. This history began in Pre-Cambrian times with the raising of the Adirondack and Green mountains, leaving between them a trough in which sediments accumulated. After

[1] BALDWIN, *op. cit.*, p. 177.

the Ordovician period the Green Mountains were raised again, and on their western edge (south of the Champlain basin) another range, the Taconic, made of sediments of the same general age as those that underlie the Hudson Valley. In the great lateral compression that made this range the rocks were metamorphosed into schist and greatly strengthened.[1] Still, there was no trough, either structural or topographic, south of the Adirondacks, the present Hudson Valley being still the margin of a wide interior sea. In this sea, sediments accumulated which are now preserved in the plateau west of the valley.

In the Appalachian Revolution at the close of Paleozoic time, the old mountain country on the east and even a part of the Adirondacks were again deformed. At this time the section here considered was itself thrown into folds which no doubt rose higher than the plateau on the west. But the deformation was not so severe as to metamorphose the rocks except moderately on the east side. All of these deformations involved faulting as well as folding. Their effect was to leave strong and weak rocks side by side so that all future erosion must be conditioned and modified by structural features.

Early Cycles of Peneplanation.—The folded and faulted rocks were further warped and faulted at intervals, but erosion preponderated and probably developed throughout this section the same pre-Schooley peneplain that is now buried by the coastal plain sediments. It is not improbable that during this peneplanation a north-flowing stream developed in the Champlain trough. To what extent such streams followed the strike in the Hudson Valley is not known. The dominant drainage after the Appalachian uplift was probably toward the Mississippi.[2] How the drainage came to be southeastward across the older highlands has been much discussed. The simplest assumption, and one whose probability is coming to be more and more considered,[3] is that the pre-Schooley peneplain was submerged on its seaward side enough to receive sediments on which drainage

[1] Just how far these effects were brought about at this time and not in the Appalachian Revolution is a question on which geologists are not wholly agreed.

[2] MILLER, W. J., Geological History of New York State, *Bull. N. Y. State Museum*, 255, p. 76, 1924.

[3] JOHNSON, DOUGLAS, "Stream Sculpture on the Atlantic Slope," Columbia University Press, 1931.

to the Atlantic was superposed.   The question is not wholly settled, and other hypotheses are mentioned on page 257.

With transverse drainage once begun across the Highlands of New York, and with the region again uplifted, the way was open for the development of a great longitudinal valley on the older and softer rocks followed by the present Hudson River. Appalachian folding had raised these softer rocks to a higher level in this belt than farther west, so that after peneplaning they were exposed here while buried elsewhere.   Longitudinal drainage should have been well begun in the Schooley cycle, which is assumed to have followed the uplift of the first peneplain.   This assumption is in accord with the evidence (page 199) that the major streams at the close of the Schooley cycle were flowing in courses not very different from those of the present.

Late Tertiary Peneplanation.—The Hudson Valley was almost erased in the making of the Schooley peneplain.   It is only since the rise of that surface that the present great longitudinal valleys came to stay (with reservations as to the future).   The Hudson-Champlain belt of weak rocks was reduced to the Harrisburg peneplain and in part to a lower one.   The Schooley peneplain covered the hard rocks of the Highlands but only fragments of narrow benches in the gorge record the work of later cycles.[1]   The narrow bench at West Point is a remnant of the rock terrace described above as an incipient peneplain, younger than the Harrisburg.   The contrast in rocks is such that a valley 1 to 2 miles wide in the Highlands corresponds to the broad lowland north of Albany.   This old valley floor must have had some southward gradient when it was developed, perhaps 1 or 2 feet per mile.   The present horizontality is the result of later crustal movements.

The slate hills on the east were first carved from the Schooley peneplain but they were greatly reduced and now represent various stages of progress toward a later peneplain.   Their western margin seems again to have reached the peneplain stage in the Harrisburg cycle.   Where limestone occurs, the drainage has in some cases become adjusted.   Thus Wappinger Creek

[1] BERKEY, C. P. (Geology of the West Point Quadrangle, *Bull. N. Y. State Museum*, 225–226, 1919), points out that such bits of the valley floor are confined to the Grenville gneiss and do not appear on the granite.

southeast of Poughkeepsie follows a belt of limestone[1] at the level of the rock terrace.

For the northern part of the section, the history given here may need modification by ascribing the depth of the valley partly to renewed faulting along old lines when the Schooley peneplain was lifted up. Some of the steeper parts of the Adirondack front have been thus accounted for.[2] However, since the line between highland and lowland is also the line between hard and soft rock, the physiographic evidence points equally to a fault-line scarp in its second (or later) cycle.

The presence of the rock terrace along the Hudson indicates post-Harrisburg uplift, and that of the inner gorge a still further rise. It is quite probable that a detailed account of uplift and erosion would be still more complex.

The Rock Gorge.—The uplift preceding the cutting of the gorge took place not long before or after the beginning of the Pleistocene. It would seem that an uplift sufficient to permit the cutting of a valley 2400 (or 4000) feet deep at the edge of the Continental Shelf, and at least one third as much in the lower Hudson, would have resulted in more general dissection than the rock surface shows elsewhere. Partly on this account, geologists have given thought to other possible origins of the submerged gorge.[3] Whatever explanation may be given for deep valleys in the Continental Shelf, there is as yet no escape from the conclusion that the basin of the Hudson was lifted some hundreds of feet. It seems necessary to conclude that the rise was very brief. It lasted only long enough to enable the Hudson to cut a

[1] GORDON, C. E., Geology of the Poughkeepsie Quadrangle, *Bull. N. Y. State Museum*, 148, p. 8, 1911.

[2] CUSHING, H. P., and R. RUEDEMANN, Geology of Saratoga Springs and Vicinity, *Bull. N. Y. State Museum*, 169, p. 145, 1914.

[3] WOODWORTH, J. B., *op. cit.*, p. 71. Reference is here made to the bibliography of the subject, especially to theories which would explain the valley by the action of bottom currents. Until recently the most complete study of the submerged gorge was that made by J. W. Spencer. For summary see, The Submarine Great Canyon of the Hudson River, *Am. Jour. Sci.* 4th series, vol. 19, pp. 1–15, 1905. A brief summary is given by J. F. Kemp, Buried Channels beneath the Hudson and Its Tributaries, *Amer. Jour. Sci.*, 4th ser., vol. 26, pp. 301–323, 1907. Volume 47 of the *Bull. Geol. Soc. Amer.* contains papers by Henry C. Stetson, also F. P. Shepard and G. V. Cohee, which give some more recent data.

deep gorge.[1] Tributaries, if not left "hanging," succeeded in cutting down to the level of the main stream only near their mouths.

Glaciation.—The work of continental ice in this section is mainly that of the last or Wisconsin stage or stages. This was a vigorous ice sheet during its advance. It polished the rocks of Shawangunk Mountain and helped to excavate its lake basins.[2] At the entrance to the Highlands it seems to have deepened the gorge by gouging, perhaps several hundred feet. It sent tongues of ice west and even northwest into the Catskills.

Concerning the manner of melting and disappearance, the evidence is less simple. Much industry and ingenuity has been devoted to correlating patches of moraine in order to outline successive positions of a retreating front. The assumption in such efforts has been that there always was a "front" to which the ice continued to advance from the north, and beyond which on the south there was no ice except local stagnant blocks. Glacial ice was always thought of as moving, even while dwindling away. In recent years there is a tendency to minimize the movement of the margin of the shrinking ice sheet. The extreme of this tendency is represented by the assumption that the whole sheet (within this area) died in its tracks.[3] On this assumption the ice would disappear, not by shrinkage on the south alone, but by thinning everywhere, dividing into patches which melted away on all sides, surviving longest where thickest. On either hypothesis ice would last longest in the axis of the valley, and deposits (largely water-laid) would accumulate on the sides, often in a series of terraces descending toward the axis with the shrinking of the ice. Where the edge was sufficiently ragged, or

[1] Effects of drainage disturbances during the advance of the ice are little known as compared with similar effects during its retreat, though they must be comparable in kind and even in magnitude. For example, if the St. Lawrence waters used the Mohawk outlet during the ice advance, they may have helped in the rapid cutting of the Hudson gorge.

[2] DARTON, *op. cit.*, p. 33.

[3] This is essentially the conclusion reached by John H. Cook (The Disappearance of the Last Glacial Ice Sheet from Eastern New York, *Bull. N. Y. State Museum*, 251, pp. 158–176, 1924). Cook (p. 160) doubts whether there is a single good recessional front in the whole Hudson-Champlain Valley. On p. 386 of this book will be found a statement of the effects of stagnant ice in accordance with more recent research.

small blocks sufficiently numerous, the terraces would consist of kames. Lakes held temporarily by ice, or less temporarily by drift, would be present on either hypothesis and would receive clay and other sediments. Such lakes would be at different altitudes.

All of these things are present and many of them are consistent with either living or stagnant ice. It is only when one comes to correlate the several fragments of moraine, terrace, or lake deposit, that the theory of a single moving glacier with a retreating front is badly strained. It is safe to say that stagnant ice was an important factor, whether the hypothesis be pressed to include the whole area throughout the whole time of ice decay, or whether it be applied mainly to a margin of limited width (*cf.* New England, page 386). Features of glacial erosion and deposition produced by moving ice disposed in lobes, and including those made by glacial waters, are intricately mixed with, or overlain by, others which could only have been made when the ice had ceased to move and resolved itself into disconnected and dwindling fragments. As such remnants were probably numerous, often blocking the natural drainage ways and vanishing one by one, the depicting of the constantly changing drainage system, with its frequent changes of local base level, is an exceedingly complicated task.

Presumably, so long as the sheet covered the Green and Adirondack mountains, the push from the north was transmitted southward. But when melting left the mountains bare, the narrow tongue of ice in the Champlain Valley may well have been incapable of transmitting the pressure.

Post glacial Waters.—As the ice melted back from the latitude of New Jersey, the sea filled the newly evacuated valley, the land being at that time somewhat lower than at present. How far north the sea followed the retreating ice is a question still in dispute. Fairchild[1] pictures the newly deglaciated valley as lying below sea level throughout its length from New York harbor to the Gulf of St. Lawrence and therefore occupied by a marine strait. Some others[2] restrict the invading sea to the ends of the long depression, *i.e.*, to the area below the Highlands

---

[1] FAIRCHILD, H. L., *Bull. N. Y. State Museum*, 209–210, 1918. Note map, Pl. 3.

[2] STOLLER, J. H., *Bull. Geol. Soc. Amer.*, vol. 30, p. 420, 1919.

at the south and to the Champlain basin at the north.   On this hypothesis the intervening valley was for a time occupied by the fresh water of Lake Albany, assumed to have been impounded by ice or drift in the gorge in the Highlands, or by a "higher stand of the land on the south."[1]   Another lake must have formed in the Champlain basin, discharging southward into Lake Albany (with or without a drop in level) so long as ice blocked the outlet to the St. Lawrence.

Either of the above hypotheses may be modified by assuming the ice to have become stagnant and to have vanished in the manner described above.   This would provide for local lakes at diverse altitudes to be followed by the unifying of all into a single body of water which received the swollen waters of the Mohawk River.   That there were such earlier and smaller lakes is clear.   Whether the ultimate water body was lake or strait would make little difference in existing land forms and must be left to historical geology.

Throughout much of the distance, strand lines were too weakly developed, and are too poorly preserved, to afford exact data for correlation.   Altitudes of shores are inferred mainly from deltas.   The one fact definitely known is that north of Troy all former shores slope south, indicating that the land at the north has been tilted up.   From other evidence it is known that similar tilting extended to the southern end of the section, but data are too vague for exact correlation.

The maximum altitude of the former water surface in the Champlain basin on the Canadian boundary is more than 700 feet.[2]   If the surface indicated was that of the sea, the tilting between northern Vermont and New York City has been about 2½ feet per mile.   On the hypothesis of a postglacial lake in the Champlain basin, the highest marine level may be between 300 and 400 feet.[3]   Woodworth mentions marine fossils up to 350 feet.

MIDDLE SECTION

The best known and in some ways most typical part of the Ridge and Valley province is in the states of Pennsylvania,

---

[1] WOODWORTH, *op. cit.*, p. 177.

[2] FAIRCHILD, *loc. cit.*

[3] WOODWORTH, *op. cit.*, p. 239.

Maryland, and the Virginias. For convenience of treatment the northeastern limit of this Middle section is placed at the limit of glaciation; for practical purposes the Delaware River (page 204). The southwestern limit is at the divide between the New and Tennessee rivers. The master streams of the Middle section are thus seen to be transverse while those of the other sections are longitudinal. Trellised drainage patterns are therefore most conspicuous in the Middle section, though not wholly wanting in the others. Another distinctive feature of this section throughout its length is the comparative absence of mountain ridges on its southeastern margin, *i.e.*, in a belt comprising a quarter to a third of the area and commonly known as the Great Valley.[1]

BOUNDARY ON THE SOUTHEAST

Between the Delaware and Schuylkill rivers the floor of the Great Valley, 600 to 700 feet high, abuts against the steep slopes of the Reading Prong. The lowland is underlain by Cambrian and Ordovician limestones and shale, both being directly in contact with the granitic rocks at many places. For most of the distance Lower Cambrian quartzite forms the flank of the range, dipping northward toward the Great Valley.[2] An outlying portion of the Reading Prong begins 8 miles west of the Schuylkill River and extends west for another 8 miles. Except for this outlier, mountains are wanting on the province boundary from the Schuylkill to a point 10 miles west of the Susquehanna, but the edge of the Triassic rocks in the Piedmont is exceptionally high (page 153) and makes the boundary distinct.

From the Susquehanna southwestward to the end of the section (and indeed to the end of the province) the steeply dipping quartzites near the base of the Cambrian continue to be part of the mountain province, while the overlying limestones in the syncline to the west, though folded in conformity with the quartzite where not separated by overthrusting, have been

[1] "Great Valley" is a popular, not a technical, term. It may be used to include most of the northern and southern sections of the province.

[2] Geologic relations in this part of the boundary are best explained by George W. Stose and Anna I. Jonas in *Bull. Geol. Soc. Amer.*, vol. 46, pp. 757–779, 1935.

reduced to lowlands.   Some of this "lowland" will be seen later to have been uplifted more than 2000 feet.

BOUNDARY ON THE NORTH AND WEST[1]

East of the Susquehanna River.—In eastern Pennsylvania the folded belt, which in central Pennsylvania is 80 miles wide, comes to an end with notable abruptness by the pitching of the folds, except for a narrow zone on the southeastern side, which continues into New Jersey and New York (see Pl. 1).   The deep synclines of the anthracite region become shallower and flatter toward the northeast and give way to the gently synclinal Pocono Plateau (p. 307).   The middle part of this plateau is protected by horizontal Catskill and Pocono sandstones which, at its western edge, dip beneath the valleys of the folded belt. These dip slopes might be expected to be somewhat less steep than the scarp slopes which bound the plateau province elsewhere. In some places this is true, but the railroads ascending to the plateau eastward from Wilkes-Barre and Scranton find the slope sufficiently impressive.   The long synclinal Wyoming Valley (northern anthracite basin) extends like an index finger 40 miles beyond its companion valleys, bounded by steep dip slopes, clearly delimited from the surrounding plateau, and ending in canoe form.

Boundary from the Susquehanna to the Potomac.—Along the boundary west of the Wyoming Valley the rocks of the Ridge and Valley province dip toward the plateau which, accordingly, is limited by a south- or southeast-facing escarpment.   From north central to southern Pennsylvania this escarpment shows two perfectly clear steps.   The surface of the lower step, or terrace, generally not more than 3 miles wide, is on the Devonian sandstones.   Its altitude is 1000 to 1100 feet in the latitude of Williamsport and becomes gradually greater toward the southwest.   It is 1600 to 1800 feet high at Altoona, sloping toward the valley, and maintains this height almost to Maryland, where it narrows and becomes negligible.   The higher escarpment is made by the Pocono in north central Pennsylvania, where its general level is 2200 to 2300 feet.   The altitude gradually increases to 2700 or

[1] More detailed descriptions of parts of this boundary are given in a paper by the author "Physiographic Divisions of the United States," 3d ed., *Ann. Assoc. Amer. Geog.*, vol. 18, pp. 297–300, 1928.

2800 feet in southern Pennsylvania where the crest is made by the Pottsville.

With remarkable continuity the foot of this double escarpment is followed by a well-developed, though narrow, valley on the Helderberg limestone. The Pennsylvania Railroad follows it for more than 100 miles in central Pennsylvania, as the Baltimore and Ohio Railroad does farther south.

Within the distance already covered in this description, as in all the distance to be covered, are certain offsets in the course of the major escarpment. By one such offset of 10 miles, a little north of Mason and Dixon's line, the province boundary

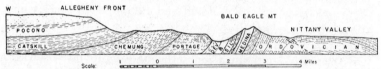

Fig. 63.—Section across the Allegheny Front in central Pennsylvania, showing two escarpments. Vertical scale twice the horizontal.

jogs to the east from the bold escarpment of the Allegheny Front west of Altoona, Pa., to that of Dans Mountain behind Cumberland, Md. Such jogs occur where an anticlinal valley not quite parallel to the province boundary runs off, splinterlike, from the valley province into the plateau.[1] The anticlinal valley behind Lookout Mountain (page 335) affords a familiar instance.

Boundary South of the Potomac River.—South of the Potomac the edge of the Carboniferous system continues to be marked by the escarpment of Dans Mountain, here resuming the name Allegheny Front, overlooking an anticlinal valley on older and weaker rocks. South of the 39th parallel the boundary jogs westward 10 miles to Back Allegheny Mountain, west of the Greenbrier Valley, in exactly the same manner as it jogged to the east in Pennsylvania.

For 200 miles from the offset in latitude 39° the province boundary fails to justify the description applied to it elsewhere. If the line be drawn at the edge of the Lower Carboniferous (Mississippian) rocks, it is true that the country northwest of it is almost uniformly a plateau on horizontal or only mildly folded beds, while on the other side are parallel ridges characteristic of eroded folds. But the ridges here are crowded so close to the

[1] These relations are clear on the geologic map of the United States (1932).

plateau escarpment that, instead of overlooking a lowland, it merely forms one side of a mountain valley. Only from an exceptionally favorable point of observation can it be seen to separate two distinct types of landscape.

After crossing the Greenbrier (lat. about 37°45′), where that stream turns westward into the plateau, the boundary is still more anomalous. Here, for many miles, the ridges of the Ridge and Valley province are higher than the plateau. Between them are, generally, only sharp narrow valleys. Where wider intervening plains occur, either well preserved or dissected, they may be as high as the plateau level or even higher.[1]   This condition

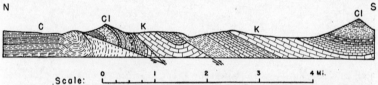

Scale:

Fig. 64.—Section in southern Virginia, showing the complicated structure of the Ridge and Valley province near the plateau boundary, which appears at the left. *K*, Knox dolomite (Cambrian and Ordovician); *Cl*, Clinch sandstone (Silurian); *C*, Carboniferous. Usually the Carboniferous makes the plateau, the Clinch sandstone makes high ridges, the harder beds in the Knox makes low ridges, and the softer beds underlie lowlands. The plateau has here no "front." (*U. S. Geol. Survey, Tazewell folio.*)

persists to the end of the Middle section, and indeed beyond it until the Clinch and Powell rivers, headwaters of the Tennessee, begin to develop broad valley floors lower than the plateau on the west.

The Delaware-Susquehanna Segment

Structure.—The Susquehanna River is approximately the western boundary of a segment of this province which has characteristics of its own both structurally and topographically. It is within this short stretch that the width of the folded belt is reduced from 80 miles at the west to one fifth of that amount at the east. Folds at such a place may well be expected to be not only closely compressed but complex in form. All of the folds here are relatively short. Anticlinal axes traced from the west converge and pitch eastward near the Susquehanna. Concurrently the intervening synclinal axes descend to great depths

[1] See topographic map of the Pocahontas quadrangle, U. S. Geol. Survey, folio No. 26; also geologic and topographic sections in the same folio.

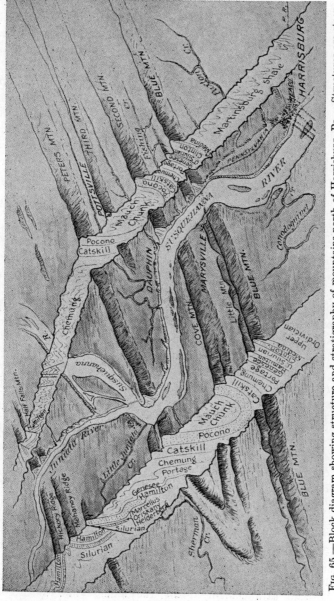

FIG. 65.—Block diagram showing structure and stratigraphy of mountains north of Harrisburg, Pa. Structures are steepened by exaggeration of the vertical dimension. Total width about 12 miles. (*XVI Internat. Geol. Congress, Guidebook.*)

in the anthracite basins and again rise and emerge on the border of the Pocono Plateau.   The dominant structural characteristics in this district are (*a*) the pitching of the folds, (*b*) their dying out at the northeast, and (*c*) the general structural depression. The depression divides itself into two parts, (1) a complex, composite, or corrugated basin, known as the southern anthracite basin, occupying the central part of the district, and (2) a simple independent syncline farther north, reaching far into the plateau province.   This last, the Wyoming syncline, or northern anthracite basin, is peculiar in being an isolated, deep, structural trough interrupting an otherwise fairly horizontal structure. Compression of the rocks of the plateau at more than one place has caused an upward wrinkle, but this downward wrinkle is almost unique.

Mountain Ridges.—Base-leveling of steep-pitching folds leaves the outcrop of any one stratum as a zigzag line or band. This is the most conspicuous feature of the geologic map of east-central Pennsylvania.   Subsequent erosion has left ridges of the same pattern.   The anthracite district of Pennsylvania is one of the world's best types of such topography.   With astonishing persistence and regularity the Pocono sandstone makes a mountain rim around the entire depressed area, following the contours of pitching folds and doubling back on its course in a series of pointed zigzags (Pl. 1).   Always there is a dip slope toward the interior of the area, and usually a scarp slope in the opposite direction, except on the side toward the Pocono Plateau. The name of the mountain changes at each sharp turn.   On the west side alone this crooked ridge bears 10 different names from Shickshinny Mountain on the north to Second Mountain near Harrisburg.

The behavior of the Pottsville sandstone (or conglomerate) is similar but, lying higher stratigraphically, it is preserved less widely.   Its ridges parallel those of the Pocono, sometimes only 2 or 3 miles away and separated by a valley or lowland on the Mauch Chunk shale.   The overlying coal measures occupy the centers of the basins, at places cut down to lowlands, elsewhere making broken uplands in which ridges and valleys have no clearly seen arrangement.   Only the highest and most continuous ridges have here been referred to.   A number of ridges on Devonian sandstone are similar except in size.

Southeast of the basins described are the older Paleozoic rocks, generally dipping northwestward beneath the basins, but there are also minor folds.   The great ridge maker here is the Tuscarora (Medina) sandstone which makes Blue Mountain,[1] which borders the Great Valley on the northwest and is practically continuous under various names from New York (Shawangunk Mountain, page 210) to Tennessee (Clinch Mountain, page 268).[2]

All statements concerning horizontality of crest and equality of altitude among ranges are relatively, not absolutely, true. The higher crests on the northern margin of this belt may average 1800 to 1900 feet at places remote from water gaps and from those sharp angles at which direction of the range changes. All crests decline toward transverse streams, present or past. The crests of all monoclinal ridges rise toward points of convergence, *i.e.*, toward the ends of pitching anticlines or synclines. At such points the altitude may approximate that of the adjacent plateau which, east of Wilkes-Barre, is not much below 2000 feet. Adjacent ridges may differ 100 or 200 feet, those of Pottsville

---

[1] Not to be confused with Blue Ridge, which is on the other side of the Great Valley. "Blue" is a very common name for mountains and hills which were first made familiar in distant views.

[2] The following column of rocks in the Ridge and Valley province in Pennsylvania and Virginia is highly generalized and incomplete but summarizes the essentials for physiographic purposes:

Mississippian
    Mauch Chunk shale
    Pocono sandstone and conglomerate
Devonian
    Catskill, Chemung, and other formations of shale and sandstone
    Hamilton and other formations, largely shale
    Onondaga limestone
    Oriskany sandstone
    Helderberg limestone
Silurian
    Clinton and higher formations of sandstone, shale, and limestone
    Tuscarora sandstone and conglomerate
Ordovician
    Martinsburg and other shales
    Trenton and other limestones
Cambrian
    Limestones and shales of Upper and Middle Cambrian
    Lower Cambrian quartzites and slates (Blue Ridge and New England
      provinces)

sandstone generally being a little higher than the Pocono, perhaps because they are nearer the center from which drainage radiates.

Ridges on the southern margin are a little lower, even the strong Tuscarora sandstone being everywhere below 1700 feet, and only 1300 to 1400 feet near the larger transverse streams.

The Lebanon Valley.—The smoothness, altitude, and extent of valley lowlands depend on the character of the rocks and their location with respect to drainage lines. Much the largest area at low levels is in the Great Valley, which is 10 to 20 miles wide. (Figs. 66 and 69 represent smaller valleys but show similar relations.) About one third of its area (one eighth to one half its width) on the southeast side is on limestone. Here the smooth surface undulates gently, dropping as low as 400 feet near the larger streams and rising to 500 feet or more between streams. The fine agricultural lowland around Lebanon and Allentown is of this character.

The remainder of the Great Valley is on the Ordovician shales or slates which overlie the limestone. The surface here is distinctly higher, the difference being 100 feet or more west of the Schuylkill and increasing eastward. The difference near the Lehigh River is more than 300 feet, the general level of the slate hills being 700 to 800 feet. This higher area is submaturely dissected by valleys 100 to 200 or 300 feet deep.

It is noteworthy that where the shale is unmetamorphosed its surface is only 100 feet above the limestone surface. The difference of 300 to 400 feet in altitude farther east is where the former shale is now slate, and where interbedded sandstones are thicker. Where the width of the folded belt is greatly contracted, compression was great and shale was metamorphosed to slate, as might well be expected. Some of the surface in this slate belt is decidedly hilly. Though imperfectly base-leveled, it represents the Harrisburg peneplain, while the lower surface on the limestone is commonly treated as a later peneplain, the Somerville. There is considerable difference of opinion with reference to the number of erosion cycles here represented. Obviously there has been at least one well-developed peneplain, indicated now by the horizon of the shale hilltops, a surface which transects dipping beds (see discussion on page 157).

Lowlands in and around the Anthracite Basins.—North of Blue Mountain the nearest resemblance to the limestone lowland of the Lebanon Valley is found near the Susquehanna. In the 50 miles from Sunbury to Harrisburg this river crosses six major ridges, besides passing the abrupt end of another. At all these crossings or water gaps, the mountain slopes rise steeply from the water's edge. Between ridges the river traverses well-developed lowlands which run east and west, some for 10 miles, some for 25 miles or more, until they narrow to a point between the zigzag ridges or disappear at some local divide.

The general level of the lowlands is 500 feet or more at Harrisburg and 800 feet or more at Sunbury where the West and North branches of the Susquehanna unite, but there is also at that place a restricted level at about 600 feet. As the river is incised at least 200 feet at Harrisburg and 450 feet at Sunbury, the submature dissection of the plains is readily understood. This dissection of the newer peneplain (one or more), along with some imperfections of development, are such as to make correlations somewhat uncertain. The question may be raised, whether the Harrisburg peneplain is represented by the 800-foot level around Sunbury or by the 600-foot level.[1] Probably there are fewer difficulties in the way of the former than of the latter. Traced upstream along the North Branch of the Susquehanna, the much dissected and sometimes questionable upper level rises to 1200 or 1300 feet at Pittston in the Wyoming Valley, where the North Branch enters from the plateau and turns to follow the valley. The 600-foot level at Sunbury is also said to be represented at Pittston by hills 700 to 800 feet high.[2] Nowhere does it extend far from the Susquehanna. This fact is adverse to correlating it with the Harrisburg peneplain which is believed to be widespread. Questions like the one here raised are numerous in this province.

[1] FRIDLEY, HARRY M., Identification of Erosion Surfaces in South-Central New York, *Jour. Geol.*, vol. 37, pp. 113–134, 1929. In this paper (p. 132) Fridley assigns the 600-foot level to the Harrisburg peneplain which Campbell correlates with the 800-foot level. VER STEEG, KARL, "Some Features of Appalachian Peneplains," Geol. Publishing Company, Des Moines, 1930. On p. 19, 2d paper, the Harrisburg peneplain upstream from Williamsport is given an altitude of 600 to 700 feet, although farther downstream in the Sunbury quadrangle, and farther from the river, this same peneplain is said to be 800 to 900 feet high. The latter agrees with Campbell's interpretation.

[2] FRIDLEY, *op. cit.*, p. 133.

CAMPBELL, *Bull. Geol. Soc. Amer.*, vol. 14, p. 291, 1903.

While, in general, the strike ridges, both major and minor, are well defined, the intervening belts on weaker rock have a great variety of aspect, ranging from well-developed lowlands to rough surfaces 1700 feet or more in height, perhaps never well peneplaned, and now dissected by valleys 400 to 500 feet deep.

The Susquehanna-Potomac Segment

Typical Character.—The features which give character to the Ridge and Valley province are best displayed between the Susquehanna and James rivers. Here is the nearest approximation to that regular repetition of similar folds on which the typical topography depends. Here the mountain ridges are most nearly parallel, most even-crested, and most continuous. Here, also, is the most frequent alternation of ridges and valley lowlands. As in other parts of the section, the folding is in places complicated by pitching, forking, and dying out of folds, and even by thrust faulting. Yet the "even crests" are not always even, and some of the smaller valley floors are hard to find. The following description applies to the area between the Susquehanna and Potomac Rivers:

Structure.—The structure of the folded belt in this segment is dominated by anticlines. In this respect it is in contrast with the segment east of the Susquehanna where the deep synclinal anthracite basins are the main features. The one extensive structural depression in this segment is near the middle. It is marked on the geologic map by the presence of coal measures on Broadtop Mountain southeast of Altoona. Two major axes of uplift are made evident by the appearance at the surface of lower Ordovician limestones. The effect of the first is seen in the Great Valley, whose rocks were borne upward on the flank of the rising anticlinorium which culminated in the Blue Ridge and Catoctin belt. The other axis lies near the northwestern boundary where the same ancient limestones are extensively exposed in lowlands. Between these parallel upfolds a broad corrugated belt was less elevated, Broadtop Mountain being relatively depressed.

Nittany Valley.—The larger topographic features of this segment can best be described in their relations to the major structural features, beginning with the long anticline or chain of anticlines near the plateau border. All the larger valleys of the series stand out on the geologic map as belts or patches of

FIG. 66.—View toward the southeast from Nittany Mountain across a branch of Nittany Valley (Harrisburg peneplain at about 1300 feet) to Egg Hill and the Seven Mountains (Schooley peneplain at 1800 to 2400 feet). The valley of Sinking Creek, entrenched 160 feet in the lowland, is overlooked. (*Photograph, Pennsylvania Department of Highways.*)

Ordovician limestone, the enclosing mountain ridges as strips of Silurian sandstone, the two being separated by a narrow zone of Ordovician shales which outcrop in the escarpments below the strong sandstone. Foremost among the valleys is the Nittany (Fig. 66), stretching parallel to the plateau front from a point south of Lock Haven to a point east of Altoona, a distance of 75 miles, with a width of 1 or 2 to 10 miles. Its floor is by no means flat, though much of it still has small relief, even though streams have entrenched themselves 300 feet or more. There are also subordinate ridges. The plain is 1300 feet high near its hydrographic center south of Bellefonte, but it declines toward, and with, the larger streams. No broad area is below 1100 feet. Except the Juniata, which crosses the southwestern end, the streams in the valley are mainly longitudinal, but they enter and leave by water gaps, indicating a complex erosion history.

The valley fingers out toward the northeast, splitting on Nittany and other synclinal mountains. Beyond the ends of these fingers are isolated coves, limestone-floored amphitheaters quite surrounded by sandstone mountains. These coves represent local humps in the anticlinal chain. Mosquito Valley near Williamsport, only 2 miles long but 700 feet deep, is a remarkable example, as is also the larger Nippenose Valley west of it,[1] with its floor perforated with sinkholes (*cf.* Burke Garden, illustrated on p. 254).

Traced toward the southwest, the Nittany trough splits on the synclinal Brush Mountain east of Altoona, sending one fork to the southwest which ends in Sinking Valley, where streams disappear in the limestone floor at an altitude of 1200 feet. The other fork continues southward and connects with Morrison Cove south of Hollidaysburg. This cove is similar in every way to Nittany Valley, most of its surface being between 1300 and 1500 feet high. South of Morrison Cove and north of the 40th parallel the anticlinal valley is interrupted by the sagging of the protecting sandstone to so low a level that it was not breached when the anticline elsewhere was unroofed. Friends Cove farther south is cut out on another dome along the same anticlinal axis.[2]

---

[1] See Williamsport, Pa., topographic sheet of the U. S. Geol. Survey. The topography and drainage of these valleys shown on this map are remarkable.

[2] All of these features are shown on Pl. 2, but comparison with the geologic map is essential to their proper understanding.

Mountains around the Nittany Valley.—Throughout this long anticlinal chain the denuded limestone is overlain by shale and, above it, by the strong Tuscarora sandstone, the latter always forming mountain ridges. Generally, on both sides of the valley, this ridge is monoclinal, presenting toward the valley a nearly straight scarp slope, made steep by the wasting of the underlying shale. Where the anticline divides into fingers, as at the northeast, the strong sandstone may make a synclinal range or, still farther to the northeast, two monoclinal ranges with a synclinal valley between. Such ranges form an east-west belt 20 miles wide south of the Susquehanna where it flows east, dying out before the river turns south. The forking of the anticlinal zone at the south end is like that at the north

The height of the ridges for long stretches on the sides of the Nittany Valley, where the folding is simple, is not much below 1800 feet or much above 2100 feet. Where pitching folds complicate the structure, altitudes are always greater. At the sharp angular turns and intersections thus produced from Altoona southward, altitudes rise to 2500 or even to 2750 feet. At the branching north end 2300 feet is about the limit.

Bald Eagle Mountain on the northwest side of Nittany Valley is remarkable for its straight and simple form and uniform height (1700 to 1800 ft.) for the 140 miles from Altoona to the bend of the Susquehanna east of Williamsport. Even more remarkable is the strike valley between it and the plateau (Fig. 63). Here the narrow outcrop of the Helderberg limestone (with a little of the shale above) forms a straight unbroken valley lowland, even where less than ¼ mile wide. The northeast-flowing Bald Eagle Creek follows it 60 miles until it enters the Susquehanna, which continues the same course. Farther south the valley is crossed by two divides between headwaters of the Juniata, but the divides rise imperceptibly and are no higher than the floor of the nearby Nittany Valley. At this place the floors of the Bald Eagle and Nittany valleys would be thought to represent the same peneplain, yet toward the northeast the floor of the former, following the strike of weak rocks, steadily descends until near Lock Haven it is 500 feet lower than that of the Nittany Valley which must be drained through water gaps in the Bald Eagle range. It is plain that among these ranges, smooth lowlands produced in the same cycle may have very different levels, the differences being determined by local conditions which favor or hinder streams in their courses.   Northwest of the Bald Eagle Valley the dip flattens and the lower bench of the plateau province appears.

Kishacoquillas Valley.—Parallel to the Nittany Valley and 20 miles to the southeast is the Kishacoquillas Valley,[1] carved out on the crest of the most important anticline between the Nittany and Great valleys.   Except for its smaller size and lower level, it is so like the Nittany Valley in its geology, topography, and history that description is unnecessary.   Its undulating limestone floor, 30 miles long and a tenth as wide, is 800 to 900 feet high, at places pitted with sinkholes.   The transverse Honey Creek ignores its existence, as the transverse Juniata River ignores the mountains to the southwest, but longitudinal creeks conform rigorously to the geologic structure.

The monoclinal mountains on either side of this anticline, scarping inward toward the valley, are as typical as any mountains of the province.   The crests are generally between 1900 and 2100 feet, the highest altitudes, here as elsewhere, being reserved for the ends of the pitching anticline where the two monoclinal ranges unite into one.   The 25-mile-long anticlinal Jacks Mountain at the south end is formed in this way.   Where crossed in Jacks Narrows by the Juniata at a level of 550 feet, the crest rises to 2350 feet.

The Kishacoquillas anticline terminates at the northeast in three pitching prongs, each anticline marked by its axial valley and each valley by its longitudinal stream.   In the intervening synclines the Tuscarora sandstone makes ranges trending toward the Susquehanna but ending where the continued pitch carries the strong sandstone to greater depths.

The Broadtop Syncline.—A broad syncline intervenes between the two main anticlinal axes described above.[2]   It is broadest, deepest, and least folded in the latitude of Morrison Cove, *i.e.*, 10 to 15 miles north of the 40th parallel.   Between that cove and the south end of Jacks Mountain a belt 10 miles wide was almost

[1] For description see Bailey Willis, "The Northern Appalachians," *Nat. Geog. Soc. Mon.* 6, p. 178, American Book Company, New York, 1895.

[2] An excellent section is shown on the Geologic Map of Pennsylvania (1931).

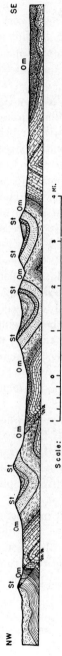

Scale:

Fig. 67.—Section in the Ridge and Valley province in Southern Pennsylvania showing monoclinal mountains. *St,* Tuscarora (Silurian) sandstone; *Om,* Martinsburg (Ordovician) shale. The section shows less than one third of the mountain belt and more than one third of the Great Valley at the right. The highest ridge, near the left, is Tuscarora Mountain. (*U. S. Geol. Survey folio No. 170 gives this and other sections with details of formations.*)

Scale:

Fig. 68.—Section in the Ridge and Valley province near the Potomac River showing synclinal mountains (Town and Sideling) and an anticlinal mountain (Cacapon). *CP,* Pocono (Mississippian) sandstone; *St,* Tuscarora (Silurian) sandstone. All other formations are relatively soft Devonian. (*U. S. Geol. Survey folio No. 179 gives this and other sections with details of formations.*)

as much depressed as the anthracite basins and has suffered very little folding. The Allegheny coal measures are here preserved below the summit peneplain. The Pottsville sandstone in the bottom of the syncline now covers and protects a plateau called Broadtop Mountain, having an elevation of about 2000 feet and bounded on all sides by outward-facing escarpments. From both eastern and western edges of this plateau the view is across valleys on Devonian shales to even mountain crests on Silurian sandstone.

The Broadtop syncline may be traced northeastward between the rims of Nittany and Kishacoquillas valleys. As the rocks are not closely folded and no strong ridge-making strata come to the surface, the topography within a belt 15 miles wide is more that of a dissected plateau than that of mountain ranges. Farther to the northeast, however, where the Nittany and Kishacoquillas anticlines come nearer together, the intervening syncline is less deep and is closely corrugated. Repeated folds here raised the ridge-making Silurian sandstones to the level at which they were truncated by the Schooley peneplain. This is the district of the Seven Mountains. All of the seven are made by Silurian sandstone, which is characteristically double in Pennsylvania. In most areas the lower division may be treated as subordinate or may be neglected, but in this vicinity both divisions are mountain makers.

Southward from Broadtop Mountain the broad syncline becomes corrugated and less deep. The main continuation is found in two long synclinal mountains, Sideling Mountain and Town Hill, reaching to the Potomac (Fig. 69).

Ridges of the Eastern Half.—Between the Kishacoquillas anticline and the Broadtop syncline on the northwest and the Great Valley on the southeast is a succession of high and low ridges separated by valleys in which well-developed lowlands are rare. The higher ridges are made by the Tuscarora sandstone and are anticlinal, synclinal, or monoclinal, according to the relative position of the strong stratum and the summit peneplain. Among these ranges is Tuscarora Mountain which, in Pennsylvania, gives its name to the strongest Silurian sandstone (Medina). Its even summit stretches 100 miles from the Juniata almost to the Potomac. Blue Mountain at the west edge of the Great Valley is continuous under various names from

FIG. 69.—View toward the west from Tuscarora Mountain over Cove Valley and McConnellsburg (Harrisburg peneplain at 940 feet) to Sideling Mountain (Schooley peneplain at 2100 to 2400 feet.) *(Photograph, Pennsylvania Department of Highways.)*

New York to southern Pennsylvania, though not without some zigzags caused by minor folds *en echelon.*

On all these higher ridges, altitudes from 1800 to 2100 feet are most common, except in the U-shape folds in the Shippensburg quadrangle. Greater altitudes here are in accordance with principles already stated. Among the lower ridges, notably on the Oriskany (Devonian) sandstone, altitudes of 1000 to 1100 feet are so common as to give some plausibility to the hypothesis that these crests are related to a later base level.[1]

Valley floors in this district are poorly developed or badly dissected. Among all the crowded ridges there is but one lowland which resembles the well-developed valley floors already described. This is an elliptical valley whose center is near McConnellsburg, 10 miles north of the Maryland boundary (Fig. 69). It is a miniature of the Kishacoquillas Valley with floor of Ordovician limestone 900 feet high and very much resembling the coves mentioned above.

Cumberland and Hagerstown Valleys.—Between the Susquehanna and Potomac Rivers the Great Valley takes its local names from Cumberland County in Pennsylvania and from the city of Hagerstown in Maryland. The contrast between the limestone belt and the shale belt in the Lebanon Valley (page 234) continues westward into the Cumberland Valley. Where the two are adjacent the latter (on the west side) is generally higher and more dissected, yet strangely enough, followed by the main streams. The same involved meandering seen in Conodoguinet Creek near Harrisburg is noted again in the Potomac and its tributary the Conococheague. Near these streams the valley peneplain must have been very close to its base level.

Near the Potomac there is not much difference in the levels on shale and limestone. There is indeed a considerable area near the river at approximately 500 feet, but it would be difficult to delimit this area from the valley floor elsewhere whose elevation, away from major streams, is generally between 600 and 800 feet. Undissected remnants of what must have been a very good peneplain are found near the 40th parallel at a height of 750 feet.[2]

---

[1] A comparison of the Millerstown and New Bloomfield topographic sheets with the geologic map of Pennsylvania will be found instructive.

[2] STOSE, GEO. W., Mercersburg-Chambersburg folio (No. 170), U. S. Geol. Survey, 1909. CAMPBELL, M. R., Chambersburg (Harrisburg)

It slopes gently toward the major streams and apparently merges with what is generally regarded as Somerville peneplain in the Potomac basin.[1]

MIDDLE SECTION IN VIRGINIA

Structure.—No abrupt change in the character of the Ridge and Valley province is noted in crossing the Potomac. As far south as the James River, folding is even more regular than in Pennsylvania, *i.e.*, the several folds are more nearly of uniform size and shape. There are no great dominating folds like the Nittany anticline or the Broadtop syncline, though a shallow extension of the latter, marked by synclinal mountains, may be traced southward for 150 miles. The Lower Ordovician limestones barely show at the surface except in the Great Valley; and the Pennsylvanian coal measures were nowhere depressed enough to escape destruction in the Schooley cycle. A few resistant formations occur and recur in anticlinal, synclinal, and monoclinal ridges from side to side of the province.[2]

A gradual change in structure which may be traced from New York to Alabama[3] begins to be noticeable in central Virginia. Toward the south the folds become more closely compressed and then overturned toward the northwest. Thrust faults make their appearance even in Pennsylvania, increasing in frequency toward the south, until in southwestern Virginia it is the rule rather than the exception that an anticline should be broken by

---

Peneplain in the Piedmont of Maryland and Pennsylvania, *Bull. Geol. Soc. Amer.*, vol. 44, pp. 553–573, 1933. Campbell designates this locality as the type for his "Chambersburg peneplain" which he had formerly called the "Harrisburg peneplain" (*Bull. Geol. Soc. Amer.*, vol. 14, 1903). The name Harrisburg is retained in this book, and the surface so named is regarded as having a gentle residual slope.

[1] CLARK, WM. B., E. B. MATTHEWS, and others, *Maryland Geol. Survey*, vol. 6, p. 89, 1906.

[2] Neither the character nor the distribution of these mountains needs further classification or analysis. For details the reader is referred to two folios of the U. S. Geol. Survey, the Monterey (No. 61) and the Staunton (No. 14). Together, these cover almost the entire width of the province and give typical sections both structural and topographic. Guidebook No. 3 of the 16th International Geological Congress, "The Southern Appalachian Region," by Charles Butts, G. W. Stose, and Anna I. Jonas, contains valuable descriptions, both general and local.

[3] CAMPBELL, M. R., Pocahontas folio (No. 26), U. S. Geol. Survey, 1896.

thrusting.   Beyond the James River, the folded belt is reduced to half its width, but the number of ridges is not decreased.   This crowding expresses itself somewhat in steeper dips but still more in thrust faults.

Thrust faulting in this part of the province has peculiar physiographic significance.   Much of the eastern boundary of the Great Valley throughout its length is at the edge of resistant rocks which were overthrust toward the west and subsequently much eroded.   Some coves in Tennessee have already been described (page 175) as windows in the overthrust block.   Similar structures occur within the Great Valley itself where Cambrian limestone and shale have been pushed many miles over rocks as young as Carboniferous.   Later erosion has exposed these Carboniferous rocks in some localities and made coal mining possible, as in the vicinity of Pulaski.[1]

Mountains of the Shenandoah Valley and Its Continuation.— The Great Valley on the southeast is continuous though drained alternately in one direction and the other.   The Shenandoah River drains it northeastward for 130 miles, but the name Shenandoah Valley is applied as far south as the constriction at Buchanan (lat. 37°30′).[2]   Down to this point the valley differs little from its Pennsylvania phase.

Primarily this great limestone belt represents the northwest limb of the Blue Ridge-Catoctin anticlinorium, but for 150 miles its median line is marked by a syncline.   North of the 39th parallel, only Ordovician shales are preserved in the syncline and the topography is little affected by difference in rocks, but for the next 45 miles the strong Silurian sandstones were suf- ficiently depressed to be preserved when the summit peneplain was made.   This accounts for Massanutten Mountain, which is a complex synclinal mass, embracing both synclinal and monoclinal ridges.   Altitudes on the monoclines are generally below 2700 feet but they rise to 3000 feet where the ranges merge.

In the same manner, and made by the same rocks, the Short Hills and other groups of high hills or mountains occur just north of the James River and all but close the valley.   Again after an

[1] CAMPBELL, M. R., The Valley Coal Fields of Virginia, *Bull. Va. Geol. Survey*, 25, 1925.

[2] STOSE, G. W., and H. D. MISER, Manganese Deposits in Western Virginia, *Bull. Va. Geol. Survey*, 23, 1922.

interval of 20 miles, the same Silurian sandstone (called Clinch in the south) forms the mountain rim of a synclinal structure 25 miles long, preserving in its axis rocks as young as the Pocono, which makes an independent range. This mountain mass, just north of the Roanoke River and west of the city of that name, divides the Great Valley into two narrow strips.

Lowlands of the Shenandoah Valley and Its Continuation.— The floor of the Great Valley is a plain, eroded to various degrees, generally not beyond maturity. At most places where it has been dissected its nearly plane surface may be hypothetically restored by sighting over hilltops. The old surface at the horizon of the hilltops, generally called the "Tertiary peneplain," is here called the Harrisburg, or simply (following Stose) the valley-floor peneplain. Near the Potomac and the lower Shenandoah, the surface is so consistently lower that a new peneplain is assumed, generally correlated with the Somerville of New Jersey. Its altitude is 500 feet or a little more in the Great Valley and a little less on the inner margin of the Piedmont province.

The altitude of the Harrisburg peneplain[1] varies from 600 feet near the Potomac to 2000 feet on the Shenandoah-James divide, and to nearly 2500 feet on the New-Tennessee divide, unless the valley floor at that place be regarded as an older peneplain (page 270). Among the factors which determined these altitudes are: (1) The heights at which the several transverse master streams cross the Blue Ridge or otherwise leave the belt here considered, or rather, the heights at which they did leave in the Harrisburg cycle; in other words, the altitude of local base level at that time. (2) The distance from the master streams. (3) Subsequent deformation. The first two factors imply that the peneplain never was, even ideally, a level surface. In a very general way the parts that are now highest were high before the cycle was interrupted by uplift. However, with all possible allowance for residual altitudes, much of the present inequality must be charged to crustal movement.

In its 60 miles north of Massanutten Mountain the Great Valley is 20 miles wide. Its floor has a gradient of less than 2 feet

---

[1] KEITH, ARTHUR, Geology of the Catoctin Belt, U. S. Geol. Survey, 14th Ann. Rept., pt. 2, pp. 293–395, 1893. Pages 374–376 give Keith's interpretation of this surface. STOSE and MISER, op. cit., pp. 5–11. Excellent description of all parts of the Great Valley.

per mile, about that of the present leisurely meandering Shenandoah. A peneplain might develop with such a gradient. In the next 45 miles, in which the valley is divided by Massanutten Mountain, the plain on the south fork (east side) rises more than 500 feet to an altitude above 1200 feet. In the same interval the plain on the north fork (west side) rises from 800 feet to more than 1500 feet. The combined plain southwest of the mountain, again 20 miles wide and everywhere higher on its northwestern side, continues to rise for another 50 miles to the well-developed and well-preserved peneplain, having a maximum height of 2000 feet on the Shenandoah-James divide. Such a slope is inconsistent not only with the development of a peneplain but with its preservation, as may be seen by the entrenchment of streams, beginning in their lower courses. This slope is not uniform but is steepest opposite Massanutten Mountain. Keith locates an axis of uplift crossing that mountain near its middle and trending North 60° West.[1]

From the Shenandoah-James divide the peneplain descends in 25 miles to 1200 feet and remains approximately at that level for many miles among the several branches of the James River, where the plain is 10 to 12 miles wide and has already been trenched 300 to 400 feet and dissected near the river. The level rises to 1500 feet on the James-Roanoke divide south of Fincastle.

The synclinal mountains in the middle of the valley west of Roanoke leave only two narrow strips of plain to represent the Great Valley. The strip on the southeast, traversed by the Roanoke River, contains a noteworthy feature. Where the river leaves the province by Roanoke Gap at the city of Roanoke, the valley floor is at 1000 feet. It rises slowly upstream (southwest) to 1100 feet at Salem, and continues rising more rapidly to 1400 feet near the forks of the Roanoke. There the two branches of the river issue from 1000-foot gorges in an upland 2200 feet high, with a ruggedly dissected escarpment known as the Pedlar Hills.[2] The tops of these hills are flat, being carved from a

---

[1] KEITH, op. cit., p. 386.

[2] See Christianburg topographic sheet, U. S. Geol. Survey. The rugged escarpment called Pedlar Hills has played an important part in habitation. In colonial times the Great Valley was the main highway between the northern colonies and the Carolinas. Travel and migration passed out through Roanoke Gap because the valley farther south was closed by "mountains"

peneplain, discernible amid dissection, for many miles to the southwest in the basin of the New River. The 2-mile strip northwest of the mountains belongs to the same level. All of these features taken together suggest that the peneplain at the upper level was developed along tributaries of the New River at the same time that the lower level was developed along the Roanoke; that the summit of the escarpment was once the Roanoke-New divide;[1] and that uplift with tilting favorable to the Roanoke caused the headwaters of that river to invade the upper level. Another interpretation is offered on page 261.

The valley peneplain in the New River drainage basin, strikingly clear at places, as around Dublin, is traceable throughout a belt 15 miles wide for a distance of 60 miles, *i.e.*, to the New-Tennessee divide. Within this belt are some unreduced divides and small residual ranges. In the plain itself there are few areas 2 miles square in which later erosion has not produced a local relief of 200 to 400 feet. The well-developed but eroded limestone plain in its eastern half, traversed by the north-flowing New River, is generally not above 2200 feet. When traced westward, up the course of the New and its tributaries Cripple Creek and Reed Creek, the plain rises to 2500 feet, at which level it passes over into the Tennessee drainage basin. The greatest interruption of the levels given here is in the semimountainous area midway between Dublin and Wytheville, where the surface is on Carboniferous rocks exposed in a window, as explained on page 246. These resistant rocks make some small monoclinal ranges and, in addition, a considerable upland of plateau aspect several hundred feet above the limestone level and perhaps representing the older peneplain. It is along the New River south of

---

(the Pedlar Hills escarpment). Except for that barrier, migration might have reached the valley floor on the New River and passed by that route northwestward into the plateau and down the Kanawha to the Ohio. With the Pedlar Hills in the way, there was no feasible line of migration into the plateau between the Potomac headwaters and Cumberland Gap at the extreme southwestern corner of Virginia, a distance of 400 miles. The New River route would have been midway between, and might have led to the settlement of the Ohio Valley before that of central Kentucky.

[1] Stose, and Miser, *op. cit.*, p. 9. Cf. Wright, Frank J., The Older Appalachians of the South, *Jour. Sci. Lab. Denison Univ.*, vol. 26, p. 207, 1931.

these hard rocks that the valley peneplain is clearly continuous with the similar strips on Reed and Cripple Creeks.

Allegheny Ridges in the Middle Section.—Among the ridges in this section interest centers, first, in those crests or segments of crests which probably indicate the level of an upraised peneplain; second, in the development of valley floors, their relation to one another and to a newer cycle of peneplanation. Crests here are higher than farther north, perhaps in some cases less even and less indicative of a former level surface. In generalizing altitudes a range of 200 or 300 feet must be allowed even when, to a casual view, the horizontality is prominent.

The altitude of the plateau edge on the Allegheny Front is about 2600 feet near the Potomac and it rises steadily southward to 4000 feet before the province boundary jogs westward from the Allegheny Front to Back Allegheny Mountain just below the 39th parallel. Its highest horizontal stretch is at 4600 feet, 20 miles west of Monterey, Va. From that place it declines and the escarpment is lost.

This 4600-foot level around the monadnock Bald Knob (lat. 38°30′, long. 80°) may be regarded provisionally as representing the summit peneplain locally bulged up, since levels decline consistently to the north, south, and west.[1] Among the Allegheny ridges there is no such consistency, but a line drawn eastward from Bald Knob would cross four ridges at least 4000 feet high and indicating very roughly an eastward decline of the summit level. This line is essentially at the jog by which the Virginia-West Virginia boundary passes from Shenandoah Mountain to Allegheny Mountain. It also marks approximately the divide between the long straight strike streams flowing to the Potomac and the similar but shorter tributaries to the James. Shenandoah Mountain, the most easterly of these high ridges, is only 8 miles from the Great Valley.

There are other intervening crests lower than these. It is also true of the highest crests, assumed to represent the summit peneplain, that their altitudes change gradually from place to place. Of two parallel crests one may decline and the other not. The impressive fact here is not a universal agreement in height,

---

[1] WRIGHT, FRANK J., The Physiography of the Upper James River Basin in Virginia, *Bull. Va. Geol. Surv.*, 11, 1925; The Newer Appalachians of the South, *Bull. Denison Univ.*, vol. 34, pp. 1–105, 1934.

but a certain limit of height which is often reached but never surpassed except by hills which are plainly monadnocks.

Consistent altitudes east of Shenandoah Mountain drop to about 3000 feet on the ridges overlooking the Great Valley and on the highest part of Massanutten Mountain. Levels also decline northward, rarely exceeding 3000 feet beyond the 39th parallel or 2000 feet near the Potomac. The decline toward the south is similar. Northwest from Roanoke Gap the horizon is generally above 3000 feet and several ridges near the northwestern boundary are over 3500 feet high. In no very great area is the prevailing crest level below 3000 feet and it rises again several hundred feet as the New-Tennessee divide is approached. Altitudes of 3500 feet are common in the Pocahontas quadrangle, and the very uniform crest surrounding Burke Garden suggests a peneplain at or above 4000 feet (Fig. 71).

In this list of altitudes, monadnocks have been ignored and all altitudes mentioned are assumed to represent a former peneplain, or the nearest surviving approach to such a surface. Altitudes given here are so few in number, and locations so generalized, that the only impression left is that of a single dome with slopes in all directions. Such a picture is incomplete rather than incorrect. A detailed study, such as Wright made of the middle part of this area, would no doubt indicate that warping has been complex. Wright finds domes, which he believes to be centers of local uplift, on which the old peneplain surface now slopes as much as 80 to 100 feet per mile in extreme cases.[1] To what extent these local bulges may be residual is a question which at present cannot receive a final answer.

The horizon within the area here referred to is sufficiently level to make it evident that certain outstanding hills are monadnocks. Thus Great North Mountain on which the peneplain is at 3500 feet, bears Elliott Knob, 4473 feet high, overlooking the Great Valley west of Staunton. The word "knob" is a common local designation for such exceptionally high residual hills.

Some of the lower ridges are sufficiently level and accordant to suggest one or more peneplains of intermediate height.[2]

[1] WRIGHT, *op. cit.*, p. 18. See also his Pl. 1, Contour Map of the Restored Upland Peneplain.

[2] STOSE and MISER, *op. cit.*, p. 21; KEITH, A., Geology of the Catoctin

Probably this explanation is correct in the immediate vicinity of some trunk streams. How far such levels may have extended is at present unknown. Levels among these ridges do not fall neatly into categories. They range from the highest to the lowest, and diverse levels may be connected by continuous slopes. The levels of most crests bear some relation to the durability of the mass beneath, *i.e.*, to the hardness and thickness of the ridge-making stratum and the breadth of its outcrop as controlled by the angle of dip (page 199). No definite limit is yet known to the possible lowering of a ridge by erosion without valleys. Many of the ridges do show by their form that they have been lowered by erosion. To assume a peneplain at every level at which some striking accordance is noted implies a greater perfection of base-leveling than is here admitted; also less liability to later degradation without dissection than is here assumed.

Valley Floors between Ridges.—The valleys in the ridged belt are much like those in Pennsylvania, except for those on the larger anticlines like the Nittany and Kishacoquillas. Along the Potomac, on both sides, tributary valleys are wider than elsewhere because that stream has chosen its course between the ends of pitching folds. Few anticlines that cross the river are high enough to bring the Tuscarora sandstone to the surface, and few synclines are deep enough to bring down the Pocono. As most of the rocks crossed are Devonian there is opportunity here for a considerable development of lowlands on Devonian shales. Near the Potomac, lowlands exceed ridges in area by a considerable margin. The prevailing level of what may be called the valley floor among the eastern ridges is 700 to 800 feet, but this is again dissected by valleys 300 to 400 feet deep, and at places a newer peneplain appears at 600 feet.[1] The level of the floor rises in each succeeding valley toward the northwest and reaches 1100 to 1200 feet.

Belt, *U. S. Geol. Survey*, 14*th Ann. Rept.*, pt. 2, p. 387, 1893; CLARK, WM. B., E. B. MATTHEWS, and others, The Physical Features of Maryland, *Md. Geol. Survey*, vol. 6, p. 88, 1906; WRIGHT, The Newer Appalachians of the South, *loc. cit.*

[1] STOSE, G. W., and SWARTZ, C. K., Pawpaw-Hancock folio (No. 179), U. S. Geol. Survey, 1912. On p. 20 of this folio elevations of the different peneplains at different places are given.

Upstream, toward the southwest, all interridge lowlands contract in width and rise in level. Near the main transverse divide 100 miles from the Potomac, the valley of the South Fork of the Potomac is a 2-mile plain over 2000 feet high. Others west of it are still higher. A comparison of altitudes in these tributary valleys would shed little light on a general base level. Even though each valley may be continuously graded, the headward rise in each is dependent on the power of its own stream and the resistance of the rocks. Throughout the mountainous area

Fig. 70.—Cumberland, Maryland, and the water gap of Wills Creek in Wills Mountain. Altitude of mountain crest, 1620–1680 feet; of Cumberland, about 620 feet. (*Md. Geol. Survey.*)

the so-called Harrisburg or "Tertiary" peneplain is a system of graded valleys, largely under independent control and having little or no relation to ultimate base level. If all the altitudes in all these valleys were plotted on a single map, it would be impossible to deduce therefrom the amount of uplift at any one place since the close of the Harrisburg cycle.

In the drainage basins of the James and New rivers the ridges are closely crowded. The only graded surface closely related to that of the Great Valley is along the New River.[1] For a few miles on either side are remnants of a rolling surface 2100 to 2200 feet high, connecting that of the Great Valley with a similar

[1] See Dublin topographic sheet, U. S. Geol. Survey.

expanse in the plateau province. Farther west the same surface rises to nearly 2500 feet (page 249).

Occasional valleys are broadened at some local base level. The most stiking of these is Burke Garden, a typical cove close to the New-Tennessee divide in the Pocahontas quadrangle. Structurally it is an elliptical dome 10 miles long, in which the

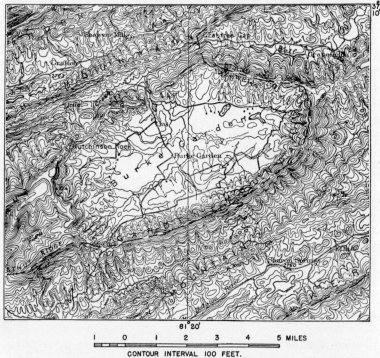

CONTOUR INTERVAL 100 FEET.

Fig. 71.—Topographic map of Burke Garden, a typical cove. The steepness of the rim is indicated by the zigzags in the road to the southeast. The gorge on the northwest is a typical water gap. The outcrop of the Clinch sandstone is indicated by the county boundary. (*U. S. Geol. Survey, Pocahontas topographic sheet.*)

strong Clinch sandstone is truncated a little above 4000 feet by the summit peneplain, exposing Cambrian and Ordovician limestones and shale. These weak rocks are now reduced to a local peneplain at 3100 to 3200 feet. All of the material was carried out through a canyon on the north side. So great is the contrast in durability between the sandstone in the rim and the limestone and shale in the center, that the latter were base-leveled over an area of 20 square miles while a barely passable gorge 1000 feet deep was being cut in the sandstone. Here, as in the coves of Pennsylvania and in many of the interridge valleys, solution is made evident by sinkholes.

HISTORY OF THE MIDDLE SECTION

Pre-Schooley History.—The materials and structures upon which erosion must work in this section were determined before and during the Appalachian revolution. The record since that time is confined to erosional forms and upwarping. As it is in the nature of erosion to erase its own records, none were preserved until nine tenths, perhaps nineteen twentieths, of the time had passed, that is, until the oldest recorded peneplain was finished. The ups and downs and cycles of erosion in this province in the several hundred million years between the Appalachian revolution and the end of the Schooley cycle may be to some small extent inferred from sediments laid down elsewhere. There is not the slightest reason to assume that the Schooley peneplain, or any other surviving in fragments, was the first in this long interval, or that it was unique in history.[1] It was indeed remarkable for its great extent and for its approach to perfection, more so than any later peneplain, but it is obvious that in a series of peneplains recorded in existing topography, none but the oldest could have been the most general.

Age of the Schooley Peneplain.—It was formerly customary to speak of the oldest surviving peneplain as Cretaceous.[2] This resulted primarily from the assumption that certain exposed land surfaces represent the same peneplain that underlies the coastal plain sediments. It was then strongly supported by showing

[1] BARRELL, J., Upper Devonian Delta of the Appalachian Geosyncline, *Amer. Jour. Sci.*, 4th ser., vol. 37, p. 103, 1914. In this and other places Barrell argues for the completion of erosion cycles in less time than has commonly been demanded. He rejects the assumption that the whole of Jurassic, Comanchean, and Cretaceous time was required in order to complete one cycle. While the estimate of the time required for a complete erosion cycle in terms of geologic periods has been progressively reduced, the relative reduction has been effected, not so much by speeding up the erosional process as by increasing the estimates of geologic time.

[2] W. M. Davis, in his Rivers and Valleys of Pennsylvania, *Nat. Geog. Mag.*, vol. 1, 1889, seems to have been the first to discuss the geologic age of this and the "Tertiary" peneplain. His conclusion was generally followed if not reached independently by others.

that the character of sediments laid down on the Atlantic border in Cretaceous times agrees with the assumption of a concurrent cycle of erosion on the land which furnished the sediments.[1]   A terminology based on this assumption came into general use, and in most of the literature down to the present, the summit peneplain is either named Cretaceous or assumed to be of that age.

Computations based on geologic measurements have made this hypothesis very improbable.[2]   Arguments against it are based on (1) the intersection, instead of continuity, of the exposed peneplain on the Piedmont and the buried peneplain beneath the Coastal Plain (page 126), (2) the great discrepancy between the relatively small amount of material eroded from the so-called Cretaceous peneplain since its making, and the great amount deposited in the coastal plain sediments in the same time and necessarily derived from the same area, (3) the vast amount of lowering necessary to cut down the Appalachian Folds to the level of the peneplain as compared with the trifling amount which the Allegheny ridges are assumed to have lost in elevation since that stage.[3]   As the prepeneplain loss may be 70 times as much as all later loss, it is argued that much the larger part of the available time must have been given to prepeneplain history and a relatively short time to post-peneplain erosion.   To these arguments might be added another, based on the absence of any remnant of a Cretaceous peneplain on strong rocks in the arid west, where an age even so great as Eocene is rarely asserted and the Pliocene seems to have been the greatest of the base-leveling periods, even on the strong rocks of the mountains.   No exact geologic date can yet be fixed for the Schooley peneplain, but it is doubtful that it was raised enough for erosion to begin cutting it away before the end of the Miocene.[4]

[1] HAYES, C. W., and M. R. CAMPBELL, Geomorphology of the Southern Appalachians, *Nat. Geog. Mag.*, vol. 6, pp. 63–126, 1894.

[2] SHAW, E. W., Ages of Peneplains of the Appalachian Province, *Bull. Geol. Soc. Amer.*, vol. 29, pp. 575–586, 1918.

[3] ASHLEY, GEO. H., Age of Appalachian Peneplains, *Bull. Geol. Soc. Amer.*, vol. 41, pp. 695–700, 1930; ref. to p. 698.

[4] Shaw, *op. cit.*, p. 586, thinks that no surface as old as Middle Tertiary has escaped "reduction and remodeling." *Cf.* BARRELL, *op. cit.*, p. 104, 1914; The Piedmont Terraces of the Northern Appalachians, *Am. Jour. Sci.*, 4th ser., vol. 49, p. 419, 1920.

This question of the geologic age of the oldest surviving peneplain has important physiographic bearings, for it involves the probability of earlier peneplains, a question which is vital in considering the problem of drainage. There may well have been a Cretaceous peneplain at the end of an erosion cycle which corresponded to the cycle of sedimentation on the Coastal Plain in Jurassic-Cretaceous time. The peneplain that is known to exist beneath the coastal plain sediments must of necessity be older than the sediments resting on it.

Reversal of Drainage.—It is agreed that the highland raised by the Appalachian revolution drained toward the interior, not toward the Atlantic. The master uplift was not far from the Blue Ridge.[1] The major streams were transverse and the New River still follows its course toward the interior. How the general drainage from the Delaware to the James was reversed has always been a major question in Appalachian physiography. If the region could be cut down to such flatness that running water stopped, it would be a simple matter to give it a new tilt to start drainage in the opposite direction. But such peneplains do not exist. So long as any slope at all remains, tilting must be very prompt to be effective. Rivers are very rarely so taken by surprise as to be turned back without a fight to save their old courses. Their method is to entrench themselves as soon as the uplift is felt. The difficulties in reversing drainage are not over even when peneplaning has been accomplished or even when tilting has once begun.

A hypothesis which gained some currency assumed that the "Cretaceous" peneplain became so flat, and rivers so sluggish, that alluvium was spread in a continuous plain, not necessarily universal but so extensive as to cover hard and soft rocks alike and thus to obscure divides.[2] On such a mantle it was assumed that slight tilting would effect a reversal of drainage. As already indicated, it is now known that the Schooley peneplain never had any such flatness. Even the still older peneplain buried by coastal plain sediments is not known to be so flat.

[1] KEITH, ARTHUR, Recently Deformed Overthrusts in the Appalachians, *Bull. Geol. Soc. Amer.*, vol. 39, p. 178, 1928.

[2] WILLIS, BAILEY, "The Northern Appalachians," Nat. Geog. Soc. Mon., vol. 1, No. 6, p. 190, Amer. Book Company Inc., New York, 1895.

A better conception of the manner in which moderate tilting may affect drainage is found in the slow migration of divides.[1] When streams are in headwater opposition, any tilt at all in the direction of one or the other adds power to the stream whose gradient is increased, enfeebles its opponent, and causes the divide to shift in the direction of the latter. A scholarly attempt to restore the original consequent drainage on the folds of Pennsylvania, and to trace the natural growth of tributaries and the migration of divides made necessary by later warping, was made by Davis[2] when the study of Appalachian cycles was in its infancy. It was concluded from this deductive study, or rather it was presupposed, that the drainage plan of Pennsylvania must have assumed roughly its present form during the cycle then designated as Jurassic-Cretaceous, *i.e.*, during the development of the peneplain indicated by the crests of the higher ridges.

Obviously the simplest way to reverse drainage on a peneplain is to submerge it beneath the sea in order to receive new sediments on which drainage will be superposed when uplift comes with a new tilt. That this hypothesis remained so long untried (or unsatisfactory when tried) was due largely to the assumption that the present summit peneplain was something unique in history. This carried with it the implication that if the drainage was superposed, it must have been by submerging the peneplain which is still in evidence. The main objection to this was the total lack of any remains of the superposed beds, but equally adverse morphologic evidence now appears. In the meantime a critical study of the drainage itself[3] has shown that present

---

[1] *Cf.* HAYES, C. W., and M. R. CAMPBELL, *Nat. Geog. Mag.*, vol. 6, p. 102, 1894.

[2] DAVIS, W. M., The Rivers and Valleys of Pennsylvania, *Nat. Geog. Mag.*, vol. 1, 1889; republished in "Geographical Essays," pp. 413–484, Ginn and Company, Boston, 1909. The enduring contribution of this classical paper is not so much in its primary thesis as in the illuminating exposition of the manner in which various types of stream patterns follow from structures on which the original consequent drainage was wholly different. Much of this discussion is just as applicable to the rivers of folded regions as it was believed to be 50 years ago. The hypothesis of superposition, now supported by many, does not do away with the significance of the extraordinary connection between structure and drainage in this province.

[3] JOHNSON, DOUGLAS, "Stream Sculpture on the Atlantic Slope," Columbia University Press, New York, 1931. The acceptance of Johnson's

features and records such as wind gaps, etc., are consistent with the superposition hypothesis.   The lack of stratigraphic evidence for such an event (remains of sediments) is rendered irrelevant by positive evidence that such superposition was not on the known summit peneplain but, of necessity, on an earlier one, now destroyed where not buried.   This older peneplain may well have been the one now preserved beneath the Coastal Plain. On this supposition Johnson has called it the Fall Zone peneplain.

A sinking of the continent brought the Fall Zone peneplain below the sea in time to receive Cretaceous sediments, at least in the Coastal Plain province.   According to the superposition hypothesis, this submergence and deposit of Cretaceous sediments extended inland across the folded belt.   When emergence occurred, the slope and drainage were seaward.

Adjustment in the Schooley Cycle.—Following the assumed superposition, uplift initiated the Schooley cycle.   Streams at the start ran fairly straight toward the sea over the new sedimentary cover.   When this was cut through, the streams were found crossing hard and soft outcrops almost at right angles. This they continued to do until strike tributaries were sufficiently developed to effect captures.   With captures began that system of rectangular turns so characteristic of Appalachian rivers. Longitudinal links alternate with transverse, so that the whole course of a river like the Potomac, within this province, becomes a series of large and small rectangular jogs.   The resulting trellised pattern is an effort at adjustment.   The development of such a pattern made good headway in the Schooley cycle, yet not so much that nothing remained to be done in the following cycle.

In the development of a peneplain the drainage pattern necessarily became fixed and divides ceased to migrate.   Drainage was fully adjusted to the structures offered *at that level*.   With uplift, and a new base level, cutting the structure lower down, a new adjustment was necessary.   Commonly used expressions, which imply that adjustment was incomplete in the one cycle merely because it began again in the next, are misleading.   There is no such thing as a final adjustment of drainage to structure unless

hypothesis of superposition is facilitated by Shaw's study on the age of the peneplain.

hard and soft rocks are separated by vertical surfaces. Otherwise all depends on the height at which the base level cuts the structure. With each change of base level the geologic map changes and adjustment begins again, though it may have been complete before. (*Cf.* Fig. 53, p. 197.)

Remarkable as the Schooley peneplain was, its perfection must not be overestimated. Streams were not left without gradient nor divides without slope. Vestiges of the peneplain where best developed indicate a relief of several hundred feet in 40 or 50 miles. All surfaces slope toward the larger existing streams, indicating that these were the master streams during the Schooley cycle and that superposition did not take place on the Schooley peneplain.[1] The peneplain on Blue Mountain is well over 1600 feet high between streams, but it declines gradually to 1350 near the Susquehanna. Similar observations are too abundant to need listing. Mountains at the ends of pitching folds are generally 200 to 400 feet higher than elsewhere, but it cannot be known now how much of this superior altitude is due to residual relief when the peneplain was made and how much to unequal reduction since its uplift. It may well be doubted that the ridges of Tuscarora sandstone, and some others, were ever so reduced that their slopes would not have been noticeable.

The Schooley peneplain was somewhat arched by uplift, the highest axis, in latitudes here considered, being near the Allegheny Front. In the latitude of New York the arching is less marked and in the southern states the greatest uplift was east of the folded belt.

Intermediate Partial Cycles.—The Schooley peneplain was elevated in a halting sort of way, hesitating long enough at some stages to allow large streams to reach their base levels and greatly widen their valleys. As some records of such halts, as in the Weverton cycle (page 168), are left on such strong rocks as quartzite, a rather extensive peneplain at that level may have developed on moderately weak rocks. Whatever its extent, this intermediate plain was largely destroyed in the Harrisburg cycle.

Harrisburg Cycle.—The Harrisburg cycle took only a small fraction of the time consumed in the Schooley cycle. This is plain from two facts: (1) It is limited to weak rocks or to the

[1] VER STEEG, cited on p. 199.

vicinity of streams.[1] (2) Its level rises upstream so much that only on large streams or lower courses can it be treated as a general peneplain whose base level was the sea. Elsewhere the base level was local, and it was different in each drainage basin. In other words, the altitude of most valley floors was a question of grade and gradient rather than of base level.

The outstanding example of this principle in the Ridge and Valley province is seen in the diverse elevations of the New and Roanoke basins (page 248). The customary correlation of the fine plain at 1200 feet around Fincastle in the Roanoke River basin and the similar one at 2200 feet around Dublin in the New River basin as parts of the same "Tertiary peneplain" rests on the assumption that the additional 1000 feet of altitude in the New River basin was no more than enough to afford the necessary gradient for the very long New-Kanawha-Ohio rivers, even on a peneplain. The distance to the sea by that route was at least 1200 miles, while the direct route from Roanoke Gap to the Atlantic was about 150 miles. A difference of 1000 feet would seem to be within reason.

On the other hand, it may be assumed that the higher of the two surfaces represents an older peneplain. If the factor of remoteness from the sea, by way of drainage lines, be used to explain why a peneplain was developed at a high level, it may also be used, and quite as aptly, to explain the preservation of such a surface, while that of adjacent areas, drained by more direct routes, is reduced to a newer peneplain. The possibility that the floor of the Great Valley in the New River basin may be an older peneplain has already been suggested in discussing the straths of the Blue Ridge province (page 190). It will be considered again in connection with the Southern section of the Ridge and Valley province (page 270).

Wind Gaps.—When the Schooley peneplain was uplifted, longitudinal streams renewed their headward growth, more captures occurred, and wind gaps were produced. As all of the wind gaps in the middle section of this province are cut below the Schooley peneplain, all of the captures that made them occurred since that cycle closed. As the depth of wind gaps is sometimes used in the reconstruction of physiographic history, some atten-

[1] For the presence of the Harrisburg peneplain on the strong rocks of the Piedmont, an explanation is offered on p. 158.

tion is given here to their distribution and significance (*cf.* page 168).

Wind gaps have sometimes been conceived of as falling into groups on the basis of altitude, the altitude of each gap being

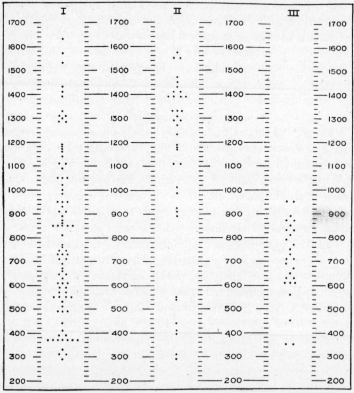

Fig. 72.—Vertical distribution of wind gaps and water gaps in eastern Pennsylvania. Each gap is indicated by a dot within a 20-foot interval. I, wind gaps and water gaps east and south of Susquehanna River; II, wind gaps and water gaps in Blue Mountain; III, wind gaps south of Lebanon Valley. Geologists are not agreed as to the extent to which concentration at certain levels is fortuitous. Hypotheses calling for a large number of base levels in Pennsylvania rest to some extent on the altitudes of wind gaps as shown in this table. (*Meyerhoff and Olmsted, Amer. Jour. Sci., vol. 27, 1934.*)

that of the stream that once flowed through it.[1] In determining this level, allowance may be made for later surficial changes. The level of the gaps in any one group is then interpreted as being

[1] BARRELL, JOSEPH, The Piedmont Terraces of the Northern Appalachians, *Amer. Jour. Sci.*, 4th Series, vol. 49, pp. 339*ff.*, 1920.

that of a valley peneplain of which surviving remnants may or may not be found. Following uplift and the growth of subsequent valleys, transverse streams were captured, the water gaps became wind gaps, and the valley peneplain was partly or wholly destroyed, perhaps leaving the wind gaps as its only record. Arguments for intermediate cycles between the Schooley and the Harrisburg have been to a considerable extent supported by such evidence.[1] A statistical study of the wind gaps of Pennsylvania casts doubt on such evidence.[2] The diversity of their levels is very great. Consistencies of level are found here and there, but they seem to point to the conditions in certain valleys rather than to general base-leveling conditions.

Wind gaps at the level of a valley peneplain necessarily resulted from successive captures by a longitudinal stream, beginning with the one nearest to the surviving transverse master stream. Each of the other transverse streams, while waiting its turn to be captured, would cut its gap lower. Hence, in a general way, the present altitudes in a series of gaps due to captures by one stream should decrease with distance from the surviving transverse stream. Examples of such a relation may be found if too great accuracy is not demanded, but the order of depth of the several notches, when not fortuitous, is found oftener to be the other way.[3] It is not improbable that an area near the mouth of the Shenandoah River was peneplaned at the Weverton level, that the three wind gaps in the Blue Ridge, mentioned on page 169, all functioned as water gaps at the Weverton level, and that the three captures occurred in succession as described above.

In using wind gaps as indicators of a former base level, the assumption is made that they served as water gaps throughout one cycle and became wind gaps by capture at some time in the next cycle. On the other hand, it is possible that transverse

---

[1] See various papers by Barrell, Bascom, and Knopf, cited in this work and mentioned in the index. Barrell, on p. 341 of the paper just referred to, lists six base levels with their altitudes.

[2] Ver Steeg, cited on page 199. Pages 94–102 of Ver Steeg's paper are largely given to tables showing numbers of gaps at various elevations. The impression is gained from these tables that wind gaps are quite as likely to become a liability as an asset to the hypothesis of intermediate peneplains. An opposite conclusion is reached by H. A. Meyerhoff, and Eliz. W. Olmsted, Wind Gaps and Water Gaps in Pennsylvania, *Amer. Jour. Sci.*, vol. 27, 1934

[3] Ver Steeg, *op. cit.*, p. 103.

streams should be first entrenched and then captured within the same cycle. In that case most captures should occur in the early part of the cycle, before maturity, for that is the time when adjustment is in progress and most of the shifting of divides occurs. Wind gaps originating in this manner would show no regularity in altitude, but most of them should be well above the peneplain that marks the end of the cycle.

A great majority of the wind gaps in Pennsylvania are higher than 1100 feet, and within the upper half of the interval that separates the Schooley and Harrisburg peneplains. This indicates that, disregarding intermediate partial cycles, capture occurred relatively early in the Harrisburg cycle. They became progressively more rare as the cycle advanced and few if any occurred in the following cycle.

Elevation of the Harrisburg Surface.—Uplift ended the Harrisburg cycle.[1] From the absence of captures since that time it might be inferred that adjustment was not disturbed and therefore that the uplift involved little or no warping. However, a tilt at right angles to the strike would not have much effect, since it would not alter the gradients of strike streams, and these are the ones that do the capturing. Such a tilt has been assumed. Campbell finds the Harrisburg peneplain at 800 feet where the Susquehanna and its west branch unite at Sunbury. This makes its gradient 5 feet per mile, whereas the river now falls but 2 feet per mile and it should have had an even lower gradient in Harrisburg time. The assumption that the post-Harrisburg uplift was accompanied by seaward tilting is common.[2] How-

---

[1] The form of this statement follows custom, but it needs criticism. It might be inferred that the peneplain ceased to be extended and perfected. The fact is that in places where the Harrisburg peneplain, or any other, has not yet been trenched, its broadening and flattening are going right on now as fast as ever. The work accomplished in such places since the uplift is exactly as much as it would have been had no uplift occurred. Sooner or later the new cycle will overtake the old, but it must be allowed that a substantial part of the Harrisburg peneplain has come into being, and other parts perfected, since the event which is commonly said to have ended the Harrisburg cycle. The same is true of the Schooley if a place can be found where it has not been trenched. This is one reason for objecting to the naming of peneplains after geologic periods, since it is a little incongruous to speak of the "Cretaceous peneplain" as still growing in North Carolina.

[2] Campbell (*op. cit.*, p. 290) thinks that at least in the Potomac basin, 90 per cent of the slope of the Harrisburg surface between the Allegheny plateau and the Piedmont is due to later deformation. It should be noted

ever, as stated before, such local peneplains as the Wyoming and Nittany Valleys at 1200 to 1400 feet, and the Potomac basin near Cumberland at 1200 feet, were no doubt developed considerably above sea level. In estimating the amount of later uplift, a liberal allowance must be made on this account.

Somerville Cycle.—After the moderate post-Harrisburg uplift came the short and still more incomplete Somerville cycle, in which a peneplain was developed where conditions were specially favorable. It has already been mentioned as preserved on the softest Triassic rocks of the Piedmont and on limestone in the Great Valley. Probably this surface is represented by the terrace-like lowland found intermittently along the Susquehanna and already mentioned as 600 feet high around Sunbury. It is identified (probably correctly) with terraces of slowly increasing altitude up both branches of the Susquehanna and also up the Potomac as high as 700 to 800 feet near Cumberland.[1] As the slope of the restored Somerville peneplain is a little steeper than the rivers, renewed rising and tilting is inferred. The Susquehanna and Potomac are entrenched less than 100 feet. Although brief, the Somerville cycle was itself composite, being interrupted by minor uplifts.

SOUTHERN SECTION

General Features.—The width of the Ridge and Valley province is a little less in the Southern section, and the area of valley floor is a larger fraction of the total. There is here no such division as there is farther north, between an eastern belt consisting mainly of lowland and a western belt of closely crowded ridges, the ridges being low or largely absent. Boundaries against the highlands on both sides continue to be clear and abrupt to within 30 miles of the southern end where the bordering uplands become very low. There is no very sharp break in passing from the Appalachian provinces to the Gulf Coastal Plain. A certain unity of character is given to the Southern

---

here that Harry M. Fridley, who accepts the hypothesis of many peneplains (Identification of Erosion Surfaces in South-Central New York, *Jour. Geol.*, vol. 37, pp. 113–134, 1929) identifies the 600-foot level around Sunbury with the Harrisburg peneplain, thus minimizing the warping. Karl Ver Steeg includes both the 600-foot surface and the one at 800 to 900 feet in the Harrisburg, thus allowing a good deal of residual relief.

[1] CAMPBELL, *op. cit.*, p. 290; G. W. Stose, (Pawpaw-Hancock folio) allows the altitude to reach 850 feet.

section of the Ridge and Valley province by its longitudinal drainage, though the difference between sections in this respect is only one of degree. As in the case of the Hudson-Champlain section, the major part of the drainage makes its final escape by a transverse valley, in this case the Tennessee (page 339).

Rocks.[1]—Several of the strong ridge-making formations of this section have the same character as those in the middle section. This is true of the Pottsville sandstone which makes ridges in Alabama and also the prominent rim of the Cumberland Plateau on the west. It is also true of the Clinch sandstone (Medina or Tuscarora of the north) which makes prominent mountain ridges north of Knoxville but is absent farther south. The basal Cambrian quartzites and conglomerates have already been mentioned (page 164) as belonging to the Blue Ridge province by reason of both topography and contiguity. An exception is found in northeastern Alabama where outlying ridges of Weisner quartzite are separated from the Piedmont province on the east by a limestone valley.[2]

[1] HAYES, C. W., Physiography of the Chattanooga District, U. S. Geol. Survey, 19*th Ann. Rept.*, pt. 2, pp. 1–58, 1899. Pages 17–19 of this paper describe the several formations with reference to topographic relations.

[2] The following column of rocks in the southern section of the Ridge and Valley province is highly generalized and incomplete, but summarizes the essentials for physiographic purposes.

Pennsylvanian
    Walden and Lookout sandstones, becoming more largely shale toward
        the south, and containing coal
Mississippian
    Pennington shale
    Bangor and other limestones
    Fort Payne chert, underlain by shale
Devonian
    Chattanooga "Black" shale, etc., (may be Mississippian)
Silurian
    Red Mountain (Clinton) and other formations of sandstone, shale,
        and some limestone
    Clinch sandstone
Ordovician
    Chickamauga limestone with minor shale and sandstone
    Knox dolomite (upper part), mainly limestone
Cambrian
    Knox dolomite (lower part)
    Conasauga, Rome, and other shales, with minor dolomite
    Lower Cambrian quartzites and slates (Blue Ridge province)

Several formations make prominent ridges in the southern section which are generally weak or wanting in the north. One of these is the Clinton (Silurian) sandstone (called Rockwood in Tennessee and Red Mountain farther south). It is important chiefly in Georgia and Alabama, being the great iron-bearing formation in the latter state. Closely associated with it is the Fort Payne (Mississippian) chert which occupies a stratigraphic position not very different from that of the Pocono sandstone in the northern states. Generally the Fort Payne and Clinton combine to make a single ridge, but at places they make independent ridges separated by a minor valley on the Devonian black shale. A number of low ridges or broad swells in the lowlands are made by cherty beds in the great mass of Cambrian and Ordovician dolomite, mainly the Knox formation, which underlies more of the valley surface than any other rock. Others are made by sandy members in the Cambrian formations which (except for the basal quartzites) are mainly shale and limestone. Most of the lowland, not on the Knox dolomite, is on Cambrian and Ordovician limestones and shales or on similar weak rocks of Mississippian age.

Structure.—As already stated (page 245) the regular open folding in the northern states gives way in Virginia and southward to closer folding, overturning toward the northwest, and thrust-faulting. In the Southern section almost every fold is broken by a thrust fault dipping toward the southeast. The combined effect of these factors is that nearly all beds dip toward the southeast. Toward the end of the province in Alabama the folding is less intense and the thrust faults fewer but of greater displacement.[1]

Province Boundary on the Northwest.—With the southwestward descent of valley floors from the Tennessee-New River divide, the great southeast-facing escarpment of the plateau province begins again to develop after the interruption described on page 229. Its height in this section is 1000 to 1200 feet except in Alabama. Its summit is held by Pottsville sandstone resting on Mississippian limestone. Its position marks roughly the change from steeply dipping to nearly horizontal beds (*cf.* Fig. 44). It is therefore on the northwestern limb or at the

[1] HAYES, C. W., Cleveland, Tenn., folio (No. 20), U. S. Geol. Survey, 1895.

foot of the last great anticline of the folded belt.[1] Generally, throughout its length in this section, this anticline was high enough to bring to the surface the weak Cambrian or Ordovician rocks. Resistant formations (Rockwood, Fort Payne) between these and the Pottsville may make hogback ridges at the foot of the escarpment. In that part of the boundary which is against the Cumberland Mountains the last great anticline is torn by a thrust fault (*cf.* Fig. 64).

As noted in Pennsylvania and Virginia (page 229), the boundary may turn backward around a sharp splinter-like projection of the plateau, behind which is a tributary portion of the Great Valley. Lookout and Pigeon mountains south of Chattanooga are the best known of such spurs. All are canoe-like synclines, and the valleys behind them are on pitching anticlines.

Province Boundary on the Southeast.—Most of the boundary on the southeast has been sufficiently described under the Blue Ridge province. Generally the contrast is sharp. South of the latitude of Birmingham (33°30′) the topographic contrast between the Talladega slate in the Piedmont and the unaltered rocks of the Great Valley is less marked. The surface on the former is but little higher or rougher than on the latter. A more distinct break in the landscape is found 10 to 20 miles farther east at the foot of the Rebecca Mountains on the western edge of the Pre-Cambrian terrane,[2] but the topography east of that ridge does not differ greatly from that on the west. Probably the best compromise is found by using the Coosa River as the boundary below the point where it enters the metamorphic rocks in latitude 33°.[3]

Mountain Ridges North of Knoxville.—The northeastern limit of the Southern section is fixed arbitrarily at the Tennessee-New River divide, where mountain ridges are numerous and valley floors narrow and high, generally near 2500 feet. Valley floors broaden and decline toward the southwest, and some of the ridges terminate while new ones appear. Clinch Mountain

---

[1] PRICE, PAUL H., The Appalachian Structural Front, *Jour. Geol.*, vol. 39, pp. 24–44, 1931.

[2] This line is adopted as the province boundary by W. D. Johnston, Jr., Physical Divisions of Northern Alabama, *Bull. Geol. Survey Ala.*, 38, 1930.

[3] Compare the topographic map of the Columbiana quadrangle west of the river with that of the Gantts Quarry quadrangle on the east.

near the median line of the province is the one great continuing feature. All of the main ridges north of Knoxville are made by the Clinch or associated sandstones. These include Bays, Clinch, Powell, and Wallen mountains, beside others at the northeastern end. In southern Virginia where the valley level is 2100 feet, Clinch Mountain is 3000 feet high and others are similar. Minor ridges or swells, in most cases only 100 to 300 feet above the streams, are so characteristic that true lowland plains are not common, except within a few miles of the larger rivers.

The crests of the higher mountains, so far as they can be seen in a single view, are prevailingly horizontal. Where such is the case they mark approximately the local level of the Schooley (Cumberland) peneplain. In the 150 miles from the vicinity of Pocahontas to that of Knoxville, the average altitude declines irregularly from more than 3500 feet to little more than 2000 feet. Considerable areas a few hundred feet above their general level are no doubt monadnocks.[1] Prevailing altitudes on these ridges are not very different from those in the plateau province to the west, except for that small part of the latter which is called the Cumberland Mountain section.

Valley Lands North of Knoxville.—The surface between mountain ridges in this part of the province is lowland only in a relative sense. Even around Knoxville the horizon is 1200 to 1300 feet high, and the surface has a local relief of 300 to 400 feet, carved since the latest peneplaning These so-called lowlands rise northeastward to 2500 feet. Broadly speaking, the relief is of two kinds. The low ridges or swells, themselves dissected, have already been mentioned. In much of the area they are near together and of nearly uniform height. Relatively low and level tracts without ridges are more extensive on the southeast side than on the northwest, largely because the Cambrian and Ordovician limestones and dolomites there are less cherty.

Another style of relief is illustrated in the basin of the French Broad River 20 to 60 miles east of Knoxville and also at other places. Here the upper Ordovician shales are preserved in a broad syncline. The once nearly level surface 1300 to 1400 feet high is not ridged but has been minutely dissected to a depth of several hundred feet, giving rise to a type of topography known

[1] HAYES and CAMPBELL, *op. cit.*, p. 78.

as "The Knobs." The tops of the knobs and low ridges apparently represent the last widespread peneplain, which is identified with the Highland Rim (Harrisburg) peneplain (page 441). Some of the streams have carved out broad valleys at a lower level which may be correlated with the Coosa peneplain mentioned below.

The restored surface at the level of the knobs and low ridges[1] has commonly been regarded as a single peneplain whose southwesterly slope is due partly to the direction of drainage and partly to differential uplift.[2] On the other hand, the same surface has been described as a series of at least three peneplains descending by steps toward the southwest.[3] No doubt, four would have been mentioned had the territory discussed extended farther south to include the Coosa peneplain. Remnants of the oldest, now 2300 to 2500 feet high, are assumed to survive at the headwaters of the Holston River. The second, now 1600 to 1800 feet high, is believed to have advanced upstream to near the Virginia line, and the third, now 1000 to 1100 feet high, to have approached the latitude of Knoxville. There is nothing inherently improbable in such an assumption. Geologists working

---

[1] Physiographers differ some in fixing the level of an old peneplain, some using the old valley levels, approximately that of the drainage, while others use the horizon of view, *i.e.*, approximately the tops of the swells and low ridges. Generally they do not state the criterion which they follow, but Hayes, in his Physiography of the Chattanooga District (*U. S. Geol. Survey, 19th Ann. Rept.*, pt. 2), adopts the former and regards the low ridges, 100 to 200 feet high, as "imperfections on the old peneplain." When the peneplain has been uplifted, as in plateaus and mountains, the valley level is often wholly destroyed. In that case the horizon of view comes into use. This may be too high where the peneplain was imperfect. However, it occurs so often that old peneplains are known only by summit levels that it would seem to be more consistent to designate the levels of all by the same criterion.

[2] That this surface is the product of a single erosion cycle is the view taken by C. W. Hayes and by M. R. Campbell in all their papers. These authors stress differential uplift. The same view has recently been reaffirmed by Frank J. Wright, who, however, lays more stress on residual slope (see references under Blue Ridge Province).

[3] KEITH, A., Some Stages of Appalachian Erosion, *Bull. Geol. Soc. Amer.*, vol. 7, pp. 519–525, 1896. It will be noted that the question of the unity *versus* composite character of the valley peneplain involves its relation to the Asheville and other local peneplains in the mountains to the east (see p. 190 of this book).

in that field disagree in their interpretation, and the published topographic maps of that region are too generalized to afford much evidence on such a point.[1]

The presence of more than one peneplain between the Schooley and the Coosa must for the present be considered as an alternative hypothesis.   If it be accepted, the Asheville and other local peneplains in the Blue Ridge province are presumably older than the floor of the Great Valley in Tennessee and the surface of the Piedmont.   In that case the difficulty with the 2500- to 2700-foot surface east of Grandfather Mountain disappears by accepting

Fig. 73.—Coosa peneplain 4 miles northeast of Cleveland, Tenn., a lowland developed mainly on Conasauga (Cambrian) shale.   Altitude about 800 feet. (*Photograph by Frank J. Wright.*)

Keith's interpretation (page 192).   Moreover, if the peneplain in the New River basin be older than Harrisburg, the same is true of the younger of two peneplains along the Kanawha. As this last is apparently older than the Lexington peneplain, the way is left open to correlate the Lexington and Harrisburg.

The Knoxville-Chattanooga Segment.—The mountain ridges described above end about 10 miles north of Knoxville.   From that latitude southward to Georgia the relief features with only one exception are of the lower order, *i.e.*, carved from the valley floor.   These features include low ridges, knobs, and all stream valleys.   They also include strips of smoother lowland below 800 feet whose maximum width in Tennessee is 5 or 6 miles along

[1] The topographic maps of this region made by the U. S. Geol. Survey are on a scale of 1:125,000.   The contour interval is 100 feet.

the main rivers, Tennessee and Hiwassee. These are classed[1] as a newer peneplain, the Coosa, more widely developed farther south (page 275).

The level of hilltops on the boundary of Georgia is rarely above 1000 feet; 10 miles north of Knoxville it is 300 feet higher. The average slope of the plain is about 3 feet per mile. The Tennessee River falls only 170 feet in the same distance. Valleys are therefore deeper and the local relief greater at the north. Hence, even the present slope of the land is greater than can be allowed for the former peneplain at the time it was made. Farther up the valley, the general slope is much steeper and all streams are actively cutting down.[2]

The Georgia Segment.—White Oak Mountain east of Chattanooga (the exceptional feature referred to above) is only the narrow northern end of a mountainous belt whose southern end is near Rome, Ga. In its southern part it broadens to 13 miles. This belt of mountains and narrow lowlands has been called the "Armuchee Ridges."[3] East and west of it the broad lowland (largely Coosa peneplain) is continuous. The presence of the mountain belt is due to a composite syncline, by reason of which certain resistant formations were below base level when the Schooley (Cumberland) peneplain was made. The Clinch sandstone does not extend so far south. The Rockwood is here the chief ridge maker and the Pottsville is next in importance. The Fort Payne cherty limestone underlies the valleys. The moderately even crests of the Armuchee Ridges reach 1500 feet in height, but long stretches are 100 feet lower. They probably represent the Cumberland peneplain, somewhat reduced because of the narrowness of the ridges.

The valley west of these mountains is 7 miles wide in the middle and twice as wide at the ends. From a divide 20 miles south of Chattanooga it drains north to the Tennessee and thereby to the Ohio, and south to the Coosa and the Gulf of Mexico. This

---

[1] HAYES, C. W., Physiography of the Chattanooga District, U. S. Geol. Survey, 19*th Ann. Rept.*, pt. 2, 1899.

[2] This is a point much insisted on by Keith in his various folios. It has a bearing on the gradient that should be allowed to a surface that has reached the peneplain stage, a factor that must be reckoned with in determining the amount of differential rise.

[3] CAMPBELL, M. R., Physical Geography of Georgia, *Ga. Geol. Survey, Bull.* 42, p. 143, 1925.

locality is one of much interest in connection with the history of the Tennessee River (page 276). Its surface is underlain by limestone, dolomite, and soft shale and is in all essential respects a continuation of the Tennessee Valley farther north. Moreover, the divide is only 250 feet above that river at Chatta-

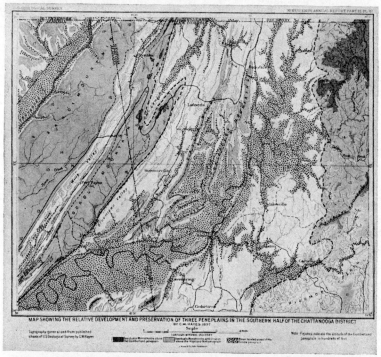

FIG. 74.—Peneplains in parts of northern Georgia and Alabama as interpreted by C. W. Hayes. Dotted area, Coosa peneplain; white, Highland Rim (Harrisburg?) peneplain more or less reduced; shaded area, Cumberland peneplain, in part reduced; dark shading, residuals above the Cumberland peneplain. Boundaries of the Ridge and Valley province shown by heavy lines.

nooga. In the study of this region made 35 to 40 years ago by C. W. Hayes[1] it was assumed that the Tennessee must have flowed this way to the Gulf. Peneplaning alone was not considered sufficient to reduce divides to such an extent. Since that time, studies of peneplains on soft rocks elsewhere have tended to reverse this judgment. The divide may well have

[1] HAYES, *op. cit.*, p. 33.

been reduced to its present flatness while the drainage had its present pattern.

East and south of the Armuchee ridges is the Rome Valley, 13 to 25 miles wide, underlain in about one half of its area by the Knox dolomite having the same topography as farther north. The other half of its surface is on Cambrian limestones and shales, more readily eroded, and worn down to a smoother plain between 600 and 800 feet high. This, with its continuation in Alabama, is the main expanse of Hayes's Coosa peneplain. It is entirely separated by divides from the smaller expanse along the Tennessee. For 80 miles southwest from Rome this smooth lowland, known there as Flatwoods, is a fertile plain.

The Alabama Segment.—South of the 34th parallel, the Ridge and Valley province is much more complex in structure and varied in topography. Great thrust faults bring to the surface the ridge-making formations in the broad belt of Cahawba ridges.[1] On either side are lowlands mainly on Cambrian and Ordovician rocks, the Coosa Valley 20 miles wide and the Birmingham Valley 4 to 8 miles wide. The ridge belt is divided longitudinally by the Cahawba Valley, a narrow lowland like those on either side and due to upfaulting of the older and weaker rocks. Crests of considerable continuity and as high as 1200 feet are found as far south as Birmingham, though most crests are a little lower. The local level of the Cumberland peneplain is about that of the highest ridges.

The most prominent ridge maker here is the Rockwood formation. With the aid of the overlying Fort Payne chert it forms Red Mountain and others from which iron ore is derived near Birmingham. Monoclinical ridges of Pottsville sandstone are also conspicuous.

Bituminous coal is found in two important fields in the Cahawba Ridges. This is noteworthy, since the Ridge and Valley province was in general so elevated that the coal measures were above base level and carried away in the first peneplaning,

---

[1] Butts, C. B., Geology of Alabama, *Ala. Geol. Survey*, 1926. W. D. Johnston, Jr. (Physical Divisions of Northern Alabama, *Bull. Geol. Survey Ala.*, 38, 1930) has more recently restricted the name Cahawba Ridges to those west of the Cahawba Valley and applied the name Coosa Ridges to those on the east, thus harmonizing the nomenclature of the ridge belts with those already in use for the coal fields.

the chief exceptions being in the synclines of Pennsylvania and in the windows in the overthrust in southern Virginia. The explanation here lies in the fact that the southern end of the province was less uplifted. In a region of such great lateral compression, it might be expected that the coal would be anthracite as in Pennsylvania, but it escaped metamorphism by reason of the fact that so large a part of the lateral compression was relieved by thrust faulting rather than by close folding.

The broad Coosa Valley on the southeast occupies half the width of the province. Much of it near the river is classed as Coosa peneplain, 600 to 700 feet high near the Georgia boundary and about 500 feet high at the edge of the Coastal Plain. All peneplains converge toward the south, and the older ones are so much eroded that accurate discrimination is not possible. Low ridges and swells continue to characterize the valley floor. The Choccolocco Mountains and several other ridges are made of Cambrian quartzite like that of the adjacent Piedmont but separated from the latter by branches of the valley lowland.

Drainage of the Southern Section.—A longitudinal profile of this section, using the general level of the hilltops in the eroded valley floor, is very flat below Knoxville and steepens progressively upstream from that point to the New River divide. A similar profile using stream levels would show a slight upturn in passing from the basin of the Tennessee to that of the Coosa. The Tennessee descends the slope for 250 miles to Chattanooga, then turns westward into the plateau. Just beyond the faint rise the Coosa begins and flows down the gentle profile. Both systems are fed by long tributaries from the southeast and receive very little water from the plateau on the northwest. Streams of both systems have broad and intricate meanders but those of the Coosa are much better developed near its source than those of the steeper headwaters of the Tennessee.

Among the mountains northeast of Knoxville the waters of the Tennessee are carried by four parallel longitudinal streams, the Powell, Clinch, Holston, and Nolichucky-French Broad. As the ridges terminate, these rivers unite to form a single stream at the foot of the Cumberland Front.

There is little direct evidence as to the time or manner in which the main features of the present drainage plan were adopted. The pattern suggests that the streams flowing northwestward from the Blue Ridge may have continued their courses as antecedents across the rising mountains and plateau to the Ohio and Mississippi[1] just as the New River continues to do. On the other hand, drainage may have been turned to the southwest in consequent streams following synclines during the rise of the folds. In the former case the change awaited the growth of subsequent streams, mainly on anticlinal axes, or at least on the weaker rocks. According to this hypothesis the branches of the growing Tennessee captured the northwest-flowing streams, one at a time, from the Hiwassee to the Watauga. Apparently the New River is safe.

Westward Course of the Tennessee River.—That the Tennessee River should follow the valley for 250 miles and then turn sharply across the plateau in a 1000-foot gorge has always been a problem. The barrier to the south is a faint divide only 250 feet above the river and not at all above the widespread valley-floor peneplain. The first explanation to suggest itself is that the Tennessee west of Chattanooga is one of the old northwest-flowing streams heading in the Blue Ridge and crossing the valley and the plateau,[2] its upper course farther east having been captured by a tributary of the Coosa.

Other hypotheses assume that the Tennessee once flowed south to the Gulf, either through the Coosa Valley or farther west. One assumption is that when the Cumberland peneplain was being finished, the Gulf of Mexico had its shore in northern Alabama.[3] With uplift and a little westward tilt the river took its westward course over the emerging sea bottom. Or the surface over which it wandered westward may have been a delta.[4]

Most of the discussion of this problem has centered around the hypothesis of capture which was the first to attract attention.[5]

[1] HAYES and CAMPBELL, *op. cit.*, pp. 101–103.

[2] WHITE, CHARLES H., The Appalachian River versus a Tertiary Trans-Appalachian River in Eastern Tennessee, *Jour. Geol.*, vol. 12, pp. 34–39, 1904.

[3] ADAMS, GEO. I., The Course of the Tennessee River and the Physiography of the Southern Appalachian Region, *Jour. Geol.*, vol. 36, pp. 481–493, 1928.

[4] BERRY, E. W., Upper Cretaceous Floras of the Eastern Gulf Coast, U. S. Geol. Survey, *Prof. Paper*, 112, 1919.

[5] HAYES and CAMPBELL, *op. cit.*, pp. 115–119. The hypothesis is restated in later papers by Hayes and was widely accepted. It is recounted at length in Chamberlin and Salisbury's "Geology," vol. 1, pp. 164–168, 1904.

It assumes that the ancestral Tennessee, the former "Appalachian River," once followed the Great Valley to the Gulf and was captured at Chattanooga by a west-flowing stream whose headward growth was favored by crustal warping, this being effected after the Great Valley was cut down almost to its present level. The strongest support for this hypothesis comes from the similarity of the lowland south of Chattanooga to that farther north, and the inevitable suggestion that the former is anomalous unless it had the same history as the latter. Additional support is found in the topographic youth of the gorge in the plateau (Fig. 98, page 340).

More recent studies[1] of this region make it clear that the low smooth divide south of Chattanooga does not require a through-flowing stream, nor is the gorge in the plateau exceptionally steep in comparison with others if the character of rock in which it is cut be taken into account (page 334). Moreover, it is inherently improbable that a large longitudinal stream following a belt of soft rock and having already a valley 1000 feet deep, should be captured by a transverse stream with its headwaters in a strong massive sandstone and having a longer course to the sea. When or why the Tennessee took its westward course may be uncertain, but it was doubtless following its present course at the level of the Cumberland peneplain before uplift and before the gorge was cut.

South of the Tennessee basin, drainage was probably longitudinal from the start, though it is reasonable to assume that the Coosa has had some headward growth, perhaps capturing an originally transverse Conasauga at the state line. Throughout the section, folds are so much broken by faults that most streams cannot be classified as anticlinal or synclinal. They are now mainly on soft rocks whether on upthrown or downthrown structures. No doubt this condition is the result of much shifting and some captures.

Summary.—The oldest recorded erosion cycle in this section is known as the Cumberland, which is identified with the Schooley. But there were, no doubt, other Pre-Cumberland cycles and

---

[1] JOHNSON, DOUGLAS W., The Tertiary History of the Tennessee River, *Jour. Geol.*, vol. 13, pp. 194–231, 1905. This thorough study takes up phases of the problem which cannot be included in this book. It includes a bibliography of the subject.

older peneplains. One of these survives beneath the coastal plain sediments and another has been pointed out at the upper surface of the marine Cretaceous.[1] Whatever direction streams may have followed immediately after folding, the drainage at the close of the Cumberland cycle probably differed little in pattern from that of the present, except that headwaters were less developed. If the Tennessee River ever followed a more direct course to the Gulf, it was probably superposed in its present course either on marine deposits or on a delta. It is more probable that this occurred in an earlier cycle than in the Cumberland.

The post-Cumberland uplift was followed by the degradation of the less resistant rocks to make the Great Valley. The cycle in which this was accomplished may have been composite. If a series of minor cycles be assumed, then the last of the series was the Coosa, in which a peneplain has been developed on the softest rocks only, or very near the larger streams. The effect of all post-Cumberland erosion in reducing the level of divides on hard rocks was moderate, but probably the crests of narrow ridges have been reduced several hundred feet.

[1] ADAMS, *op. cit.*, p. 487. While Adams extends the Cumberland peneplain over the top of the Upper Cretaceous sediments, Charles Butts ("Geology of Alabama," 1926) places it at the bottom.

CHAPTER V

THE APPALACHIAN PLATEAUS

The Appalachian Revolution involved more than the making of a narrow chain of folded mountains from the St. Lawrence to the Gulf Coastal Plain. It raised out of water the horizontal rocks of the interior. Over a wide strip near the mountains the surface became a sloping plateau. Though largely base-leveled one or more times, it has suffered repeated uplift. The mountains, as originally made by folding, have been destroyed and the adjacent margin of the plateau at most places rises above the folded belt. The plateau province is everywhere dissected but the extent and style of this dissection differs from place to place. It is partly on this basis that the province is treated here in seven sections.

Province Boundaries.—Elevation decreases so gradually toward the interior that the line between highland and lowland is in part debatable. Moreover it has shifted with the fortunes of uplift and erosion. As the rocks near this line dip gently toward the plateau some prominent and long continuous outfacing escarpments are developed. This is notably the case in Tennessee and Kentucky at the western limit of the Pennsylvanian (Upper Carboniferous) system. This escarpment, 1000 feet high in Tennessee, is the conventional boundary of the province here treated. This is not ideal, since the surface at the foot of the escarpment is also plateau-like, and it shared in the Appalachian uplift in a noteworthy way (page 440).

In southern Ohio and northern Kentucky the province boundary is at the west-facing escarpment of Mississippian (Lower Carboniferous) rocks, but north of Columbus, where there is no escarpment, the limit of the plateau is fixed empirically by the contrast of its topography with the smoother surface of the Till Plains. Eastward from Cleveland an escarpment again develops. To a point south of Buffalo it follows no single geologic horizon, but from there eastward it is in turn at the edge of the

279

FIG. 75.—Escarpment of an outlier of the Allegheny Plateau, 400 feet high, west of Chillicothe, Ohio.   Till Plains in the foreground.
(*Hyde, Geol. Surv. of Ohio.*)

Portage sandstone, and the Tully, Onondaga, and Helderberg limestones. The province boundary follows this escarpment only to a point west of Utica. From there it swings back to the northwest, following no one outcrop but lying at the fairly definite west foot of a high cuesta sloping away from the Adirondack province. The Black River at the foot of the scarp on the east side of the cuesta divides the plateau from the Adirondacks (page 325). The boundary, both here and farther east, is at the contact of the Paleozoic rocks of the plateau with the crystalline rocks of the Adirondacks. The remaining boundaries of the plateau province have already been described (pp. 204, 228). The sharp folds of the mountain belt give way gradually through low mild undulations of less and less amplitude to the horizontal beds of the interior. The surface on the gentler folds is distinctly plateaulike, and the province boundary on the east, or southeast, is clear.

Rocks and Structure.—Throughout four fifths of its periphery the plateau province is higher than its neighbors. This fact might suggest that it is underlain by hard rocks. For much of the area, especially in the south, this is true, but it is not universally so. In a large and general way the province is a shallow syncline. If the boundaries be located at the foot of outfacing escarpments it follows as a matter of course that the edges are underlain by relatively strong strata, but the central syncline may, and does, contain a large proportion of shale. All of the formations, however, contain sandstone members at intervals. In the process of degradation, these sandstones persist for a longer time than an equal thickness of shale or limestone. Hence, at any one time, sandstone may be represented at the surface in larger proportion than in the mass. This principle has its bearing on both topography and soils and it is not surprising that the province as a whole is not greatly favored agriculturally.

Southwest of West Virginia the rocks of the plateau are mainly sandstones and conglomerates of the Pottsville series.[1] The beds thicken toward the south until, in Tennessee, a single stratum, the Walden sandstone, not only makes the surface of the plateau but constitutes most of its mass. Toward the

---

[1] While not customarily included in the "coal measures," as that term is used in Pennsylvania, the Pottsville, even in the north, contains thin seams of coal, and in the south it affords important coal fields.

FIG. 76.—The Helderberg Escarpment, separating the Allegheny Plateau from Hudson Valley lowland. The lower plateau in the middle of the picture is upheld by Helderberg limestone. Hamilton beds make the higher plateau in the background. (*Photograph by E. J. Stein.*)

northeast the trough deepens and is filled with younger rocks of the coal measures. While sandstone is important throughout the entire series, shale is more abundant. Limestone is a minor element. The several series differ in topography and soil as they do lithologically.

The most valuable generalizations are afforded by the geological map of the United States. The Dunkard group (Permian or "Upper Barren Measures"), which is mainly a thick mass of red shale and sandstone, occupies a belt stretching southwest from near Pittsburgh to near Huntington, W. Va. Outcropping around it in successive elliptical zones are the Monongahela ("Upper Productive"), Conemaugh ("Lower Barren"), Allegheny ("Lower Productive") and finally the Pottsville, relatively thin here but obdurate and physiographically important. Most of the limestone and the best coal beds are in the Monongahela formation. The elliptical form of outcrop is lost before the border of Mississippian shale and sandstone is reached. In southern New York and northern Pennsylvania, on the margin of the synclinal basin, only older rocks are left. From south to north the surface is successively on Devonian, Silurian, and Ordovician, some of whose characteristics are mentioned below in local descriptions.

Subdivision into Sections.—For any adequate discussion it is necessary to divide this large and varied province into seven sections. About the only true statement that can be made of all is that they are plateaus in process of dissection or degradation. Sections differ in the character of their underlying rocks, in altitude, in degree of dissection, and in the presence or absence of glaciation. The largest and most typical section is the *Unglaciated Allegheny Plateau*, approximately mature in its dissection. Between it and the Ridge and Valley province is a higher strip whose topography, though distinctly plateaulike, is much affected by open folds. This strip has always been known as the *Allegheny Mountains*. North of these two sections, mainly in southern New York, is the *Glaciated Allegheny Plateau* which, apart from changes due to ice, is much like its correlative on the south. The *Catskill Mountains* are a higher and more deeply dissected plateau rising above the last-mentioned section on its eastern margin. North of the Allegheny Plateau, and separated from it by a north-facing escarpment, is the *Mohawk section* on dip slopes rising toward the Adirondack Upland.   Beginning in southern Kentucky and extending to the Gulf Coastal Plain is the *Cumberland Plateau,* underlain by strong nearly horizontal sandstone beds, and having, in its most typical part, a submature topography.   East of it rise the *Cumberland Mountains,* analogous to the Allegheny Mountains in the north.

THE ALLEGHENY MOUNTAIN SECTION

Distinctive Character.—The high eastern margin of the plateau province from northern Pennsylvania to central West Virginia is called the Allegheny Mountains.   This use of terms involves no inconsistency, since any surface of varied and high relief is properly called mountainous.   In general the mountain section is higher and more deeply carved than those that border it, but this is not true in central West Virginia.   There the adjacent Allegheny Plateau is as high as the "mountains," 3500 feet with local swells rising 1000 feet higher, and the delimitation of the two sections is not very satisfactory.   The distinction stressed here is between areas dendritically dissected and areas in which erosional forms are more or less controlled by structure.

Throughout the mountain section the rocks are mildly folded. Erosion of folds has given rise to topographic belts, anticlinal, synclinal, and monoclinal.   The mention of these types might seem to class the Allegheny Mountain section with the Ridge and Valley province.   It will be seen, however, that not only are many of the mountains of this section themselves plateaulike, but they are separated by strips of deeply dissected plateau, not by valley lowlands as in the adjoining province.

Types of Structure and Topography.—Anticlinal mountains are best exemplified by two parallel ridges, Chestnut Ridge and Laurel Hill[1] on the western margin of the section in the southern half of Pennsylvania.[2]   These anticlinal ranges are arches of sandstone, at places Pocono, elsewhere Pottsville, according to the amount of uplift.   Relative altitudes of 1000 feet are common.   Between and around them the rocks of the coal measures make broad plateaus.   Other anticlines between these ridges and the Allegheny Front were raised higher, so that both Potts-

---

[1] The name Laurel is applied to the eastern ridge, except near the Maryland boundary where it is attached to the western ridge.

[2] See Masontown-Uniontown folio (No. 82), U. S. Geol. Survey, 1902.

Fig. 77.—View down the West Branch of the Susquehanna River in Clinton County, Pennsylvania. The locality is in the Allegheny Mountain section. The flat horizon at an elevation of about 2200 feet is on the Pottsville sandstone. (*Photograph by W. M. Gaylor, Sag Harbor, N. Y. Reproduced from N. Y. State Museum Bull. 255.*)

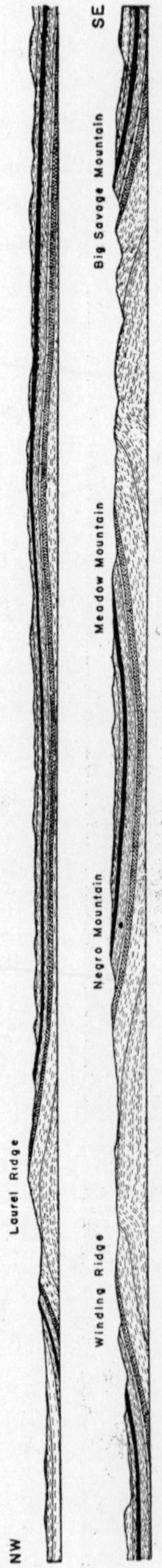

FIG. 78.—Cross section of the Allegheny Mountain section in southern Pennsylvania and Maryland. The Pottsville sandstone is shown in black, the Pocono is dotted. The lower section is the eastward continuation of the upper. Total length of section about 46 miles. Vertical exaggeration small. (*U. S. Geol. Survey folios Nos. 82 and 160.*)

ville and Pocono were eroded from their crests and now form monoclinal ridges several hundred feet high.[1] Between these ridges, on the axes of the anticlines, Devonian rocks are exposed, but instead of making lowlands, as do the older Paleozoics in the Ridge and Valley province, they underlie plateaus 2500 to 2700 feet high cut by valleys to a maximum depth of over 1000 feet.

The traveler on the old Cumberland Road, now the National Highway, going east from Uniontown, Pa., first crosses Chestnut (Laurel) Ridge. Then, after 20 miles, of plateau, he crosses in succession at intervals of 5 or 6 miles Winding Ridge and Negro, Meadow, Big Savage, and Dans mountains, all monoclinal ridges on the Pottsville or Pocono, and all about 2900 to 3100 feet high, except the last, which is several hundred feet lower. The tops of these mountains are much like those in the Ridge and Valley province, except that they are less even. If they were removed from the landscape, the topography would be typical of the Allegheny Plateau. The surface rises from 2100 to 2200 feet on the west to 2600 or 2700 feet farther east, and is cut by valleys 300 to 500 feet, in extreme cases 1000 feet, deep. Dips are gentle, and in the shallow synclines are coal fields, typical of the plateau. The somewhat knobby crests of the higher ridges may indicate that they were not reduced to the Schooley base level or that they have suffered later erosion.

In the northern half of Pennsylvania the folds are more open. Here the rela-

[1] See Accident-Grantsville folio (No. 160), U. S. Geol. Survey, 1908.

tion of the strong sandstone to the folds is generally such that it is now preserved only in the nearly flat synclinal troughs. These strips now constitute the "mountains" which are, in reality, only narrow strips of very rough plateau, alternating with lower plateaus on the older rocks of the anticlines. Near the New York boundary the summit level of the mountains is 2300 to 2500 feet and that of intervening tracts 300 to 500 feet lower.[1] Even without folding, this part of the province would be so deeply eroded as to be mountainous.

Fig. 79.—Valley of Monroe River in western Maryland, representing the Allegheny Mountains in the Appalachian Plateau province. Relief about 1000 feet. (*Md. Geol. Survey.*)

The Allegheny Front is a southeast-facing escarpment on the northwestern flank of the last great anticline of the folded belt[2] (Fig. 63). Generally at least 1000 feet of the rise is an almost unbroken slope over the edges of the Pocono and Pottsville sandstones. Equally general in Pennsylvania is a bench at the foot, 4 to 6 miles wide, on the less obdurate Devonian rocks, mainly shales. Its average elevation is 1500 to 1600 feet, but it declines toward the Susquehanna and rises toward the south,

[1] See Gaines folio (No. 92) and Elkland-Tioga folio (No. 93), U. S. Geol. Survey, 1903.

[2] Well shown on the structural map in the Ebensburg folio (No. 133), U. S. Geol. Survey, 1905.

almost disappearing before Maryland is reached.   It has a strong slope away from the escarpment toward the limestone valleys, which are several hundred feet lower.   The surface of the bench is a minutely dissected plateau which may represent a peneplain or may be merely a stripped surface.   Northwest of the great escarpment the strong cliff-making formations soon dip below the surface of the plateau, only to reappear in the anticlines already mentioned.

The Schooley Surface.—It is a fair assumption that the summits of the Allegheny Mountains represent an imperfect phase of the Schooley peneplain.[1]   As seen at a distance, say from one of the Allegheny ridges, the horizon strongly suggests a peneplain, but any attempt to fix its position requires that some of the higher masses be regarded as rising above it.   It will be recalled that in the Ridge and Valley province altitudes are closely related to the breadth of outcrop of the mountain-making sandstones.   Other things being equal, low-angle dips, as at the ends of pitching folds, are accompanied by higher altitudes.   It is only to be expected, therefore, that the gentle folds of the Allegheny Mountains would be imperfectly reduced to the Schooley level.   That the structure was an important factor in controlling the level of the surface, both during the Schooley cycle and later, is indicated by the manner in which altitudes rise and fall with changing hardness, thickness, and dip of a resistant formation.[2]   For many miles Chestnut Ridge (called Laurel in the Uniontown quadrangle) declines in altitude toward the north whereas the parallel Laurel Ridge, a few miles to the east, rises in the same direction, the heights of both being apparently controlled by the Pocono sandstone.   It must be assumed that this agreement between altitude and structure reflects not only the imperfections of the Schooley peneplain but also unequal subsequent lowering of that surface.

With these elements of uncertainty in mind, the altitude of the Schooley surface, where it most strongly suggests a former base level, may be tentatively placed at 2300 to 2500 feet in

[1] Called Kittatinny by those who do not treat the Schooley and Kittatinny peneplains as identical.

[2] For good illustrations see G. H. Ashley, Studies in Appalachian Mountain Sculpture, *Bull. Geol. Soc. Amer.*, vol. 46, pp. 1395–1436, 1935.

northern Pennsylvania,[1] a little higher in the middle, and at 2700 feet in western Maryland.[2]

The surface on the Pottsville in middle Pennsylvania rises in ridges and swells as high as 2900 feet, or a probable 400 feet above the peneplain level in that locality. In western Maryland and adjacent states the monoclinal ridges, mentioned above, rise locally above 3100 feet, or 400 feet, above the general level. Altitudes continue to increase toward the south in West Virginia. Where the mountain ridges end, in latitude 38°30′, many points on their crests are above 4000 feet and a few reach 4500 feet. Similar altitudes are found on the horizontal rocks of the adjacent plateau. Wright treats these high points as elements of the warped Schooley peneplain.[3] If judged by the same standards as those applied above to Pennsylvania it is not improbable that a few hundred feet would be allowed for local relief at the close of the Schooley cycle.

Possible Later Cycle.—There is some evidence of a base level lower than the Schooley. The lower levels in northern Pennsylvania, 1800 to 2000 feet, may represent a later peneplain. It is also conceivable that, after uplift and during the dissection of the Schooley surface, the surface on softer rocks was lowered somewhat uniformly without approaching a new base level and without developing a new peneplain. In southern Pennsylvania and western Maryland are considerable areas, either along streams or on the softer rocks of the coal measures,[4] having a surface a little below or a little above 2000 feet and not everywhere on softer rocks. Martin interprets the 1900-foot level

[1] CAMPBELL, *op. cit.*, 1903; also, FULLER, M. L., and W. C. ALDEN, Gaines folio (No. 92), U. S. Geol. Survey, 1903, and Elkland-Tioga folio (No. 93), U. S. Geol. Survey, 1903. The area described in these folios is, strictly speaking, in the glaciated section but the change by glaciation is small. With respect to erosion surfaces it is typical of the northern end of the mountain section.

[2] MARTIN, G. C., Accident-Grantsville folio (No. 160), U. S. Geol. Survey, 1908. On p. 3 is a good summary of altitudes in western Maryland, classified according to structural relations.

[3] WRIGHT, FRANK J., The Physiography of the Upper James River Basin in Virginia, Va. Geol. Survey, *Bull.* 11, p. 18, 1925.

[4] CAMPBELL, M. R., Masontown-Uniontown folio (No. 82), U. S. Geol. Survey, 1902; ref. to p. 2.

along the Youghiogheny River in Maryland as indicating a base level. This question is mentioned again on page 293.

THE UNGLACIATED ALLEGHENY PLATEAU

Rocks and Their Influence.—The Unglaciated Allegheny Plateau covers much of western Pennsylvania, Western Virginia,

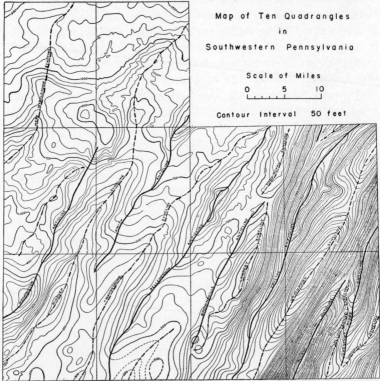

Map of Ten Quadrangles
in
Southwestern Pennsylvania

Scale of Miles
0   5   10

Contour Interval   50 feet

Fig. 80.—Map of southwest corner of Pennsylvania showing contours at intervals of 50 feet on the horizon of the Pittsburgh coal. Anticlinal axes are indicated by solid lines, synclinical axes by broken lines. The amplitude of folding in the Uniontown quadrangle at the southeast (Laurel Ridge) is 4000 feet, and the dip may reach or exceed 1 foot in 3. Elsewhere the amplitude rarely exceeds 500 feet, and dips are generally from 10 to 100 feet per mile. [*This map, on a larger scale, is found in U. S. Geol. Survey folio (No. 180).*]

eastern Ohio, and eastern Kentucky. This section embraces most of the rock formations listed above. The topography therefore is carved from a mass which is more largely shale than sandstone. The surface truncates and bevels the edges of 3000 feet of strata lying in the broad syncline. As inequalities in resistance generally fail to cause more than minor irregularities in altitude, it is plain that general base-leveling occurred at some time in the history of this section.

The influence of different rocks is, however, not negligible. In addition to the dips toward the central syncline, there are others due to low folds parallel to the mountains on the east, having an amplitude of several hundred feet and widths of 5 to 10 miles. Dips are generally less than 100 feet to the mile. It is not uncommon that anticlines and synclines of such dimensions present, at the surface, rocks of contrasted character. Low broad ridges or swells are thus produced, often not noticeable to the eye as elevations but well distinguished with respect to smoothness or fertility. It is not uncommon that the small synclines retain beds of coal which have been eroded away on the anticlines.[1] The latter, in many cases, are the oil and gas fields.

Altitude and Relief.—The western edge of the Allegheny Plateau in central Ohio and northern Kentucky is 1200 to 1300 feet high and has a local relief not greater than 200 or 300 feet.[2] The surface rises faintly toward the Allegheny Mountains, the horizon being but rarely above 1400 feet in southwestern Pennsylvania, though occasional hills rise above 1500 feet, the maximum on the Ohio-Monongahela divide being more than 1600 feet. In a broad outlook the surface is undulating; smooth in proportion to the distance, or to the height, from which it is viewed. Actually, no point is very far from valleys several hundred feet deep, even 400 or 500 feet near the larger streams. Most slopes are steeper below than above. Most land of moderate slope is between valleys rather than in them, though valleys are very important in transportation and industry.

Toward the north from latitude 41 degrees, the surface rises steadily to more than 2100 feet on the New York boundary. On both sides of that line scattered hills or patches of upland rise

---

[1] See U. S. Geol. Survey folios Nos. 94 (Brownsville-Connellsville), 110 (Latrobe), 178 (Foxburg-Clarion), and 180 (Claysville).

[2] There is no exact definition of "local relief." "Total relief" within a given area is the difference in altitude between its highest and lowest points. A more useful element in the description of the landscape is the difference in elevation which may be noted in a single view or a single ascent or descent. Necessarily, this cannot be stated with exactness.

200 to 300 feet higher. Altitude favors deeper valleys, and the presence of the Pottsville and other strong sandstones at the surface makes them angular. An extensive district east of the Allegheny River, largely in this section but partly in the Allegheny Mountains, is still known as the "Forest counties" of Pennsylvania. The relation between forests and rough surface is obvious.

From southern Ohio southeastward, for some miles beyond the Ohio River, the general level not only does not rise but is interrupted by a broad zone along the river in which the horizon is not above 1000 feet. Farther to the southeast it rises, slowly at first, but with increasing steepness as the Allegheny Front is approached. In the middle of West Virginia the eastern margin of the Allegheny Plateau rises to elevations of 3500 to 4000 feet, with exceptional tracts still higher.[1] It will be observed that the high eastern margin of the province, corresponding to the Allegheny Mountains farther north and the Cumberland Mountains farther south, is not here differentiated from the Allegheny Plateau, though its relief reaches 1000 to 2000 feet.

Altitudes within this section in Kentucky exceed 2000 feet only in the extreme eastern part and fall off rapidly toward the west and north. With deep valleys all around to lower the local base level, and with sandstones at the surface to preserve the hilltops, the higher part of the plateau in eastern Kentucky is deeply, steeply, and minutely dissected.

Into this general picture certain more local features must be fitted: (1) There are occasional abrupt changes of level. In southern Ohio there are two west-facing escarpments 20 miles apart corresponding to resistant formations. Their crests are at the local level of the plateau, about 1300 feet. From the crest of each escarpment an eastward dip slope descends to about 1000 feet, which is the level of the lowland farther west.[2] (2) In the higher parts of West Virginia, the altitudes given above are reached only by the higher hills and divides. A level 100 feet lower at the west and 1000 feet lower at the east is equally prominent. The higher levels are in some cases on harder rocks, in others on divides of long standing. (3) In Pennsylvania and

[1] For detail between lats. 37°30' and 39° see F. J. Wright, *loc. cit.*

[2] Well described by J. E. Hyde, Geology of the Camp Sherman quadrangle, Geol. Survey Ohio, *4th Ser. Bull.* 23, p. 161, 1921.

Ohio, on relatively soft rocks and near large streams (one or both of these conditions being fulfilled) the surface is commonly about 100 feet lower (see Worthington peneplain, page 300). Still lower strips closely following the streams are noted below. The topographic effect of low folds has already been mentioned.

Relation to the Schooley Peneplain.—On the relation of the plateau surface to the Appalachian peneplains previously described, there is no general agreement. Westward from the Allegheny Mountains in northern Pennsylvania and southern New York the general level of hilltops on Pottsville and Pocono sandstones is only a little lower than in the mountains and is quite as likely to represent the Schooley surface since all levels decline toward the northwest.

The typical Allegheny Plateau around Pittsburgh, underlain by the coal measures, has its horizon at about 1300 feet. When traced eastward, this horizon is seen to rise not more than 100 feet until the Pottsville sandstone is encountered in Chestnut Ridge. There the level rises abruptly and is maintained whereever the harder rocks reach the surface. Likewise, northward from Pittsburgh, the plateau surface rises a little more than 100 feet before reaching the Pottsville outcrop, beyond which the rise of the surface is at least 10 feet to the mile, which is less steep than the dip. The corresponding outcrop is reached in east-central Ohio without significant westward slope of the plateau surface. From Pittsburgh southwestward to eastern Kentucky the level is lower, especially near the Ohio River, except on some divides which antedate the present drainage plan (page 317). In northeastern Kentucky at the level of about 1200 feet, the Pottsville formation again appears at the surface. Thence south to Tennessee and southeast to the Cumberland Mountains the surface rises in general (not exact) agreement with the dip. Southeastward from the Ohio River the surface does not rise above 1200 feet until the Pottsville comes to the surface at Charleston, W. Va., beyond which point the rise is rapid toward the southeast, *i.e.*, in conformity with the structure. The general picture described here is that of a basin of Pottsville sandstone, filled to an almost horizontal surface with softer rocks.

The close relation between altitude and hard sandstone strongly suggests that the relics of the Schooley peneplain

(wasted and lowered, of course) should be sought on the rim of
Pottsville and Pocono formations, ignoring hills and ridges of
exceptional height.   A hypothetical surface determined by such
criteria would slope northwestward from the Allegheny Front to
central Ohio where its altitude would be about 1300 feet.   A
bulge near the New York-Pennsylvania boundary may be due
to deformation at the time of uplift.   Here the Pocono sandstone
reaches heights of 2400 feet, while differential erosion (perhaps
not involving a new cycle) has lowered the general surface to
2100 feet.[1]   The eastern margin of the Schooley surface was
imperfectly peneplaned and the western margin may (as some
believe) have been peneplaned again, but that remains unproved.

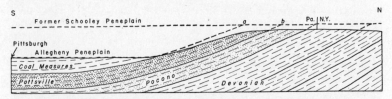

Fig. 81.—Diagram to illustrate the erosional history of western Pennsylvania.
Northern Pennsylvania and southern New York are represented as Schooley
peneplain somewhat reduced.   The Pottsville formation has been reduced where
it reached the Schooley surface, *a* to *b*, denuded farther south and reduced in
proportion to the length of time exposed.   The coal measures have been cut
down to a later peneplain.

Less risk would be involved in asserting that the Schooley surface at the west *coincides* with a later peneplain.   (*Cf.* Fig. 82.)

As the structural basin within this great sandstone rim was
filled with weaker rocks, the surface on these was lowered with
relative rapidity while the sandstone rim was wasting slowly.
With progressive removal of the softer rocks, the underlying
Pottsville sandstone was more and more laid bare.   In the
stripped zone the present surface cuts across the bedding of the
Pottsville because the sandstone has been lowered in proportion
to the time exposed (Fig. 81).   This gives a deceptive appearance of peneplaning, because truncation or beveling is not
limited to beds directly underlying the old peneplain, but likewise
affects beds exposed by stripping.   Thus it may be tentatively
assumed that (1) the outer rim of the Allegheny Plateau, con-

[1] GLENN, L. C., Devonic and Carbonic Formations of Southwestern
New York, *Bull. N. Y. State Museum,* 69, pp. 967–989, 1903.

sisting of Pocono and Pottsville sandstones, represents the Schooley peneplain modified only by such slow and nearly uniform wastage as does not involve a new cycle; (2) that inside this outer zone is another, within which downcutting by streams has been limited by the Pottsville. Within this zone both altitude and topographic forms are accounted for by stripping, weathering, and valley cutting. These processes left a surface that cuts across the bedding and strongly resembles a peneplain dissected almost to maturity by valleys of rather angular style.

The Allegheny Peneplain.—The surface on the coal measures is either a younger peneplain or the Schooley surface dissected and reduced without loss of horizontality of sky line. The latter alternative assumes a continued state of maturity, old age perhaps being prevented by continual uplift. In either case the vertical interval between the old surface and the new is 1000 feet at the east and little or nothing at the west. The close relation between altitudes and hard rocks is thought by some[1] to nullify all arguments for a peneplain younger than the Schooley. If this surface were approached from the east it would, without hesitation, be pronounced a later peneplain. It is only when traced to the north or south and found to pass without break into a similar (though more angular) surface that is structurally controlled, that one is tempted to question whether the forms require the assumption of any base level between the Schooley and the present.

According to one suggested hypothesis (not yet definitely disproved), the plateau surface in western Pennsylvania and parts of adjacent states is merely the dissected and lowered Schooley peneplain.[2] Yet the level of hilltops inside the rim of Pottsville sandstone is so nearly uniform for several hundred miles that it strongly suggests a peneplain. The surface truncates the rocks of many formations, in which differences of physical character are by no means negligible. There can be little doubt that the surface did at one time come under the influence of base level and at least approach the peneplain condition. That was before the last series of moderate uplifts

---

[1] ASHLEY, *loc. cit.*

[2] This hypothesis was at one time preferred by the author. See *Proc. Geol. Soc. Amer.*, p. 78, 1933. Its latest and fullest expression is by Geo. H. Ashley, *Bull. Geol. Soc. Amer.*, vol. 46, pp. 1395–1436, 1935.

which gave rise to renewed valley cutting.   Between the steep-sided valleys many divides are only moderately rolling.

If this former surface of low relief be regarded as a peneplain (as is done here tentatively), it can be identified with the Harrisburg or assigned to an intermediate cycle.   Generally it has been called Harrisburg.[1]   In that case it is contemporaneous with the extensive peneplain in western Ohio and adjacent states at an elevation of 1000 feet or less.   The abrupt change in level along

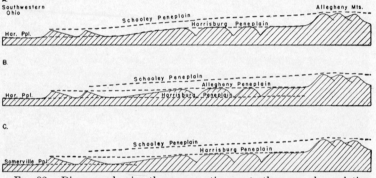

Fig. 82.—Diagrams showing three assumptions as to the age and correlation of the Allegheny peneplain. *A*, the plateau surface is Harrisburg peneplain, as is also the Central Lowland. *B*, the Allegheny peneplain is younger than the Schooley and older than the Harrisburg. *C*, the plateau surface is Harrisburg and is older than the Central Lowland.

the province boundary in southern Ohio is then explained by assuming that the marginal cuestas are surviving remnants of the Schooley surface (Fig. 82*A*).   This in itself is not improbable.   In northern Ohio where there is no abrupt change in level at the province boundary it may suffice to say that the newer peneplain was poorly developed.

It may be urged, on the other hand, that the forms of valleys in the Allegheny Plateau indicate a more eventful (hence probably longer) history than that of the surface farther west.   On

[1] CAMPBELL, M. R., Geographic Development of Northern Pennsylvania and Southern New York, *Bull. Geol. Soc. Amer.*, vol. 14, pp. 277–296, 1903. In this paper the Harrisburg peneplain (including what is here called Allegheny) was first named and systematically differentiated from the Schooley and from other post-Schooley surfaces.   Campbell's contoured map showing the warped surface of this peneplain makes it cover not only the coal measures but the surrounding higher zones which are here interpreted otherwise.

this assumption the plateau surface may be treated as a peneplain older than the Harrisburg. It is much lower than the Schooley on its eastern side and may or may not coincide with it at the west (Fig. 82B). Still another hypothesis correlates the plateau surface with the Harrisburg peneplain and the lowland west of it with the Somerville (Fig. 82C). Though often implied and sometimes expressed in the literature of the subject,[1] this hypothesis is not regarded as probable.

Fig. 83.—View up the Ohio River in the Allegheny Plateau about 12 miles east of the Central Lowland. The river at low-water stage is 463 feet high and the horizon 1100 to 1200 feet high. It represents the "Allegheny" peneplain, which at this place is probably very near the theoretical position of the restored Schooley peneplain. (*Ky. Geol. Survey.*)

Tentatively it is concluded that the summit level in eastern Ohio and parts of adjacent states is related to a former base level and is properly called a peneplain. So long as doubt remains with respect to its correlation, it seems best to give it a local name, which may be discarded later if it is proved to be the equivalent of the Harrisburg. The term "Allegheny peneplain," though abandoned by its author,[2] who gave to it somewhat greater scope,

[1] SHARP, HENRY S., The Geomorphic Development of Central Ohio, *Bull. Denison Univ.*, vol. 27, pp. 1–46, 1932.

[2] ASHLEY, GEO. H., Scenery of Pennsylvania, Pa. Geol. Survey, *Bull. G-6*, pp. 23*ff.*, 1933. See also FRIDLEY, H. M., and NOLTING, J., Peneplains of the Appalachian Plateau, *Jour. Geol.*, vol. 39, 749–756, 1931. These authors credit the term to Ashley.

is a suitable designation for the surface on the coal measures and has the advantage of being noncommittal as to correlation. As the uplift of the Schooley peneplain diminished toward the west it is not probable that the Allegheny and the Schooley can be differentiated in central Ohio if the former is not identified with the Harrisburg.

Erosion Cycles in West Virginia.—Near the Allegheny Front in the middle of West Virginia, it is agreed that the Schooley peneplain is indicated approximately by the highest uplands and that it slopes northwestward, but there is much difference of opinion as to whether some exceptionally high areas are residual or due to local warping. In a study covering some 5000 square miles of the plateau, Wright[1] delineated the older peneplain as warped into domes, two of which on the Allegheny Front near the latitude of Charleston rise above 4600 feet, another farther north, above 4400 feet, and another farther south, above 4200 feet. If local warping be ignored, his Schooley surface, represented only by remnants, declines northwestward from these altitudes to 1200 feet in 100 miles. As the point thus reached (lat. 39°, long. 81°) is still more than 30 miles from the Ohio River and the descent continues, the difficulty of determining the westward extent of the Schooley peneplain is readily seen. Where two surfaces, each with its own local relief, come so near together that the interval between them is less than the relief of either, discrimination is hazardous and diverse interpretations may be expected.

West of the New River in southern West Virginia the Schooley surface seems to be indicated at an altitude of about 3500 feet[2] on knobs and ridges which constitute the smaller part of the surface. Toward the northwest these remnants decline both in absolute and in relative height.

A line drawn parallel to the Ohio River, 20 or 30 miles southeast of it, would mark the approximate limit of the area within which the Schooley peneplain can plausibly be said to be indentifiable. The supposed limit is both vague and irregular. Southeast of that line, elevations believed to represent the Schooley

---

[1] WRIGHT, FRANK J., *loc. cit.*

[2] Altitudes not taken from Wright's paper are taken from U. S. Geol. Survey folios Nos. 34 (by J. A. Taff and A. H. Brooks), 69, 72, and 77 (all by M. R. Campbell), and 184 (by W. C. Phalen).

surface increase in number and relative altitude toward the
Allegheny Front. Within this area appears the probable correlative of the Allegheny peneplain. This is a wide zone reduced to
a lower level near the Kanawha River and its upper course, the
New River. It is dissected now but still preserves its flat
horizon and is continuous from the Great Appalachian Valley

Fig. 84.—Gorge of the New River above Nuttall, W. Va., eroded in a peneplain younger than the Schooley. Depth 1000 feet. The rock is Pottsville sandstone. (*Photograph by M. R. Campbell, U.S. Geol. Survey.*)

to the Ohio.[1] This surface is 1100 feet high near Charleston
where low residuals rise 100 feet or more above it and the river
cuts a gorge 500 feet deep. The general level rises steadily
upstream to a height of 2600 feet at Hinton, near the Allegheny
Front, where the gorge is 1100 feet deep and residual masses (at
some distance) are 1000 feet high. Upstream (south) from

[1] CAMPBELL, M. R., and MENDENHALL, W. C., Geologic Section along the
New and Kanawha Rivers in West Virginia, U. S. Geol. Survey, 17*th Ann.
Rept.*, pt. 2, pp. 473–511, 1896. This paper does not apply names to
peneplains.

Hinton the general level declines, showing that an uplift, with its axis near the Allegheny Front, has occurred since the peneplain was made.

The well-developed peneplain along the New-Kanawha River is apparently an extension of the plateau surface that prevails over western Pennsylvania and parts of adjacent states. Apparently also, it is a continuation of the same peneplain which makes the floor of the Great Valley where crossed by the New River in southwestern Virginia. It is clearly younger than the Schooley surface and there is some reason to think that it is older than the Harrisburg. This possibility with respect to the valley in southwestern Virginia is stated on page 261. Reasons for such an inference with respect to the Allegheny Plateau are given below.

The Worthington Peneplain.—Along the larger streams, especially where the rocks are soft, the surface is so consistently about 100 feet lower that a later subcycle of erosion, the Worthington, has been assumed.[1] This lower and generally smoother surface, found in straths which are often 2 to 3 miles broad in Pennsylvania and broader in Ohio, seems at many places to be too well outlined and too clearly separable from the general level to be regarded as merely valley bottoms of the Allegheny cycle.[2] In Pennsylvania, West Virginia, and much of Ohio, wherever the lower surface has definitely been regarded as the product of a distinct subcycle of erosion, it consists of broad valleys only.[3] Even in the Beaver, Pa., quadrangle, which is next to the Ohio line, traversed by the Ohio River and by the main line of pre-glacial drainage (page 316) the Worthington surface does not extend more than 4 miles from the river. Conditions are similar in the adjacent part of Ohio where the Allegheny-Worthington interval is 140 feet.

Farther west are broader strips, and in several counties of southeastern Ohio on the coal measures the general level is

[1] BUTTS, CHARLES, Kittanning folio (No. 115), U. S. Geol. Survey, 1904. The vicinity of Worthington in this quadrangle is the type locality.

[2] STOUT, W., and LAMBORN, R. E., Geology of Columbiana County, O., Ohio Geol. Survey, *4th Ser. Bull.* 28, p. 40, 1924. Geologists of the Ohio Survey call the plateau surface Harrisburg peneplain and make the Worthington 140 feet lower in Columbiana County.

[3] STONE, R. W., Physiography of Southwestern Pennsylvania, Pa. Geol. Survey, *Rept. for* 1906–1908, pp. 120–127, 1908.

mainly that of the lower peneplain.[1] The elevation there is 1000 feet or less, and the same is true of a considerable strip on the West Virginia side of the river. The limits of this surface in the plateau province have not been accurately traced, but it merges at the west with the Lexington peneplain, which covers western Ohio and much of the Mississippi Valley. The broad development of the Worthington surface near the Ohio seems to be related both to the weakness of the upper coal measures and to its proximity to the main drainage lines, present or past.

Ages of Peneplains.—The assignment of greater age to the Allegheny peneplain than to the Harrisburg rests on the assumptions (1) that the Worthington peneplain is the product of a distinct cycle (or subcycle) and (2) that it is the equivalent of the Lexington peneplain. The Harrisburg cycle was the last one of major importance on the Atlantic slope. The Lexington has the same distinction in the Central Lowland. The remains of the Lexington peneplain are probably more extensive than those of any other on the continent. To treat this important cycle as post-Harrisburg is to correlate it with the minor Somerville episode in which only narrow local peneplains were developed on soft rocks near the sea. In view of the many chances of error in correlation by tracing surfaces from place to place, it is believed that the extent to which a peneplain was developed and subsequently eroded, taking all factors into account in both cases, is a safer guide. The Nashville Basin and other post-Lexington lowlands of the interior should have required quite as much time in the making as all that passes under the name of Somerville peneplain.

The Parker Strath.—More obvious than the Worthington surface is a terrace about 200 feet lower. Its original width was 1 or 2 miles, but it was in larger part destroyed as streams were again rejuvenated and cut deeper valleys. No large stream in the region is without this feature. This terrace is the so-called Parker strath.[2] Certainly most of it, and probably all of it, is former flood plain, a planation surface limited by bluffs. Its rock

[1] HYDE, J. E., Geology of the Camp Sherman Quadrangle, Ohio Geol. Survey, *4th Ser. Bull.* 23, p. 164, 1921.

[2] BUTTS, *loc. cit.* Strictly speaking this is a strath terrace, not a strath (see footnote, p. 181). The term is here retained because it has in this case passed into use as part of a proper name.

floor is covered by gravel, sand, or silt to maximum depths of
more than 100 feet. This is largely of glacial origin along streams
which flowed from the ice and of local origin elsewhere. While
the larger streams were entrenching themselves to this level
and widening their bottoms, their tributaries dissected the
nearby older surface to approximate maturity.

Abandoned Valleys.—The terrace of the Parker stage is of
special interest in connection with drainage changes, some of
which are described here, while others must be deferred to the
treatment of the glaciated section of the Allegheny Plateau (page
317). Some of the larger streams, from the Kanawha and Ohio
on the south to the glacial boundary on the north, have abandoned portions of their old valleys at the Parker level in favor
of new courses which are generally, but not always, shorter.
These broad smooth valleys several hundred feet below the
adjacent hilly surface, and not now followed by streams, are
conspicuous features of the landscape. As their bottoms are
at the level of the Parker Strath, the changes of stream courses
must have followed the downcutting, the planation, and the
deposition, all of which made that terrace. No one explanation
of these changes is universally accepted. No doubt, in a few
cases, meanders, even though entrenched, were cut off by continued lateral corrasion, but in other cases the new channel is
miles in length and no straighter than the old. In most cases it is
necessary to assume valley filling at the Parker stage, sufficient
to cover some local divides, thus enabling the stream to elect a
new course.

At least three hypotheses have been advanced which deserve
attention: (1) Complete obstruction of northward drainage by
ice, which ponded the waters, in which sediments then accumulated to the necessary height.[1]   (2) Local dams of ice, which
held back the streams and caused the necessary deposition on
their upstream sides.[2]   (3) Overloading of streams which flowed
from the ice, causing aggradation, not only of their own valleys

[1] WHITE, I. C., Origin of the High Terrace Deposits of the Monongahela
River, *Amer. Geologist*, vol. 18, pp. 368–379, 1896; abst. in *Science*, vol. 4,
p. 385, 1896.
[2] CAMPBELL, M. R., Masontown-Uniontown folio (No. 82), U. S. Geol.
Survey, 1902.

but of north-flowing streams with which they united.[1] Any one
of these three conditions might result in the filling of valleys to a
level above that of local divides and the adoption of a new course.

No one of these suggestions can yet be wholly discarded.
As all the preglacial drainage of the section is believed to have
escaped to the north (Fig. 93, page 318), nothing is more certain
than that the main streams were blocked by the Pleistocene ice
and lakes must have formed.   At none of the places in question

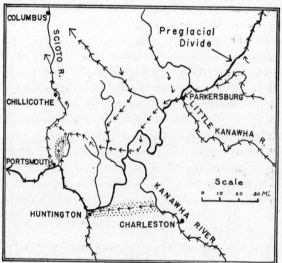

Fig. 85.—Present and former drainage of southeastern Ohio and adjacent part
of West Virginia. Solid lines represent present streams. Arrows indicate the
courses of former drainage. (*Data from W. G. Tight, U. S. Geol. Survey.*)

have lake sediments been actually observed at levels high enough
to superpose the drainage along present lines.

Evidence of important lacustrine deposits is weak in the
Monongahela basin, for which the hypothesis was first put forward.   It is much stronger in the valley of the old Kanawha
which followed the course of the Ohio to a point about 7 miles
east of the Scioto and flowed thence northward through a spacious
valley now abandoned and once filled, at least partially, with
lacustrine clay and alluvial silt.   It is here that superposition

[1] Shaw, E. W., High Terraces and Abandoned Valleys in Western Pennsylvania, *Jour. Geol.*, vol. 19, pp. 140–156, 1911.   Shaw gives references to
the principal contributions before 1911.

on the old lake filling makes its strongest appeal. All the tributaries of this main valley are likewise partly filled. Small streams follow the old valleys, some in the original direction, some in the opposite. They enter and leave the old valleys without notice, crisscrossing the divides in an irresponsible manner which suggests superposition. Remnants of clay have been found as high as 860 feet,[1] and all requirements of the superposition hypothesis would be met by filling to a level somewhat below 900 feet. It is probable that the hypothesis of superposition on lacustrine filling (supplemented by alluvium) is correct in this case.

The hypothesis of ice dams, originating as jams in the larger streams, was suggested with primary reference to the Monongahela Valley. It involves some difficult questions and perhaps need not be invoked. Overloading and aggradation of the Allegheny River during a late glacial stage explains fairly well the abandoned valleys along that stream and its tributaries, and perhaps also along the Monongahela, whose gradient must have been reduced by a fill of more than 100 feet at Pittsburgh. But this hypothesis does not explain the features in southern Ohio where the sediment in old valleys is lacustrine.

THE GLACIATED ALLEGHENY PLATEAU

Were it not for the accident of glaciation, the northern section of the Allegheny Plateau might be included in the description already given for the southern section. Even as it is, the extent of dissection is much the same and the relief is similar in amount though qualitative differences are noteworthy.

Underlying Rocks.—The rocks underlying this section dip mainly south toward the synclinal basin in West Virginia. Because of this dip and the prevailing northward slope a large number of different formations outcrop in irregular east-west bands. While none of these rocks are highly resistant, the difference between firm sandstone and weak shale is reflected at places in abrupt, or at least noticeable, differences in altitude

---

[1] RICH, J. L., Drainage Changes and Re-excavated Valleys, *Proc. Geol. Soc. Amer.*, 1934; p. 102, 1935; see also STOUT, W., and S. DOWNS, The Minford Silts of Southern Ohio, *Bull. Geol. Soc. Amer.*, vol. 42, pp. 633–672, 1931. The last-named authors give 820 feet as the highest known limit of clay at the time of their writing.

and style of surface. The most conspicuous of such contrasts
is along the northern boundary, which is at most places an escarpment. Along this margin, where dips are a little steeper than
farther south and the northward slope of the surface is very
pronounced, the outcrops of the several formations are narrow.[1]
In some parts the Allegheny Plateau breaks off at the north by a
series of rock terraces, among which it is not always clear which
edge should be adopted as the section boundary. In the fol-

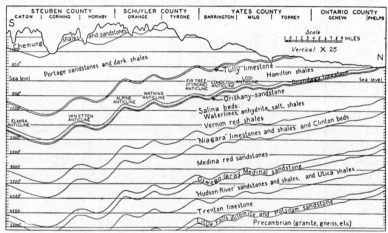

Fig. 86.—Cross section of New York State on the 77th meridian. The
plateau at this place owes its existence to the sandstones of the Chemung formation. Note the general southward dip and the gentle folds (whose steepness is
here multiplied by 25) increasing in amplitude toward the south, just as they
increase toward the east in Pennsylvania. (*N. Y. State Museum, Circ.* 7.)

lowing generalized column of Devonian rocks, only such characteristics are mentioned as have physiographic significance.

DEVONIAN ROCKS IN NEW YORK

Catskill: Important sandstone in eastern New York, with minor amounts
of shale.

Chemung: Shale and sandstone, the latter predominating near the top but
thinning out in western New York.

Portage: Shale and sandstone, the latter predominating in east central
New York but, toward the west, limited to members near the top.

Tully: A thin limestone between weak shales in west central New York.

Hamilton: Thick shales with subordinate sandstones in eastern New
York; becoming thinner and more exclusively shale toward the west.

[1] Best seen on the geologic map of the State of New York, 1901.

Onondaga: Massive limestone
Oriskany and other thin sandstones, shales, and limestones.
Helderberg: Massive limestone.

Boundary on the North.—The boundary between the plateau and the Hudson Valley has already been traced (page 204). East of the meridian of Schenectady, the Helderberg escarpment overlooks the Hudson Lowland. West of that line to the meridian of Utica, a distance of 50 miles, while the altitude of the plateau edge is well maintained, the scarp itself is relatively low because much of the surface to the north has considerable elevation (see Mohawk section, page 324). The lowest rock terrace is made by the Helderberg limestone and is 1300 to 1400 feet high at the east and 1600 feet high south of Utica. Three to ten miles back of this edge is generally another upward step (or a series of such) due to the harder sandstones of the Hamilton. South of this rise, the altitude is generally 2000 feet or more in the east and less farther west.

West of Utica the escarpment again overlooks a low plain, the eastern extension of the Central Lowland (page 449). The drop here is from an average altitude of 1300 to 1400 feet to a level of 400 to 500 feet. In the meantime the Onondaga limestone has taken the place of the Helderberg at the edge of the section. In the Finger Lake district there is a long descent from the plateau to a smooth surface not much above 700 feet. Here the outcrop of the Tully limestone makes a minor escarpment which serves as a conventional boundary. Farther west the sandstones of the Portage group support the plateau surface and make an escarpment to a point south of Buffalo. Beyond that the limit of the plateau seems to have been controlled more by erosion in the Erie basin than by the strength of any one formation. A well-marked escarpment extends almost to Cleveland, except for the interruption by the Grand River lowland described on page 316. Farther west, as the boundary of the Allegheny Plateau leaves the lacustrine plain and lies against the Till Plains, it is recognized less by difference of altitude and more by topographic contrast.

Boundary on the South.—The southern boundary of this section is, by definition, the limit of glaciation. As the interest here is in topography, not in geologic history, it is better in practice to limit the section to the area in which the topography

is clearly influenced by glaciation, mainly by the Wisconsin ice
sheet. An early ice sheet probably advanced 50 miles down the
Susquehanna and other valleys into territory whose present land
forms show nothing of its effects (Fig. 87).[1] Again in northwestern Pennsylvania, a 20-mile strip of old and scattered glacial
drift is disregarded, and the boundary drawn at the edge of the
Wisconsin drift sheet. Both here and in Ohio this edge is
marked by glacial topography sufficiently distinctive to make
the section boundary moderately clear.[2]

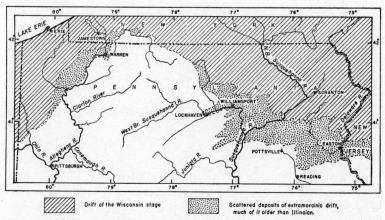

Fig. 87.—Map of Pennsylvania showing glacial deposits. (*Data from Leverett.*)

The glaciated section, east of the longitude of Buffalo, is almost
confined to Devonian rocks, which are weaker than the Pocono
and Pottsville formations preserved in the synclines on the other
side of the boundary. One important exception is the Pocono
Plateau east of the Wyoming Valley, an upland 2000 feet high on
nearly horizontal Pocono sandstone, distinctly glaciated almost
to its southern edge.

The Plateau Surface. Most of the surface of the Glaciated
section lies between the altitudes of 1200 and 2000 feet. The
highest altitudes are near the southern margin. South and

[1] Warren folio (No. 172), U. S. Geol. Survey, p. 7, 1910.
[2] Locally the glacial geology is quite complex, as recently shown by
George W. White, The Pleistocene Geology of the Region of the Reentrant
Angle in the Glacial Boundary in North Central Ohio, Abstracts of Doctors'
Dissertations, No. 13, Ohio State University, 1934; also, An Area of Glacial
Stagnation in Ohio, *Jour. Geol.*, vol. 40, pp. 238–258, 1932.

southwest of the Catskill Mountains, a level of 2000 feet or more is preserved on the major divides and the harder rocks. The eroded surface declines southeastward toward the Great Valley and toward the Delaware River, reaching levels as low as 1300 feet between streams. The plateau is everywhere separated from the Great Valley by an escarpment, but where the valley floor reaches levels of 800 or 900 feet (page 209), the escarpment may be less than 500 feet high and not abrupt. The plateau surface in this locality is on relatively soft Devonian rocks. East and southeast of the Wyoming Valley is the Pocono Plateau, an uneven surface on the strong Pocono sandstone. It is probably an imperfect peneplain, eroded after uplift and glaciated. On its western and southern sides, steep dip slopes descend to the Ridge and Valley province. On the east is a sharp escarpment, called Pocono Mountains, overlooking the worn-down surface on Devonian shales. Much of the high surface is still in forest.

The plateau north of the Catskill Mountains is 2000 feet high and cut to a depth of 1000 feet by Schoharie Creek and its tributaries. West of this the Mohawk-Susquehanna divide is very near the crest of the highest north-facing escarpment. A height of 1800 to 1900 feet is maintained to the Finger Lake district. The level in the Susquehanna basin declines a little toward the south but rises again to 2100 feet on the Delaware-Susquehanna divide in northeastern Pennsylvania where the sky line is smooth despite valleys 800 feet deep.

Among the Finger Lakes the surface is much reduced. The high level of 1800 to 1900 feet is found only around their heads, *i.e.*, their southern ends. A line drawn south through Cayuga Lake would pass through a slight depression from which the level rises eastward toward the Catskills and westward to the low dome mentioned on page 291.[1] Even the lower northern margin of the plateau in this district has valleys 300 to 400 feet deep. Relief farther south is 500 to 800 feet.

South and southwest of the Finger Lakes the Pocono and Pottsville sandstones come in, and the two levels described on page 289 make their appearance, the lower level being continuous

---

[1] FRIDLEY, HARRY M., Identification of Erosion Surfaces in South Central New York, *Jour. Geol.*, vol. 37, pp. 113–134, 1929. His Fig. 8, p. 130, shows contours on what he calls the Schooley (Campbell's Harrisburg) peneplain. These are not surface contours but the difference is not great.

with the surface in the Finger Lake district and farther east. This also is the surface which makes the low dome 2100 to 2200 feet high on the New York-Pennsylvania boundary (page 291) just within the conspicuous northward bend of the line which marks the limit of glaciation (Fig. 87). From this dome the upland level slopes imperceptibly north and northwest to the beginning of the steep descent which limits the province. Traced southwestward to Ohio, the upland level declines to 1300 feet or less. Relief decreases with altitude, from steep forested hills to rolling farmlands.

In northeastern Ohio there is another sag in the upland, bringing much of the surface down to a level below 900 feet in a north-south belt 8 to 12 miles wide and 40 miles long, drained by the north-flowing Grand River and the southeast-flowing Mahoning. This low, smooth, deeply drift-covered surface, an exceptional feature in the plateau, is explained on page 316 as the valley of a preglacial trunk stream.

The relation of the plateau surface to the Schooley peneplain has already been discussed on page 293. The surface on the Pottsville sandstone, assigned to the Schooley peneplain in northwestern Pennsylvania, is continuous with that of the glaciated section. The plateau around the Catskill Mountains is a fairly representative peneplain (now dissected), having roughly the same altitude as the higher ridges of the Folded Appalachians on the south, the prevalent level among the Taconic Mountains on the east and the Adirondack upland (aside from monadnocks) on the north. All of these are believed to be products of the Schooley cycle, and there is no good reason for assigning a different age to the plateau at the foot of the Catskills.[1] The only reason for assigning to it a different age is the absence of any break in the continuity of the plateau surface from southeastern New York to southwestern Pennsylvania, where it is lower and apparently more recent. The reason for this continuity is explained on p. 293.

It is fair to assume that the Schooley surface has been lowered, but evidence for one or more subsequent cycles in the Glaciated

---

[1] It is treated as "Cretaceous" peneplain by H. L. Fairchild, W. J. Miller, H. P. Cushing, and others of the New York Geological Survey. (*Cf.* citations under Catskills, p. 322.)

section is doubtful.[1] Probably the lowering has been much at one place and little at another, as the rocks vary in hardness and the proximity of main drainage lines favors dissection. That the Schooley level should be well preserved around the Catskills is to be expected from the prevalence of resistant sandstones in the

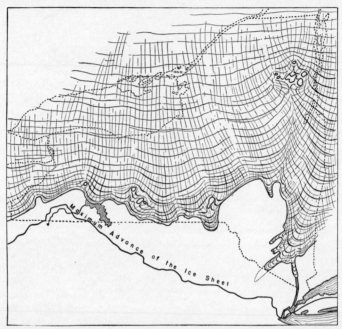

Fig. 88.—Indication of some recession of the ice front from its maximum advance. An area in the lee of the Catskills is deglaciated, but small lobes go up the mountain valleys. The highest of the Adirondacks and a few spots near the ice edge are laid bare.

Figs. 88–91.—Stages in the waning of the ice sheet in New York State. (*After Fairchild in N. Y. State Museum Bull.* 160.) Glacial lakes are indicated by stippling.

upper Devonian rocks in east central New York. The high altitude in southwestern New York is apparently due in part to later crustal warping.

Glaciation.—In considering the present day topography, attention is directed primarily to the last, or Wisconsin, ice sheet. At the time of its greatest extension it was sufficiently thick to

[1] The case for several cycles is stated by Harry M. Fridley, Identification of Erosion Surfaces in South Central New York, *Jour. Geol.*, vol. 37, pp. 113–134, 1929.

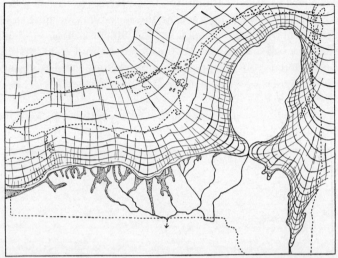

Fig. 89.—The ice has almost disappeared from the Adirondack province but wraps around it in two lobes, meeting near Little Falls. Lakes fill valleys sloping toward the ice.

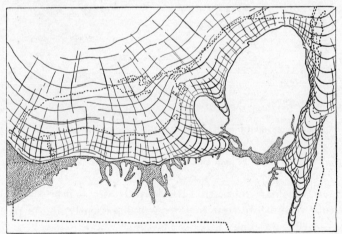

Fig. 90.—The Tug Hill cuesta stands out, causing further lobation. The waters of Lake Schoharie in the Mohawk Valley follow the foot of the Helderberg escarpment to the Hudson. Glacial lakes farther west drain to Lake Warren and the Mississippi.

move southward as a single mass, covering plateau and mountains alike.[1] It was only when it was weakening and wasting that the sheet began to split on the higher divides and move forward in lobes over the lowlands (Fig. 89). A suggestion of this tendency is seen in the reentrant angle in the glacial boundary in southwestern New York, at the place where the upland is domed.

West of this angle the effect of glaciation is apparent in rounded hills and partly filled valleys, a general reduction of relief, and

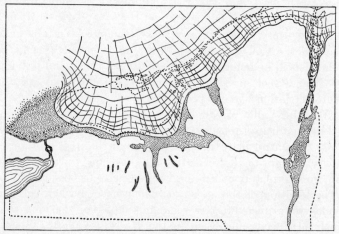

Fig. 91.—The ice in the Ontario basin is giving way to Lake Iroquois whose waters escape at Rome into the Mohawk Valley and thus to Lake Albany. The Niagara River and Falls have come into existence.

the omnipresence of boulder clay, also in a moderate number of lakes. Eastward from the angle to the North Branch of the Susquehanna, there is a considerable margin which must have been covered by ice for a short time only. There are no continuous moraines near the limit of ice advance, and scarcely even erratic boulders on some of the uplands. Valleys may contain glacial drift, but there is little of it on the hills. Even the soil is largely residual.[2] Farther east the Delaware-Susquehanna

[1] FAIRCHILD, H. L., Pleistocene Geology of New York State, *Bull. Geol. Soc. Amer.*, vol. 24, p. 135, 1913. The estimate is here made that its surface over the Adirondack Mountains was 9000 to 12,000 ft. above the sea.

[2] TARR, R. S., Watkins Glen-Catatonk folio (No. 169), p. 16, U. S. Geol. Survey, 1909.

divide and the Pocono Plateau are clearly glaciated and dotted with lakes.

It was not until the ice front had retreated almost to the southern ends of the present Finger Lakes that a long halt occurred and substantial moraines were built.[1] These are known collectively as the Valley Head moraines, and they mark approximately the present divide between the Ontario and the Susquehanna drainage except for the Genesee River. North of this line of moraines the time of ice occupation was much longer than south of it and the ground moraine is more important. However, it is not to be understood that the glacial drift on the plateau is very thick at any place except in certain valleys. South of the Finger Lakes and over much of the area between them, the till in general is less than 10 feet thick, and it averages less than 3 feet on the uplands.[2] The topography as it was before glaciation has not been greatly changed.

Even the Valley Head moraines do not constitute a single, well-defined belt of terminal moraine outlining the edge of the ice across the entire plateau. In this rough country, moraines are patchy. Maps of the retreating ice sheet, or of areas of stagnation, must probably continue to be tentative (*cf.* page 386).

The lobation of the ice sheet, which ensued when the higher divides were uncovered, is seen first of all in the long tongue which advanced southward in the Hudson Valley. When the surface of the glacier fell below that of the Adirondacks the ice parted, following the Hudson and St. Lawrence valleys. It spread westward from the former in a lobe which advanced up the Mohawk Valley almost to Utica. At the same time a lobe west of the Adirondacks spread to the south and southeast from the St. Lawrence Valley and met the other lobe coming from the east. The difficulty which the ice encountered in climbing the Allegheny Plateau and advancing southward was less in the Finger Lake district where the surface was lower and smoother. Here an incipient lobe developed, having the form of a semicircle (Fig. 88).

The Finger Lakes.—Two groups of long narrow lakes in west-central New York suggest fingers spread apart and pointing southward, hence the name of the groups. Obviously these

[1] *Cf.* FAIRCHILD, N. Y. State Museum, *Bull.* 160, Pl. 11.

[2] TARR, *op. cit.*, p. 16.

lakes are in the valleys of preglacial streams, and just as obviously their basins above the water level have been seriously modified by moving ice.   These are about the only facts relating to their origin which have not been disputed.[1]   The largest lakes, Cayuga and Seneca, 40 miles long, are undoubtedly in the valleys of streams that flowed north.   The direction of former flow in some of the smaller basins is less certain.   The four smaller lakes of the western group drain to the Genesee River, and their axes converge toward its mouth just north of Rochester.   The seven lakes of the eastern group drain to the Seneca River and their axes converge toward a point in Lake Ontario.

Lake Cayuga, 381 feet above the sea, has its bottom 54 feet below sea level.   Lake Seneca, 444 feet above the sea, reaches a depth of 174 feet below sea level.   A drilling nearly 600 feet below the bottom of this lake did not reach the rock floor of the old valley,[2] which is partly filled by outwash.   East and west from these two large lakes the others increase in altitude to almost 900 feet, while decreasing in depth and size.

The question of greatest interest is how these basins attained their great depth.   Ice erosion is suggested by the forms of the exposed slopes.   They are wonderfully smoothed, increasing in steepness toward the lakes with a gently convex curvature. Except for a few postglacial ravines, the contour lines are almost as straight as the lakes.   For many miles together the absence of tributaries is almost complete.   Not only were the lateral ravines of preglacial time filled, but the divides between them were smoothed off.   Nothing but a glacier could have made the sides of these lake basins so simple.

[1] It is impossible to allow the necessary space here for a critical discussion of points in controversy.   The following papers, among others, contain valuable information and discussion.   Some of them also give further references to the literature of the subject.

DRYER, CHARLES R., The Finger Lake Region of Western New York, *Bull. Geol. Soc. Amer.*, vol. 15, pp. 449–460, 1904.   TARR, R. S., Watkins Glen-Catatonk folio (No. 169), U. S. Geol. Survey, 1909.   SPENCER, J. W., Hanging Valleys and Their Preglacial Equivalents in New York, *Bull. Geol. Soc. Amer.*, vol. 23, pp. 447–486, 1912.   FAIRCHILD, H. L., Pleistocene Geology of New York State, *Bull. Geol. Soc. Amer.*, vol. 24, pp. 133–162, 1913; Ice Erosion a Fallacy, *Bull. Geol. Soc. Amer.*, vol. 16, pp. 13–14, 1905. MONNETTE, V. E., The Finger Lakes of Central New York, *Amer. Jour. Sci.*, 5th ser., vol. 8, pp. 33–53, 1924.

[2] FAIRCHILD, H. L., *Bull. Geol. Soc. Amer.*, vol. 24, p. 142, 1913.

The dominance of the glacial agency at the surface inevitably suggests downcutting in the axis of the valley. This meets with grave difficulties long before the rock bottoms of the basins are reached. Difficulties do not wholly disappear if the agency of preglacial or interglacial rivers is invoked. In order that rivers might cut gorges which are now more than 700 feet below sea level, it is necessary to assume a temporary uplift, greater than is known to be required at any other place along the line of drainage from these lakes to the sea, whether the direction of that drainage was north or south. Only the gorge of the Hudson is deeper. On the whole, perhaps, rivers afford a better field for speculation than glaciers. The topographic work of the latter was important in the upper parts of the valleys, but it can not now be confidently affirmed that these basins owe their great depths to the erosive work of ice. So far as known, the water in these basins is held entirely by morainic deposits at their northern ends. It has not been definitely shown that longitudinal profiles of the rock surface would show basins. Crustal movements are, however, raising the surface at the north.

Preglacial Drainage of the Allegheny Plateaus.[1]—The northern end of the Allegheny Plateau first rose above the sea as a coastal plain sloping southward from the old Canadian and Adirondack highland. Streams heading on the highland flowed south across the plain to the Appalachian trough in Pennsylvania. Cuestas inevitably developed with the growth of subsequent strike streams. After the great upheaval in the Appalachian Revolution the northeastern part of the plateau province was a relative lowland stretching far to the east, bounded by the Pre-Cambrian highland on the north and by the newly made mountains on the south and east. It is commonly believed that the water which descended the slopes from the mountains escaped to the west by one or more major streams.

As the weak Cambrian and Ordovician beds were exposed on the northern margin, important subsequent valleys were opened on their outcrops, *e.g.*, the Ontario and Mohawk valleys. The

[1] FAIRCHILD, H. L., The Susquehanna River in New York and Evolution of Western New York Drainage, *Bull. N. Y. State Museum*, 256, 1925. Some of the opinions expressed in this paper are disputed. For a map of preglacial drainage as assumed by Fairchild, see *Science*, vol. 76, p. 426, Fig. 2, 1932.

streams that made these valleys grew headward, capturing and diverting, one by one, the older consequent streams from the north. A similar strike valley, cut in the soft Devonian shales, is now the basin of Lake Erie. There is little question that the original drainage of these subsequent valleys west of the Adirondacks was toward the interior, but whether this was the case just before Pleistocene glaciation, or whether the drainage was then following an ancestral St. Lawrence is not yet determined.[1] Whichever way the master stream flowed, its old valley is now filled with drift and obscured.

The bottom of Lake Ontario is 591 feet below sea level and its rock floor may be still deeper.[2] From such a deep strike valley it is natural to expect that obsequent tributaries would send their heads far to the south. This was better illustrated before the changes due to glaciation, but the Genesee continues to drain its old basin. The Mohawk Valley farther east is relatively shallow by comparison, and it developed only short obsequent tributaries. Hence the beheaded members of the Susquehanna system (North Branch) continue to drain the plateau, almost from its northern edge.

For some distance southwest of the Genesee, the lines of preglacial drainage led from the Allegheny Mountains to the Erie basin (Fig. 92). The principal stream in the Pennsylvania part of the plateau was the Monongahela, continued northwestward along the line of the Beaver and Mahoning rivers (reversed) and the Grand River to the Erie Basin. It was the lower valley of this large stream that became, after glaciation, the smooth lowland mentioned on page 309.[3] Farther south, the Kanawha and Big Sandy joined and flowed north to Chillicothe, Ohio, through the now abandoned valley mentioned on page 303.

---

[1] A brief but lucid statement of alternatives is given by F. Leverett in his Outline of History of the Great Lakes, Mich. Acad. Sci., *12th Ann. Rept.*, p. 21, 1910. J. W. Spencer advocated an eastward outlet; see Origin of the Basins of the Great Lakes of America, *Amer. Geologist*, vol. 7, pp. 86–97, 1891; also a more exhaustive paper in the *Quart. Jour. Geol. Soc. London*, vol. 46, 1890. The argument for a westward outlet is presented by A. W. Grabau in his Niagara Falls and Vicinity, *Bull. N. Y. State Museum*, 45, 1901, in which he cites older opinions.

[2] The extent to which this depth is due to glacial scouring is unknown.

[3] LEVERETT, F., Glacial Formations and Drainage Features of the Erie and Ohio Basins, U. S. Geol. Survey, *Mon.* 41, p. 74, 1902.

Farther north and west the old valley is lost beneath the drift. It may have reached the Mississippi or one of the Great Lakes.[1]

Changes Due to Glaciation.—The coming and going of a continental ice cap made little difference in the drainage where the flow was southward, *i.e.*, away from the ice front. The

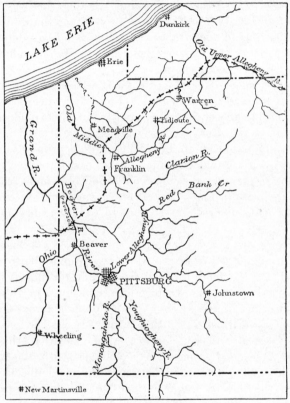

Fig. 92.—Sketch map showing probable preglacial drainage of western Pennsylvania. The line of crosses is approximately the edge of the glacial drift. (*Leverett, U. S. Geol. Survey.*)

Delaware suffered no major change. The facts about the Susquehanna are less certain.[2] Farther west the drainage was toward the ice and was compelled to seek new courses. Each stream, as it reached the ice, was ponded. It filled its valley first with water, then partly or wholly with sediment. Ultimately the

[1] LEVERETT, F., *op. cit.*, p. 103, discusses several possibilities.

[2] See reference in footnote, p. 315.

level of one or the other rose above a col leading over to the next basin. By thus breaking over from basin to basin, the water followed the most available of the old valleys, some of them upstream and others down. The final result was a piecing together of formerly distinct valleys into a continuous stream from the head of the Allegheny to the lower Ohio (compare Fig. 93).

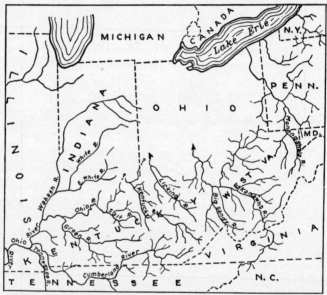

Fig. 93.—Map showing old drainage systems before combining to form the Ohio River. (*Leverett.*)

The most noteworthy of these changes was the permanent obstruction of the old stream which led from Pittsburgh to the Erie Basin. This stream received a tributary which flowed northeast from the site of New Martinsville on the Ohio River near Mason and Dixon's Line prolonged westward. The ponded waters backed up this stream and overflowed a col into another valley leading southwestward. This became the new course of the Ohio. The position of the old divide is marked by an exceptionally deep, steep, and narrow gorge.[1] A series of

[1] TIGHT, W. G., Drainage Modifications in Southeastern Ohio and Adjacent Parts of West Virginia and Kentucky, U. S. Geol. Survey, *Prof. Paper* 13, p. 29, 1903.

similar events at points in front of the ice between New York and southern Ohio, resulted in a continuous stream, the Allegheny-Ohio, roughly parallel to the edge of the ice (*cf.* the Missouri River, page 564).

South of the Finger Lakes the cols by which the ponded waters finally escaped were at the heads of the north-flowing streams, *i.e.*, on the old divide in northern Pennsylvania on the Pocono or Pottsville sandstone. While the front of the retreating ice sheet was halting at the present "Valley Heads" the new channels leading over into south-flowing streams were so deepened that they remained in permanent use, the postglacial divide being along the Valley Head moraines.

THE CATSKILL MOUNTAINS

Relation to Underlying Rocks.—The Catskill Mountains in southeastern New York are surrounded by the Glaciated Allegheny Plateau, except on the east side where they border the Hudson Valley. The rocks that make the mountains may be thought of as a nearly horizontal hard plate which was wasted but slowly and still continues to protect the beds below. Meantime the protective cover has been deeply carved, but its divides still rise several thousand feet above the plateau. The protecting rock is a coarse, porous sandstone or conglomerate which resists erosion partly because of its induration and insolubility, and partly because of its porosity, which is adverse to the concentration of water into streams. Toward the west and south this character is gradually lost. Within the mountain section the formation seems to be an old delta or alluvial fan, hence the gradual change.[1]

In common with other rocks of the region, the Catskill formation is tilted slightly northwestward from the Hudson Valley and southward from the Mohawk. Structurally it forms a very gentle syncline pitching toward the southwest (*cf.* page 206 and Fig. 57). It is cut off on the southeast and northeast by the bold "Catskill Escarpment." On the southeast this escarpment descends to the Hudson Valley with a drop, at places, of 3000 feet.

[1] The rather complex relation of this formation to the rest of the Devonian is well shown by R. C. Moore, "Historical Geology," pp. 244–246, McGraw-Hill Book Company, Inc., New York, 1933.

On the northeast and north it descends only to a broad and deeply cut bench 2000 feet high, the local representative of the Allegheny Plateau.

The limiting escarpment on the northeast fronts a rugged cuesta whose dip slope declines southwestward to the upper Schoharie Valley, beyond which is another and similar cuesta breaking off toward the northeast in the "Central Escarpment." A dozen miles south of the Central Escarpment is the Southern Escarpment, facing south and overlooking the plateau. Between the Central and Southern escarpments is the main expanse of mountains including the highest summits. The summit level declines southwestward with a long and rugged dip slope which, at a distance of 30 to 40 miles, merges with the plateau surface.[1]

Erosional Forms.—The cuestas mentioned here would scarcely appear as such to the casual traveler. The scarps are obvious, but the dip slopes are known by generalization and are not comprehended in a single view. The whole is maturely dissected into mountains of diverse height but becoming lower toward the southwest and west where summits become broader and more uniform in height. A few summits, mainly near the escarpments, are a little above or a little below 4000 feet (Slide Mountain 4204 feet). There are scores of summits and divides between 3000 and 4000 feet, some of them 2000 feet above the nearby mountain valleys. A striking characteristic of Catskill topography is its coarse texture. Valleys are relatively few, and the intervening masses are correspondingly bulky. The paucity of small tributaries may well be due to the permeability of the rocks.

The surrounding plateau is plainly a former lowland. When streams ran over this surface, instead of in trenches as at present, the low gradient of the Schoharie extended up that stream and some of its branches well toward their heads in the mountains. Their valley floors in the mountains were straths 2 or 3 miles wide, continuous with the plateau and rising only moderately upstream. At present the Schoharie trenches the plateau more than 1000 feet deep. The sharp young valley goes up the strath, but its depth and width become less and less until the headwaters

---

[1] A good discussion of this section is by John L. Rich, Glacial Geology of the Catskills, *Bull. N. Y. State Museum*, 299, p. 11ff., 1934. Also *Amer. Jour. Sci.*, 4th ser., vol. 39, pp. 137–166, 1915.

are found to be draining old wide valleys made in the former cycle.

Drainage.—The development of drainage in this part of the plateau province was modified somewhat by the obduracy of the Catskill rocks. It was pointed out (page 316) that the headward growth of southern tributaries to the Mohawk has been small. But the headwaters of the Susquehanna could not have been protected against their competitors on the north had the main stream been cutting in strong rocks. Former streams may well have flowed southwest across the hard rocks of the Catskill area. If so, their upper courses had little cutting power and gradually yielded their domains to the obsequent Schoharie. The latter, in its continued headward growth, either developed or captured the subsequent stream between the cuestas. Meantime the Susquehanna continues in its consequent course down the original slope and dip. So also do the branches of the Delaware flowing southwest from the Central Escarpment.

The growth of east-flowing streams awaited the excavation of the Hudson Valley. Then the subsequent Catskill Creek developed at the foot of the Northern Escarpment, and the obsequent Esopus Creek cut far back into the central upland, beheading branches of the Delaware. This rapid development of obsequents on the east side is a continuing process. Among the fresh records of recent capture are two cases at the head of the Schoharie system, the captors being the Kaaterskill and the Plaaterskill.[1] When it is remembered that a capturing stream receives a sudden increment of volume and power, the exceptional sharpness of these two gorges is partially explained.[2]

Erosion Cycles.—The sky line of the Catskill Mountains is not very uneven despite the range of heights within a restricted area.[3] Some geologists find in this fact satisfactory evidence of a former peneplain. Others find the old hypothetical surface no flatter than might be expected on a wasting mass of slightly

---

[1] DARTON, N. H., Examples of Stream Robbing in the Catskill Mountains, *Bull. Geol. Soc. Amer.*, vol. 7, pp. 505–507, 1896. Plate 23, which accompanies this paper, shows the relations clearly.

[2] See U. S. Geol. Survey Topographic Map of the Kaaterskill Quadrangle.

[3] RICH, JOHN L., *Amer. Jour. Sci.*, 4th ser., vol. 39, p. 139, Fig. 2, gives a panoramic sketch in which evenness of sky line is very pronounced.

dipping hard rocks brought down to less than 2000 feet above the surrounding plain, which was for a long time near base level.[1] Among those who affirm a summit peneplain, some would correlate it with the Schooley (or Kittatinny if that be higher), others with an older peneplain, elsewhere destroyed.[2]

If a summit peneplain be postulated, its altitude must be nearly 4000 feet at the highest place. This is 1500 to 2000 feet higher than what is believed to be the Schooley surface on Shawangunk Mountain or in the Adirondacks or New England or northeastern Pennsylvania. There is no collateral reason for assuming such a decided bulge at this place. Moreover, it might be expected *a priori* that the Catskill conglomerate would fail to be base-leveled. Monadnocks of various other rocks, both sedimentary and igneous, are scattered from the St. Lawrence to the Carolinas, and the Catskills are here assigned to the same category. The summit level may or may not represent an older peneplain. In any case it is now eroded to late maturity and beginning to be subdued.

Glaciation.—The Catskills were entirely covered by the early Wisconsin ice sheet and again partly covered during the last advance.[3] Most of the area southwest of the Central Escarpment was covered only by the older ice sheet. Data on the movement of the glacier pertain mainly to the last invasion. The ice came from a direction at right angles to the escarpments, *i.e.*, from the north-northeast. Even at the time of its greatest vigor it veered somewhat to avoid the highest mountains. In its later stages, when thinned, weakened, and relatively warmed, it followed the valleys with astonishing plasticity. The ice entered the upper Schoharie Valley between the cuestas, partly by way of the river valley, partly over the escarpment farther east, the several lobes crowding one another and producing a confused tangle of moraines. Having filled the valley it pressed over several passes in the Central Escarpment. The same passes were later

---

[1] Wm. J. Miller, (The Geological History of New York State, *Bull. N. Y. State Museum*, 255, 1924) states definitely on p. 70 that the Catskills stood above the "Cretaceous" peneplain.

[2] FAIRCHILD, H. L., The Susquehanna River in New York, etc., *Bull. N. Y. State Museum*, 256, p. 16, 1925. The suggestion is made by Fairchild that the summit peneplain is of Jurassic age.

[3] Data on this subject are taken mainly from John L. Rich, *Bulls. N. Y. State Museum*, 196 and 299.

cut deeper by water from the retreating ice front and remain today as scenic features known as "notches." The lobe in the Hudson Valley spread laterally into the mountain valleys in a surprising manner, (Fig. 88). The ice pushed out in minor lobes not only westward but northwestward in the Rondout and Kaaterskill valleys.

Like other mountains of northeastern United States, the Catskills supported local alpine glaciers, probably both before and after general glaciation. It would be natural to expect alpine glaciers during the advance of the ice sheet rather than during its retreat, *i.e.*, at a time when the climate favored ice formation, rather than when it was making the continuance of ice impossible. However this may be, certain moraines unquestionably indicate that some local glaciers did follow the ice cap.[1] Cirques and glacial troughs are poorly exemplified in the Catskills but are clearer in the White Mountains (page 383).

Features due to ice erosion are not noteworthy. The topography is affected mainly by deposition in the valleys, where boulder clay, outwash gravel, or lake clays may raise the level 200 feet.

THE MOHAWK SECTION

Rocks and Their Relations.—Between the Allegheny Plateau and the Adirondack highland is the strike valley of the Mohawk River. Relative to the plateau, this valley is a lowland, but it is by no means all low or all smooth. Most of the rocks are Ordovician shales and limestones, the relative weakness of the Hudson River shale being the main factor in differentiating the Mohawk Valley from the Allegheny Plateau. However, the upper beds of this series, which appear only west of the Adirondacks, are stronger, and these rocks, together with a locally overlying Silurian sandstone, constitute a high cuesta whose scarp slope faces the Adirondacks and whose dip slope descends to the Ontario lowland on the west. Immediately below the shales in the scarp slope is the soluble Trenton limestone, the wasting

---

[1] It would be inappropriate to enter upon this discussion here. Reference is made to John L. Rich, Local Glaciation in the Catskill Mountains, *Jour. Geol.*, vol. 14, pp. 113–121, 1906; also to D. W. Johnson, Date of Local Glaciation in the White, Adirondack and Catskill Mountains, *Bull. Geol. Soc. Amer.*, vol. 28, pp. 543 and 552, 1917. For further mention and references see White Mountains, p. 383 of this volume.

of which has made the Black River Valley between the cuesta
and the Adirondacks.   Below the shales farther east in the
Mohawk Valley, the stronger Beekmantown limestone appears
at the surface on upfaulted blocks.   The surface on these blocks
is relatively high, not because of their original uplift, but because
the faults bring the more resistant rock to the surface.[1]

Altitudes and Topography.—The low valley of the Mohawk
affords a connection between the Hudson Valley and the Interior
Lowland.   This is the route of the Erie Canal, whose highest level
in central New York is approximately 450 feet A.T.   This
striking and often mentioned fact may lead to an exaggerated
impression of the lowness and smoothness of the valley.   The

Fig. 94.—General relations of the Allegheny Plateau, Mohawk Lowland, and
the nonmountainous edge of the Adirondack Upland.   Exposed Paleozoic rocks
are Ordovician, Silurian, and Devonian.   *SN* represents the Schooley peneplain
somewhat reduced.   The valley floor is an imperfect Late Tertiary (Harrisburg?) peneplain.   *BC* is a pre-Paleozoic peneplain exposed by stripping since
the Schooley peneplain was uplifted.   Vertical scale about eight times the
horizontal.   (*Altered from H. P. Cushing, N. Y. State Museum Bull.* 95.)

strip of land at the level of the canal and the New York Central
Railroad is merely a flood plain, varying in width from zero to
1 or 2 miles.   At most places the flood plain is bounded by steep
slopes or actual bluffs leading up to levels of at least 700 or
800 feet.   From these levels the surface continues to rise irregularly to the limits of the section both north and south.   At places,
especially on the fault blocks mentioned above, levels of 1100 or
1200 feet approach close to the river.   Elsewhere are structural
benches, drift-covered but made evident by escarpments.   West
of the meridian of Schenectady are several such benches of
intermediate height, fronted by escarpments facing east and
north (see topographic maps of the Amsterdam and adjacent
quadrangles).   The lowest of these extends north of the river
with a height of more than 1000 feet in the Glenville Hills.   The
inclusion of these benches in the Mohawk section is made necessary by the adoption of the Helderberg escarpment as the limit
of the Allegheny Plateau.

[1] Comparison of the topographic sheets of the U. S. Geol. Survey with the
geologic map of New York is instructive.

In general, the surface of the section is not that of a well-developed peneplain, but rather that of a glacial plain of considerable relief, interrupted by higher tracts reflecting inequalities of the underlying rock surface. At intervals are steep-sided young valleys in process of being graded to the level of the Mohawk.

The surface here described gives way to that of the Hudson Lowland near the 74th meridian. In part the boundary follows a north-south fault, west of which the harder limestone is at the surface (*cf.* page 206), also the rock terraces mentioned above. The surface is high and strongly undulating and declines westward from an altitude of 1200 or 1400 feet to 1000 feet in about 25 miles. Farther west, as far as Little Falls, is a low plateau of rounded forms 700 to 900 feet high. This description applies to both north and south sides of the river from the Hudson Lowland almost to Little Falls. The edge of the crystalline rocks (Adirondack province) is indicated by a continued northward rise rather than by a well-defined escarpment. Abrupt rises are noted mainly on those parts of the boundary where knobs or ridges surmount the general level of the crystalline surface, but these are rather frequent.

Near Little Falls, 20 miles east of Utica, the surface is high and rough on both sides of the river, with a horizon at 1200 to 1400 feet. The explanation is that a preglacial divide at this place was located on one of the upthrown fault blocks mentioned above as bringing the Beekmantown limestone to the surface. In this case Pre-Cambrian crystalline rock is brought up above the river's bed.

West of Little Falls the stronger Upper Ordovician rocks, which make the great cuesta farther north, begin to appear in benches and ridges. Ignoring such minor features, the Helderberg escarpment south of Utica separates two plateaus at altitudes of about 900 feet and 1300 feet, respectively.

The Tug Hill Cuesta.—North of Utica and Rome, the distinctive features are the Black River Valley and the cuesta known as Tug Hill. The Black River runs northwest along the nearly straight edge of the Adirondack province, descending from a level of 1200 feet northeast of Rome to 700 feet, where it turns west around the cuesta before entering Lake Ontario. The slopes of its wide, open valley rise eastward across old lake plains to the low edge of the Adirondacks (page 395), and westward by a series of remarkable limestone terraces[1] to the main escarpment, very steep, 500 feet high, and 4 to 6 miles from the Black River.

The top of the cuesta, midway of its length, is 2000 feet above the sea, the river at its foot being at 760 feet. The crest declines toward both ends, and the long dip slope to the west brings down the surface in 25 miles to the Ontario lacustrine plain at 500 feet. On its higher part the surface is smoothly glaciated with very

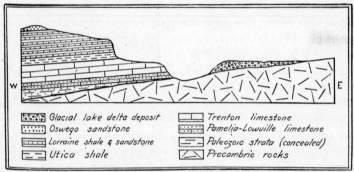

Glacial lake delta deposit   Trenton limestone
Oswego sandstone   Pamelia-Lowville limestone
Lorraine shale & sandstone   Paleozoic strata (concealed)
Utica shale   Precambric rocks

Fig. 95.—East-west section across the Black River valley 2½ miles north of Lyons Falls, N. Y., showing the terraced character of the Tug Hill cuesta and the glacial lake deposits on the east. Vertical scale greatly exaggerated. (*W. J. Miller, N. Y. State Museum Bull.* 193.)

moderate relief, hills as well as valleys being elongated from northwest to southeast. Postglacial drainage is very young, many depressions being still swampy.

Drainage.—The major features of the Mohawk section are the products of its drainage history, which, in turn, was the necessary result of its geologic structure. With major streams cutting down in the Hudson Valley and the Ontarian basin, it was inevitable that subsequent streams should grow headward along the outcrop of the weak strata. Streams growing from the two ends came into headwater opposition at Little Falls.[2] Doubtless,

[1] FAIRCHILD, H. L., The Glacial Waters in the Black and Mohawk Valleys, *Bull. N. Y. State Museum*, 160, p. 9, 1912. Fairchild states that drift on the west side is scanty, though all of these terraces except the highest are below the level of his Pleistocene lake at its second stage, whose old outlet at the south is 1240 feet A.T. See the Port Leyden topographic sheet of the U. S. Geol. Survey.

[2] First clearly stated by T. C. Chamberlin, Preliminary Paper on the Terminal Moraine of the Second Glacial Epoch, U. S. Geol. Survey, 3d *Ann. Rept.*, pp. 295–402, 1882. Ref. to p. 362.

this divide would have been farther west had not the east-flowing stream been checked from place to place in its headward growth by hard rocks brought up by faulting. At the last of these obstructions it met the opposition of its west-flowing competitor. The manner in which the latter stream was reversed between Rome and Little Falls is described below under Glaciation (page 328). Both streams in developing headward captured others which previously flowed south from the Adirondacks across the plateau, mainly into the Susquehanna. The headward elongation of the Black River southeastward from the master stream in the Ontarian basin is similarly explained by the outcrop of the soluble Trenton limestone.

In its erosional history the Mohawk section shared the events already recounted. The Schooley peneplain was continuous from the Adirondacks southward across the plateau, all scarps being substantially erased. In a post-Schooley cycle this section was worn down below the Allegheny Plateau. In its lower parts, 700 to 900 feet, it again attained old age, but rock terraces and remnants at intermediate levels indicate the incompleteness of the cycle. The massive cuesta west of the Black River rises essentially to the Schooley level. Later uplift brought about the entrenchment of the rivers and the dissection of the older surface.

Glaciation.—As the great southwest-moving ice sheet weakened, its movements followed more and more the great preglacial valleys[1] (Fig. 89, page 311). The Mohawk lobe was an expansion of the greater mass in the Hudson Valley. It spread to the west, even north of west, up the valley to the old divide at Little Falls. The moving stream of ice covered the edge of the Allegheny Plateau but was mainly if not wholly north of the escarpment made by the Hamilton sandstone. It is surmised by some[2] that the rough plateau farther south may have remained covered with stagnant ice for some time while the lobes continued to move. At all events the limestone upland north of the sand-

---

[1] CHAMBERLIN, T. C., *op. cit.*, pp. 361–365.

[2] COOK, JOHN H., The Disappearance of the Last Glacial Ice Sheet from Eastern New York, *Bull. N. Y. State Museum*, 251, pp. 158–176, 1924; ref. to p. 160. Also BRIGHAM, A. P., Glacial Problems in Central New York, *Ann. Assoc. Amer. Geogr.*, vol. 21, pp. 179–206, 1931; ref. to p. 190. See also Brigham's Glacial Geology and Geographic Conditions of the Lower Mohawk Valley, *Bull. N. Y. State Museum*, 280, 1929.

stone escarpment was severely scrubbed and finally left covered with thin drift disposed in drumloid hills elongated east and west, either made wholly of drift or merely veneered.

At the same time the main stream of ice in the St. Lawrence Valley, after passing the Adirondack Mountains, spread freely to the south and southeast. Thus a lobe moved up the Black River Valley, advancing as far as Little Falls, where it met the Mohawk lobe, the two together making a broad band of ice between the Adirondacks and the plateau.

Necessarily there was much derangement of drainage while the ice lasted, and changes while it was coming and going. Lakes, small and large, accumulated in valleys draining toward the ice. Their extent and their outlets changed as the ice front retreated and uncovered lower divides. The number of these short-lived outlets is great. Each new outlet meant a new shore line, to be abandoned like its predecessors, generally leaving few marks of its presence, or none at all. Most of these shifting waters left little effect on the larger landscape and cannot be mentioned here. A bit of shore line may be detectable on an occasional exposed slope, but such occurrences are extremely scattered. Deltas and lake clays were deposited in some of the basins, but no extensive area at present has soils of this origin. The study of these temporary drainage features is a specialized line of much interest, but it concerns the historical geologist more than the physiographer.[1]

The most important change in this section, the beginning of eastward drainage over the divide at Little Falls, is best discussed in connection with the history of the Great Lakes (page 495). It is enough to say here that the ice lobe in the Mohawk Valley melted away while the St. Lawrence outlet remained obstructed; also that the divide which was uncovered at Little Falls was lower than the previously used outlet of the Pleistocene Great Lakes at Chicago; that therefore the waters from one or more of the lakes of that time escaped eastward to the Hudson. Much of the gorge cutting at Little Falls was done by the swollen stream of that time. It also built the broad delta in the Hudson Valley, described on page 215.

[1] FAIRCHILD, H. L., Glacial Waters in Central New York, *Bull. N. Y. State Museum*, 442, 1909.

THE CUMBERLAND MOUNTAINS

Structural Relations.—The Cumberland Mountain section embraces a strip about 150 miles long and 25 miles wide on the southeastern margin of the plateau province in Virginia, Kentucky, and Tennessee. It is distinguished empirically by its altitude and relief, being everywhere higher than the adjacent Cumberland Plateau. These features are the result of differential erosion. The extent of the higher area is determined by structure and stratigraphy. Its largest and most characteristic part is a great fault block thrust northwestward at least 6 miles with some upturning at the edges, bringing the resistant Lee conglomerate (basal Pottsville) to a level above that of younger and softer rocks to the northwest. Adjacent to the southwestern end of this block, and included in the mountain section, is a considerable area in Tennessee underlain by the very strong Anderson conglomerate (uppermost Pottsville), the surface on which is at least as high and rough as that on the fault block adjacent.

The overthrust block is terminated at the northeast and southwest by cross faults.[1] In general, the structure within the area outlined by faults is a shallow syncline in which the most prominent formation, the strong Lee conglomerate, is turned up at the edges like the rim of a pan.[2] Its edges, at places almost vertical, make monoclinal mountains, Pine on the northwest and Cumberland, continued as Stone Mountain, on the southeast. The overlying strata within the syncline, which now make the highest mountains, have been saved from erosion partly by their own massive and resistant sandstones and partly, no doubt, because the drainage must necessarily cross the barriers of Lee conglomerate. The same rocks that are called Anderson conglomerate in Tennessee make the even-topped divides here.

A structural feature of secondary importance is a north-south fault on the line between Pine Gap and Cumberland Gap, the

---

[1] WENTWORTH, CHESTER K., Russell Fork Fault of Southwestern Virginia, *Jour. Geol.*, vol. 29, pp. 351–369, 1921.

[2] ASHLEY, GEO. H., and L. C. GLENN, Geology and Mineral Resources of the Cumberland Gap Coal Field, Ky., U. S. Geol. Survey, *Prof. Paper* 49, 1906. See Pls. 40*A* and 40*B*, geologic maps, and sections.

latter being where the three states, Kentucky, Tennessee, and Virginia, come together. The upthrown block on the east is Rocky Face Mountain. The fault is not known to extend north to Pine Gap, but this fault or another extends south to Cumberland Gap. The location of both gaps along this line is noteworthy. The crest of Cumberland Mountain changes its level suddenly at the Gap, being several hundred feet lower on the west than on the east. West of the Gap, and on the downthrow side of the fault, is the Middlesboro basin, 4 miles in diameter,

Fig. 96.—Escarpment of Cumberland Mountain near Cumberland Gap. The bed at the top is the conglomeratic Lee (Pottsville) sandstone. Ordovician rocks underlie the valley. Cumberland Mountain is the southeastern rim of a shallow syncline whose northwestern rim is Pine Mountain. (*Ky. Geol. Survey.*)

which is filled with recent alluvium at a level of less than 1200 feet. This is lower than the floor of the Ridge and Valley province on the other side of Cumberland Mountain. Such a low basin, situated on the downthrow side of a fault, partly filled with alluvium and draining north to the Cumberland River through a narrow valley, strongly suggests that faulting has been recent.[1]

Topography.—Cumberland Mountain is a part of the long Cumberland Front, or edge of the plateau province in the south, analogous to the Allegheny Front in the north. As seen from

[1] Rich, John L., Notes on the Physiography of Cumberland Gap, *Bull. Geol. Soc. Amer.*, vol. 44, p. 96, abs. 1933.

the valley of Powell River on the southeast, it is much like Powell Mountain on the other side of the valley and the parallel Clinch Mountain farther to the southeast, except that it is generally higher. Altitudes between 2500 and 3000 feet are most common, but the surface may be several hundred feet above or below these limits, the higher part being toward the northeast. The approximate horizontality of the crest as seen from many points leaves no doubt that the strongly dipping Lee conglomerate, where not actually peneplaned, was subdued to low ridges or knobs.

Pine Mountain has the same character with a little lower altitude, generally 2100 to 2300 feet in its southwestern half and 2600 to 2800 feet in its northeastern half, with a long swell rising above 3000 feet. As seen from the plateau on the northwest, this even-topped mountain stands little if any above the horizon near the Tennessee-Kentucky border but rises progressively northeastward until its relative altitude becomes 600 to 800 feet. A similar rise, though less abrupt, is seen in approaching the section from the northeast. At the southwestern end, where the surface of the fault block is lower, reaching 2500 feet only on isolated ridges, the neighboring plateau underlain by the Anderson conglomerate has hills and divides above 3000 feet. This exceptionally high part of the plateau, included in the mountain section, gives way rather abruptly on the west to the normal plateau level for this latitude, that is, 1600 to 1700 feet. The high part is coextensive with the hardest rock.

The mountains in the broad syncline between Pine and Cumberland mountains are deeply carved, mainly from nearly horizontal sandstone whose position is apparently accountable for considerable stretches of almost level profile. The highest and most continuous mass, near the northeastern end, is known as the Black Mountains. Their summit level is about 4000 feet. Near the middle, numerous small ranges of different names (the Log Mountains are best known) have a common horizon at about 3000 feet but declining southwestward.

Drainage.—Cumberland Mountain constitutes the main divide, the drainage being northwestward toward the Ohio. It has been surmised that the former drainage of the southern Blue Ridge province was all in this direction, *i.e.*, that streams crossed the folded Appalachian belt, ultimately reaching the

Ohio.[1] It is assumed that these northwest-flowing streams were captured by the subsequent headwaters of the Tennessee, in this case the Powell. The very existence of Cumberland Gap and the marked depression in the summit level north of it tempts the surmise that a stream once flowed through it to Pine Gap. This may well have been the case during the Cumberland cycle, but the assumption requires that the cutting occurred since the uplift of the Cumberland peneplain. This order of events involves grave difficulties. The level of the small stream now flowing from the Gap to Powell River is a full 200 feet higher than that of the stream on the opposite side, tributary to the Cumberland. Unless very significant crustal movements can be assumed to have followed the gorge cutting, Cumberland Gap must be accounted for mainly by weathering and local wash due to the crushing and weakening which resulted from faulting. Whatever headwaters the Cumberland may have had in a former cycle, its main upper course now is a long subsequent tributary on the shale outcrop at the southeast foot of Pine Mountain.

Erosional History.—The crest of Pine Mountain has long been regarded as a remnant of the Cumberland (Schooley) peneplain. Absolute flatness is not assumed. When the peneplain was at its best it may well be that the outcrop of the Lee conglomerate made a low swell or a series of long elliptical embossments, one of them being possibly 200 feet high but of exceedingly gentle slope. As this ridge affords the best evidence of a former nearly level surface, its altitude is taken to indicate the present local level of the peneplain. This is a little under 3000 feet at the northeast (*cf.* page 298), 2300 feet where the Cumberland River emerges, and at least 2100 feet near the Kentucky-Tennessee border.

Cumberland Mountain is, on the whole, a little higher and in parts much higher, as for 20 miles northeast of Cumberland Gap, but the stronger undulation of its crest makes its relation to a former base level less certain. No doubt it was imperfectly reduced.[2] Higher mountains between the Pine and Cumberland

---

[1] First proposed and discussed by Hayes and Campbell, *Nat. Geog. Mag.*, vol. 6, p. 101*ff.*, 1894. See also Ashley and Glenn, *op. cit.*, p. 17.

[2] ASHLEY and GLENN, *op. cit.*, p. 16, exclude a part of Cumberland Mountain from the peneplain, also a large part of the higher mountains between Cumberland and Pine. Campbell (U. S. Geol. Survey, folio No. 12) admits only a few monadnocks above the Cumberland peneplain.

ranges appear to be residual masses above the Cumberland peneplain. Flat segments of the summit level apparently owe their form and their altitude to the strong sandstone called Harlan or Wise at the northeast[1] and Anderson at the southwest.[2] To regard this summit level as an older peneplain would be unwarranted. Its altitude above the Cumberland peneplain in the Black Mountains near the northeast end of the section is more than 1000 feet. The difference decreases to 100 or 200 feet at the southwest end of the fault block. In northern Tennessee, beyond the limits of the fault block, the same formation lies at a higher level and has preserved a surface 1000 feet higher than the adjacent Cumberland plateau, whose altitude is approximately that of the Cumberland peneplain.

That the Cumberland peneplain was more or less warped during uplift has always been assumed. The difference of several hundred feet in the level of the mountain crest east and west of Cumberland Gap suggests post-Cumberland faulting. The alluviation of the Middlesboro basin reinforces this suggestion and points to a relatively recent date.

It thus appears that the superior altitude of the Cumberland Mountains is due in part to incompleteness of peneplanation in the Cumberland cycle; elsewhere (notably in Pine Mountain) to subsequent lowering of the adjacent surface. The history and correlation of the adjacent surface on the northwest is discussed on page 341.

THE CUMBERLAND PLATEAU

General Relations and Character.—The plateau which is called Allegheny in the north is called Cumberland in the south. If a boundary is specified at all, it must be arbitrary. None the less, the two names are useful, partly for mere geographical reasons, and partly because the character changes somewhat with latitude. The following discussion covers all that part of the province which lies in the drainage basin of the Kentucky River and south of it.[3] In a very general way the rocks in this southern

---

[1] Estillville folio (No. 12), U. S. Geol. Survey, 1894. The name Harlan has been used in inconsistent ways.

[2] Briceville folio (No. 33), U. S. Geol. Survey, 1896. The question of exact equivalence is not important.

[3] This agrees fairly well with popular usage. On the author's map of Physical Divisions of the United States (U. S. Geol. Survey, 1930) an

part are more resistant, and this must be taken into account in explaining the topography; but a division based strictly on this criterion would have to assign to the southern section all of the western margin of the plateau as far north as southern Ohio. Also, in a very general way, the southern section is less dissected than the northern, but the upper basin of the Kentucky River affords some of the roughest land in the United States. The surface of the southern end of the section in Alabama is likewise carved to maturity.

Rocks and Structure.—The Cumberland Plateau is underlain largely by rocks of Pottsville age. These are stronger than most of the rocks of the Allegheny Plateau, but they contain shales in alternation with sandstones, thus favoring the stripping of the latter. It was noted (page 292) that in southern Ohio the Mississippian rocks on the western margin of the Allegheny Plateau form cuestas rising to the full height of the plateau. The prominence of these cuestas diminishes toward the south, but they continue to form a narrow belt included in the plateau as far as latitude 37°30′, beyond which the Mississippian rocks (all except the uppermost) spread widely to the west at a lower level and belong to a different province. Farther south the strong conglomerates or sandstones at the base of the Pottsville (Rockcastle group) underlie and support the margin of the plateau. All beds here dip slightly to the east, and the strong basal formations are to some extent stripped, leaving at places a decided eastward dip slope. As the stripped belt widens toward the south, and the province narrows, the entire width of the Cumberland Plateau in Tennessee and Alabama comes to be on the strong formations here known as Walden and Lookout sandstones.

For nearly 200 miles along the median line of the province in Tennessee and Alabama, runs the straight Sequatchie anticline, broken on the west by a thrust fault. If left uneroded, it would form a range of mountains, as it still does at its northern end where the Crab Orchard Mountains are in line with the perfect anticlinal valley which marks the rest of the uplift (Fig. 97). Like the more extensive and complex Allegheny and Cumberland Mountains, this anticline represents the propagation into the plateau of the compressive stress by which the Ridge and Valley

---

attempt is made to draw a line between a maturely dissected Allegheny Plateau and a submaturely dissected Cumberland Plateau.

province was folded. Parallel to this feature, and 15 miles to the east is the similar Wills Creek anticline, marked by the valley west of Lookout Mountain.

Description of Boundaries.—The west-facing escarpment is everywhere conspicuous until gradually lost in Alabama by reason

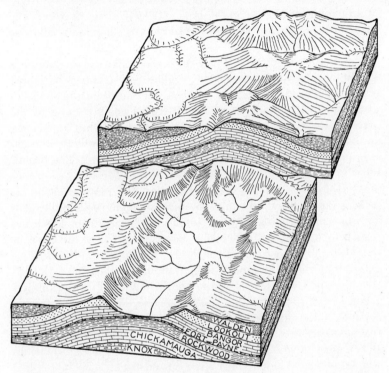

Fig. 97.—Block diagram showing the relation of Grassy Cove to the Crab Orchard Mountains. The Sequatchie Valley and Grassy Cove were formed where the Lookout and Walden sandstones were arched high enough to be cut off by erosion in the Cumberland cycle. The valleys were made in a later cycle. At the pitching end of the anticline the strong sandstones remained as a monadnock on the Cumberland peneplain. (*Diagram by Anneliese S. Caster.*)

of diminishing height. At places the slope is almost uninterrupted; at others it is terraced by formations of Chester (Mississippian) age. Everywhere its steepness is due to sapping. Its course is straight in general but ragged in detail, made so by young valleys. In the Kentucky River basin the escarpment rises from the Lexington peneplain (page 441) at 950 or 1000 feet

to heights ranging from 1300 to 1500 feet.   The lower level on
the west extends south through Tennessee into Alabama with
little change.   From the Kentucky River southward the height
of the plateau edge rises gradually, reaching 1800 feet on the
northern boundary of Tennessee and a maximum of more than
2000 feet in the southern part of that state.   Thence it declines
to 1400 feet before crossing the Tennessee River, where the
escarpment turns to the west and faces north, overlooking the
Tennessee Valley.

The boundary between the Plateau and the Gulf Coastal Plain
has no marked features.   In the margin of the former, hills may
be capped by remnants of coastal plain sediments.   In the
margin of the latter, streams cut down into the older rocks of the
plateau.   Between these two phases there is gradation.

The boundary on the east, known as the Cumberland Front, is
also an escarpment, which grows in clearness and height toward
the north.   The close folding (with marked faulting) on the east
side of the valley gives way gradually to milder and isolated folds
on which anticlinal valleys alternate with synclinal plateaus and
the province boundary is somewhat arbitrary.   Thus the
Cahawba and Coosa coal fields in Alabama (page 274)are isolated
from the plateau province, of which they are logically outliers,
and embraced in the Ridge and Valley province.   On the other
hand, Blount Mountain, and Lookout Mountain farther north,
each with an anticlinal valley to the west, are obviously parts of
the plateau.   The famous scarp face of Lookout Mountain shows
the same formations which appear in the long, nearly straight,
1000-foot escarpment from Chattanooga to Knoxville, between
which points the summit level reaches 2000 feet.   The boundary
between this section and the Cumberland Mountains is described
on page 329.

The straightness of the Cumberland Front is in strong contrast
with the frayed character of the scarp on the other side of the
province.   Sapping is the important factor in both cases.   In the
Cumberland Front it is due to weak Bangor limestone at the base
of the escarpment.   As mentioned before, the position of the
Front is on the western limb of an anticline.   The beds therefore
dip beneath the plateau.   The fold is sufficiently simple and the
dip sufficiently steep to cause the formations, when cut off by a
horizontal surface, to outcrop in narrow, nearly straight bands;

hence the straightness of the escarpment. The eastward dip at the western edge is very slight.

The Plateau Surface.—In its more typical part, mainly within the state of Tennessee, the Cumberland Plateau has an undulating surface submaturely dissected by young valleys whose steepness and depth increase toward the edges. Its foremost characteristic is seen in broad remnants of a surface in which only shallow valleys of an older generation are found. This part of the surface is underlain by the sandstone or conglomerate called Walden and Lookout here, Rockcastle in Kentucky, and Lee in the Cumberland Mountains. Weaker beds at the surface are negligible topographically, but enough of them remain to show by their beveling that the surface is a true peneplain.[1] The immaturity of the topography in the current cycle is due partly to the hardness of the sandstone, and partly to its great thickness, 600 to 700 feet, by reason of which sapping is impossible except at the edges.

In the Kentucky portion, where the province broadens, immaturity is seen only in a belt some 25 miles wide along the western edge, and even there it is less striking than in Tennessee. The same rocks noted in Tennessee underlie this belt, but they are less massive here. The beds dip eastward beneath other formations whose surface is higher and whose topography is quite different. The surface in this 25-mile strip is plainly a dip slope, apparently stripped since the last peneplaning. Its altitude of 1300 to 1500 feet at the province boundary declines southeastward to 1100 or 1200 feet in east-central Kentucky, which is only 100 to 200 feet above the lower province to the west. From this low level the surface rises eastward over formations of shale and sandstone to the foot of Pine Mountain. It also rises southward, merging with the 2000-foot level in Tennessee. The basin of the Upper Kentucky River is sharply and maturely dissected, with a relief of 500 to 1000 feet.[2] A common summit level is still observed and gives evidence of a former peneplain, though all of the hilltops have no doubt been reduced below the old level.

The plateau extends 135 miles south of the Tennessee-Alabama boundary. Its elongation is toward the southwest, but its slope

[1] HAYES, C. W., Physiography of the Chattanooga District, U. S. Geol. Survey, 19*th Ann. Rept.*, pt. 2, pp. 23–25, 1899.

[2] See the Hazard and adjacent topographic sheets of the U. S. Geol. Survey.

is more nearly southward, about 10 feet to the mile. The old peneplain, preserved in large patches at the north, is progressively more eroded toward the south. No flat uplands are left in the last 30 or 40 miles. South of the Tennessee River, where the inner boundary of the province runs east and west, it forms a broken cuesta with a scarp slope toward the river and an altitude of 1000 to 1200 feet. It is capped and protected by the same sandstone that supports the plateau in Tennessee, but the sandstone is thinner here and is cut through and sapped by the Tennessee and its tributaries; hence the mesa-like forms of the remnants. With approach to base level farther south, sapping and escarpments disappear.

Anticlinal Valleys.—The Sequatchie and Wills Creek anticlines, mentioned above, divide the plateau into three parts, Lookout Mountain east of the Wills Creek anticline, Walden Ridge (plateau) between the two folds, and the plateau west of the Sequatchie which bears no local name other than Cumberland Plateau. On both of these anticlines, when erosion had once breached the arch of thick sandstone and exposed the limestone and dolomite, axial valleys were developed. The present valley floors are in all respects like that of the folded province on the east. Indeed the floor of the Wills Creek anticline is as truly a part of the Great Valley as Lookout Mountain is a part of the plateau, but the outlying part of the plateau is so much larger that it seems better to include the narrow valley in the plateau province than to take the other alternative. Both valleys are bounded by escarpments, made steep and kept steep by the easier weathering of the weaker rocks below the sandstone cover. The straightness of the valleys merely reflects the straightness of the structural contours. In the case of the Sequatchie anticline, base-leveling of the upturned hard rocks on the flanks was never complete. These remain as a low monoclinal rim interrupted at intervals by gaps cut down to the general level.

The tendency of streams to develop on the axis of the anticline began whenever and wherever the sandstone arch was cut through. The gaps in the rim may have been made by transverse streams of an older drainage system.[1] Longitudinal

[1] Hayes, C. W., Physiography of the Chattanooga District, U. S. Geol. Survey, 19th *Ann. Rept.*, pt. 2, Pl. 4, 1899.

tributaries no doubt began in the Cumberland cycle, but their integration into a single south-flowing stream was probably accomplished in the later cycle.

Crab Orchard Mountain.—At both ends of the Sequatchie anticline the uplift was too little to make sapping effective and the fold continues to stand in relief, making Crab Orchard Mountain, 1000 feet above the plateau at the north, and similar though smaller mountains in Alabama. A singular development is now in progress in the Crab Orchard Mountains. The core of the mass is Bangor limestone which shared in the folding. With the cutting of valleys through the overarching sandstone, the limestone was exposed to solution, which deepened and spread from one or many centers until a great local depression 5 miles long and 2 miles wide now occupies the axis of the fold. This is Grassy Cove, a completely encircled basin whose flat floor is nearly 500 feet below the plateau. This steep-sided solution basin is only a mile from the equally steep head of Sequatchie Valley, whose floor is still lower, but the two are separated by a mountain whose lowest pass is nearly 1000 feet above the cove. Streams in the cove lead only to sinks at the northeast end.[1] The water there enters passages in the limestone, turns underground to the southwest, and issues again in the Sequatchie Valley.[2] The rock carried away to make the basin has followed the same course. The processes now at work in Grassy Cove, and others of the same kind though smaller, were no doubt active in the destruction of the range farther south during the Cumberland cycle.

Drainage.—The peculiarity of the Tennessee River in departing from its longitudinal course in the Great Valley of East Tennessee and crossing this province is described on page 276. The belief is there expressed that the present course was followed before the close of the Cumberland cycle. Its ancestral headwaters may or may not have crossed the Great Valley from the mountains on the east as other streams farther north may also have done (page 275). At present the Tennessee, after crossing Walden Plateau, turns from its transverse course and follows the Sequatchie Valley for 75 miles before turning again to the west. These rectangular turns, by which the river follows alternately

[1] Represented in Fig. 97.
[2] HAYES, C. W., Kingston folio (No. 4), U. S. Geol. Survey, 1894.

longitudinal and transverse courses, suggest adjustment by capture, but no other features remain to suggest that the Tennessee ever followed a different course.

Erosion Cycles.—It is commonly agreed that the Cumberland peneplain, which is seen on the upland in this section and on some of the higher ridges of the valley province, is correlative with the Schooley peneplain. It is well developed in eastern

Fig. 98.—Gorge of the Tennessee River in Walden Ridge west of Chattanooga, Tennessee, from Signal Hill.   (*Courtesy Cline Studios, Chattanooga, Tenn.*)

Tennessee, but not without a few monadnocks, among which the Crab Orchard Mountains are most prominent. It is parallel in general, but not in detail, to the bedding of the Pottsville formation.

The relation of the plateau surface to the underlying rocks is such as to raise the question whether the former surface of low relief may be primarily the stripped surface of the Walden sandstone rather than a peneplain produced near base level. Approximate parallelism of the plateau surface with the bedding and the fact that some large masses of the resistant sandstone remain at higher levels where it is arched up in the Sequatchie anticline give some plausibility to the explanation of the plateau as a stripped surface. This explanation becomes inadequate when it is remembered that the parallelism of surface with bedding is only approximate and that some of the beds at the surface, even in Tennessee, are soft. Beveling is general. Moreover, if the plateau level in Tennessee be projected northeastward it merges with the summit level of Pine Mountain, in which the resistant sandstone is upturned and truncated. The gradual rise of this level to nearly 3000 feet at the northeast is accounted for by inequality of uplift.

It is likewise true that the plateau surface may be traced northward from Tennessee, west of the Cumberland Mountain section, with no abrupt change in altitude. In general there is a gradual decline except near the southeastern edge, *i.e.*, near the sources of the streams. Therefore, in the latitude of Pine Mountain there are two levels, both continuous with the plateau surface in East Tennessee but separating northward like a pair of shears. Both of these levels have been identified with the Cumberland peneplain. Pine Mountain may be a little too high (page 332) but is no doubt the best representative of that peneplain in this locality.

The origin of the plateau level west of Pine Mountain, and indeed of the entire northern part of the Cumberland Plateau. must be considered in the light of the discussion on page 293. Northward from Tennessee to the Ohio Valley, the strong basal sandstones of the Pottsville are overlain by weaker rocks. The plateau surface on these weaker rocks is maturely dissected. All divides are sharp, and the general level of hilltops is being lowered. The horizon is still essentially flat and is properly said to "represent" a peneplain. If the last peneplain developed was the Schooley, then the one essential difference between the surface on Pine Mountain and that on the plateau to the northwest is that the former has wasted but little since the uplift and the latter has wasted much. This explanation alone would account for the difference in height. On the other hand, if it be asserted that a later peneplain was developed on the plateau in eastern Kentucky, the statement would be difficult to disprove. There is good reason to think that a newer peneplain (the tentative Allegheny) was developed farther north (page 295).

The summit level is essentially the same from the vicinity of Pittsburgh to central eastern Kentucky. Provisionally, it may be stated that, northward from Tennessee, the well-preserved Schooley peneplain gives way, first to a dissected and reduced Schooley peneplain on softer rocks, and then to the "Allegheny" peneplain, also minutely dissected.

CHAPTER VI

THE NEW ENGLAND PROVINCE

THE PROVINCE AS A WHOLE

Geologic Relations.—In a sense, the New England province is made up of the northward continuations of the Piedmont, the Blue Ridge, and the Ridge and Valley provinces (*cf.* page 123). Theoretically the New England area might be divided up and its parts assigned to the provinces named. Such a treatment would emphasize certain geologic relations, but it would sacrifice the geographic and geomorphic unity of this broad northern area, whose connection with the more southerly provinces is at best by a very narrow neck. The unity of the New England province and its differentiation from the others are further emphasized by glaciation.

The province has this in common with the Older Appalachians to the south, that its rocks have been greatly compressed, generally metamorphosed, uplifted, and deeply denuded. Most of them attained their present character under the weight of a great overburden, since removed by erosion. Present elevations are only indirectly related to upheaval. It happens in some cases that areas of ancient uplift are high today, but this is because of the hardness of the rocks in the cores of old anticlines or in Paleozoic intrusions. Present-day altitudes are related mainly to rock resistance and distance from the sea. Near the shore, some very strong rocks underlie low surfaces. To these factors must always be added the mere fortunes of erosion, for, even where rocks are uniform, residual masses are often found on divides.

Among the rocks most readily recognized as resistant are the intrusive igneous rocks, largely granite, of late Paleozoic time. Though underlying only about one sixth of the surface, they are widely distributed, making many of the mountains as, for example, the main mass of the White Mountains. Granite also

343

underlies large areas of plateau and, near the sea, some relatively low areas.

If the remaining rocks be classified in a few very comprehensive groups,[1] the order of hardness will be roughly that of age except for limestone. Essentially as resistant as the intrusives just mentioned are the Pre-Cambrian (Archean?) gneisses seen in the Green Mountain section and south of it to the Reading Prong. Younger sedimentary schists (in part Algonkian) underlie fully half of New England except for northern Maine. They are generally less obdurate than the granites and gneisses, and their surface is characteristically, though not universally, plateaulike. Relatively strong schists of Cambrian and Ordovician age make most of the Taconic Mountains (page 355).

Cambrian and Ordovician limestones, despite their age and metamorphism, are conspicuous valley makers. Their occurrence is limited to the long north-south valleys west of the Green Mountain axis. Rocks of the other Paleozoic periods are mostly of intermediate strength. Carboniferous phyllites and even conglomerates, from Rhode Island to southern Maine, lie at relatively low altitudes, bordered by granites and schists at higher levels. The widespread Silurian (with some Cambrian and Devonian) rocks in northern Maine underlie the most extensive upland in the province. The Triassic sandstones and shales of the Connecticut Valley, not very strong by any standard, underlie lowlands completely enclosed by the upland on more enduring rocks.

The entire province was laterally compressed almost at the beginning of recorded time and at intervals throughout its history. The structural effects of this recurrent strain are seen in two major zones of uplift, one west of the Connecticut Valley marked by the Green Mountains, the other marked by the broad upland east of the river. Beyond and between these deeply truncated uplifts are structural depressions.

Dominant Topographic Features.—The present surface of the province is mainly that of a plateaulike upland declining toward

[1] On Emerson's geologic map of Massachusetts and Rhode Island, published in U. S. Geol. Survey, *Bull*. 597, there are 101 symbols, each representing a distinct type of rock. These are comprehended in eight groups on the geologic map of the United States. For the purpose here in hand this grouping is quite satisfactory.

the sea, surmounted by residual mountains standing singly or in groups and ranges. Except in the presence of mountains, the horizon is fairly level. Its relief is negligible when compared with the great vertical displacement of the rocks. That there has been peneplanation on a large scale is too obvious to argue. Any more exact interpretation runs at once into questions which remain unsettled. The main feature of the true picture may be that of a single peneplain, not only retaining its primitive seaward slope but warped up to a level of more than 2000 feet around the Green Mountains; or it may be a series of partially developed and partially preserved peneplains descending stairlike from the oldest in the interior to the youngest near the shore; or it may be faceted by peneplains of different age and slope, intersecting at very low angles, the oldest being nearest the sea (page 372); or it may be in part a series of marine terraces. The essential fact here is that the plateau exists, and that it is to a large extent independent of structure.

It is equally plain that the surface has been for some time above its base level. This is made evident by the prevalent, though not yet complete, dissection. Generally the valleys are narrow, but lower peneplains have been developed on such weak rocks as the limestone of the Taconic section, the sandstone and shale of the Connecticut Valley, and the Carboniferous rocks in some local basins. Even those are now above base level.

Subdivision into Sections.—In its different parts the New England province presents at least five distinct aspects, each represented by a different area. Of these the *New England Upland* section, already briefly characterized as plateaulike, is most widespread. It extends into Canada and has been interpreted as crossing the Hudson in the Reading Prong, known as the "Highlands" in southeastern New York and northern New Jersey (page 165). As the surface slopes down to the shore, there is necessarily a strip of relatively low land between upland and sea. This is treated as the *Seaboard Lowland* and is, perhaps, distinguished by its erosional history, hence by characteristics other than mere altitude (page 370). There are several large areas of lowland not embraced in this marginal slope; the most important is the *Connecticut Valley*. The *White Mountain section* consists in large part of residual mountains, but the plateau surface invades its margins, at places merely in strips along the streams, elsewhere surrounding closely set monadnocks. The *Green Mountain section* is a linear north-south uplift which remains above the general level, probably because of the strength of the rocks at its core. The *Taconic section* on the west consists largely of mountains but includes the prominent limestone valleys of western Vermont and Massachusetts.

THE WHITE MOUNTAIN SECTION

What the Section Includes.—It is not possible to define and delimit the New England mountain sections except in a very general way. The White Mountain section as outlined here is straggling and not very coherent, but in a morphologic description it serves fairly well as a unit. The White Mountains proper are a continuous and extensive mountain mass, but they are loosely connected with other masses, around and among which the plateau surface is studded with more or less isolated monadnocks. The boundary line used here represents merely an attempt to delimit the area within which mountains are sufficiently abundant to dominate the landscape in a general view. It is nowhere far from the generalized contour line of 1500 feet.[1] In this way about 10,000 square miles are assigned to the White Mountain section, less than a tenth of which belongs to the White Mountains, strictly so called.

The White Mountains are commonly understood to include the Franconia Mountains west of "The Notch" traversed by the Maine Central Railroad. A hundred and fifty miles to the northeast, in central Maine, is the smaller but comparable Katahdin group, connected with the White Mountains by a continuous zone of monadnocks or mountain groups. Parallel to this zone, and on the International Boundary, is a similar one called by Keith the Boundary Mountains. Between these mountainous zones is a troughlike depression, 5 to 10 miles wide, containing such well-known lakes as Moosehead and the Rangely

---

[1] From an unpublished map by Arthur Keith. Contours on this map indicate the level of the horizon in a distant view, exclusive of monadnocks. F. W. Toppan in a paper on the Physiography of Maine (*Jour. Geol.*, vol. 43, pp. 76–87, 1935) gives four profiles showing a southeast-facing escarpment. The localities indicated are near the line that is here treated as the boundary of the White Mountain section. His elevations are taken from railroad profiles and are therefore lower than Keith's.

group. It is not the valley of any one stream, nor is it clearly related to the rock structure, though in a general way both the trough and the ranges follow the trend of folding. Another line, the Caledonia Mountains, lies west of the Upper Connecticut River. It bends toward the east in Canada and merges with the Boundary Mountains. It is also contiguous at other points with outlying groups of the White Mountain section.

Relation to Structure.—The White Mountains proper are a group rather than a range.[1] Their primary reason for existence is the presence of a great granitic intrusion, outcropping here in an area 35 miles long and 25 miles wide. Nothing definite is known of the original form of the intruded mass, or of the surface on which erosion began to work,[2] though northeast-southwest lineaments are more pronounced than any other. Whatever the original form of the mass or plan of drainage, streams now radiate from the center. All surface forms are due directly to the work of water and ice. Similar statements might be made about the Katahdin group. Rock resistance is a primary factor, but there is no close correlation of altitudes with geologic formations. The case is not very different throughout the northeast-southwest belts mentioned above. The influence of structure is seen more convincingly in their general direction than in their boundaries. The linear plan of the Caledonia Range agrees more closely with the structure than any other in this section. Throughout the White Mountain section are granite areas, but they are not everywhere high. The limited outcrops of extrusive igneous rocks are generally mountainous, but there remains a considerable part of this section whose mountains are due to the

---

[1] The term "mountain range" when used technically designates the product of a single orogenic event (Standard Dictionary). The range is understood to be an orogenic unit. In this sense the use of the term must almost be restricted to mountains of the first generation, those whose relief is due to constructional forces, not to those which result from selective erosion. Ordinarily, even among geologists, the term "range" is used in a merely descriptive sense to designate any assemblage of mountains in which a linear plan is suggested. There is no limit in size or complexity. A large and complex range may embrace constituent ranges.

[2] A. C. Lane makes some surmises (White Mountain Physiography, *Amer. Jour. Sci.*, 5th ser., vol. 1, p. 350, 1921). He suggests, for example, the location of several axes of folding, also that at certain places the present surface is not far from the original contact of intrusive with overlying rock.

hardness of metamorphosed Algonkian and early Paleozoic rocks.[1]

Topography.—As treated here, the White Mountain section is bounded by a much generalized contour line of 1500 feet. Within the area thus enclosed are hills and mountains of all altitudes up to that of Mount Washington, 6290 feet. Most of the summits above 5000 feet are in the Presidential Range, a rather limited portion of the White Mountains proper. Second only to that group is the Katahdin group in central Maine, where

Fig. 99.—The Westmore Mountains in northern Vermont, a part of the Caledonian range on the western edge of the White Mountain section. The highest mountain in view is a little more than 3000 feet. The sky line is typical of subdued mountains. The type is widely distributed through New England, the Adirondacks, and the southern Appalachians. (*Vt. Geol. Survey.*)

the highest mountain is 5200 feet high, and a score of others approach or exceed 4000 feet. The Caledonia range is one of irregular altitudes with a maximum in Vermont of about 3500 feet. All of these mountains are the remains of greater masses.

It is not probable that the surface of the entire area was once even with the mountain tops, but there is nothing in these forms to indicate that such was not the case. Probably the mountains have survived more than one cycle of erosion. The surrounding New England upland may be taken to indicate the last long-enduring cycle in this locality. In it the peneplain, now 1000 to 1500 feet high, was in places well developed up to the very base of the White Mountains, in their marginal valleys, and among their

[1] The geologic map of the United States may be checked with the topographic sheets.

outer monadnocks.[1] There are indications that denudation halted at several levels before this one was reached. Keith[2] finds summits near 1600 feet in altitude, and again near 2100 feet, so numerous as to suggest former peneplains at those levels. The remains of these are mainly west of the Connecticut River and are treated here as belonging to the New England Upland (page 358). Many slopes in the mountains are also flattened, or old valleys broadened, at levels between 2600 and 3000 feet. Lane[3] interprets these features as indicating that the sea once met the mountains near the present 2600 foot contour and stood there while the valleys above were broadened and the supposed submarine "Becket Terrace" was carved, a hypothetical surface assumed to be represented by hills in Massachusetts at a height of 2450 feet (page 360).

The most striking areas of gentle slope in the White Mountains are found at high altitudes and are known as "lawns." They are what would be called in the West "boulder fields," ranging from below 4000 feet to above 5000 feet. Near their lower limit they flatten as if they once merged at that level with old valley bottoms, but if so, the old valley bottoms are now replaced by gorges of a younger cycle. Goldthwait[4] was "inclined to look favorably" on the suggestion that the hypothetical old valley bottoms were parts of the New England peneplain, which was later domed up to about 4000 feet (present level) and then destroyed in the making of the present surface. These gentle slopes near the summits are, indeed, topographically unconformable with the steep slopes of the gorges below. There is nothing improbable about an interrupted rise, but "lawns" and "alpine meadows" are not in all cases accepted as remnants of an older topography. A similar mountain topography in Iceland is believed to have resulted from the work of an ice sheet which barely covered the gentle slopes in question.[5] The effects

[1] LOBECK, A. K., The Position of the New England Peneplain in the White Mountain Region, *Geog. Rev.*, vol. 3, pp. 53–60, 1917.

[2] KEITH, ARTHUR, unpublished work for U. S. Geol. Survey.

[3] LANE, A. C., see reference, p. 347.

[4] GOLDTHWAIT, J. W., Remnants of an Old Graded Upland on the Presidential Range of the White Mountains, *Amer. Jour. Sci.*, 4th ser., vol. 37, pp. 451–463, 1914.

[5] WRIGHT, F. E., Some Effects of Glacial Action in Iceland, *Bull. Geol. Soc. Amer.*, vol. 21, pp. 717–730, 1910. Wright states that the mountains

of glaciation in the White Mountains are mentioned on page 383.

Gentle slopes at high levels in the Katahdin Mountains are so prevalent, and the lower slopes so steep, that in a distant view the entire group has a tabular appearance. The sloping upland is generally 2500 to 4000 feet in altitude with the higher edge at the south, where it breaks off in an imposing escarpment. The rise from the 1000-foot upland to the summit of Katahdin at 5200 feet is thought by some to be the most impressive mountain slope in New England.[1] Little is known of these thickly forested mountains, but the abruptness with which the summit upland gives way to the steep sides leaves a strong impression of an older surface.

From the above description it is apparent that all the mountains of the section are mere residual masses, left in the process of erosion. Any differential uplift whose results survive is speculative. While erosion around the mountains may be found to have comprised several cycles, it can not be affirmed that a peneplain was ever developed above the surrounding plateau level, though suggestions occur as high as 1600 feet or possibly 2100 feet.

THE GREEN MOUNTAIN SECTION

General Relations.—From Canada to northern Massachusetts the Green Mountains rise distinctly above the New England upland. The ultimate reason for their existence is found in resistant rocks, mainly the Archean core of a very old anticline. The direct topographic effect of that uplift has long since been destroyed. South of central Vermont it may have initiated the divide which persists to the present time. Where that is true a double reason exists for higher altitude. In northern Vermont the main divide is on the Caledonia Mountains, and the Green Mountains are ignored by the Winooski and Lamoille rivers, which flow across them to Lake Champlain. Here as elsewhere the oldest rocks on the axis of the anticline constitute local divides but they do not outcrop continuously. For 50 miles

---

of northern Iceland have the appearance of "an undulating mature topography approaching that of a peneplain."

[1] TARR, R. S., Glaciation on Mount Ktaadn, Maine, *Bull. Geol. Soc. Amer.*, vol. 11, pp. 433–448, 1900.

south of the Canadian border the range is somewhat scattered.[1] Most of the rocks not belonging to the Archean core are old and intensely metamorphosed sediments.

Topography.—In a distant view the crest of the Green Mountains is notably regular. Maximum heights are above 4000 feet but the prevalent altitude in the higher (middle) parts of the range is not much above 3000 feet. Students of these mountains find that certain ranges of altitude are more abundantly represented than others. Thus a 3000- to 3200-foot level is pointed out as represented only by summits. Summits above 3200 feet cannot be correlated, and indications of peneplains above 2800 feet in the Green Mountains are not positively affirmed. Meyer-

ALTITUDES OF ACCORDANT SUMMIT LEVELS OR TERRACES IN WESTERN NEW ENGLAND[1]

Southern New England, Barrell		Taconic section, Pond	Eastern and central Vermont, Meyerhoff and Hubbell	Western Massachusetts, Keith
Terrace	Elevation	Elevation	Elevation	Elevation
Dorset[2]...........	....	3200	(?)3000(?)–3200	
Braintree[2]........	....	2700	2700 –2800	(?)2800
Becket............	2450	2500	2300(?)–2500	
Canaan...........	2000	2000	2000 –2150±	2050–2200
Hawley[2]..........	....	....	(?)1820 –1920	
Cornwall.........	1720	1700	1660(?)–1720	1600–1700
Goshen...........	1380	....	1360 –1420	
Litchfield........	1140	....	1180 –1240	1100–1200
Prospect..........	940	900±	(?) 980 –1080(?)	
Towantic.........	740	700+	780 – 900(?)	
Appomattox.......	540	....	540 – 620(+)	500
New Canaan......	450	....	420 – 480	
Sunderland........	240	....	(?) 260 – 300	
Wicomico.........	120	....	(?) 160 – 180	

[1] MEYERHOFF, H. A., and M. HUBBELL, The Erosional Land-forms of Central Vermont, *16th Rept. Vt. State Geologist*, pp. 315–381, 1928. This table, except the last column, is found on p. 324. Elevations credited to Keith are taken from U. S. Geol. Survey, *Water Supply Paper* 415, p. 14, 1916.

[2] The name Dorset has been proposed by Pond; the names Braintree and Hawley are proposed by Meyerhoff and Hubbell; all others are Barrell's.

[1] For description see Geo. B. Perkins, The Physiography of Vermont, *Science*, vol. 49, pp. 77–81, 1919.

hoff and Hubbell, working in central and eastern Vermont, found that summits were relatively numerous at certain levels, or within certain ranges of altitude, shown in the table on page 351. They interpret this fact as indicating that incipient or imperfect peneplains were developed during intermittent rising of the land. All observations in the field, and the testimony of maps, agree that a level of 2000 to 2100 feet is prominent in the Berkshire Plateau, *i.e.*, the New England Upland south of the Green Mountains in western Massachusetts. As for most of the other levels, the extent to which accordance of hilltops, though prominent in certain localities, represents the influence of successive base

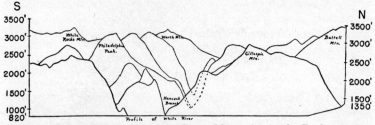

FIG. 100.—Projected profile of the Green Mountains in the Rochester, Vt., quadrangle, representing a stretch of about 10 miles south of the 44th parallel, and showing accordance of peaks at the 3200-foot (Dorset) level. The forms of composite slopes are believed to suggest levels at 2800 feet, 2150 feet, and 1850 feet. Profiles of this character constitute a part of the data underlying the hypothesis outlined on page 362. (*Meyerhoff and Hubbell, Vt. Geol. Survey, 1928.*)

levels, and not mere coincidence, is not yet agreed upon by geologists.

If there is a steplike descent from the crest of the Green Mountains down to 1000 feet or even lower, a decision as to where the mountains end must be more or less arbitrary. Around their southern end the 2000- to 2100-foot level is quite as much a part of the plateaulike New England Upland as is any other level. East of the Green Mountains the plateau is not extensively developed at any one level. In some localities it may seem to abut against the mountains at 2100 to 2200 feet; elsewhere, at 1600 to 1700 feet. The large valleys in the mountains are commonly broadened at the level of the adjacent upland. Valleys cut below that level comprise a very small fraction of the area of the mountain section.

If the levels mentioned above are recognized, the eastern slope of the Green Mountains is crudely terraced. The highest terrace at any one place, and the residual peaks above it, are on the western edge of the range, the descent to the valley on that side being, in central and southern Vermont, almost a single slope. In northern Vermont the plan is different. There, there is a suggestion of two ridges separated by a narrow strip of upland 1200 to 1600 feet high. The western, somewhat interrupted, ridge bears Mt. Mansfield (4393 ft.), the highest peak in the range.

Of the various levels named above, the one at 2000 to 2100 feet has been most generally recognized and correlated with the Schooley peneplain. Consistent levels at higher altitudes are not universally acknowledged. Thus far but few students have studied these mountains from this point of view. The subject is discussed further on pages 360 to 364.

THE TACONIC SECTION

General Character.—West of the Green Mountains, and of the New England Upland farther south, is the Taconic section, consisting mainly of mountains. Between the Taconic Mountains and the highlands on the east is a long, narrow lowland, treated here as a part of the Taconic section. Justification of this grouping is found partly in geological history and partly in mere convenience. The mountains consist of strongly metamorphosed sediments now largely schist. The effect of east-west compression is seen not only in metamorphism but in a prevalent north-south strike. Mountains and valleys have their dominant trend in that direction. The continuous valleys on the east, and some others less continuous, are on limestone or its metamorphic equivalent, marble.

Boundaries.—From latitude 41°35′ to 43°45′ a line may be drawn, generally 5 to 15 miles west of the eastern boundary of New York, which marks the western limit of the schist and stronger rocks, and of the Taconic Mountains. This limit is not a simple escarpment. At places the relief is strong on both sides, but an eastward view from almost any high point 3 to 10 miles west of the line would show mountains rising above the general level. The horizon of hilltops on the west (omitting exceptional heights) is generally less than 800 feet, rarely more than 1000 feet. The general level of mountain tops on the east is 2000 feet or more at the north. It declines southward to about 1200 feet east of Poughkeepsie, where the slate and glacial hills on the west are not above 700 or 800 feet.

The eastern boundary of the Taconic section is between the limestone valleys described below and the Green Mountains or, farther south, the New England Upland. The rise is generally abrupt, though in some parts the line is far from straight.

Topography

The Rensselaer Plateau.—The abrupt rise which marks the edge of the Taconic section 10 miles east of Albany is the western

Fig. 101.—View northeastward to the Taconic Mountains from West Pawlet, Vt. The relatively level foreground is on the slate belt of the Ridge and Valley province. The mountains of Berkshire schist belong to the New England province. (*T. Nelson Dale, U. S. Geol. Survey.*)

edge of the Rensselaer Plateau, a tract roughly 20 miles long and 9 miles wide, with a plateau surface ranging from less than 1500 to more than 2000 feet high. It is therefore far from flat, but its relief is expressed in broad swells and long slopes, not in the sharp valleys and steep slopes of the mountains.[1] It is held up by a

_____

[1] See Berlin topographic sheet, U. S. Geol. Survey. Contrast the western half (Rensselaer Plateau) with the eastern half (Taconic ranges).

strong folded and metamorphosed Cambrian (?) grit or quartzite. The soil cover on this siliceous rock would be poor and thin even if glaciation had not made it rocky. The once densely forested slopes are now deforested, rocky and boulder-strewn. The glacier left lakes and swamps but even less good soil than in the steeper mountains.[1] The general accordance of hilltops is sufficient to indicate approximate peneplanation.

Taconic Ranges.—Although the Rensselaer Plateau contains only 175 square miles, it is much the largest part of the Taconic section not affording elongated topographic forms which suggest longitudinal structures. Almost everywhere mountain masses are longer than they are broad. Among streams or valleys having any continuity, the direction is generally north and south. The Taconic Mountains have sometimes been compared to the Folded Appalachians, but the feature here mentioned is about all that the two regions have in common. Taconic mountains and valleys have no such straightness, parallelism, and continuity as exist in Pennsylvania; no such regularity of width and elevation. Valleys, even where longitudinal, are generally narrow and without valley lowlands. The expression is that of mountains carved from rock that is more uniformly hard than the rocks of central Pennsylvania. Aside from the few limestone belts, streams have not been guided by the outcrops of particular formations.

Summit levels in the Taconics are far from uniform. Considerable areas rise above any demonstrable peneplain. That a former peneplain, regarded here as Schooley, has been raised 2000 feet or more in the north, and less toward the south, cannot well be doubted, but it was imperfect at best, and it has been unequally worn down. No traces of a peneplain much above 2000 feet are at all convincing. Near the latitude of Albany the range for many miles rises from 200 to 800 feet above that level. Among monadnocks of exceptional height are Mt. Greylock in Massachusetts (3505 ft.), and Equinox Mountain (3816 ft.) and Dorset Mountain (3436 ft.) in Vermont.

Limestone Valleys.—In the intense folding which altered the Cambrian and Ordovician shales to Berkshire (Taconic) schist,

[1] DALE, T. NELSON, The Rensselaer Grit Plateau in New York, U. S. Geol. Survey, 13*th Ann. Rept.*, pt. 2, pp. 297–337, 1893. Plates 98 and 99 in this paper show structure and geologic relations.

there were also involved the Cambro-Ordovician limestones.   As the limestone underlies the shale, it appears now in strips along anticlinal axes and along the eastern margin next to the underlying but uplifted rocks of the Green Mountains.   Generally, but not universally, the limestone strips are now lowlands. Much the most important and continuous of these is the one on the eastern margin, separating the Taconic from the Green Mountains in Vermont and from their southward continuation, confusingly called Berkshire Hills[1] in Massachusetts.   Valleys on the same limestone extend southward through northwestern Connecticut and eastern New York between the New England Upland in Connecticut and the Reading Prong.

The valley that constitutes the main southern extension is 400 to 800 feet deep but not more than 1 to 2 miles wide.   Much of its floor, choked by glacial hills, is swampy.   Northward, through Connecticut and Massachusetts, the valley broadens and branches, enclosing islandlike ridges of schist.   Even the limestone is not everywhere low or even "gently" rolling, but the entire belt, locally 12 miles wide, affords the most habitable country between the Connecticut and Hudson valleys.   Pittsfield, North Adams, and Williamstown are among its centers. In southern Vermont the valley is almost absent south of Bennington and is reduced to a gorge opposite Dorset Mountain, but it is generally 2 to 3 miles wide.   The level falls off northward to 540 feet at Rutland and to 350 feet near Brandon, where the Taconic Mountains come to an end and the limestone lowland merges with the Champlain Lowland.   Other valleys similar in origin are generally narrow and irregular.

The degree and character of metamorphism in the limestone differ from place to place.   Other factors than mere compression are involved in the making of marble.   In the Vermont portion

---

[1] The term "Berkshire Hills" has been used in a loose way for the highlands in Berkshire County, Mass., and that usage is here accepted.   T. Nelson Dale (*op. cit.*, 1893, p. 297) restricts the term to the Taconics, and excludes the mountains east of the valley.   The use of the term "Berkshire schist" for the rocks of the Taconics adds to the tendency to use the term "Berkshire Hills" in the same connection.   On the other hand, B. K. Emerson (Holyoke folio, No. 50) limits the term Berkshire Hills to the highland east of the valley.   So also does Arthur Keith (U. S. Geol. Survey, *Water Supply Paper* 415).

of this valley, especially near its northern end in the Rutland district, the transformation was such as to produce the leading marble deposits of the United States.

The limestone lowlands probably represent the work of the Harrisburg cycle, though even where good peneplains were produced, their base levels may have been local. The lowland is now well above base level, and the larger streams run in newer valleys 100 or several hundred feet deep. Some of them are now cutting down, and no doubt all would be doing so had their gradients not been disturbed by glaciation.

That the ice, whether "live" or stagnant, disappeared sooner at the south than at the north is indicated by the evidence of lakes in valleys draining northward, and their absence in valleys draining southward, notably the Housatonic. The valley of the north-flowing Hoosic was flooded in Massachusetts, Vermont, and New York to a height of 1110 to 1120 feet (present altitudes). This produced the largest of the glacial lakes, known as Lake Bascom or Lake Hoosic. Its significance lies in the fact that it is typical of north-flowing streams, whose basins contain lake clays and deltas but no valley trains, while south-flowing streams, like the Housatonic, have valley trains but no features due to ponding.[1]

Attention is called to the fact that many of the hills surmounting the Champlain Lowland (an extension of the valley surface here considered) rise to an almost uniform level of 900 to 1000 feet. These have been interpreted[2] as representing an intermediate peneplain, but if this is true, its relation to known peneplains elsewhere remains to be determined.

Summary.—In the Taconic section, as elsewhere, certain earlier events are of interest, not because of any surviving topographic effect, but because ancient convulsions imposed structural and lithologic conditions on all erosion to the end of time. Such was the effect of the great post-Ordovician lateral compression which made the original Taconic Mountains, long since destroyed. The same deformation made the anticlines whose truncation left

[1] TAYLOR, FRANK B., The Correlation and Reconstruction of Recessional Ice Borders in Berkshire County, Massachusetts, *Jour. Geol.*, Vol. 11, p. 329, 1903.

[2] BAIN, GEO. W., Geologic History of the Green Mountain Front, *Rept. State Geologist Vt.*, 1924–1926, p. 236. Pond, Adela, *Rept. State Geologist Vt.* 1928.

the limestone (or marble) exposed in strips. It also caused the metamorphism and determined the extent of the schist which constitutes the present residual mountains.

Mountain-making forces were active again, at least during the Appalachian Revolution, but geologists are not in agreement as to the work accomplished in the mid-Paleozoic and the post-Paleozoic orogenies, respectively. All direct topographic effects of these and even later disturbances were probably erased before the oldest detectable peneplain, now 2000 feet high, was made. This is probably the same as the one noted at a similar level in the New England Upland, and the same as the highest and oldest one recognized in the Appalachian Mountains, *i.e.*, the Schooley peneplain. Low, subdued mountains rose above it 1200 to 1500 feet, differing from the White and Adirondack Mountains only in having a more linear form.

THE NEW ENGLAND UPLAND

Description of Type.—The typical upland in New England is an upraised peneplain[1] bearing occasional monadnocks and dissected by narrow valleys. Uncut remnants on some divides may be several miles wide. Near large valleys dissection is complete. Some of the smaller streams run in mere ravines, others in well-graded and rounded valleys. A few large tracts at relatively low level may represent incipient younger peneplains. Moderately level surfaces are found more largely at the level of the horizon than at stream levels. The depth of valleys varies with the altitude. It is common to see streams in their middle courses cut one third to one half way down to sea level. With altitudes ranging from below 1000 to above 2000 feet, this statement implies a landscape in which steep slopes are common. It

---

[1] It should no longer be necessary to protest against calling this peneplain imperfect merely because it is not flat. In a sense all peneplains are imperfect, and if it were flat it would not be a peneplain. This subject is sufficiently discussed by W. M. Davis under the title of The Peneplain, *Amer. Geologist*, vol. 23, pp. 207–239; 1899; see also, Baselevel, Grade and Peneplain, *Jour. Geol.*, vol, 10, pp. 17–111, 1902. Both articles are reprinted in "Geographical Essays," pp. 350–412, Ginn & Company, Inc., Boston, 1909. There is more excuse for confusion in speaking of surfaces not yet sufficiently reduced to justify the term peneplain. It is because of the want of a short and convenient term to designate such surfaces that the term peneplain has been overworked.

is a country of winding roads, whether on ridges or in valleys. Features due to glaciation are described below.

Monadnocks.—Monadnocks are residual hills or mountains surrounded by peneplain.[1] Such unreduced remnants are apt to be of exceptionally hard rock. Many of the New England monadnocks are of granite, but favorable location with respect to drainage lines is also important. The original Mount Monadnock in southwestern New Hampshire, 3166 feet high on a peneplain 1100 to 1200 feet high, consists mainly of schist not

Fig. 102.—Mount Monadnock seen from Beech Hill, N. H., looking over the New England Upland. (*Courtesy of the Geography Supply Bureau.*)

known to be peculiarly resistant.[2] Southward from it, across Massachusetts, extends the fairly straight divide between the Connecticut basin and the Atlantic, surmounted by Mount Wachusett, 2000 feet high, and others composed of the same rocks that underlie the peneplain. Monadnocks increase in number toward the White Mountain section, in which large areas of granite occupy the hydrographic center of the province.

[1] The term *monadnock* is most distinctive and useful if reserved for an isolated eminence which may be seen in its true relation to the peneplain on which it stands as a remnant.

[2] PERRY, JOSEPH H., Geology of Monadnock Mountain, New Hampshire, *Jour. Geol.*, vol. 12, pp. 1–14, 1904.

As the drainage has probably had at least 200 million years to adjust itself, this relation is not surprising.

Origin of the Upland.—The upland described above is typical of central Massachusetts where the horizon is 1000 to 1100 feet high. From there it (together with the Seaboard Lowland) may be traced in all directions with minor variations to the limits of the province. Whether this surface is genetically the same throughout, or whether it embraces a series of surfaces of different age, and even of different origin, is not yet determined. Most of the study given to this problem has been west of the Connecticut River and south of central Vermont. The first conception was that of a single peneplain, near sea level along Long Island Sound and rising to more than 2000 feet in and around the Green Mountains.[1] That this hypothesis, with slight modification, still contends for the mastery[2] is evidence, at least, that it is in harmony with the impression gained from a general view, and further, that the features which would disprove it are debatable in character.

Hypothesis of Marine Terracing.—It is well known that the gradation from low to high altitudes in western New England is not everywhere uniform. Profiles[3] constructed from contour maps indicate that at some places the level of summits or upland tracts rises terracelike from the sea to the Green Mountains. While it is not true that all profiles show terraces, the recurrence of moderately level surfaces or of accordant summits at certain elevations or within certain limits is noteworthy; especially so when different workers, in widely separated districts, and following different procedures, find the so-called terraces at similar

---

[1] DAVIS, W. M., The Physical Geography of Southern New England, *Nat. Geog. Mon.* 9, Nat. Geog. Soc., 1896; republished under title, "Physiography of the United States," pp. 269–304, American Book Company, Inc., New York, 1896.

[2] This hypothesis is at least tentatively accepted by Douglas Johnson in his "Stream Sculpture on the Atlantic Slope," p. 11, Columbia University Press, 1931.

[3] Three types of profile are in use: (1) The linear profile or simple topographic cross section; (2) the projected profile, used by Joseph Barrell, in which all the hilltops within a given zone are projected on a vertical plane at one side of the zone, the highest lines representing the horizon; and (3) a simpler form of projected profile (called zonal profile by Meyerhoff), in which the horizon only is thus projected.

altitudes. Observations in the field agree with conclusions drawn from profiles, but the points of observation must be suitably chosen. That such places exist is not questioned, but only here and there are the terraces distinct. There is as yet no general agreement among geologists that each of these so-called terraces represents a distinct event in geomorphic history. In interpreting profiles the subjective factor necessarily enters when a decision is to be made between fortuitous coincidence and law.

Barrell[1] recognized eleven such terraces separated by "escarpments" (*i.e.*, steeper slopes) and occupying the territory between Long Island Sound and the Green Mountains, hence averaging about 9 miles in width and separated by vertical intervals averaging 200 feet (see table, page 351). As these terraces were determined by projected profiles,[2] their levels are those of the hilltops, some of the hills being isolated monadnocks. The assumption was that each level represents a wave-cut terrace on which no islands or stacks were left standing above sea level. Hence present hills were ascribed to later erosion. If the surface be considered as a series of peneplains, monadnocks must be ignored. The level of each terrace in that case would be at the base of monadnocks, not at their summits. As this assumption alters the altitudes of the several assumed terraces, it also alters their boundaries. Some of them may even disappear.

On the supposition that the terracing was done by wave erosion, theoretical considerations make it necessary to assume that the cutting of each terrace was followed by a decided uplift, and later by sinking sufficient to bring the sea up again to the proper level to cut the next lower terrace. It was also necessary to

[1] BARRELL, JOSEPH, Piedmont Terraces of the Northern Appalachians and their Mode of Origin, *Bull. Geol. Soc. Amer.*, vol. 24, pp. 688–690, 1913, abstract; also, Post-Jurassic History of the Northern Appalachians (abstract with discussion), *ibid.* pp. 690–696. More detail of Barrell's work is set forth in a group of posthumous papers edited by H. H. Robinson and published in the *Amer. Jour. Sci.*, 4th ser., vol. 49, pp. 227–258, 327–362, and 407–428, 1920. An extension of Barrell's work to the area east of the Connecticut River was made later by Laura Hatch, Marine Terraces in Southeastern Connecticut, *Amer. Jour. Sci.*, 4th ser., vol. 44, pp. 319–330, 1919.

[2] Barrell's profiles are shown in the 1920 paper, cited above, as Pl. 5, opposite p. 246. In the same paper, Fig. 1, p. 247, is his preliminary map.

assume that in the time interval between emergence and renewed submergence the zone which was next to be subjected to wave planation was greatly reduced by normal erosion so that the work remaining for marine planation was largely the truncation of hills and ridges and the development of a sea cliff.[1] With these requirements met, it appears that much the larger part of the work of reducing the surface was, in any case, done by normal erosion. The higher terraces were, of course, exposed to erosion throughout the partial cycles of normal and marine erosion in which the lower terraces were made. So it is not surprising that the older members of the series are badly wasted, and the planation surfaces postulated by Barrell are at the tops of present-day monadnocks. It is remarkable that these older terraces should be sufficiently preserved to be recognizable.

No doubt oscillations of land and sea levels are common and, in any long period of time, inherently probable.[2] It has, however, been pointed to as improbable that such oscillation should occur eleven times in succession at uniformly diminishing intervals, always with the correct amplitude to allow for the right amount of stream erosion and to leave the continent with a net gain of about 200 feet in altitude. But this question of rhythm confronts any hypothesis for explaining these terraces. Failure to find remnants of marine sediment, even in depressions of the youngest terraces, has also been urged as an objection, especially in view of the fact that these same young (Pleistocene) terraces are assumed by the hypothesis to be the northern correlatives of the coastal plain terraces farther south.

Terracing by Normal Erosion.—Farther north, as stated on page 351, a detailed study of the slope from the Green Mountains to the Connecticut River has resulted in depicting that slope as a series of 14 terraces.[3] Five of these, ranging in altitude from 160 to 900 feet, belong to the slope of the narrow Connecticut Valley. Three others, between 2300 and 3200 feet, are allotted to the Green Mountains. The remaining six, ranging from 980 to 2150 feet, fall within what is regarded as the New England Upland. Most terraces of this series correspond in

---

[1] BARRELL, op. cit., pp. 233, 410, 1920.

[2] Barrell (op. cit., p. 328, 1920) points out that there are 13 unconformities in the coastal plain sediments of the Patuxent, Md., quadrangle.

[3] See reference to Meyerhoff and Hubbell, p. 351.

altitude to those of Barrell (see table, page 351) with which they are believed to be continuous.

The total range in altitude among the ten higher terraces is a little more than 2400 feet. Each terrace is assigned, not one fixed level, but a vertical range averaging 115 feet for each. There remains an average interval of 127 feet between terraces, but it is not to be assumed that there are no hilltops within these intervals. As the breadth of the terraced belt is only 15 to 20 miles, the average width of each terrace would be little more than a mile if all were straight north-south strips. Since they are deeply crenulate, running in and out of side valleys, their actual width is much less. It may also be much greater where some of the terraces are crowded out. However, a part of the available width is occupied by the intervening slopes or "escarpments." It is to be remembered that all surfaces are deeply dissected and that each terrace level is a hypothetical plane determined by accordant summits.

These terraces are described as being essentially (or approximately) horizontal. If they were plotted on a map, their boundaries would appear as contour lines running in and out, around valleys and spurs, though much broken and interrupted. On this account the hypothesis of marine terracing is excluded.[1] A similar study in the Taconic Mountains[2] showed evidence of seven terraces, also corresponding in altitude to those noted elsewhere. In this case a marine hypothesis is excluded on account of the highland which intervenes between the sea and the area in question.

The authors of the two studies cited above explain the terraces as the result of successive uplifts, alternating with incipient peneplaning. It is assumed that erosion at the edge of the mountains reached the stage of incipient peneplaning, *i.e.*, of wide valley floors or straths. After uplift new valley floors would develop at lower levels, beginning downstream and

---

[1] Barrell gives only a much generalized sketch map (*op. cit.*, p. 247, 1920) which does not show the pattern of the boundaries between terraces. Neither Pond nor Meyerhoff and Hubbell give any maps at all, but descriptions by all of these writers agree that each terrace, along its inner margin, sends tongues up the river valleys.

[2] POND, ADELA M., Preliminary Report on the Peneplanes of the Taconic Mountains of Vermont, 16*th Rept. Vt. State Geologist*, pp. 292–314, 1929.

spreading laterally and headward, each lower strath being separated from its older and higher neighbor by a steeper slope,
called, for convenience, an escarpment.   Each of the old straths
would thus gradually be consumed by the encroachment of
the new, except for the fact that it itself, being as yet unaffected
by rejuvenation, continues to grow both laterally and headward
at the expense of the original highland.   This process may
be repeated any number of times, each strath being progressively
consumed on its lower (streamward) side and growing constantly
along its outer boundary at the expense of a higher strath or of
the original highland.

As stated here, the hypothesis assumes that the steep slopes
separating the several straths (now strath terraces) would retain
their steepness during recession.   On this point geomorphologists
disagree.[1]   If, in the process of recession, an escarpment tends to
be graded down, or is much dissected, the former strath terraces
would disappear.

Summary.—There are some localities in New England in
which no geologist can fail to see a suggestion of eroded terraces.
There are other places in which some see terraces and others do
not.   Subjective differences among workers are no doubt important.   Also, the part that chance coincidence plays cannot easily
be evaluated.   Both marine and fluvial agencies have received,
and are receiving, respectful attention, but the extent of the
evidence is disputed, and both hypotheses are challenged on
theoretical grounds.   No single explanation of terracing can yet
be said to be generally accepted.

Hypothesis of a Single Upland.—Little intensive work of the
kind described above has been done east of the Connecticut
River.   A few projected profiles between the White Mountains
and the coast[2] were tacitly assumed to indicate a single erosion
surface.   These profiles indicate a maturely dissected plateau
1000 to 1100 feet high, clearly distinguishable despite monadnocks, reaching to the very foot of the White Mountains.   This
upland with minor interruptions maintains its level to within

---

[1] This question is closely related to that of "knick points" in streams.
It is considered critically by W. M. Davis in his paper on Piedmont Benches
and Primärrümpfe, *Bull. Geol. Soc. Amer.*, vol. 43, pp. 399–440.   His conclusions are adverse to the continued recession of knick points of cyclic origin.

[2] LOBECK, A. K., see reference p. 363.

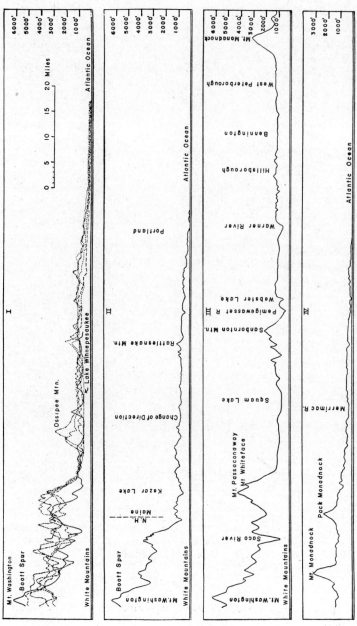

Fig. 103.—Profiles of the New England Upland south of the White Mountains. (*Lobeck, Geogr. Rev., vol. 3.*) I. Five profiles from the White Mountains south by east, being partly in the basins of the Salmon Falls River and Lake Winnepesaukee. II. Profile from Mt. Washington eastward into Maine and turning southeastward to Portland. III. Profile from Mt. Washington south by west to Mt. Monadnock. IV. Profile from Mt. Monadnock eastward across the Seaboard Lowland to the Atlantic.

25 or 30 miles of the coast and then declines. Toward the southwest from the White Mountains the general level is continuous to central Massachusetts. Interruptions are seen in broad irregular bands along streams, or in former stream valleys, notably in the region of Lake Winnepesaukee. Within these bands the general level is broken down, and some lowlands, occupied by lakes or outwash plains, are 400 to 500 feet below the upland. It is evident that these lower belts represent renewed erosion after a general uplift.[1] (*Cf.* Fig. 103.)

The hypothesis of marine planation has been applied to southern New Hampshire and southwestern Maine[2] by correlating the general upland surface with Barrell's Litchfield terrace, which is 1140 feet high in western Connecticut and Massachusetts. The necessary assumption is made that the higher members of the series were cut away.

The Upland in Northern New England.—North of central Vermont and central New Hampshire the upland becomes less and less of a plain. Numerous monadnocks rise to various altitudes. None the less, an 1100-foot level has been traced from Massachusetts to Canada, being generally in valleys in the northern part. A level spoken of as "the 1600-foot plateau" is more widespread than any other in Vermont east of the Green Mountains.[3] There is also a 2100-foot level, especially around the mountains. Practically the whole of the New England Upland above 1000 feet has been described by Keith as dominated by the levels here named, with slight variation. Approximately, they agree in altitude with the Litchfield, Cornwall, and Canaan terraces recognized by Barrell, who treats them as marine plains, and by Meyerhoff and Hubbell, who treat them as fluvial plains. Presumably these latter writers cited would find

---

[1] The ambiguous verdict of many profiles is indicated by the fact that Professor Lobeck who made these profiles regarded the upland surface as a unit (except for more advanced erosion in some places), while others see in the same profiles a series of terraces.

[2] LANE, A. C., White Mountain Physiography, *Amer. Jour. Sci.*, 5th ser., vol. 1, pp. 349–354, 1921.

[3] For information on these little-studied parts of New England the writer is indebted to Arthur Keith who generously permitted the use of his unpublished manuscript, representing the work of several years for the U. S. Geol. Survey.

in northern New England about the same number of terraces as are listed farther south.

The "levels" here spoken of are, of course, generalizations based on summit altitudes. The summits that fall exactly in these planes are few. Considerable deviation must be allowed, and there are many hilltops at intermediate altitudes. Whether the hills rising to each of the favored levels represent the remains of a former, more continuous and more extensive surface, or whether all owe their heights to unequal uplift and unequal degradation of a single surface in a long erosional process, not now separable into cycles, is a question that future study must decide.

Altitudes in northern Maine must be stated very generally. It is a land of primeval or second-growth forest and lakes, with not a little swamp land, settled sparsely or not at all, most of it not topographically surveyed. In its general level, as in its topographic style, there is no great change as one passes from the 1000 to 1100-foot upland in central Massachusetts through southern New Hampshire and southwestern Maine around the White Mountain section into northern Maine. There, north of Moosehead Lake, is the largest expanse of plateau in New England, its horizon being at 1100 to 1250 feet.[1]

The same surface extends east some miles beyond the 69th meridian. Farther east is the broad basin of the upper Penobscot River, also that of the Aroostook and other tributaries of the St. John and of the St. Croix, which forms the state boundary farther south. Most of the surface within these basins is below 700 feet. Probably this low altitude is due to erosion since the uplift of the peneplain which, in somewhat dissected form, constitutes the surface of the upland in northwestern Maine. At places there is an east-facing escarpment.[2] Locally this can be correlated with a contrast in rocks. Elsewhere it may be due to the fact that streams flowing east have the advantage of a direct course to the sea while those flowing west follow a roundabout course. However, as the divide is some miles west of the escarpment, it is necessary to assume that east-flowing streams have been working headward in the current erosion cycle.

[1] KEITH, ARTHUR, unpublished data used by permission.

[2] TOPPAN, FREDERICK W., The Physiography of Maine, *Jour. Geol.*, vol. 43, pp. 76–87, 1935.

According to the outline of provinces and sections followed here, the New England Upland extends southeastward to the Seaboard Lowland. An adequate description would require the mention of units of a smaller order. The wide lowland along the St. John and its tributaries in northeastern Maine is connected across low divides with the similar valley of the Penobscot, and that again with the valley of the Kennebec. Thus a continuous lowland, 2 or 3 miles to 25 miles wide, called by Keith the Bangor Lowland, extends northeastward from the lower Kennebec River, connecting the Seaboard Lowland with the valley of the St. John. Southeast of this depression is a somewhat larger area of upland to which the name Norumbega Hills has been applied. It is in all essential respects an outlying portion of the New England Upland, a plateaulike expanse, youthfully dissected and bearing a pronounced range of monadnocks from which it takes its name.

The Reading Prong

Extending southwestward from the south end of the Taconic section into Pennsylvania, is the Reading Prong, a belt of low mountains commonly called the Highlands in New York and New Jersey, and by various local names in Pennsylvania. The end of the belt is marked approximately by the city of Reading in the transverse valley of the Schuylkill River, west of which is only a smaller outlier. The total length is 150 miles and the maximum width about 25 miles.

Almost all that has been said about the topography and the geomorphic history of the Blue Ridge (page 164) is true of the Reading Prong, but there is, between the two, a gap of 50 miles (page 165). On the other hand, the Reading Prong is contiguous with the Taconic Mountains and the New England Upland. The Pre-Cambrian rocks that constitute its core are essentially those of the Green Mountains and the high western edge of the New England Upland, called the Berkshire Upland.[1] With respect to elevation the Prong is more like the adjacent Taconic Mountains. The sky line is continuous from one to the other at an elevation of 1200 feet or more. Where the south end of the Taconic Mountains lies between the Highlands on the west and

[1] Berkshire Hills, if that term is restricted to the highland east of the limestone valley. See footnote, page 356.

FIG. 104.—View up the Hudson from West Point, in the Highlands. A typical drowned river in a region of hard rocks and great relief. The mountains rise 1400 feet above the river, whose surface is at sea level while the old, now buried, rock channel is 600 to 800 feet below the river, as shown in Fig. 62. (*N. Y. State Museum Bull.* 255.)

the New England Upland on the east, the three divisions have approximately the same summit level. But if the New England Upland be traced to the south and west from the Berkshire Upland, around the end of the Taconic section to the Reading Prong, the level of the upland is found to be not more than 600 to 800 feet where it meets the Prong at 1000 to 1200 feet.

As the Highlands are a relatively narrow and elevated tract between the Great Valley on one side and the Triassic lowland on the other, they are cut by rather deep, narrow valleys. Some of the valleys, structurally controlled, are parallel to the trend of the Prong. This causes parts of the Highlands to be characterized by ridges, and thus to resemble those parts of the Taconic Mountains in which summits are moderately accordant. Where drainage is not structurally controlled, the broadly rounded interstream masses have an aspect not very different from those in the Berkshire Upland.

On the map of Physical Divisions of the United States,[1] the Reading Prong appears as an extension of the New England Upland. From the above descriptions it will be observed that it may be desirable at times to correlate it with other sections according to the purpose in hand.

THE SEABOARD LOWLAND

Extent and Description.—In its larger aspect the relatively low coastal border of New England is merely the sloping margin of the upland. The distinction is geographically important because population and industry are to a remarkable degree concentrated on this lowland and in the Connecticut Valley. Worcester, Mass., and Waterbury, Conn., are the only large cities on the Upland and these are near the edge. Everywhere this coastal strip is not only lower but smoother than the adjacent upland. At most places the change in topography is observed between the 400- and the 500-foot contours. Limited in this way the Seaboard Lowland is 6 to 16 miles wide in Connecticut, exclusive of the Connecticut Valley Lowland, which is treated separately. In Rhode Island and Massachusetts the boundary is a nearly north-south line located 10 or 12 miles west of Providence and a similar distance east of Worcester. The lowland in these states is not without its monadnocks, like

[1] U. S. Geol. Survey, 1930.

Blue Hill south of Boston, and larger tracts of rocky hills like the Middlesex Fells on the granite north of Boston.

From its north-south course in Massachusetts the boundary line turns to the northeast through New Hampshire and Maine, lying at first about 20 miles from the coast, but gradually diverging from it. Before reaching the New Brunswick border it lies 60 miles inland (Pl. 1). East of the Kennebec River the Seaboard Lowland, properly so-called, lies between the Norumbega Hills and the sea, but from the standpoint of human occupation the Bangor Lowland is the real and important continuation of the coastal belt. It is more important (at least at the present time) than the coastal strip outside the Norumbega Hills with its miles of forest and many lakes, its islands, peninsulas, and beaches, and very few people.

Rocks and Their Relations.—The relatively low altitude of the Seaboard section is not due primarily to a difference in rock resistance, though the parts underlain by Carboniferous sediments are lower and flatter than the rest. Where these are contiguous with the Upland, as at places in Massachusetts and New Hampshire, that fact gives sharpness to the boundary, but in general the boundary is not thus marked. One such area of Carboniferous rocks is the Boston basin, in which most of the surface is lower than 100 feet and the area above 200 feet is very small. The Middlesex Fells on the north and Blue Hill on the south are granite. The much larger Narragansett basin, partly submerged in the bay of that name, is likewise in Carboniferous rocks, but the rougher granite areas east and west of it also belong to the so-called lowland. Southeastern New Hampshire and southwestern Maine exhibit the same types of topography, and for the same reason.

Along the Maine coast east of Portland, contrasts in rock resistance are mainly between granite and schist. Among other eminences, the former constitutes Mt. Desert Island[1] east of Penobscot Bay, famed for its beauty ever since its first description by Champlain. In a distance of 10 miles the Mount Desert Range comprises a dozen peaks, the highest of which, Cadillac Mountain, is 1532 feet above the sea.

[1] BASCOM, F., The Physiography of Mount Desert (Island), *Bull. Geog. Soc. Phila.*, vol. 17, pp. 117–130, 1919.

Interpretation of the Seaboard Lowland.—In explanation of the Seaboard Lowland, the simplest hypothesis would be that it is merely the less elevated portion of a widespread peneplain most of which is now an upland.   There is, however, some reason to believe that the history of the lowland is different.   As evidence of this it is pointed out that, if all valleys made in the current cycle were filled, the surface of the lowland would still be flatter than that of the upland; also that the gradation in altitude from one section to the other and the transition between the two types of topography are too abrupt, too much confined to a narrow zone, to agree with the simple hypothesis stated above.

In the case of the southern margin fronting Long Island Sound, it is probable that a zone at least a few miles wide was formerly

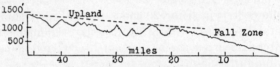

Fig. 105.—Reduced profile showing the slope of the upland and Fall Zone peneplains in Connecticut.   (*Sharp, Conn. Geol. Survey Bull.* 46.)

covered by Cretaceous formations of the Coastal Plain, now stripped away.   Such a zone must be part of a pre-Schooley peneplain (the Fall Zone peneplain) having a steeper seaward slope than that of the upland as stated in discussing the Fall Line (page 126).   This sub-coastal plain floor is known to have very small relief.

On this hypothesis the stripped zone and the later developed upland would be facets intersecting at a very small angle.   That such relations were developed during the stripping need not be doubted, and it may well be that a part or all of the Seaboard Lowland in Connecticut represents the older peneplain, now stripped.[1]   As yet there is no proof that these two surfaces are coextensive.[2]   From Massachusetts northward, submergence has probably obscured all traces of the Fall Zone peneplain.

[1] SHARP, H. S., The Physical History of the Connecticut Shoreline, Conn. State Geol. Nat. Hist. Survey, *Bull.* 46, 1929; see his Fig. 10, p. 37.   JOHNSON, D., "Stream Sculpture on the Atlantic Slope," pp. 25–27, 1931.

[2] Geo. T. Renner, in the paper cited on p. 127, states (p. 282) that the basement peneplain is exposed for a width of 14 miles in western Connecticut and 5 miles in eastern Connecticut.   As the width of the lowland is only 6 to 10 miles in western Connecticut and 10 to 15 miles in eastern Connecti-

Another hypothesis is based on relatively late submergence and marine planation of the seaward margin of the province since the New England peneplain was uplifted.[1] This explanation of the Seaboard Lowland is in agreement with Barrell's interpretation of the New England Upland, the plausibility of which is greater when applied to the margin of the land than when applied to the interior. It is possible to make certain combinations of this hypothesis with the one previously described.

THE CONNECTICUT VALLEY LOWLAND

Geographic Relations.—A north-south strip of lowland, sharply distinguished from the bordering upland on both sides, crosses Massachusetts and Connecticut. It is 95 miles long and, for much of its length, 20 miles wide. The Connecticut River follows it to a point 20 miles from Long Island Sound. Its moderately level or rolling floor is 400 feet high at the foot of the lateral escarpments at the north end, and slopes south with fair uniformity down to sea level.

Geologic Relations.—This well-marked geomorphic unit is quite as clearly outlined geologically as topographically. Its underlying rocks are Triassic sandstone, conglomerate, and shale, all relatively soft, with included igneous sheets, extrusive and intrusive, both familiarly known as trap rock. The latter are about as hard as the rocks of the upland. All of these younger rocks give way abruptly on both sides, along nearly straight lines, to the schists and granites of the upland. It is plain that the valley belt has been structurally depressed, and equally plain on the east side that this depression has been by faulting. Locally this is true also of the west side, and the entire belt is treated by some as a graben.[2] For much of the distance the monoclinal structure described below is sufficient to

---

cut, it is plain that Renner's work does not show any exact correlation between the Seaboard Lowland and the denuded subcoastal plain floor. It is not yet clear what might appear if large allowance were made for later erosion of the landward margin of the stripped peneplain.

[1] Research based on this hypothesis is now proceeding under the direction of Prof. H. A. Meyerhoff.

[2] EMERSON, B. K., Geology of Massachusetts and Rhode Island, U. S. Geol. Survey, *Bull.* 597, p. 16, 1917. See also DAVIS, W. M., The Triassic Formation of Connecticut, U. S. Geol. Survey, *18th Ann. Rept.*, pt. 2, p. 9, 1898.

account for the abruptness and general straightness of the escarpment on the west side without faulting.[1]

The Triassic sediments are at least several miles thick and the volcanic sheets add not less than 500 to 600 feet to the total thickness and the depth of the structural trough. All of the rocks dip east at angles of 15 to 20 degrees, the base of the series being on the west side where the old crystalline surface passes under the sediments at a similar angle. The entire belt, 20 miles in width, is divided into blocks by roughly parallel north-south faults, each block being upthrown on its west side and down-

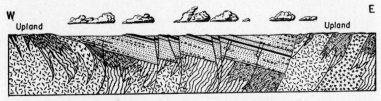

Fig. 106.—Structural section across central Connecticut. Triassic lavas are shown in black. The faulted and tilted sediments are Triassic. Metamorphosed Paleozoics are closely folded in the pre-Paleozoic complex. (*Barrell, Conn. Geol. Survey.*)

thrown on the east. It is probable also that the total uplift west of the belt was such as to incline the whole region eastward.[2]

Topographic Development.—With such a structure, the major topographic features follow almost as a matter of course. The New England peneplain, being made near sea level, was necessarily continuous at the same level over the Triassic area. Doubtless it was flatter on the softer rocks. Probably the outcropping volcanic rocks caused visible swells on the surface, but only to the height of other low swells on the adjacent peneplain. A few hills rose a little higher, but the same was true on the crystalline rocks. With the uplift of the New England peneplain the weak sediments were worn down to a new base level. Meantime the masses of igneous rock were but little reduced by erosion. They now constitute the well-known Trap Ridges (*cf.* page 147), whose summits are essentially even with the adjacent uplands.

[1] RICE, WM. N., Manual of the Geology of Connecticut, Conn. Geol. Survey, *Bull.* 6, pp. 213–215, 1906.

[2] It should be noted that the structure of the Triassic rocks in the Piedmont of New Jersey, with their included volcanics, is like the mirror image of the Connecticut Valley structure, dips in New Jersey being toward the west.

It is important to note that, in the main, the reduction of the soft sediments here as elsewhere was not by planation by meandering streams, but by *peneplanation*, the essence of which is wearing down between streams (*cf.* footnote, page 181). It is therefore not necessary, as was once supposed, that the Connecticut River should at one time have followed the lowland to Long Island Sound. The well-known Connecticut terraces are a later feature below the level of the peneplain. These will receive further mention in the treatment of glaciation.

Course of the Connecticut River.—At Middletown, Conn., 20 miles from the sound, the Connecticut River, here less than 20 feet above sea level, abruptly leaves the lowland and turns southeastward to cross the upland in a narrow valley. Attempts to interpret the history of the Triassic belt in a way that shall be consistent with this striking fact have led to various assumptions. Perhaps the one most often cited[1] is that, following the making of the New England peneplain, a slight subsidence permitted the deposition of coastal plain sediments to a distance of at least 20 miles inland. On emergence with a southeastward tilt the river was superposed in its present course. A parallel is suggested with the Hudson River, which also leaves a soft-rock lowland to cross a crystalline upland. In neither case is there any strong evidence that the stream ever followed the lowland farther than at present. The sudden southeastward turn of the Housatonic River in western Connecticut has also been included in this suggestion.

There is nothing improbable about an overlap of sediments as assumed above. Indeed, the latest suggestion[2] would call for coastal plain sediments and superposed drainage as far inland as the Green Mountains and northeastern Pennsylvania. According to this last hypothesis, most or all of the streams flowing into the Atlantic from the northern states took their original courses on such overlapping coastal plain sediments. The lower, southeastward courses of the Connecticut and Housatonic are assumed

---

[1] Davis, W. M., The Triassic Formation of Connecticut, U. S. Geol. Survey, 18*th Ann. Rept.*, pt. 2, p. 155, 1898. In this paper Davis cites the various hypotheses proposed up to that time, crediting R. S. Tarr with suggesting superposition.

[2] Johnson, Douglas, "Stream Sculpture on the Atlantic Slope," Columbia University Press, 1931. See pp. 25–31, especially Fig. 11, p. 29.

to be all that those streams have left of their original courses, their headwaters being diverted and now known by other names. On this hypothesis the entire Connecticut river above Middletown is subsequent, owing to the headward elongation of a tributary along the soft Triassic belt as far as northern Massachusetts and along older sedimentaries on the Vermont-New Hampshire boundary.

An older assumption is that, in the post-Triassic block faulting and eastward tilting, the former Connecticut lost its way and took a consequent course to the sea. The subject of southeastward drainage in its broader relations is considered in the chapter on the Ridge and Valley province.

No one of these hypotheses can yet be rejected. Two of them are consistent with the assumption that the Connecticut River once followed the Triassic belt to the sea at New Haven, but this remains unproved. On none of them can the river be assumed to have cut down the present lowland below the upland level south of Middletown. The valley in the upland from Middletown to the sea is apparently of the same age as other valleys in the upland. It seems to have been begun when the New England peneplain first began to be dissected.

THE NEW ENGLAND SHORE

General Statement.—The eastern shore of North America is divided by the Hudson River into two strongly contrasted parts. The southern half has already been described (Chap. I) as originating by emergence of the marginal sea bottom, occasional downward movement being subordinate. From New York to the Arctic Ocean the shore line is plainly one of submergence.[1] In each case the sweeping statement must be modified by an admission of complexity and of minor movements in the opposite direction. One characteristic of the shore line of submergence is its irregularity. In the case of New England, the zone of irregularity increases northeastward, with increasing

---

[1] JOHNSON, DOUGLAS, "The New England-Acadian Shoreline," John Wiley & Sons, Inc., New York, 1925. This volume treats the subject in detail with abundant citations. Its conclusions are here accepted.

The contrast between shores north and south of New York must not be interpreted too narrowly. It must not be assumed that there was a hinge line in this latitude and that sinking of the northern shore corresponded in time to rising of the southern.

submergence, to a broad fringe of intricately commingled islands, peninsulas, bays, and channels. Local variation is due to differences in rock resistance, to the relation which the direction of the shore bears to that of rock structures and drainage, and to minor crustal movements, for example to a small, late but not final, rise.

Topography before Submergence.—The factor of greatest immediate significance was the topography of the land before submergence. The seaward border of Connecticut was relatively level. At least in part, it was probably the old peneplain (Jurassic or early Cretaceous) that extends beneath the Coastal Plain, covered and later denuded but never much dissected. Here the amount of recent sinking was too small to reach inland beyond the smooth surface. Had it extended to northwestern Connecticut and Massachusetts, the shore would have been very different. In the latitude of Maine, submergence reached farther inland, where the elevation had been greater and deeper valleys had been carved.

Influence of Rocks and Structure.—The effect of hard rocks on the character of the shore is found partly in their effect on the pre-existing land topography and partly in their resistance to the later work of waves. In the short time that has elapsed since submergence, shore processes have accomplished relatively little toward altering the original contours of the steep-sided branching valleys in the stronger rocks. The shores east of Casco Bay (long. 70°) are abrupt, very crooked, and often rocky, but the abruptness is not generally that of the receding cliff; it is more often the steepness of the hillside. High monadnocks among the islands occur at intervals. The Mount Desert Range (page 371) is much the highest.

Rocks of less strength, for the most part Carboniferous sandstones and shales or slates, underlying relative lowlands, are marked in some cases by such deeply reentrant bays as Narragansett, Boston, and Casco on which Portland is located. Shores rise to less height and, where not cliffed by waves, they rise less abruptly than those on harder rocks. On the other hand, cliffs are much better developed. Some are many miles long and are believed to have receded several thousand feet. As the Carboniferous cliffs frequently recede 6 inches in a year, and some of them a foot in a year, there is no evidence that the present level of the sea dates back more than a few thousand years.[1]

Among the most notable contrasts in plan of coast line, is one that depends on its relation to structure rather than to hardness. The coast southwestward from Portland is remarkably simple as compared with that to the northeast. Inspection of the geologic map shows that the shore to the southwest is parallel to the axes of folding, while that to the northeast crosses the structural grain. As the rocks, however hard, are not uniformly hard, drainage and topographic features tend to be oriented with the strike.

The Narrow Coastal Plain.—Another factor, which at places affects the simplicity or complexity of shore lines, is best exemplified in this same segment between Portland and Cape Ann. This feature is a narrow coastal plain brought into being by a postglacial rise. At some places the width of this plain reaches 5 to 10 miles, but it is exceedingly variable because its landward boundary is in the fringe or among the islands of a drowned coast; also because the coastal plain merges with the outwash plains of the broader valleys. Its effect is to reduce the irregularities of the shore line.

The narrow, fragmentary, and very recent coastal plain mentioned here is not to be correlated with the Coastal Plain province south of New York. The latter has its correlative in Long Island and the islands east of it; probably also in the sea bottom of the Gulf of Maine which is, with good reason, regarded as submerged coastal plain[2] (page 14). To drown this part of the Coastal Plain province required a sinking of at least 1200 feet. The time of sinking cannot be stated with exactness, but the land is known to have been depressed while the ice rested on it and, in part at least, for that reason.[3] It is known to have been

[1] JOHNSON, *op. cit.*, p. 366.

[2] JOHNSON, *op. cit.*, Chap. VIII, pp. 255–314. STETSON, H. C., Bed Rock from the Georges Bank Canyon, *Proc. Geol. Soc. Amer.*, p. 112, 1934. WOODWORTH and WIGGLESWORTH, Museum Comp. Zool., Harvard College, *Mem.* 52, 1934, 322 pp. and excellent maps.

[3] While on the one hand the glacier depressed the land by its weight, on the other hand it lowered the sea level by withdrawing a part of its water to make the glacial ice. The latter effect may have amounted to several hundred feet. The relative position of sea and land during glaciation is therefore a complex question. It is briefly but instructively discussed by E. Antevs, Late Quaternary Changes of Level in Maine, *Amer. Jour. Sci.*,

lower than at present when the ice disappeared from the coast. Recent marine deposits are found inland to a distance of 80 miles and to heights of nearly 500 feet, and faintly etched postglacial shore lines are found 300 to 400 feet above the present sea level.[1] When they were made, the land was probably already rising. Continued rising made the narrow coastal plain, originally broader than at present. The most recent record is one of moderate submergence. Antevs estimates that the shore may have been laid bare of glacial ice 30,000 years ago and that the final sinking may have left the shore at its present position 3000 to 6000 years ago.[2]

Valleys in the Continental Shelf.—Previous to the sinking mentioned above, New England seems to have been bordered by a coastal plain like that of New Jersey at the present time, but broader. Probably the shore was near the outer edge of the Continental Shelf, more than 200 miles from the coast of Maine. Just within that line is Georges Bank, a submerged cuesta increased in volume by glacial drift. Between the cuesta and the present coast is the old inner lowland, some of it 1200 feet below sea level.

Both in the inner lowland and on the outer slope of Georges Bank, soundings indicate valleys whose form suggests that they are stream valleys, cut when the land stood higher.[3] Probably this suggestion would be accepted without question were it not for their great depth. Some of them at the edge of the Continental Shelf descend to depths of more than 8000 feet.[4] The supposition that the continent stood that much higher in late Tertiary time is so hard to harmonize with some other known facts that other possible ways of making submarine valleys are still being investigated (page 223). There can be no doubt that

---

5th ser., vol. 15, pp. 319–333, 1928; more fully discussed by R. A. Daly, "The Changing World of the Ice Age," New Haven, pp. 151*ff*., 1934.

[1] KATZ, FRANK J., Late Pleistocene Shoreline in Maine and New Hampshire, abst., *Bull. Geol. Soc. Amer.*, vol. 29, p. 74, 1918; Also STONE, GEO. H., The Glacial Gravels of Maine and Their Associated Deposits, U. S. Geol. Survey, *Mon.* 34, 1899; ref. to Pl. 2, p. 58.

[2] ANTEVS, *op. cit.*, p. 328.

[3] SHEPARD, F. P., Canyons off the New England Coast, *Amer. Jour. Sci.*, vol. 27, pp. 24–36, 1934.

[4] STETSON, H. C., Bed-rock from the Continental Margin on Georges Bank, *Trans. Amer. Phys. Union*, 16th Ann. Meeting, 1935.

some submerged valleys began as normal subaerial valleys. The "canyon" of the Hudson across the Continental Shelf is no doubt related in origin to the gorge of the Hudson in the Highlands. The deep valleys in Georges Bank are not known to be related in any way to streams of the present.

GLACIATION

Casual Evidence.—Continental glaciation in the Western Hemisphere was first demonstrated in New England. Its effects there are of the most obvious kind. Stones of all sizes[1] up to that of a house litter the surface, making agriculture at many places

FIG. 107.—Stone fences near Alfred, Me. The glacial drift is here so stony that fields must be cleared of stones before plowing. (*Courtesy of the Geography Supply Bureau.*)

impossible until they are cleared away. Some of them are built into fences. In many cases the kind of rock is unlike that of any ledge in place within hundreds of miles. In every glaciated country such erratics are the ones that attract attention, but for every thousand stones of strange or remote origin, ten thousand have come from ledges near at hand, perhaps from one to 50 miles away.[2] The evidence of drainage and topographic features is

[1] ALDEN, WM. C., The Physical Features of Central Massachusetts, U. S. Geol. Survey, *Bull.* 760, pp. 13–106, 1925. Page 58 gives a good description of the great variety of boulders.

[2] FLINT, RICHARD F., (The Glacial Geology of Connecticut, State Conn. Geol. Nat. Hist. Survey, *Bull.* 47, 1930) states (p. 73) that considerably

quite as convincing but less direct. There is little reason to doubt that continental ice from the north covered this province several times, but so far as the mainland is concerned the work of ice invasions before the last have been so far obliterated as to be inconclusive. Only when the islands, Martha's Vineyard, Nantucket, Long Island, etc., are taken into account, does it become clear that the ice advanced its front more than once. This subject will be mentioned again under the head of End Moraines (page 385).

Thickness of Ice and Direction of Movement.—The ice sheet spread southward from Labrador, covering all the mountains of this province and also the Adirondacks. Its thickness at any given place may be estimated roughly by assuming that its surface descended to sea level at Long Island with a slope 30, 40, or 50 feet to the mile (judging by other ice sheets)[1] for the last 50 or 100 miles, but with less slope farther north. At all events Mount Washington was well covered, and streaks of boulder clay were left on its top.[2] The same is true of Mount Katahdin.[3] While the dominant movement was southward it was influenced also by the orientation of the broader slopes, and by more and more restricted slopes as the sheet thinned and lightened. On the east it spread seaward, almost at right angles to the coast of Maine (Fig. 108). The Hudson-Champlain Trough favored a large lobe, which tended to spread both right and left over the highlands. With the wasting of the ice the Connecticut Valley developed its own lobe, and the minor basins of eastern Massachusetts did the same (page 386).

Erosive Work of Ice.—In so rough a country as New England it may well be expected that the ice should bear heavily on the hilltops. The summits of all mountains were well scrubbed, but there are very few places at which ice erosion accomplished much below the weathered zone. On the other hand, little soil

more than 90 per cent of the stones in the drift in Connecticut are of local origin.

[1] ALDEN, *op. cit.*, p. 37.

[2] GOLDTHWAIT, J. W., Remnants of an Old Graded Upland on the Presidential Range of the White Mountains, *Amer. Jour. Sci.*, 4th ser., vol. 37, p. 458, 1914.

[3] TARR, R. S., Glaciation on Mount Ktaadn, Maine, *Bull. Geol. Soc. Amer.*, vol. 11, p. 436, 1900.

or weathered rock was left anywhere, except in narrow valleys
or pockets where the ice may not have shared the forward motion
of the sheet.[1]   A vigorous ice sheet ending in a rough country
may develop narrow lobes in valleys which are approximately
parallel to the direction of movement.   Such tongues of ice

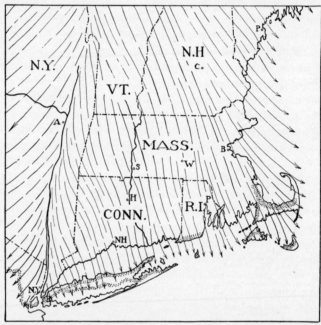

Fig. 108.—Map of southern New England showing generalized directions of
movement of the last ice.   Dotted belts indicate end moraines.   (*Alden, U. S.
Geol. Survey, modified by R. F. Flint.*)

erode their valleys after the manner of alpine glaciers, making
rounded glacial troughs which, if partly below sea level, consti-
ture fiords like those of Greenland.   Such erosive work of ice is
exemplified on the Coast of Maine, but only in one locality,
Mount Desert Island.[2]   Here is at least one good fiord, Somes

[1] Burt, Frederick A., Pleistocene Ice Stagnation in the Valleys of
Western Vermont, *Bull. Geol. Soc. Amer.*, vol. 43, p. 177, 1932, abst.   The
preservation of soft Miocene sediments and pre-Wisconsin talus in some of
these valleys is here explained by relative stagnancy of ice in the valley,
while the main sheet sheared over it in a diagonal direction: see also Flint,
op. cit., p. 46.

[2] Johnson, Douglas, "The New England-Acadian Shoreline," John
Wiley & Sons, Inc. New York, 1925.   Pages 90–100 discuss fiords in general

Sound; likewise half a dozen other U-shaped valleys, deeply scoured and containing lakes.[1] Other bays, inlets, and headlands of the coast show severe glacial scrubbing and removal of weathered rock but do not indicate depth of erosion by ice.

Distinct features due to alpine glaciation show that the White Mountains and the Katahdin group, as well as the Adirondack and Catskill groups and the Green Mountains, were centers of outward moving valley glaciers, whose direction of movement bore no relation to that of the general ice sheet. Necessarily, this alpine glaciation occurred either before or after the continental glaciation, no doubt both before and after. The chief evidence is found in cirques, the "gulfs" of the White Mountains. Some of them are excellent examples of their kind and point without doubt to a climate quite different from the present. All theoretical considerations indicate that the climate during the advance of the continental ice was more favorable to local glaciers than during its wasting or retreat. Some observations in the field also indicate that the cirques had essentially their present form when overridden by the ice sheet.[2] On the other hand, it is to be expected that the moraines of pre-Wisconsin valley glaciers would be made unrecognizable by the passing of the ice sheet. It is also to be expected that any post-Wisconsin valley glaciers in these same cirques and valleys, even though less vigorous than their predecessors, would leave clearer records. It is probably true that certain moraines were made by such belated valley glaciers.[3]

The Drift Mantle.—The mantle of ice-laid drift is nowhere thick, except in an occasional deep valley favorably situated.

---

and Mount Desert Island in particular. Francis P. Shepard (*Bull. Geol. Soc. Amer.*, vol. 42; *Jour. Geol.*, vol. 39, pp. 345–360) has treated the Bay of Fundy as due in large part to glacial erosion. This paper contains valuable data, but Shepard's conclusion is not here followed.

[1] U. S. Geol. Survey, Topographic Atlas, Lafayette National Park sheet.

[2] Clear evidence is found by Richard P. Goldthwait—Glacial Striations Date Cirque Cutting in the White Mountains, *Proc. Geol. Soc. Amer.*, 1936. See also, GOLDTHWAIT, J. W., Glaciation in the White Mountains of New Hampshire, *Bull. Geol. Soc. Amer.*, vol. 27, pp. 263–294, 1916; LANE, A. C., White Mountain Physiography, *Amer. Jour. Sci.*, 5th ser., vol. 1, p. 349, 1921.

[3] JOHNSON, DOUGLAS, Date of Local Glaciation in the White, Adirondack and Catskill Mountains, *Bull. Geol. Soc. Amer.*, vol. 28, pp. 543–552, 1917.

It is estimated to average between 5 and 10 feet over the whole state of Connecticut[1] and perhaps 10 to 15 feet over central Massachusetts.[2]   It may be deeper in some parts of the province, especially in some low basins near the coast, but in general it is only a small fraction of the preglacial relief. As glacial erosion was similarly small, it is plain that the topography was changed only in minor ways. As deposition was preponderantly in valleys, the total effect was to diminish relief. The concentration of water-laid drift in the valleys is an important factor in producing this effect.

In two classes of deposits, thick drift rises visibly above the general level. One of these is terminal moraines, the other is drumlins. The latter are conspicuous to a degree quite out of proportion to their total area, which may reach a very few hundred square miles in the entire province.[3] Heights between 50 and 100 feet are most common. As the typical drumlin is smoothly rounded, not too steep to cultivate, and generally freer from boulders than the average drift, most of these hills are cleared and farmed.

Effects on Drainage.—The general aspect of the landscape was altered more by derangement of its drainage than by changes in relief. Most hills and most valleys could be identified on corresponding contour maps made before and after glaciation, but there were no preglacial lakes. Most of the present lake basins are caused by the unequal thickness of the drift in pre-glacial valleys, the thicker masses constituting dams. Thousands of such basins held lakes or ponds when the ice vanished. Many have since become swamps, or meadows, like the intervales of the White Mountains.

While a very large amount of drift would be required to obliterate a valley, a very small amount may block a channel. Most streams remained in their old valleys, but many of them lost their channels. Streams thus compelled to seek new courses

---

[1] Flint, *op. cit.*, p. 47.

[2] Alden, *op. cit.*, p. 39.

[3] Alden (*op. cit.*, p. 42) gives average measurements of about 300 drumlins in an area of 1835 square miles in central Massachusetts, the several drumlins averaging about ⅛ square mile and altogether occupying perhaps 2 per cent of that area.   Many of these are rock drumlins with only a veneer of drift. His Pl. 13 is a map of Massachusetts showing all listed drumlins.   See also Flint, *op. cit.*, pp. 73–77.

have no guidance except the slope of the drift surface, a good guide for the moment, but as soon as the stream cuts through the drift, it may find itself crossing a ridge or ledge of hard rock, over which it develops falls or rapids, and in which a gorge is eventually carved. New England's water power is due to such accidents. At least six manufacturing cities on the Merrimac alone owe their locations to water power where the river failed to find its old channel when the glacier vanished. It is fair to assume that, in the long preglacial cycles, drainage had gone far toward finding rocks of least resistance where option was allowed, and in grading channels across harder rocks where it was necessary to cross them. In wiping out such lines the glacier set back the work of adjustment by some millions of years. The features due to this derangement, lakes, swamps, falls, and gorges, affect the landscape to a degree quite disproportionate to the amount of change in relief.

As indicated above, drainage changes caused by the ice were mainly of a minor sort. Most of them involve new channels rather than a rearrangement of drainage basins. They are not to be compared in magnitude with the changes made by slow adjustment in the interval between the uplift of the New England peneplain and the coming of the ice. The magnitude of glacial changes may be seen in the case of the Farmington River in northern Connecticut.[1]

End Moraines.—At its maximum extension the ice sheet had its front on Long Island and the islands east of it as far as Nantucket. The terminal moraine on these islands is described on page 16. No doubt it is continued northeastward on the present sea bottom. It may add both breadth and height to Georges Bank, having the same relation to that shoal which it has to the islands named.[2] Retreat and readvance of the ice front caused a second moraine to be built farther north on Long Island and a chain of little islands leading to the southwestern corner of Rhode Island. Between that point and Cape Cod are the only considerable stretches of ridgelike terminal or recessional moraine in the province. Even these are short and

[1] FLINT, R. F., *Amer. Jour. Sci.*, vol. 27, pp. 88–90, 1934. Also Conn. Geol. Nat. Hist. Survey, *Bull.* 6, p. 252, and *Bull.* 47, p. 116.

[2] SHEPARD, F. P., and others, Origin of Georges Bank, *Bull. Geol. Soc. Amer.*, 44, abst., 1933.

interrupted. The development of two marginal lobes, one in the Narragansett basin, the other in Cape Cod Bay, reflects the topography, and indirectly the geology, of the preglacial surface. Between the two lobes, and responsible for their separation, is a low granite upland. East of that feature the drift is very deep and little is seen of the underlying rock of the Coastal Plain, but enough to indicate that the east-west part of the Cape Cod peninsula is a preglacial divide. The ice eroded so little that the form of the old drainage basin on the north is known to have been not very different from that of Cape Cod Bay.[1] The eastward continuation of this second moraine is not known, but it was well outside the present coast of Maine. Both of these terminal moraines are classified as Wisconsin in age.[2]

Disappearance of the Ice.—In other parts of the United States the front of an ice sheet is known to have receded by excess of melting while the ice continued to move forward. During halts of moderate duration recessional moraines were built (page 514). The absence of such in New England, together with the forms, structure, and distribution of water-laid drift, has led to a different conception of the manner in which this province was deglaciated. The ice sheet may be thought of as diminishing progressively both in thickness and extent. Such wasting, over a surface of considerable relief, may result in a margin of unknown width, consisting of islands and peninsulas of ice, the former stagnant, and the latter in process of becoming so as connection with the main moving mass grows more and more tenuous. Under such conditions water-laid deposits accumulate in the interspaces, but recessional moraines marking the position of an "ice front" are precluded. Patches of drift, thicker or more hummocky than the average, are found here and there in valleys. On the assumption that these are bits of end moraine, older studies of glaciation correlated them in such a manner as to represent successive stages of a receding ice front.[3] If the

[1] SHALER, N. S., Geology of the Cape Cod District, U. S. Geol. Survey, 18*th Ann. Rept.*, pt. 2, p. 516, 1897.

[2] FULLER, M. L., The Geology of Long Island, New York, U. S. Geol. Survey, *Prof. Paper*, 82, p. 210, 1914.

[3] TAYLOR, F. B., The Correlation and Reconstruction of Recessional Ice Borders in Berkshire County, Massachusetts. *Jour. Geol.*, vol. 11, pp. 323–364, 1903; ALDEN, W. C., The Physical Features of Central Massachusetts, U. S. Geol. Survey, *Bull.* 760, pp. 13–105, 1924; ref. to pp. 94*ff*.

margin of the wasting ice sheet be visualized as described above, the conception of a receding front becomes inapplicable. The masses of drift referred to may be in part ground moraine but are mainly bits of kame terrace.

Water-laid Drift.—A surprising thing in southern New England is the large amount of sand and gravel laid down by melt water.[1] Such sediments partly fill all valleys except some of the smallest. In part these deposits are ordinary valley trains, involving no obstruction to drainage, but merely an excessive supply of sediment from the melting ice. In part, they are kame terraces, made by filling the trough between a valley side and a surviving ice tongue or ice block in the valley. The ice in that case may be either moving or stagnant. If stagnant, the edge of the terrace in contact with the ice should show by casts the characteristic forms of a decaying glacier, its indentations, enlarging crevasses and outlying residual blocks. Such ice-contact faces are common in the larger valleys. Much of the assorted drift is less definitely related to the ice, having been deposited because free drainage was impeded by isolated masses of ice which lingered in the valleys after the main body had melted back a few miles or many miles. Conditions under which the water-laid drift accumulated will be understood if the gradual disappearance of the ice sheet be conceived of as described above.

Waters locally and partially dammed by remnants of glacial ice form sluggish streams or lakes, or any gradation between the two, according to the spread. The approach to stream or lake conditions may be known by the substance and structure of the deposit. Whether deposition was in lakes or by streams, in immediate contact with the ice or in pools held by ice dams, the water descended from one level to another by passing over or around the barriers in spillways. Since many of the barriers were ice, the spillways shifted from time to time and the streams and lakes fell to new levels. Some of the temporary basins were filled, and the surface of the gravel deposit is now seen to accord with an abandoned spillway which determined its level. Since the disappearance of the ice, the streams are rehandling the sediments, laying them down again on flood plains which slope

[1] Well shown on the Map of Glacial Geology of Connecticut by R. F. Flint, State Conn. Geol. Nat. Hist. Survey, scale 1:125,000, 1930.

continuously toward the sea instead of descending by steps. Some of the newer alluvial surfaces are already terraced.

The Connecticut Valley.—The Connecticut Valley has long been famed for its terraces.   The lower members among these are

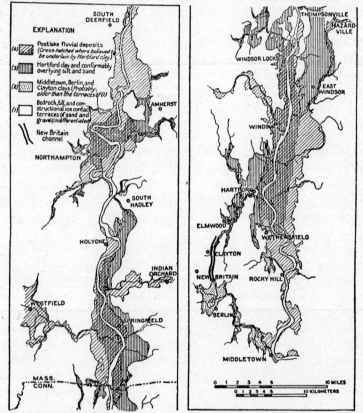

Fig. 109.—Late Glacial sequence of deposits in the Connecticut Valley, showing relation of lacustrine clays to earlier ice-margin deposits and later fluvial terraces.   (*R. F. Flint.*)

postglacial stream terraces, to be mentioned below.   The highest members, and first to be developed, are composed of sand and gravel deposited by late glacial waters between the ice and the valley side.[1]   It is agreed that ice lasted longer in the valley

[1] FLINT, R. F., Late Pleistocene Sequence in the Connecticut Valley, *Bull. Geol. Soc. Amer.*, vol. 44, pp. 965–988, 1933.

than on the uplands, also that the melting of this mass in the valley began at the margins. It was there that deposition by glacial waters began making kame terraces. In many cases these are pitted by the melting out of ice blocks, or hummocky where pits are very close. The ice in the valley was at first a mere extension of the main ice sheet and shared its southward movement. Later there was gradation, as described above, between the moving, but shrinking, ice sheet and outlying stagnant blocks. The width of this fringe is not known, but there is no doubt of its existence. Its several fragments blocked the valley here and there, dividing it into irregular areas of deposition as the melt water followed changing channels determined by the wasting ice and the newly exposed bedrock surface.

So long as this condition lasted, sand and gravel were being laid down at lower and lower levels, making a series of depositional terraces, not necessarily linear or parallel to the valley. Many ice-contact faces show by their form that the ice was stagnant. Such faces may be on any side of the terrace, including the south. Most of the water, for most of the time, was moving in streams. From time to time and from place to place the waters were expanded and lacustrine sediments were deposited.

With the melting of the ice from the Connecticut Valley its deeper part became a single lake of considerable extent. The sediments in the middle of this newer lake were mainly clay or fine glacial rock flour known now as "Hartford clay" and by other local names. This is varved clay, known to have been deposited in fresh water. The deposit is analogous to the "brick clays" of the Hudson Valley and, like them, frequently covered with sand which washed in as the lake became shallow.[1] The reason for a lake in the Connecticut Valley is to be found primarily in a dam of drift, probably supplemented by stagnant ice. The depression of the ice-covered surface to the north, and the consequent low southward gradient of the valley at that

---

[1] In treating this lake as later than the kame terraces, the author follows Richard F. Flint. B. K. Emerson (Holyoke folio) allowed much importance to lakes, apparently ascribing to lacustrine conditions most of the deposition in the kame terraces which Flint in his later papers ascribes mainly to stream work. Emerson seems not to separate these two types of deposition with respect to time.

time, caused the lake to extend much farther north than it otherwise would.[1]

All lakes ultimately disappeared and, with the gradual rise of the continent at the north, the Connecticut River incised its channel in the steadily rising surface, all the time preserving its graded profile except for a few crossings of hard rock. The result of steady downcutting with coincident meandering was to carve a series of alluvial terraces, not generally matched as to elevation on opposite sides of the river.[2] These terraces are, in the main, carved in the stream-laid and lake deposits already described.

This description of the Connecticut Valley applies mainly to that broad portion whose floor is the Triassic lowland. Similar features confined to a much narrower belt are found at places in the upper valley; for example, the lacustrine plain on which Hanover, N. H., stands.[3]

The lower terraces in such a series necessarily indicate a narrower meander zone than the upper and older terraces. Unwarranted inferences as to the former size of the river have at times been drawn from this fact. The limitation of lateral swing of the later meanders may best be explained by the form of the underlying surface of hard rock which slopes toward the axis of the valley. As the river cuts down, its possible swing is more and more restricted by cutting into solid rock. Older terraces are thus "defended" and preserved.[4]

Alluvial terraces are not limited to the peculiar conditions in the Connecticut Valley. They characterize valleys which for any reason were partly filled by unconsolidated deposits, especially where profiles have been steepened by postglacial tilting.

[1] ANTEVS, E., Recession of the Land Ice in New England, *Bull. Geol. Soc. Amer.*, vol. 33, p. 86, abst., 1922. Alden (*op. cit.*, p. 90) allows also for the effect of dams of drift to the south. Flint (Late Pleistocene Sequence in the Connecticut Valley, *loc. cit.*) stresses particularly the probable damming by drift with possible aid of surviving ice blocks (pp. 977–978).

[2] DAVIS, W. M., River Terraces in New England, *Bull. Harvard Coll. Museum Comp. Zool.*, vol. 38, pp. 281–346, 1902. The reference here is to p. 291.

[3] GOLDTHWAIT, J. W., Glacio-lacustrine and Postglacial Features of the Connecticut Valley near Hanover, N. H., *Science*, vol. 32, p. 126, 1910.

[4] DAVIS, *loc. cit.* Pages 297–326 discuss the Theory of River Terraces with many illustrative drawings.

These conditions are met in the valleys of Maine[1] where valleys were partly filled with marine sediments (p. 378). Both here and farther south, overloaded waters from melting ice left kame terraces or valley trains, or both, in which subsequent terracing has been easy.[2] Postglacial time has also been long enough for the cutting of moderate gorges by streams which were displaced and superposed on hard rocks.

Résumé of Glaciation.—The continental ice first spread over New England from the north at a time when the surface stood higher than at present. The surface was, then as now, very rough and must have impeded the ice movement unless the ice that filled the valleys was overridden by that above the hilltops. The ice cover vanished first from the southern margin and by slow degrees toward the north, occupying somewhat more than 4400 years in its retreat from Hartford, Conn., to St. Johnsbury in northern Vermont.[3] Nowhere is there a clear recessional moraine. Indeed, the present conception of the manner in which the ice sheet wasted away is such as to preclude anything that might properly be called recessional moraine.[4] It seems safe to affirm, at least, that during the wasting of the general cover, a broad margin was so broken up that the several blocks were no longer in contact and therefore no longer pushed forward.[5] Drift, largely water-laid, accumulated all around them, as seen by the fact that ice-contact edges now face in all directions. The isolated blocks for a long time must have interfered with free drainage. This helps to explain the very abundant glaciofluvial drift.

[1] Smith, Geo. Otis, Geology of the Kennebec River Basin, U. S. Geol. Survey, *Water Supply Paper* 198, 409, 1907.

[2] Alden, *op. cit.*, p. 56.

[3] Antevs, *op. cit.*, p. 47, 1922.

[4] Papers by Richard F. Flint in 1929 and 1930, referred to above, emphasize considerations favoring stagnation of the entire ice sheet. His later papers (Deglaciation of the Connecticut Valley, *Amer. Jour. Sci.*, vol. 24, pp. 152–156, 1932; Late Pleistocene Sequence in the Connecticut Valley, *Bull. Geol. Soc. Amer.*, vol. 44, 1933) harmonize the evidences of stagnant ice with a progressive disappearance from south to north.

[5] This view does not necessarily conflict with that of Alden (*op. cit.*, p. 93) "that the ice did not disintegrate throughout the area as a wholly stagnant mass."

CHAPTER VII

THE ADIRONDACK PROVINCE

GEOLOGIC CONDITIONS

Relation to Other Provinces.—The Adirondack province is a highland, in part mountainous, covering a little more than 10,000 square miles in northern New York. It occupies the point of a wedge between two structural troughs, the Great Appalachian Valley on the east and the St. Lawrence Valley on the northwest. Both of these depressions are major features of Appalachian physiography. Except for them the country has the same general character from Long Island Sound and the coast of Maine to northern Ontario, everywhere a rough, plateau-like upland surmounted by monadnocks or larger residual masses.

The Hudson-Champlain Valley is narrow (10 to 20 miles) and the view across it is much the same, whether looking east or west. Against this troughlike depression the highland ends abruptly. In addition to the geosynclinal character of the trough it is known to be faulted down.

The St. Lawrence Valley is much wider, 60 miles or more, and the margin of the Adirondack province merges with it by a more gradual descent. The province boundary is the line along which the Pre-Cambrian rocks disappear beneath the sedimentary beds preserved in the syncline. The area described in this chapter extends to the St. Lawrence River, thus including a strip, nowhere wider than 25 miles, which belongs properly to the St. Lawrence Valley province, not otherwise treated in this volume.

The remaining part of the boundary is a curved line on the south and southwest determined by the retreating edge of a former sedimentary cover. The Black River marks the western part of this line with considerable accuracy. Farther east the Mohawk flows in a subsequent valley only a few miles south of the boundary.

Rocks.—The rocks of the Adirondack province are mainly Pre-Cambrian igneous and very old. Granite (including syenite)

392

is most abundant. This is more resistant than most sediments, being comparable to the core of the Green Mountains (page 350). About one sixth of the area in the eastern part is occupied by intrusive rocks, the Adirondack batholith, mainly anorthosite but embracing some gabbro. The former, at least, is more resistant than the granite, and makes at least half of all the mountains, including all of the highest and steepest. Within the granite area are smaller irregular patches, several of them 25 miles long, of Pre-Cambrian sediments known as the Grenville formation. That part of this formation which was originally shale and sandstone is now metamorphosed to schist, and reacts to erosion much like the surrounding granite. But a part of the Grenville is limestone, distinctly more erodible than the rest, hence always a valley maker.

On the northern side the surface on the granite descends gradually beneath the nearly flat-lying Potsdam (Cambrian) sandstone, which is often classified as quartzite[1] and is in places (not everywhere) harder than the underlying crystallines. Above it are the Ordovician formations, first limestones and then shales, the resistance decreasing upward.

Structure.—The Adirondack region is one which has more than once been raised above its surroundings. Before Paleozoic time began, there were mountains here whose trend was northeast-southwest near the present St. Lawrence River and in the western part of the province. In the southeastern part the trend was generally east-west but with local irregularities. These directions are known by the present trend of foliation in the gneiss.[2] Remnants of the Grenville series are elongated in the direction of the old folding, and some valleys follow these remnants because of the relatively weak rocks which they contain. Others are believed to mark lines from which the Grenville has disappeared.

Since the ancient mountains were made and base-leveled, in Pre-Cambrian time, there has been folding in the geosyncline on the east but none in the Adirondacks. Faulting has, however,

[1] KEMP, J. F., The Physiography of the Adirondacks, *Pop. Sci. Monthly*, vol. 68, p. 195, 1906.

[2] BUDDINGTON, A. F., Granite Phacoliths and Their Contact Zones in the Northwest Adirondacks, *Bull. N. Y. State Museum*, 281, 1929; see especially Fig. 44, map.

been noteworthy, especially in the eastern part, where the mountains are. Cushing finds strong evidence that the eastern boundary of the province is in part a fault scarp not yet reduced by erosion. The steep ascent west of Lake Champlain is over a series of abrupt rises unrelated to the drainage and in rock of uniform hardness, hence not to be accounted for by differential erosion. Recent step faulting is inferred.[1] Similar evidence, not everywhere equally clear, occurs at intervals throughout the eastern boundary.

The direction of most faults is north-northeast to south-southwest, hence generally at variance with the older structure. Most of the demonstrated and mapped faults were made during or at the close of the Paleozoic.   In either case, or even if made in Triassic time, their scarps have long disappeared. If any show at present, they are second-cycle (fault line) scarps. The question of age has no importance here, so long as the scarps are known not to be in their first cycle, but the distinction between fault scarps (first cycle) and fault-line scarps (later cycle) is important because of its bearing on the explanation of drainage lines (see below). The question of later faulting, sufficiently recent to affect the topography directly, is considered on page 401.

Much of the faulting which is believed to be young is known only by physiographic evidence and must be mentioned in discussing the topography.   Generally the rocks traversed are the same on both sides, hence the faults do not appear on the geologic map.   Those which do so appear, mainly on the south and southeast, are old, their scarps being revived by subsequent erosion.[2]

PREGLACIAL TOPOGRAPHY

The Plateau Surface.—The western half of the Adirondack province and parts of the southern and northern margins farther east are plateaulike and belong to the extensive upland which includes Eastern Canada and New England.   Genetically it is an old peneplain (or approximately such), lifted and dissected. In evenness of sky line it is comparable with the New England

---

[1] Cushing, H. P., Geology of the Northern Adirondack Region, *Bull. N. Y. State Museum*, 95, p. 432, 1905.

[2] Cushing, *op. cit.*, p. 431; *cf.* Miller, W. J., Geological History of New York State, *Bull. N. Y. State Museum*, 255, pp. 74–75, 1924.

Upland. Monadnocks are similar in number and size. Valleys are also much the same in depth, though more of them are wide, and the filling of glacial drift is generally deeper. Lakes are more abundant, especially in and near the mountains. It is for the most part a wild country, sparsely populated, retaining much of its original dense forest and the charm of the wilderness. Where forests have been destroyed by logging or by fire the scene is desolate.

The surface here described averages about 2000 feet high, lower at the edges and higher near the center of the province. The most pronounced general slope is toward the west. The approximate agreement in elevation with the Schooley peneplain east and south of this province seems to warrant the assignment of this surface to the same cycle. The greater altitude of the central part no doubt indicates differential uplift,[1] but it is also probable that the peneplain here retained considerable relief even aside from definite monadnocks. The most distinct impression of an old, now uplifted, plain is gained by looking across the Black River Valley from the west. There the observer may stand on the flat top of the Tug Hill cuesta 2000 feet high (page 325) and look eastward to the horizon on the Adirondacks at about the same level. Similar views may be had at places near the northern margin.[2]

At no place on the north, west, or south does this old surface reach the province boundary. Everywhere it is cut off by a steeper slope descending to the edge and passing beneath the sedimentaries (Fig. 94, page 324). As both surfaces are dissected, it would be hard to locate the line of their intersection, but the zone allotted to the steeper marginal slope is generally between 5 and 15 miles. This steeper slope is a Pre-Paleozoic peneplain, brought to view again by the stripping of the weaker sediments from the more resistant and enduring crystalline floor. It is constantly being broadened by further stripping on its outer edge and destroyed by erosion on its inner margin.[3] On the west and south the Pre-Paleozoic peneplain was fairly level, and the

[1] MILLER, WM. J. The Adirondack Mountains, *Bull. N. Y. State Museum*, 193, p. 56, 1917.

[2] CHADWICK, C. H., The Paleozoic Rocks of the Canton Quadrangle, *Bull. N. Y. State Museum*, 217, p. 47, 1920.

[3] Similar relations in the Piedmont province are described on p. 127, and in the Superior Upland in Wisconsin, on p. 552.

present edge of the sediments is moderately straight except for offsets due to faulting. The corresponding surface on the north retained considerable relief[1] and the edge of the Potsdam sandstone is correspondingly irregular. East of Canton (a little west of the 75th meridian) a rise of 500 to 1000 feet in passing from the sedimentary rocks to the crystallines is accomplished in a very few miles. Farther west the slope is gradual.

Fig. 110.—Western margin of the Adirondack Upland east of the Black River and southeast of Carthage, N. Y. Elevation 700 to 800 feet. Probably the Pre-Cambrian peneplain, now stripped. The surface at this place was scrubbed by the ice sheet, which removed the preglacial soil, exposing residual knobs of granosyenite. (*A. F. Buddington, N. Y. State Museum, Bull.* 296.)

The Lower Peneplain.—Both of the surfaces mentioned above are cut by valleys, some of them wide, leading down to lowlands in the adjacent provinces. These latter, the floors of the St. Lawrence, Hudson, and lower Mohawk valleys and the Ontario Lowland, represent a younger peneplain (one or more) developed in late Tertiary time. Their altitudes rarely reach 500 feet. Some of the Adirondack valleys leading down to them are graded for considerable distances and have developed wide floors or straths which are correlated in age with the late Tertiary peneplain (tentatively Harrisburg). They are themselves incipient peneplains, but the altitude at any one point is determined more by the stream gradient than by ultimate base level. Hence altitudes cannot be relied on to indicate the amount of later

[1] Cushing, H. P., Geology of the Northern Adirondack Region, *Bull.* N. Y. *State Museum*, 95, p. 433, 1905.

uplift. Elevations vary from valley to valley. Although their significance as indicators of later uplift is very limited, they are all, none the less, parts of a single surface, the product of an unfinished erosion cycle interrupted by uplift not long before the glacial epoch.

In none of these valleys is grading so perfect as to eliminate all rapids. In all of them, rapids are encountered soon after entering the Adirondack province. Graded stretches extend from one rapids to the next, it may be 10 miles or 30 miles away. Hence wide valleys with peneplaned floors of the younger cycle are all more or less local. This does not affect their age or their correlation, but it casts doubt on any inference as to the amount of later uplift, based on the elevation of local peneplains. At present these wide valleys are in large part floored with deep drift and in part occupied by lakes or swamp. On account of glaciation they may or may not be on the main lines of present drainage.

The St. Lawrence Valley.[1]—The St. Lawrence Valley is a smooth glacial plain whose lower part is made still more smooth by a covering of marine clay. The thick mantle of glacial and marine deposits rests on the late Tertiary peneplain, which bevels at a very low angle the strong Cambrian sandstone and the weaker Ordovician limestones and shales. These dip gently from the Adirondacks to the St. Lawrence and should form cuestas scarping toward the highland as the same formations do south of the Frontenac axis which crosses the St. Lawrence at the Thousand Islands.[2] Such cuestas may well be present,[3] obscured by the thick drift, for the underlying rock is rarely seen.

Altitudes are generally less than 500 feet, dropping below 200 feet along the St. Lawrence. But near the eastern limit of the highland (east of the 74th meridian) there is a marked elevation. Here is probably an upwarp along a north-south axis in line with the main range of the Adirondacks. On this

[1] The lowlands on sides other than north are treated elsewhere. This paragraph on the St. Lawrence Valley is placed here because that province receives no other treatment in this volume.

[2] Cushing, H. P., Geology of the Thousand Island Region, *Bull. N. Y. State Museum*, 145, p. 21, 1910.

[3] Ruedemann, R., The Tangential Master Streams of the Adirondack Drainage, *Amer. Jour. Sci.*, vol. 22, p. 434, 1931.

axis the Paleozoic sediments reach a height of more than 1000 feet. This upwarp of the stratified rocks affords one of the arguments for the tentative conclusion that the Adirondack area was unequally raised since peneplanation.

Relief in the St. Lawrence Valley is almost wholly within the glacial drift. One hundred feet is near the maximum. Drumlins are the most conspicuous forms.[1]

Mountainous Portion of the Adirondacks.—It is only in its eastern half that the Adirondack province is mountainous. Even here the level of the horizon is not above that of the western half except in a northeast-southwest belt near the divide between the St. Lawrence and the Hudson-Champlain Trough. At the north this belt lies between 20 and 30 miles west of Lake Champlain. In the latitude of Mt. Marcy (a little north of lat. 44°) the mountain belt is fully 30 miles wide, approaching within 15 miles of the lake. Here it jogs westward and continues south-southwest past Lake Pleasant toward Little Falls, running out into more or less isolated knobs before the province boundary is reached. In this ill-defined strip are two summits above 5000 feet and fourteen others above 4000.[2] The country east of this zone is also truly mountainous, though its summit level differs little from that of the peneplain west of the mountains.[3]

The northern end and the southern half of the mountain belt consist of the same rocks that make the broad upland. The inference is that the mountains owe their existence, at least in part, to location near an old divide. The remaining (north central) part of the range is on the old batholith whose rocks are more resistant. Here are most of the high mountains. The slopes are also steeper and the forms less rounded than elsewhere. These features are consistent with the inference that the mountains are residual. Probably the sufficiency of this explanation would never have been questioned had it not been for certain valleys of striking form, obviously related to faults. Most of these lie east of the high mountains.

[1] CHADWICK, C. H., The Paleozoic Rocks of the Canton Quadrangle, *Bull. N. Y. State Museum*, 217, p. 49, 1920.

[2] For a list of these 16 peaks and their altitudes see *Bull. N. Y. State Museum*, 138, p. 12, 1910.

[3] A good generalized topographic map in colors, on a scale of 12 miles to 1 inch and showing contours at a 200-foot interval and also the main divides, is issued by the N. Y. State Museum.

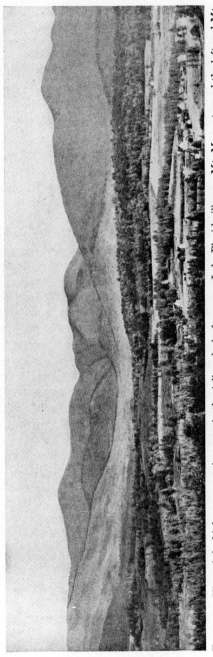

FIG. 111.—View of the highest mountain group in the Adirondacks from near Lake Placid village. Mt. Marcy toward the left and Mt. MacIntyre at the right. (Photograph by Melvil Dewey of the Lake Placid Club. Reproduced from N. Y. State Museum Bull., 193.)

A feature quite out of harmony with the assumption of a purely residual origin is the relatively low surface in and around the Saranac Lake district just north of the jog in the mountain belt. This district is likewise on the batholith, whose rocks are quite as hard here as elsewhere. Yet a considerable area containing no mountains lies below the level at which the Schooley peneplain might be expected. It is inferred by Cushing[1] that the surface here is that of the upland peneplain dropped below its surrounding level by faulting when a general uplift was in progress. It has been rather generally assumed by New York geologists that such postpeneplain faulting did occur, and that it is in part at least responsible for the mountains. The features most appealed to in support of this hypothesis are the narrow, straight valleys, discussed below.

East of the belt of highest mountains the relief is less, though everywhere of mountainous dimensions unless it be near the southern edge. The average elevation of the horizon is little if any greater than in the western half, but the sky line is broken and valleys are cut to greater depths. There is no suggestion of a plateau. The mountainous aspect is enhanced by the prevalence of a northeast-southwest alignment (more strictly north-northeast and south-southwest) caused by straight valleys.

Valleys in the Mountains.—Adirondack valleys are of two general types.[2] There is first the fairly open valley with moderately sloping sides and a smooth or rolling bottom, sometimes a mile or several miles in width, the type to be expected in any well-subdued mountain country, and abundantly illustrated in the western half of the province. Glacial filling or lakes, of course, alter the present aspect. Such is the valley that contains Schroon Lake, or the southern third of Lake George, or the Keene and other valleys in the Mt. Marcy quadrangle, or that of the Cedar River south of Blue Mountain. Such valleys follow no one direction and are not straight for long distances. Some of them agree in direction with the faulting. Some of them follow the weaker rocks of the Grenville series. Some others occupy zones in which the Grenville is believed to have been present

[1] CUSHING, H. P., Geology of the Northern Adirondack Region, *Bull. N. Y. State Museum*, 95, p. 429, 1905.

[2] KEMP, J. F., The Physiography of the Adirondacks, *Pop. Sci. Monthly*, vol. 68, pp. 195–210, 1906; ref. to p. 200.

when the stream's course was chosen. Still others are not known to be related to structure. These valleys represent the normal development of the last well-marked erosion cycle, barring the cutting of gorges.

Valleys of the second type are notably straight, parallel, narrow, and steep, their direction being the most prominent element in the lineaments of the landscape. They are found both in the belt of higher mountains and farther east. Long and Lower Ausable lakes occupy such valleys in the higher mountains. Farther east the valley marked for 30 miles by Indian Lake and Indian River is a striking lineament on any map of the region. A glance at the Schroon Lake quadrangle, or the Newcomb west of it, will reveal others not occupied by lakes. That this system of valleys is related to a system of faults is not questioned. To account for these valleys in such a manner as will be consistent with their features, and which will at the same time admit of the older, broader, less regular valleys, is one of the main problems of Adirondack physiography.

Relation of Faulting to Valleys.—The prevalent and perhaps correct assumption is that faulting accompanied the uplift of the Schooley surface, perhaps even that which followed the making of the wide valleys (tentatively correlated with the Harrisburg cycle). Some valleys may be actual fault troughs or grabens.[1] Others, or all, may be subsequent along lines weakened by brecciation or by slicing.[2] All scarps are preglacial and, since they lie in the direction of the ice movement, were probably freshened and steepened by the ice which carried away their talus. As the rock traversed by any one of these lines is of uniform character both laterally and vertically, it is not possible to say of any one fault what was the amount of throw, or even its direction. The existence of the faults is known only by the forms of valleys not otherwise explainable. Neither the resulting constructional surface nor the amount of subsequent erosion is known. A fuller knowledge of the structure would facilitate a reconstruction of the erosional history.

[1] KEMP, *op. cit.*, p. 201.
[2] KEMP, J. F., and R. RUEDEMANN, Geology of the Elizabethtown and Port Henry Quadrangles, *Bull. N. Y. State Museum*, 138, 1910. Page 16 of this paper states that the trellised drainage follows the faults because of the weakness along those lines.

A district of considerable interest in this respect lies east and south of Mt. Marcy where the drainage exhibits a rather striking trellised pattern.[1]   The larger streams flow northeast or southwest and receive their longer tributaries from the northwest. It has been assumed that blocks made by a series of parallel faults have been tilted southeastward, each fault having its downthrow on the northwest side.[2]   Such a relation between structure and drainage implies relatively little wasting of the original fault blocks.   This interpretation is not universally accepted.   The interstream blocks show no distinct contrast in slope between their northwest and southeast sides.   Moreover, doubt is cast on the assumed northwestward throw by the fact that in most of the well-demonstrated faults in the Adirondacks the throw is the other way.   It is suggested by Cushing[3] that on a series of fault blocks stepping down toward the southeast the growth of tributaries from the northwest would be favored and the present drainage pattern would result.   As compared with the hypothesis mentioned above, this one assumes more time to have elapsed since the faulting, but both assume the faults to be recent and the valleys to result directly from them.

The evidence for faulting since the Schooley cycle is fairly impressive.   It does not follow, however, that the faults here referred to were initiated at that time.   It is not improbable that they represent renewed slipping along old lines.   As old zones of shattered rock would be subject to rapid trenching after the late preglacial uplift, and to erosion by ice which followed their direction, the extent to which late faulting must be invoked is still uncertain.[4]

Estimate of Postpeneplain Faulting.—The extent to which the mountains of this province are, on the one hand, residual and, on the other hand, made by postpeneplain faulting is not yet

[1] BRIGHAM, A. P., Note on Trellised Drainage in the Adirondacks, *Amer. Geologist*, vol. 21, pp. 219–222, 1898.

[2] OGILVIE, IDA H., Glacial Phenomena in the Adirondacks, *Jour. Geol.*, vol. 10, pp. 397–412, 1902.   KEMP, J. F., Geology of the Mt. Marcy Quadrangle, *Bull. N. Y. State Museum*, 229–30, p. 7, 1921.   In the discussion of the Elizabethtown and Port Henry Quadrangles (*Bull. N. Y. State Museum*, 138, p. 16) Kemp and Ruedemann ascribe the rectangular stream pattern to two systems of faults at right angles.

[3] CUSHING, H. P., *Bull. N. Y. State Museum*, 95, p. 440, 1905.

[4] DAVIS, W. M., *Science*, vol. 23, pp. 630–631, 1906.

settled. The proximity of the higher mountains to the main divide favors their explanation as residuals. So also does the fact that the group of peaks on the hard intrusives averages 1500 feet higher than the next highest group on the less resistant rocks in the Indian Lake quadrangle. On the other hand, faulting is obvious and there is good reason to think that some of it occurred after the Schooley cycle and added its effect to the height of the mountains. It is rather common among New York geologists to assume that certain moderately flat summits or shoulders represent uplifted portions of a faulted peneplain. Such features are seen in the Paradox Lake quadrangle[1] at altitudes of from 1700 to 2200 feet; also in the Blue Mountain quadrangle[2] at elevations of from 3000 to 3500 feet. All such occurrences are extremely inconspicuous on topographic maps. Of themselves they are unconvincing. There remains, however, the reasonable assumption that a former peneplain, which is so evident in the western half of the province, was not wholly absent from the eastern half. This, with the known facts regarding faulting, gives plausibility to the generalization that the mountains of this province, while mainly residual, owe some part of their relief to recent faulting. So far as any peneplain existed in the region affected by faulting, it seems to have been broken up into flat-topped blocks.[3] There seems to have been a doming of the old surface both in the uplift of the Schooley surface and again in the late uplift which caused the wide valleys to be trenched.[4]

GLACIATION

Thickness and Movement of the Ice.—As elsewhere in New York and New England, the visible effects of glaciation are those of the last glacial stage, though it is known that prior invasions occurred. The movement of the ice was south by west, but it suffered some deflection in the direction of the great

[1] OGILVIE, I. H., Geology of the Paradox Lake Quadrangle, *Bull. N. Y. State Museum*, 96, p. 468, 1905.

[2] MILLER, W. J., Geology of the Blue Mountain Quadrangle, *Bull. N. Y. State Museum*, 192, 1917.

[3] KEMP, J. F., *Pop. Sci. Monthly*, vol. 68, p. 209, 1906.

[4] CUSHING, H. P., 18*th Ann. Rept.*, State Geologist, New York, 1898, cited by I. H. Ogilvie who finds the same evidence in another part of the province, *Jour. Geol.*, vol. 10, p. 409, 1902.

depressions, the Champlain and St. Lawrence valleys. When the ice had its maximum thickness and extent, this tendency to split on the higher Adirondacks was unimportant. The movement then was a little west of south[1] and the highest mountains were probably buried. This last conclusion is reached deductively[2] and also by inference from the known burial of the White Mountains, which are about 1000 feet higher than the Adirondacks. The conclusion has been questioned[3] on the ground that Mt. McIntyre (5112 ft.) shows at its summit only fragments of the local rock not demonstrably moved. Casual observation might leave the same impression of Mt. Washington, but search has revealed erratics among fragments of local rock at places not otherwise suspected of being passed over by the ice.[4]

With its disappearance from the highest places, the ice fell more and more into lobes and tongues occupying the great valleys and accommodating their movements to the contours rather remarkably. In this way a west-moving lobe in the Mohawk Valley met an east-moving lobe from the Ontario basin and probably a southeast-moving lobe in the Black River Valley (Figs. 89 and 90, page 311).

In crossing so rough a surface as the central Adirondacks, one of the two assumptions may be made: (1) The ice may have been retarded by the constant necessity of remolding its lower surface to fit its uneven bed. There was a tendency within the mass to follow valleys leading off obliquely, and thus to jam and interfere with the general motion. This effort to fit the glacier to its bed would not only be hard on the ice but on the bed as well. Vigorous scour might be looked for at all depths. (2) It may have been found easier for the upper ice to move over the lower than for the latter to move over the rugged surface, always making the necessary changes of form. This assumption seems to give a truer picture than the other, as the scouring of surfaces

[1] OGILVIE, I. H., Glacial Phenomena in the Adirondacks, *Jour. Geol.*, vol. 10, pp. 397–412, 1902; Pl. 1, p. 398, shows the direction of striae.

[2] For estimates based on the profile of the glacier see H. L. Fairchild, Pleistocene Geology of New York State, *Bull. Geol. Soc. Amer.*, vol. 24, p. 135, 1913.

[3] COLEMAN, A. P., Extent and Thickness of the Labrador Ice Sheet, *Bull. Geol. Soc. Amer.*, vol. 31, p. 325, 1920.

[4] GOLDTHWAIT, J. W., "The Geology of New Hampshire," p. 14, Concord, 1925.

and the rounding of forms at high altitudes is quite out of proportion to that in valley bottoms. Below a certain level no striae are recorded,[1] and only favored valleys show that they were occupied by moving tongues of ice. It is not necessary to postulate complete stagnation, though this may have occurred locally. The essential in the picture is a movement of the upper ice over the lower. During the decay of the ice sheet, when movement was concentrating in the bordering valleys, it may well be that considerable areas of ice in the mountains, having become

Fig. 112.—A granite boss in the Thousand Islands district, Alexandria, N. Y., quadrangle. The rounded form of the hill suggests the severity of glacial scouring. (*H. P. Cushing, N. Y. State Museum Bull.*, 145.)

isolated, were allowed to melt in place, wasting on all sides simultaneously. Since residual blocks of ice occur in valleys, not on hills, free drainage is obstructed and lakes are characteristic. This is one of the reasons why the glacial drift in this province has been so largely rehandled by water.

Proglacial Lakes.[2]—It may be assumed that the continental ice disappeared first from the highest area and that the bare spot grew slowly in all directions. As drainage was, then as now, mainly radial, this meant that each outflowing stream was ponded, becoming an ice-dammed lake with constantly changing outline, area, and altitude. As the barrier receded, lower outlets were uncovered, and lakes merged. In this way all the valleys

---

[1] OGILVIE, *op. cit.*, p. 400.

[2] Lakes in valleys draining toward the ice.

and lower lands of the province were washed by a gradually expanding ring of ponded waters, very irregular and broken. This is another reason for the predominantly water-laid character of the glacial deposits. Drift is relatively thin on the hillsides, and the old valleys are characteristically floored, often to depths of several hundred feet, with more or less assorted drift.

The general procedure here outlined is exemplified in the basin of the Ausable River, which flows northeast from the Mt. Marcy quadrangle to Lake Champlain. The area of ponded waters has been plotted at six different stages, beginning with a lake surface 2210 feet high near the central divide and passing by various stages to a lake in the lower basin with its surface 1017 feet above the sea.[1] If all these temporary lakes were plotted on a single map along with a corresponding series for the Hudson, the Saranac, the Raquette, and all the other rivers, their combined area would cover a large part of the province. Parts of the total area, but only the lower parts, received sediments enough to make flat plains, such as the flat meadow in the valley at Elizabethtown, 560 feet high.[2] The many fine deltas built in these lakes are also exemplified at Elizabethtown by the flat bench on which the village stands, 40 feet above the old lake bottom.

With periodically shifting limits and falling levels, it is but natural to expect the old lacustrine flats to be terraced. Other terraces have been carved by postglacial streams. Both kinds, along with deltas, are covered with gravel, sand, or silt. To these may be added an occasional kame terrace made by glacial outwash between an ice tongue and the valley wall.[3] Altogether, terraces are a rather familiar feature of the Adirondack valleys.

The best known and perhaps the most typical proglacial lake in the province occupied the valley of the Black River.[4] A southeast-moving glacial lobe completely filled the valley, over-

[1] ALLING, H. L., Geology of Mt. Marcy Quadrangle, *Bull. N. Y. State Museum*, 229, pp. 68–80, Figs. 9–14, 1921.

[2] KEMP, J. F., and RUEDEMANN, R., Geology of the Elizabethtown and Port Henry quadrangles, *Bull. N. Y. State Museum*, 138, p. 19, 1910.

[3] OGILVIE, I. H., *op. cit.*, p. 407.

[4] FAIRCHILD, H. L., The Glacial Waters in the Black and Mohawk Valleys, *Bull. N. Y. State Museum*, 160, 1912. This bulletin contains a series of maps showing the gradual disappearance of the ice sheet from the state of New York.

lapping on Tug Hill to the west and the Adirondack upland to the east (Fig. 90). The proglacial lake began when the rim of ice around the highland was complete and the outlet to the south was across the ice of the Mohawk lobe. When the shrinking ice lobes first failed to meet in the Mohawk Valley, the space between them was occupied by Lake Herkimer, with an arm in the Black River Valley, its surface standing at an altitude of 1440 feet.[1] As the ice front receded, the water found new outlets, stood at different levels, and covered different areas. A different name is applied to each stage. After the Herkimer stage a lower outlet to the Mohawk Valley was uncovered and the water level fell to 1240 feet (Forestport Lake). More shrinkage of the ice revealed a westerly outlet which was cut down to 1130 feet (Port Leyden Lake). Near the 44th parallel Tug Hill comes to an end. When the receding ice front approached that latitude the lake spilled over the northern slope in a series of outlets, each lower than its predecessor. With further withdrawal of the ice the lake in the Black River Valley became a bay of the extensive Lake Iroquois (page 495).

The successive glacial lakes in the Black River Valley rested against the rock-terraced scarp slope of the Tug Hill cuesta. Their waters expanded mainly over the gentler slope of the Adirondack province. Here is a succession of lake flats, dropping at intervals from a maximum height of 1440 feet to a little more than 800 feet. For the most part these flats are deltas, at places pitted by the molds of ice fragments.

Postglacial Lakes.—For lakes amid mountains the Adirondacks are noteworthy. There are thousands of lakes in the glaciated part of Eastern United States, and still more in Canada, but most of them are in plains or plateaus. An ascent of several scores of feet, or at most of several hundred feet, leads in most cases to a fairly level horizon. Even in the mountains of New England, lakes are few. On the other hand, the Adirondacks are said to have 2000 lakes and ponds. Fully half of them are in the mountains. It is here that the Lake District of England finds its counterpart both physiographically and esthetically. None of these lakes are known to be preglacial, despite the fact that

[1] Such statements refer to the present altitude of the old shore. Later crustal movements are here ignored.

some are in fault valleys of youthful appearance. All of the larger ones are in stream valleys crossed by dams of drift at one end as in the case of Schroon Lake, or at both ends as in the case of Lake George. In the latter case preglacial streams flowed both ways in a fault valley from a divide near the middle.[1] All of the larger lakes, Placid, Saranac, Raquette, etc., which are not distinctly linear, are in obstructed parts of the valleys classed above as "wide" and tentatively ascribed to the Harrisburg cycle. Long and Indian lakes are in fault valleys which may be of later date.

A few basins afford suggestions of glacial scouring as a factor in their making.[2] In a region where the movement of the basal ice was so much impeded and deflected into divergent or convergent currents by mountains, it would not be surprising if an occasional place were found where the ice bore so heavily on the rock as to gouge out a shallow basin. But evidences of such action are sparse. More frequent, and much more certain than rock basins, are the depressions in water-laid drift due to melting out of ice blocks. Lakes and ponds of this origin are found in the drift-filled valleys of the Saranac basin, and more obviously in the old lake flats in the Black River Valley (see topographic map of the Port Leyden quadrangle). As all the lakes are of recent origin, so all are hastening to extinction. All stages in this process are illustrated. Already many meadows or "vlies" show the final stage.[3]

Local Glaciation.—Like the Catskills (page 323) and the mountains of New England (page 383), the Adirondacks were centers of local glaciation of the alpine type, probably both before and after being covered by the continental ice sheet. Arguments on the date of such glaciation are the same here as elsewhere. The cirques and glacial troughs in these mountains, while genuine, are not the best types of their kind. Examples are seen on the north side of Sentinel Range and the east side of Whiteface in the Lake Placid quadrangle. The Giant Washbowl on the

[1] MILLER, WM. J., *Bull. N. Y. State Museum*, 193, p. 64, 1917.

[2] OGILVIE, *op. cit.*, p. 411; also *Bull. N. Y. State Museum*, 96, 1905. Kemp (*Pop. Sci. Monthly*, vol. 68, p. 210, 1906) cites these observations with endorsement.

[3] For description see C. H. Smyth, Jr., Lake Filling in the Adirondack Region, *Amer. Geologist*, vol. 11, pp. 85–90, 1893.

southwest side of Giant Mountain in the Elizabethtown quadrangle is another example.

Drainage Changes.—All that is known about drainage lines
in the Adirondacks before the Schooley cycle is based on the
inference that consequent streams on a structural dome should
be radial. It is assumed that the province was nearly or quite
covered by Paleozoic sediments and that consequent drainage on
them became superposed on the Pre-Cambrian rocks. It is
also safe to assume that during the slow paring back of the edge
of the strata, the ancestors of the Black and Mohawk rivers
followed their tangential courses at or near the edge of the sediments, slipping down the hard rock surface as denudation
progressed.[1]

Two assumptions are quite common: (1) That the Black and
Mohawk rivers originated as subsequent streams after the
uplift of the Schooley peneplain, and (2) that in their headward
growth they captured the radial streams from the Pre-Cambrian
area. These two assumptions, if accepted, mean that the radial
streams of the Schooley and all previous cycles continued their
courses to the Ontario Lowland on the west and the Allegheny
Plateau on the south. This assumption limits the down-dip
shifting of the tangential streams to Tertiary time and to a very
narrow zone. As the Schooley cycle came relatively late in the
long history of denudation, and was doubtless preceded by other
long cycles, it seems gratuitous to assume that the development
of these strike valleys was so long delayed. No satisfactory
criterion is yet known by which their geologic age may be
determined.

The position of residual mountains at the close of the Schooley
cycle warrants the inference that the main divides were then not
far from their present location. Following the post-Schooley
uplift, there were no doubt significant drainage changes in the
faulted eastern half of the province, whether the faulting was
renewed at that time or whether the rejuvenated drainage was
merely given additional opportunity to develop subsequent

---

[1] RUEDEMANN, R., The Tangential Master Streams of the Adirondack
Drainage, *Amer. Jour. Sci.*, vol. 22, pp. 431–440, 1931. Ruedemann would
have all such sedimentary scarps which face the stripped Pre-Cambrian
called by the Scandinavian term "glint." Such streams as the Black and
Mohawk would then be "glint streams."

streams along old fault lines. A glance at the course of the Upper Hudson in the Newcomb and adjacent quadrangles is sufficient to show its relation to two fault systems.

Then came the glacier. A way in which glaciation altered drainage indirectly has already been suggested in the mention of ice-dammed lakes. It is in the nature of such lakes that they spill over their rock rims while the former water courses are still buried by ice. Some of these improvised outlets become permanent. Other changes are clearly accounted for by morainal dams. Prominent among such changes is that by which West Canada Creek (see Pl. 1) was turned south at Trenton Falls instead of continuing its former westward course to join the Rome River flowing west to the Ontario basin.

It will be observed that the upper course of West Canada Creek, the Sacandaga River, and a link in the Hudson form an east-west line 80 miles long, nowhere more than 30 miles from the Mohawk. The divide between the two drainage lines is only 15 to 18 miles from the Mohawk, which seems to have received much longer preglacial tributaries from the north. Apparently this divide is due to the marginal moraine of the Mohawk lobe which turns all south-flowing streams eastward to the Hudson.[1] This obstruction prevents the Sacandaga from flowing south to the Mohawk in its old course past Gloversville. It also turns the Hudson eastward from Corinth to Glens Falls. In this part of its course the Hudson, having been first crowded to the southwest at Warrensburg out of its old direct southeastward course, was compelled to cross a second divide at Corinth to find a valley leading east to join its old course.[2]

[1] CUSHING, H. P., *Bull. N. Y. State Museum*, 95, p. 441, 1905. BRIGHAM, A. P., Glacial Geology and Geographic Conditions of the Lower Mohawk Valley, *Bull. N. Y. State Museum*, 280, p. 24, 1929.

[2] MILLER, W. J., *Bull. N. Y. State Museum*, 255, p. 112; also Fig. 36, p. 111, 1924.

CHAPTER VIII

INTERIOR LOW PLATEAU

Use of Terms.—The coupling of the words "plateau" and "low" calls for explanation. It is not possible to define "plateau" and "lowland" by exact limits of elevation. Popular usage, generally influenced by relation to adjacent areas, cannot be ignored. If a surface 1000 feet high is seen to be in process of active dissection by headward-growing streams, or if it is seen to be exposed to such dissection by reason of its relative altitude, it is unhesitatingly called a plateau. If, however, it is bordered by higher land, or if it is so extensive or so far from the sea that the possibility of dissection is not considered, it will be called a lowland. When these terms are used in proper names, still more allowance must be made for relativity, for a large area is designated only by those characteristics that are most general. Thus it comes about that an area between the Ohio River and the Coastal Plain is called a plateau while another area of equal height north of the Ohio and extending far to the west is called the Central Lowland. Only a broad generalization justifies these names. The term "upland" is always used in a relative sense. "Highlands" should be actually high, but "uplands" need only be relatively so. A "lowland" should not lie high enough above its local base level to admit of sharply incised valleys. In choosing proper names for the several physiographic divisions of the United States, much respect has been paid to custom.

Boundaries.—The westernmost member of the Appalachian Highlands (so far as they can be outlined by province boundaries), is the Cumberland Plateau, typically developed on the heavy sandstones or conglomerates at the base of the coal measures. West of that, and typically developed on Mississippian (Lower Carboniferous) rocks, is the Interior Low Plateau. Its lower altitude excludes it from the Highlands, but in its history it has much in common with the Appalachian provinces. In its old, well-indurated rocks and angular forms it is strongly contrasted

411

with the Coastal Plain province which bounds it on the west, and it is also wholly different from the Till Plains on the north, in which an older topography like that of the Interior Low Plateau is buried.

The eastern boundary in Tennessee is the west-facing escarpment of the Pottsville sandstone, gashed by steep young valleys which make it irregular in detail, but a commanding feature 1000 feet high. Its relief decreases toward the northeast, where the rocks of the Pottsville group are less uniformly hard, and head-waters of the Cumberland River have broken down the

Fig. 113.—Escarpment of the Allegheny Plateau 40 miles east of Lexington, Ky. The view is northward from a valley on Devonian shale in the Knobs belt, indenting the western edge of the plateau. The rocks at the top are Mississippian limestones except at the extreme right where the Rockcastle sandstone (Pottsville) appears. Similar views may be found on the southern and western borders of the Bluegrass section. (*Ky. Geol. Survey.*)

surface of the higher plateau. In the London quadrangle, southeast of central Kentucky, the Pottsville escarpment is little more than a broad belt of hills separating surfaces of no great relief and not very different altitude. From this place to the edge of the glacial drift in Ohio, the Mississippian beds form only a belt of knobs, or at most benches, which are included in the Cumberland and Allegheny plateaus, being several hundred feet higher than the Bluegrass section on the west. West of this rough country, which includes also the narrow outcrop of Devonian shale, is the relatively smooth surface of Silurian limestone, a narrow band belonging to the Bluegrass section.

Likewise, toward the south from central Tennessee, the Pottsville escarpment becomes less high. It is cut to pieces where the Tennessee River leaves the higher plateau on the east to enter the lower plateau in northern Alabama. South of that river the escarpment trends east and west along the northern edge of the synclinal Warrior Basin (coal field) and overlooks a limestone bench on the north. Though not high, as in Tennessee, it is a well-recognized feature almost to the Coastal Plain.

The western boundary of the province is essentially at the Tennessee River in its northward course across West Tennessee, though the hard rocks of the upland province appear at places west of the river, mainly in the deep valley, and the Cretaceous beds of the Coastal Plain cover many divides east of the river, especially near the Alabama line (*cf.* page 67). The landscapes west and east of this somewhat ambiguous boundary are of different types.

The boundary on the north is determined by the edge of the glacial drift. It is like that on the west in separating topographies of strongly contrasted type, like it also in being a zone rather than a line, and in being difficult to locate with exactness. In practice the difficulty on the west side is solved by arbitrarily adopting the Tennessee River. In the same way on the north, the Ohio River is arbitrarily followed from Louisville to a point 40 miles above Cincinnati. Actually, glacial drift is found a dozen or more miles south of the river, but with no influence on the topography. Where the glacial mantle fails to reach the river, it thins gradually toward the margin. The difficulty of locating the exact limit is shown by the discrepancies of different surveys.[1] For our purpose it is desirable to locate the boundary as nearly as possible where the topographic effects of the drift cover begin to be apparent, hence preference is given to the older lines which restrict the glaciated area most narrowly.[2]

Rocks and Structure.—The relation between stratigraphy and structure on the one hand and physiography on the other is very close in this province. The topography on each formation

---

[1] MALOTT, CLYDE A., The Glacial Boundary in Indiana, *Proc. Ind. Acad. Sci.*, pp. 93–107, 1925. See especially his Fig. 5, p. 103.

[2] The line here used does not differ greatly from that given by Leverett in U. S. Geol. Survey, *Mon.* 53, Pl. 6, 1915, and in his older publications. As this map includes contour lines at intervals of 100 feet, it shows fairly well the significant relation between the drift border and the rock surface.

or group, if not uniform through the area, is at least so closely related to it that an explanation of the surface forms involves constant reference to the underlying rocks.   The stratigraphic groups indicated here are comprehensive, and only such descriptions are given as are needed in the explanation of topography. Additional names and descriptions are given as required in the discussion of the several sections.   The following Paleozoic groups are named in the order of their occurrence, beginning at the top:

GENERALIZED COLUMN OF ROCKS IN THE INTERIOR LOW PLATEAU PROVINCE

Pennsylvanian.

2. Many hundred feet of shale and sandstone, with beds of coal and rarely a few feet of limestone, comprising the Carboniferous coal measures, most of which is of Pottsville age.   Generally easily eroded.

1. Mansfield (basal Pottsville) sandstone, at places 300 feet thick. A strong stratum which makes uplands and cuestas.

Mississippian:

3. A series of alternating sandstone, limestone, and shale, embracing most of the Chester group, in which sandstone formations dominate the topography.

2. A thick series of limestones embracing the basal Chester, St. Louis, and Warsaw (named in descending order), remarkable for caves and solution topography.

1. Some hundreds of feet of shale and sandstone (more sandstone in the upper part) formerly called Waverly in Kentucky and Knobstone in Indiana (Kinderhook and Osage in the standard section of Missouri).   Toward Tennessee the upper part becomes more limy and passes into the resistant Fort Payne chert which rests on several hundred feet of Mississippian (New Providence) shale.

Devonian:

In the northern part, limestone (the old "Corniferous") is overlain by shale (called New Albany shale in Indiana); each is 100 feet thick, more or less according to locality.   In the southern part the lower and middle Devonian limestones and shales are succeeded by the Chattanooga shale (late Devonian or early Mississippian).

Silurian:

Several hundred feet (in Kentucky) of limestone and dolomite, mainly of Niagaran age.   Very thin and unimportant in Tennessee.

Ordovician:

3. Limestone with subordinate shale beds embracing the Richmond group and much of the Maysville (called Leipers in Tennessee).

2. A thick mass of shale with subordinate limestone beds, embracing the Eden group and part of the Maysville.

1. A succession of limestones, soluble and easily reduced to plains, most of it belonging to the Trenton and Chazy groups.

All of these rocks dip gently to the northwest from the Appalachian highlands. The gentle regional dip is interrupted by two low structural swells, one centering in the Bluegrass section of Kentucky, the other in the Nashville Basin. A line connecting their centers marks the axis of a very low, broad anticline. The saddle between the two low domes is part of a broad, shallow, transverse syncline which extends northwestward and deepens greatly to form the coal basin of western Kentucky, Indiana, and Illinois. This is the only part of the province in which the coal measures lay below base level in the last great peneplaning cycle. Elsewhere, base level was somewhere in the Mississippian series or, in case of the domes, in the Ordovician.

Sections of the Interior Low Plateau.—Owing to the structure here described, the province falls naturally into four sections, each underlain by rocks within a certain range of age and character. The largest and most representative is the *Highland Rim section* underlain by Mississippian rocks, mainly limestones. Locally a narrow strip of Devonian shales is exposed in the bordering escarpment and included in the same section. The *Nashville Basin* and the *Bluegrass section*, or Lexington Plain, result from the truncation of the two low domes and the resulting exposure of Ordovician rocks with a narrow border of Silurian limestone. The shallow syncline in western Kentucky and adjacent states is distinguished by topographic features due to the preservation of sandstones of Chester and Pennsylvanian age. This is the *Shawnee section*. On the whole it is lower than the Highland Rim, but near its boundary the surface rises above the general level and forms the outfacing Dripping Springs escarpment.

THE HIGHLAND RIM SECTION

Highland Rim is the name given to the lower plateau on Mississippian rocks at the foot of the Pottsville (Cumberland) escarpment.[1] This same upland entirely surrounds the Nash-

[1] The entire section is here called by the name popularly applied to the upland around the Nashville Basin. Carl O. Sauer treats the Kentucky portion as "The Pennyroyal district" (Geography of the Pennyroyal, *Ky. Geol. Survey*, ser. 6, 1927), the name being taken from popular usage in southwestern Kentucky but, unfortunately for the purpose here in hand, including the wide margin of Chester sandstone in the Shawnee section.

ville Basin, goes south and west to the Tennessee River and north to the glacial boundary in Indiana. It embraces much rolling land between sharply incised valleys. Near the larger streams it is generally cut to maturity. The term "barrens" was applied by early settlers to extensive prairies but without reference to natural fertility. The word has since been applied much more extensively so as to include the "cedar glades" of Tennessee. These are areas largely in forest, often of scrub cedar, especially in, and east of, the Nashville Basin. Parts of the Highland Rim are indeed unproductive but their location and extent bear little relation to the limits of forest.

Relation to Other Sections.—The popular use of the term Highland Rim by dwellers in the Nashville Basin indicates that the upland ends abruptly in the escarpment that surrounds the basin. The relation is perfectly clear despite the young valleys which deeply notch the escarpment and carve it into branching spurs and outliers. Altitudes of the upland east of the basin reach 1100 to 1300 feet. On the west they decrease from 900 or more to less than 700 feet near the Tennessee River. At places on the east the slight dip of the rocks away from the dome is noticed in the slope of the surface.

The relation of the Highland Rim to the Lexington Plain in Kentucky is less simple. On the east side, the Rim is too narrow and fragmentary to be separated in treatment from the Appalachian Plateau. The Mississippian outcrop widens near the Ohio River, but here, as farther north, its elevation equals that of the plateau on the east. On the south and west of the Bluegrass basin there is an escarpment of several hundred feet facing inward. From the crest of this escarpment, known as Muldraugh's Hill, the surface slopes outward with the dip of the beds around the dome. Within a short distance this outward slope brings the level of the Highland Rim down to that of the Lexington Plain, *i.e.*, to 900 or 1000 feet. In this cuestalike margin of the Highland Rim the slope is influenced by the bedding. West of the Bluegrass basin both regional dip and regional slope of the Highland Rim are toward the Shawnee section, but in passing from the older rocks of the former to the younger rocks of the latter the general slope is interrupted by an abrupt rise known as the Dripping Springs escarpment. In general, throughout the section, the formations are beveled by erosion, and the outcrop of each major group requires its own physiographic description.[1]

Eastern Margin.—Description may well begin with the eastern margin, the Highland Rim strictly so called, *i.e.*, the limestone bench 10 to 15 miles wide between two west-facing escarpments, the one limiting the Cumberland Plateau, the other overlooking the Nashville Basin and Cumberland River. The rocks dip faintly to the east and are beveled by a smooth or rolling upland 1000 to 1300 feet in height. The strong Fort Payne chert (sandstone in Kentucky) makes the escarpment at the west, but the surface passes eastward without a break over higher limestones and shales to the valley floors in the frayed Cumberland escarpment. The peneplain cannot be questioned, though at places the general slope for many miles agrees in direction with the southeastward dip. This may be due wholly or in part to postpeneplain erosion. Such structural control within minor limits should not distract attention from the widespread beveling of slightly dipping beds, even though one bed may form the surface for a dozen miles.

In its gentle slopes, its solution features, and its mellow soil, the Kentucky portion of the Eastern Highland Rim is an outlying portion of the greater limestone upland farther west (page 419). On the east are the ragged spurs and outliers of the Cumberland Plateau, separated by limestone valleys at the level of the Highland Rim and properly belonging to it. These valleys are not all mere ravines due to surface erosion. Many of them are "coves" due in large part to solution. They are often wide in proportion to their length and have steep head walls and ungraded floors with underground drainage.[2] Where the limestone upland is adjacent to the deep valley of the Cumberland River, it is much better preserved than is the Waverly surface in the same situation. Though underlain in large part by limestone, most of this district is infertile. Its typical character is seen along the Cincinnati Southern Railroad.

The Waverly-Fort Payne Outcrop.—The truncation of the faint anticline connecting the two domes exposes the rocks of the Waverly (Knobstone) series in a northeast-southwest belt, whose

---

[1] Reference to the geologic map is essential to profitable reading.

[2] Elk Spring Valley on the Monticello topographic sheet (U. S. Geol. Survey) is a fair example.

width may reach 40 miles, but erosion has made its boundaries highly irregular.   Near its eastern side it is traversed by the Cumberland River in a valley 300 to 400 feet deep, near which the plateau is cut into narrow rugged ridges.   Even without this special reason for dissection, the siliceous rocks of the lower Mississippian have been more carved by streams than the higher limestones which underlie adjacent areas and have been more subject to solution and underground drainage.   None the less, a level horizon begins not far from the river, and districts remote from the larger streams have rolling uplands of considerable extent which typify the Highland Rim peneplain.   As in the Knobs around the Bluegrass basin, these sandy rocks are poor soil makers, though the district is more favored topographically, hence not quite so unproductive.[1]   The rim of Fort Payne chert around the Nashville Basin is a continuation of the same geologic outcrop.   The strata become more cherty and hence more resistant toward the south, and the valleys more angular.   The soil has a large admixture of chert, and the productivity, or lack of it, is much the same as farther north.

The Knobs.—The rocks exposed around the truncated anticline form a cuestalike rim on three sides of the Bluegrass section. In Kentucky and Indiana the term "Knobs" has both a descriptive and a regional[2] significance.   The hills thus designated are carved from the escarpment of the Highland Rim from which the belt of Knobs is not clearly separated.   It surrounds the Bluegrass section in Kentucky and extends northwestward in Indiana to the glacial boundary.   These hills are carved largely from the sandy and fairly strong beds of the Waverly or "Knobstone" series, *i.e.*, from the scarp slope of Muldraugh's Hill whose highest summits (south of the Bluegrass) are 1200 to 1400 feet high.   Where erosion has cut through to the shales below (either Mississippian or Devonian), the sandstone tends to stand up in isolated rounded hills separated by wide valleys or shale-floored

---

[1] A good brief description of this district is given by Arthur Miller (The Geology of Kentucky, *Ky. Geol. Survey*, ser. 5, *Bull.* 2, p. 197, 1919).   A more complete geographic and physiographic treatment is given by Carl O. Sauer in The Geography of the Pennyroyal, *Ky. Geol. Survey*, ser. 6, vol. 25, pp. 54–70, 1927.

[2] For a map of this region in Kentucky and for its human geography see W. G. Burroughs, Geography of the Kentucky Knobs, *Ky. Geol. Survey*, ser. 6, vol. 19, 1926.

lowlands.[1] Conical forms are common except where remnants of a hard bed make flat tops. Not infrequently the thin, cherty, Warsaw limestone serves this purpose. The characteristic topography and poor soils of the Knobs give way to those of the Bluegrass section at the contact between the New Albany shale (Devonian) and the underlying Jeffersonville limestone. It is not uncommon, however, to speak of the "Bluegrass Region" as limited to Ordovician rocks and to include the surface on all Silurian and Devonian rocks in the belt of Knobs. This zone of Knobs in Kentucky, 10 or more miles wide, is a barren and backward country, with a primitive people whose chief money crop is

Fig. 114.—Topography in the Knobs Country of Kentucky, on the Devonian outcrop. (*Ky. Geol. Survey.*)

tanbark from the chestnut oak. Industries (carried on by outside enterprise) consist of the manufacture of some clay products and of ax and pick handles.

The Pennyroyal District.—The name Pennyroyal[2] is used here in its most restricted sense, designating only the limestone plateau south of the western Kentucky coal field. The terrace of Chester sandstone, limited on the south and east by the Dripping Springs escarpment, is not here included. The Pennyroyal district is a part of the extensive surface on middle Mississippian limestones, stretching from Indiana to Alabama. Its southward extent is not defined, but the area west of the Nashville Basin is here treated separately.

The plane of the hilltops is continuous with that of areas already described on the Waverly, but it declines gently westward from 700 or 750 feet near Glasgow Junction (south of

[1] MILLER, *op. cit.*, pp. 86 and 184.
[2] SAUER, *op. cit.*, p. 21.

Mammoth Cave) to 400 or 500 feet before the Tennessee River is reached.

In its typical development this limestone plateau is without deep or steep valleys. Over large areas its local relief is due more to solution than to surface streams, but it differs much from place to place. The limestone is not a single homogeneous formation but a group of formations and members differing in solubility. Their several outcrops no doubt differed in relief even when the peneplain was at its best, the purest limestones being lowest and most nearly flat. All parts of the surface have been lowered since uplift, some parts perhaps peneplaned again, others lowered by solution, either by general wasting of the surface without involving much local relief at any time, or by passing through a cycle of subterranean erosion (see below). On the whole, high solubility and low altitude go together. This is illustrated in the Bowling Green quadrangle where the sinkhole plain rarely rises above 600 feet, while the horizon of the more hilly surface in the southeastern part, free from sinks, is 700 to 750 feet high.

A major part of the area in which solution features are prominent[1] is characterized only by isolated, generally funnel-shaped, sinks, obviously due to the solvent action of descending water. Other parts of the area have extensive basins or "valley sinks" or "blind valleys," in some cases several miles in length, rimmed by irregular rock ridges or uplands.[2] Surface drainage is out of the question. The floors of these basins are themselves uneven, often subdivided into minor basins, all drained into sinks. The larger basins may result from the coalescence of enlarging sinks, whose walls recede like other escarpments, or from the falling in of the roofs of caves. A tendency to exaggerate the frequency of this latter process probably arises from the steepness, even verticality, of many sink walls.

Sinks often cease to function by reason of clogging with waste, like any other drain. Small ponds result, or lakes or swamps in the larger basins. No large lakes exist now, but some plains

[1] For description see W. R. Jillson, American Karst Country, *Pan-Amer. Geol.*, vol. 42, 1924. His map showing Karst areas in Kentucky is reproduced as Fig. 124 in this book.

[2] LOBECK, A. K., The Geology and Physiography of the Mammoth Cave National Park, *Ky. Geol. Survey*, 1928.

several miles in extent, known as "flatwoods," owe their existence to the filling of lakes thus caused. It is generally agreed that
cultivation has contributed greatly to the stopping up of sinks.
Springs often issue from their walls, and early settlers, whose
houses were located by such springs, have been compelled to
seek other sources of water as the basin floor rose gradually
above the level of the spring.[1]

The Cavern Cycle.—It is not improbable that some of the
lower parts of the limestone plain are younger peneplains, in the
making of which underground solution and erosion have played a
critical part.[2] Cave streams bear the same relation to such
erosion as surface streams do to surface erosion. They run at
the level of the water table, and ultimately the land surface is
reduced to about the same level. The process begins with the
enlargement of passages in joints and bedding planes, producing
galleries and shafts. Sinks are the surface expression of descending passages. As the growth of openings is gradual, the drainage
of the area is slowly withdrawn from surface streams and con-
ducted below. When all the drainage is subterranean and sinks
dominate the surface, the cycle is in its mature stage and the
surface is typical karst. After that, the sinks continue to
enlarge. The rock between them is consumed, partly by solution, partly by breaking off in blocks from the steep (sometimes
vertical) sides. Ultimately sinks coalesce, leaving the irregular
remains of their former walls standing in flat-topped mesas or
rocky hills and ridges, or only as low irregularities on the new
surface at the level of the old cave bottoms. When the surface
is said to have "collapsed," the word is to be understood as
referring generally to this gradual process of destruction, not
often to the falling in of a broad roof in a catastrophic event
(see footnote, page 437).

The process here described produces "blind valleys," or
"valley sinks," separated by ridges or plateaus of the original
mass. External drainage is impossible, except as it passes under
the surrounding uplands. Generally the uneven floor itself

---

[1] SAUER, *op. cit.*, pp. 40, 47, 51.

[2] BEEDE, J. W., Features of Subterranean Drainage as Illustrated in the
Bloomington, Ind., Quadrangle, *Proc. Ind. Acad. Sci.*, 1910, pp. 1–22.
DAVIS, W. M., Origin of Limestone Caverns, *Bull. Geol. Soc. Amer.*, vol. 41,
pp. 475–628; ref. to pp. 528, 546.

consists of numerous separate basins, the drainage from which in time goes down through sinks to a still lower level. Caves at the level of the now exposed floor (or higher or lower) may be continuous beneath the uplands. At least one deeper level is indicated by the presence of sinks in blind valleys. In this region it is indicated also by maps of large caves, like the Mam-

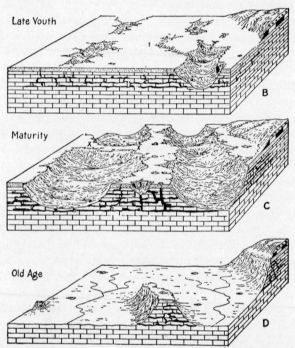

Fig. 115.—Topographic development of a plateau having underground drainage. *B*, youth; *C*, maturity; *D*, old age. Diagram *C* illustrates the conditions found in much of the Mammoth Cave region. (*Lobeck, Ky. Geol. Survey.*)

moth, which appear to spread beyond the limits of the upland, apparently beneath the adjacent valley sinks.[1]

The end of the process here described comes with the reduction of the area to a peneplain near the level of the subterranean streams. Probably this has been accomplished over considerable areas at the foot of the Dripping Springs escarpment, which now lie below the level of the Highland Rim peneplain. The process is now seen in various stages, from isolated sinkholes coexisting

[1] DAVIS, *loc. cit.*

with surface drainage, through maturity, to the stage of extensive blind valleys alternating with honeycombed uplands. Sinkholes in the otherwise smooth plain near Bowling Green and elsewhere indicate the beginning of another cycle.

Areas showing the features described above lie partly without and partly within the line of the Dripping Springs escarpment, Mammoth Cave itself being mainly beneath a terrace of the Shawnee section which is thinly covered with Chester sandstone (p. 436). The great caves in Indiana, Wyandotte, Marengo, etc., lie at the foot of the Chester escarpment but not far away, generally in bays which indent it.

Features West and South of the Nashville Basin.—The belt described above, in which the effects of solution are prominent, is mainly in Kentucky. Farther south the rocks are less soluble and the surface is that of a dissected upland on which the outcrops of harder and softer beds cause faint corrugations.[1] West of Nashville, dissection is about mature, with the horizon at 800 to 900 feet and a rather sharp local relief of 200 to 300 feet.[2] To the south as far as Alabama there is no great change in altitude or relief.[3] Coastal plain sediments cover the upland near the Tennessee River, but they are soft and thin and have little or no effect on the topography. The southward dip around the plunging end of the Nashville dome carries the surface down to a level below 600 feet in Northern Alabama, where the Tennessee River flows west in a strike valley on the St. Louis limestone at the foot of Little Mountain, a cuesta 800 feet high on the same sandstone[4] that makes the Dripping Springs escarpment. Solution features are found at intervals throughout the area in Tennessee and Alabama in soluble limestones like the Bangor.

The immediate valley of the Tennessee River here is on the St. Louis limestone. While the general dip of the rocks is south

[1] Flint, R. F., Natural Boundaries in the Interior Low Plateau Physiographic Province, *Jour. Geol.*, vol. 36, pp. 451–457, 1928. Existing maps do not yet make possible a more adequate description of these features.

[2] For description see C. W. Hayes, Columbia folio (No. 95), U. S. Geol. Survey, 1903.

[3] Miser, Hugh D., Mineral Resources of the Waynesboro Quadrangle, Tenn. Geol. Survey, *Bull.* 26, 1921; Jewell, W. B., Geology and Mineral Resources of Hardin County, Tenn., Tenn. Geol. Survey, *Bull.* 37, 1931.

[4] Called Hartselle sandstone on the geological map of Alabama, 1926; see also W. D. Johnston, Jr., Physical Divisions of Northern Alabama, Geol. Survey, Ala., *Bull.* 38, 1930.

toward the edge of the province, faint minor swells are common. One of these brings up the hard Fort Payne chert above the bed of the river for 35 miles above Florence, Ala., causing rapids and falls throughout this distance, with a total fall of 140 feet. Muscle Shoals is the main rapid near the end of the series.

With such regulation of the river as existed in 1935, the Wilson Dam at Muscle Shoals provided for the development of 67,000 primary horsepower, about one fiftieth of the power ultimately available at Niagara Falls (if the scenic effect is to be in a measure preserved), or one fifteenth of what is now permitted by treaty, or two fifteenths of our country's share. The total primary and secondary power at Muscle Shoals, available for 43 per cent of the time after the construction of other dams upstream, is believed to be five times the primary, or 335,000 horsepower. The completion of the Norris Dam alone raises the primary power at Muscle Shoals to 220,000 horsepower.[1]

The Pennyroyal and Knobs in Northern Kentucky.—North of the Green River the Highland Rim extends northwestward in a strip 15 to 20 miles wide between Muldraugh's Hill (top of the Knobs cuesta) on the east and the Dripping Springs escarpment (Chester sandstone) on the west. The same soluble limestone continues, also the solution features, but the drainage is less exclusively subterranean. There are more streams and stream valleys.[2] Corresponding to the greater relief is a greater tendency of the soil to wash away under cultivation. The soluble limestones of this province produce a characteristic red-clay subsoil. If allowed to accumulate, this develops a darker, often chocolate-colored topsoil. A distant view is sufficient to tell by the color of the landscape whether the good soil is being washed away. Red colors are accordingly much more abundant here and among the headwaters of the Cumberland River than on the smoother uplands south and southwest of Mammoth Cave.

[1] Letter of C. A. Bock, Ass't Chief Engineer of the Tennessee Valley Authority, to Prof. L. C. Glenn of Vanderbilt University. *Cf.* also Samuel S. Wyer, Power Possibilities at Muscle Shoals, Paper before Amer. Inst. Elec. Eng., 1925. An excellent map of the Tennessee basin showing existing dams and reservoirs, proposed dams and "run-of-river" projects is found in Tenn. Geol. Survey, *Bull.* 40, 1931, Surface Waters of Tennessee, by Warren R. King.

[2] SAUER, *op. cit.*, p. 46. Sauer describes this as the Elizabethtown area.

The Highland Rim in Southern Indiana.[1]—The stratigraphic and topographic relations of the Highland Rim continue north of

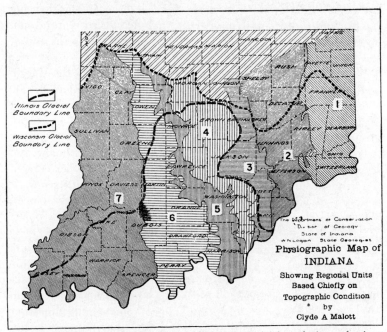

FIG. 116.—Map of Southern Indiana showing glacial boundaries and minor physiographic divisions determined by underlying rocks. (*Clyde A. Malott, Ind. Geol. Survey.*)

(1) Dearborn Upland, part of the Lexington peneplain on Upper Ordovician limestone and shale; maximum elevation 1,100 feet; trenched several hundred feet by minor streams.

(2) Muscatatuck Regional Slope, largely a stripped surface on Devonian and Silurian limestones; flats between young valleys of moderate depth.

(3) Scottsburg Lowland, on Upper Devonian shale; axis 500 to 600 feet high south of the Wisconsin drift.

(4) Norman Upland, whose eastern edge is the Knobstone escarpment; a roughly dissected upland on rocks of the Osage (Mississippian) group, mainly sandstone.

(5) Mitchell Plain, a west-sloping plain on the St. Louis and other Mississippian limestones; many solution features.

(6) Crawford Upland on the clastic rocks of the Chester and Pottsville groups; eastern edge is a ragged escarpment with many outliers.

(7) Wabash Lowland on Pennsylvanian coal measures.

the Ohio River. The Knobstone escarpment, where not obscured by glacial drift, is the most prominent topographic feature in

[1] As it will appear from the following paragraph, it is impossible to treat the Highland Rim section logically without extending it into Indiana. The

Indiana.   East of it lies a lowland on Devonian shales, belonging
to the Till Plains section of the Central Lowland.   Glaciation in
the Knobs is detected only by careful search.   Streams descending the dip slope of the Knobs cuesta have carved it into sharp
crested hills and V-shaped valleys.   Its summit is a mature
plateau on arenaceous rocks, called by Malott the Norman
Upland[1] and corresponding to the Waverly district in Kentucky.
This rugged upland has a maximum width of 40 miles.

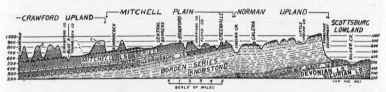

Fig. 117.—Cross section in Indiana near the Ohio River.   The escarpment
of the Crawford Upland (Chester) is the continuation of the Dripping Springs
escarpment in Kentucky.   Caves characterize the Mitchell limestone series on
both sides of the escarpment.   Figures on the margin indicate altitude above
sea level.   Length of section 32 miles.   Vertical scale twenty five times the
horizontal.   (*Malott, Ind. Geol. Survey.*)

As the dip of the rocks is here 30 feet to the mile and the surface
slope is somewhat less, the sandy rocks of the Norman Upland
pass beneath the soluble limestone, and the topography gives
way to the Mitchell plain, a surface much like that on the corresponding formations in Kentucky.[2]   The limestone plain, very
narrow at the north but broadening toward the Ohio River, is
limited on the west as in Kentucky by the outcrop of Chester
sandstone, *i.e.*, by the Dripping Springs escarpment.   This
escarpment is several hundred feet high near the Ohio, but

---

same is necessary when treating the human or commercial geography of
small areas.   On the other hand, in the study of large areas, as in plotting
or tabulating census data for the United States, it is probably neither feasible
nor desirable to separate this narrow strip in Indiana from the Shawnee section.   This strip, like that section, is for the most part a rough country,
the smooth part being too narrow to receive separate recognition when large
areas are being considered.

[1] Malott, Clyde A., The Physiography of Indiana, Part 2 of "Handbook
of Indiana Geology," p. 91, 1922; see also, by the same author, Some Special
Physiographic Features of the Knobstone Cuesta Region, *Proc. Ind. Acad.
Sci.* (for 1919), pp. 361–383, 1921.

[2] The outcrops of several formations within this limestone zone have
different topographies, giving rise to physiographic units too narrow to be
treated here.   See Beede, *op. cit.*, p. 3; also various papers by Malott.

farther north its clearness depends less on its height than on the contrast in topography on its two sides.

In general the surface on soluble limestones is a local peneplain of a relatively late subcycle, either of the normal or the cavern type. At places, however, the Mitchell plain slopes with the dip

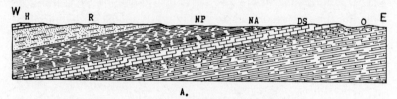

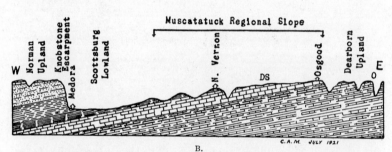

Fig. 118.—Diagrammatic cross section in southern Indiana, showing in diagram *A* the restored Lexington peneplain, and in diagram *B* the present surface in a later erosion cycle. *H*, Harrodsburg limestone; *R*, Riverside sandstone (Knobstone); *NP*, New Providence shale (Knobstone); *NA*, New Albany shale; *DS*, Devonian and Silurian limestones; *O*, Ordovician limestone and shale. Section 70 miles long; the base is 200 feet and the upper surface about 1000 feet above sea level. Vertical scale about sixty four times the horizontal. This figure also illustrates conditions at the edge of the Bluegrass section in Kentucky. (*Malott, Ind. Geol. Survey.*)

and appears to be controlled by structure rather than by a former base level.[1]

THE BLUEGRASS SECTION[2]

The "Bluegrass region," as the term is used in Kentucky, has variously defined limits. In its most inclusive sense it embraces

[1] MALOTT, CLYDE A., The Physiography of Indiana, "Handbook of Indiana Geology," p. 192, 1922.

[2] The term Bluegrass is frequently written as two words, but it has long ago lost all literal significance. As a geographic term neither word has any separate significance. The common understanding, as well as the pronunciation, is that of a single word. It is so spelled by Arthur M. Miller

the entire area bounded by the semicircle of the "Knobs Country" and the Ohio River. The term "Bluegrass section" is used here in that broad sense with the inclusion of a small triangle in Ohio bounded by the river, the edge of the glacial drift, and the escarpment of the Allegheny Plateau (Pl. 2).

The Inner Bluegrass.—The structural dome which is accountable for this section involves a maximum uplift of about 2000

Fig. 119.—View in the flatter part of the Inner Bluegrass district, Kentucky.
(*Courtesy of the Cincinnati Southern Railway.*)

feet. On the crest of the dome in Jessamine County, south of Lexington, the Lower Ordovician limestones are exposed. The surface on these rocks is the "Inner Bluegrass," an area of 2400 square miles, fertile and rich, the center of Kentucky history and tradition. Its distinguishing features are due to its soluble phosphatic limestones, the basis of its rich soils.[1] They were well peneplaned, and even now, since uplift and erosion, the surface is relatively smooth, much of it but mildly rolling, at a level of

---

in his "Geology of Kentucky," Ky. Dept. Geol. and Forestry, 1919. For general treatment see Davis, D. H., Geography of the Bluegrass Region, *Ky. Geol. Survey*, ser. 6, vol. 23, 1927.

[1] This long-standing explanation of the rich soils is still true, though it is now known that the factors which control the physical character of soils (mainly topographic, climatic, and ground-water conditions) are equally important.

900 to 1000 feet. Sinkholes are characteristic but in no large area is surface drainage wholly absent. However, the small amount of entrenchment by the smaller streams is often remarked.

The influence of underlying rocks is so pervasive that this Inner Bluegrass district may be again divided into two nearly equal areas, the innermost being underlain by the Lexington limestone and the remainder by the Cynthiana limestone. It is the former, with its chocolate-colored soils, that has given Kentucky its great reputation for horses. It is the central and

Fig. 120.—Gullied slopes in the Eden shale belt of the Bluegrass section, Kentucky. (*Ky. Geol. Survey.*)

richest part of the section. The Cynthiana limestone with its more reddish soils supports mainly cattle.

The Eden Belt.—The limestones of the Inner Bluegrass dip gently outward beneath the Eden shales, which outcrop in an irregular ring with an area of 2500 square miles. In topography, soil, culture, and wealth this district and the Inner Bluegrass are strongly contrasted.[1] Only the altitude is similar. The former plain on the Eden is angularly and maturely dissected by small valleys several hundred feet deep, leading to rivers entrenched 400 feet. The yellowish soil, even where present, is not rich, and it is progressively washed away after careless cultivation of

[1] Compare the U. S. Geol. Survey topographic sheets of the Lexington and Lockport quadrangles.

steep slopes, leaving them littered with limestone slabs. Some abandoned fields have a small value as pasture, others become covered with bushes and trees of little value.

The Outer Bluegrass.—Outside the zone of Eden shale is another ring on the higher Ordovician formations (Maysville and Richmond), in which limestone is abundant or predominant. Locally there is a narrow outer border on Silurian limestone which belongs topographically (though not with respect to soils) in the same unit. This very irregular ring, aggregating over

Fig. 121.—Limestone sinks, Covington, Ky., in the Outer Bluegrass district.

3000 square miles, is the Outer Bluegrass. In topography and soil it resembles the central area, but solution features are almost absent. There is a tendency to slope down the dip of the dome to the encircling belt of Knobs, no doubt because the Devonian and basal Mississippian shales have been stripped from the sloping Silurian limestone surface. The trough thus produced at the foot of the Knobs is specially significant south of Louisville since it gives prominence to the Knobstone escarpment whose crest is here no higher (generally lower) than the level of the Bluegrass section.[1]

[1] For topographic relations south of Louisville see Charles Butts, Geology and Mineral Resources of Jefferson County, Kentucky, *Ky. Geol. Survey*, 4th ser., vol. 3, pt. 2, 1915.

Erosion Levels.—With due allowance for the general lowering of the surface on soft rocks, the upland level in this section indicates a peneplain. The main or through-streams are now incised to a maximum depth of nearly 500 feet. It appears, however, that erosion below the peneplain is the work of several partial cycles. At places the present steep-walled trenches are seen to be cut in shallow valleys, the floors of which (benches above the present valleys) retain patches of clay, sand, or gravel that indicate old flood plains. Along the Kentucky River near

Fig. 122.—Old valley of the Licking River above Falmouth, Ky., occupied by the river at the Parker stage but now abandoned. (*Photograph by L. H. Desjardins.*)

the Cumberland Plateau such old alluvium is called the Irvine formation.[1] Similar sediments in similar position are found elsewhere in this section near the larger streams, and likewise north of the Ohio River. Near the Ohio these old valleys may be at least 200 feet deep, and their courses often deviate from those of present streams (Fig. 122). Their relations appear to be identical with those of the abandoned valleys in the Allegheny Plateau (page 302) and of the so-called Parker Strath.[2]

THE NASHVILLE BASIN

General Relations.—The structural dome in middle Tennessee is very low. Its significance to physiography is due to the fact

---

[1] Campbell, M. R., Richmond folio (No. 46), U. S. Geol. Survey, 1898.

[2] Unpublished work of Louis H. Desjardins, University of Cincinnati, 1934. F. Leverett, The Pleistocene of Northern Kentucky, *Ky. Geol. Survey*, ser. 6, vol. 31, pp. 4*ff.*, suggests that the Irvine formation may represent older valleys than those described here.

that the strong cherty limestones (Fort Payne and higher), which once covered it, were necessarily thinned when the first general peneplain (Cumberland) reduced the dome to the level of its surroundings.   The strong cover may have been entirely removed from the center of the dome when the leveling was repeated in the making of the Lexington (Highland Rim) peneplain.   This removal exposed the weaker Ordovician rocks.   The limestones exposed in the present basin are lower in the series than those of the Inner Bluegrass district of Kentucky.[1]   The development of a topographic basin was merely a matter of locally widening the stream valleys, mainly the Cumberland.   With the broadening and coalescence of the valleys, the protecting cherty limestone was undercut, producing an escarpment.   With the retreat of this escarpment down the dip of the dome, the protecting bed became thicker and the retreat was slowed up.   Sapping is no longer as effectual as it was.   The growth of the basin in its early stages was no doubt very rapid.   This fact and some features of the topography indicate that the Nashville Basin is of relatively recent origin.

Topography.—The present basin is a valley 400 to 600 feet deep, 60 miles wide, and 120 miles long (including the Elk River basin) in a direction parallel to the Appalachian folds.   At the northeast the basin begins with the abrupt widening of the Cumberland Valley at Carthage, near where the river crosses the 86th meridian.[2]   Above this point the fine, sweeping meanders of the Cumberland are deeply entrenched between bluffs from ½ to 2 miles apart.   Below Carthage the valley walls suddenly part, the right- and left-hand bluffs becoming respectively the northern and eastern escarpments overlooking the basin.

[1] For geology of this section see R. S. Bassler, The Stratigraphy of the Central Basin of Tennessee, Tenn. Div. Geol., *Bull.* 38, 1932; J. J. Galloway, Geology and Natural Resources of Rutherford County, Tenn., Div. Geol., *Bull.* 22, 1919; C. W. Hayes and E. O. Ulrich, Columbia folio (No. 95), U. S. Geol. Survey, 1903.

[2] In this part of the boundary the topmost limestones of the Ordovician are cherty and resistant, and unite their effect with that of the Fort Payne chert to form the Highland Rim plateau.   The boundary of the basin on this side cannot be drawn from a geologic map unless individual formations are indicated as in the maps by Bassler, *loc. cit.*   On these maps the Cannon limestone, cherty at the top, is seen to make uplands.

The elevation of the lowland may average 600 feet, being 200 feet lower where the Cumberland leaves the basin, near Nashville, than in its remoter parts. Much of the surface, though topographically old, retains too much relief to be called a peneplain. Local relief of more than 100 feet is common. Exceptional monadnocks rise almost to the level of the Highland Rim, notably on the divide between the Cumberland and Duck rivers. South of the Duck River basin is that of the Elk, so crowded with monadnocks that its inclusion in the Nashville Basin is questionable.[1] Near the larger streams a late peneplain is well developed, the most noticeable present relief being due to limestone sinks. This is called the Central Plain. The immediate valley of the Cumberland River is younger and 100 to 150 feet lower.

Glades.—On the whole it will be observed that the floor of the basin is not base-leveled, though broad strips of incipient peneplain appear on the purer limestones near the main rivers. Contrary to what might be expected, these are by no means universally covered with good soil, though fertile areas are sufficiently extensive to make the Nashville Basin the center of wealth and culture in Tennessee. A characteristic habit of weathering results in what are known as "glades," areas of bare, or nearly bare, rock whose level is nearly that of the surrounding plain.[2] Some of these areas support red cedar trees in their scanty soil in joints of the rock. These "cedar glades" occur on patches of a platy limestone (the Lebanon) which rise a little above the plains developed on the massive jointed (Ridley) limestone in the Stones River and other valleys. This latter rock has its own glades, more or less covered by hardwood trees (hence called "hardwood glades") which grow in the joints between the blocks. Weathering gradually enlarges the joints and reduces the blocks, so that there are all gradations between the continuous rock floor, in which joints are widely spaced, and the floor of good red soil in which stumps of bedrock are seen here and there. The cedar glades alone occupy fully a fourth of Rutherford County in the Stones River Valley, the most central

[1] In the dimensions given above, the Elk River drainage is included. It is excluded on the map of Physical Divisions of the United States, U. S. Geol. Survey, 1928.

[2] For the use of the term "glade" in Tennessee, see Galloway, *op. cit.*, p. 13.

and typical county of the Basin. In addition, patches of hard-wood glade occur in almost every square mile of the massive limestone.[1] It is not improbable that the rapid weathering indicated by the glades may help to explain the exceptional widening of the Cumberland Valley to make the Nashville Basin.

Erosion Cycles.—Doming, partly accomplished in Paleozoic time, was renewed after the Highland Rim peneplain was made and continued into the Pliocene,[2] the center of the dome being raised an additional 300 to 400 feet with respect to the sides. Streams were able not only to maintain their courses across the rising dome but to widen their valleys more than elsewhere. With cessation of rising, these wide valley floors expanded some miles from the larger streams, together constituting the local peneplain which is now 500 to 700 feet above sea level and known as the Central Plain. Neither the rise nor the erosion was uninterrupted. When the surface was 80 to 100 feet above the present level, there was a significant pause. Wide valleys were cut in the adjacent Highland Rim, that of Duck River on the west side being well preserved.[3] Some flood plains within the limits of the basin were aggraded with gravel 50 feet deep, remnants of which now form ridges or mesas 80 to 100 feet above the rivers.

The last peneplain, the present basin floor, is believed to have developed in Pleistocene time.[4] A final rise enabled the Cumberland River to cut a wide valley 100 to 150 feet below the Central Plain. Entrenchment extends in diminishing amount up all tributaries but has not reached the remoter parts of the basin.

THE SHAWNEE SECTION[5]

Boundaries.—This section has been defined as an area bounded on the east and south by a continuous outfacing sandstone escarpment and characterized by a maturely dissected surface on

---

[1] GALLOWAY, *op. cit.*, pp. 13–16.

[2] GALLOWAY, *op. cit.*, pp. 20, 22.

[3] Columbia folio (No. 95), U. S. Geol. Survey, 1903.

[4] GALLOWAY (*op. cit.*, p. 23) assigns its date to Mid-Pleistocene.

[5] The name "Shawnee Hills Section" is suggested by R. F. Flint (Natural Boundaries in the Interior Low Plateau Physiographic Province, *Jour. Geol.*, vol. 36, pp. 451–457, 1928.) This and other geographic names date back to the temporary occupation of the lower Ohio Valley by the Shawnee Indians.

sandstones and shales. For a short distance near the western end the southern boundary is drawn arbitrarily westward from Princeton, Ky. By so doing the section is made to include a small area underlain by the Highland Rim limestones whose topography here is peculiar (page 438). The rest of the boundary is against the Coastal Plain and the Ozark Highland on the west, and the Till Plains on the north. The Ozark Highland is made to begin (somewhat arbitrarily) where the deformation is sufficient to bring to the surface rocks older than Carboniferous.[1]

The escarpment referred to above is made by the lowest strong stratum in the Chester series. In Kentucky it is called Cypress sandstone. In Indiana it is at the base of the Huron group. The horizon of the lowest sandstone is not everywhere exactly the same, but throughout the length of the eastern and southern boundary there is a scarp-making sandstone at about the same horizon, with just enough weak beds below to cause sapping, and everywhere below them the great Mississippian limestone. Above the Cypress are several hundred feet of sandstone and shale, with minor limestone beds, but no formation of conspicuous strength until the massive Mansfield (Caseyville or "Millstone Grit") sandstone or conglomerate at the base of the Pottsville is reached. Then follow more than 1000 feet of relatively weak coal measures.

Topography.—This succession of rocks, depressed in a syncline pitching northwestward, and all beveled by an old surface now dissected, is accountable for the major features of relief. These are two curving cuestas, scarping outward and sloping inward with the dip to the low area near the mouth of the Wabash. The outer cuesta on the Cypress sandstone, fronted by the Dripping Springs escarpment, is continuous and generally more than 150 feet high. Throughout most of its length it makes an important divide. The Pottsville is unimportant as a divide but forms a belt of higher and steeper hills. In Indiana the two cuestas are poorly separated. The two together form a wide belt of rugged country, particularly so near the Ohio River, Perry County being the most rugged county in Indiana. Aside from this sharp dissection near the deepest valley, the relief of both cuestas is greatest near the Green River, which, except in its

---

[1] See geologic map of Illinois or of the United States. Topographic maps show that this line has also topographic significance.

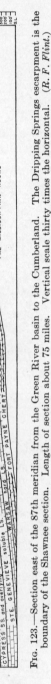

FIG. 123.—Section east of the 87th meridian from the Green River basin to the Cumberland. The Dripping Springs escarpment is the boundary of the Shawnee section. Length of section about 75 miles. Vertical scale thirty times the horizontal. (*R. F. Flint.*)

lower course, marks approximately the axis of the syncline. In the middle of the syncline, *i.e.*, in the western Kentucky coal field, the surface is maturely dissected, but because of the weakness of the rocks the slopes are less steep. Moreover, since the general level declines toward the west, the valleys are less deep, but rarely less than 200 feet.

Dripping Springs Cuesta.—The name Dripping Springs was originally applied to the escarpment in Edmonson County which contains Mammoth Cave. Here the escarpment, 160 to 240 feet high, is in clear view from the Louisville and Nashville Railroad, which runs at a distance of ½ mile to 5 miles from its foot between Glasgow Junction and Bowling Green. At its top is the thin edge of the Cypress sandstone, which here dips northward 200 feet in the first mile but gradually flattens.[1] The northward slope of the surface is almost as great. Both dip and slope are probably at their maximum in this locality. For some distance west of the 86th meridian the dip slope is smooth except for sinkholes, which the sandstone cover is too thin to prevent. The same is true at various places throughout the length of this cuesta, notably around Hardinsburg in northern Kentucky. The Hardinsburg sandstone, a little above the Cypress, underlies the smoother parts of the dip slope.

The Great Cave District.—Over most of this plateau the porous Cypress sandstone allows easy access of surface waters to the underlying soluble limestone. Sinkholes are therefore common where the sandstone cover is not too thick. East of the 86th meridian the surface has reached or passed the karst stage, *i.e.*, the

[1] WELLER, JAMES M., The Geology of Edmonson County, *Ky. Geol. Survey*, ser. 6, vol. 28, p. 179, 1927. A number of the facts stated here are taken from this paper.

stage in which all the surface slopes toward sinks and all drainage is underground. This is the area containing Mammoth Cave and others comparable in size. The porous sandstone, instead of protecting the limestone, has favored percolation at the expense of runoff. It may also to some extent have helped to hold up the surface while caverns were being enlarged. Large caves are also favored here by the deep gorge of the Green River which drains off the water from the cave level and makes free circulation possible. Many of the sinks leading down to lime-

Fig. 124.—Karst and sinkhole tracts in Kentucky.   (*Jillson, Ky. Geol. Survey.*)

stone caverns have enlarged to the point of coalescing, so that over large tracts the cave roof has disappeared,[1] making "valley sinks," "blind valleys," or "dolines." At least one half of the surface is occupied by such "blind valleys" several hundred feet deep, arranged in lines which converge dendritically toward the Green River gorge.[2] Between the steep-walled valleys are uplands, some of which are gently rolling farm lands. Beneath these may be perched water tables which make surface wells

---

[1] The term "collapse" is much used and often objected to. The falling in of large areas of cave roof at one time is believed to be very rare. On the other hand, the rock does fall, block by block, both from roofs and sides of caves and from the walls which surround sinks.

[2] WELLER, *op. cit.*, p. 15.

possible.[1]   The great caves lie mainly beneath these uplands, their openings being in the sides of the valley sinks or in the gorge of the Green River.   Some of the lower galleries, however, are known to extend under the adjacent basins.

Mammoth Cave is commonly said to have its galleries at five different levels,[2] with Echo River at the lowest.   On the assumption that all caves are developed at or above the water table, this multiplicity of levels is interpreted as indicating intermittent uplift of the land, the galleries at each level marking a still stand. This is now questioned.   Davis[3] has assembled much evidence for the hypothesis that caves may develop below as well as at the water table, in which case all levels may be of the same age. The distinctness of the five levels is also questioned.

Brush Creek Hills.[4]—On the divide north of the Green River, following the axis of the syncline, a tongue of rugged upland extends eastward for 40 miles.   It is a rough, still largely forested and primitive country with sharp ridges and steep narrow valleys as much as 400 feet deep.   Its character is due in part to remnants of Tertiary sandstone, formerly mistaken for Pottsville and so indicated on the older geologic maps.   Indeed, the aspect of this strip is very similar to that of the plateau in eastern Kentucky or to the sandstone cuestas in the west.   None the less, it lies outside the logical limits of the Shawnee section and is treated here as an exceptional feature of the Highland Rim.

The Faulted District at the West.—The two cuestas continue westward through Kentucky and southern Illinois almost to the Mississippi River, *i.e.*, to the Ozark uplift.   The western part of the section includes an area south of the cuestas, traversed by a great number of faults.   In some cases these are followed by small streams, but since the faults antedated the last peneplain they do not affect the landscape, except where the rocks on opposite sides differ in hardness.   This condition is met chiefly

[1] LOBECK, A. K., The Geology and Physiography of the Mammoth Cave National Park, *Ky. Geol. Survey*, 1928.

[2] HOVEY, H. C., Mammoth Cave, Kentucky, 1912 (not consulted). WELLER, *op. cit.*, pp. 30*ff.*, finds seven levels of various grades of distinctness in the surrounding topography.

[3] DAVIS, W. M., Origin of Limestone Caverns, *Bull. Geol. Soc. Amer.*, vol. 41, pp. 475–628, 1930; also *Science*, vol. 73, pp. 327–331, 1931.

[4] Term taken from Sauer, *op. cit.*, p. 48.   For life in this rugged country see Lobeck, *op. cit.*, p. 11; also Miller, *op. cit.*, p. 199.

north and west of Princeton, Ky., and in the adjacent part of Illinois, where the rocks at the surface are either the limestones of the Highland Rim or the lower members of the Chester. Differential erosion since the last peneplaning has resulted in a topography quite equal in relief to that of the nearby cuestas, and in contrast with that of the relatively smooth limestone surface farther south and east. The present hills and ridges are mainly on downthrown blocks. The constructional topography of the first cycle is thus reversed in the second.[1] This is the great fluorite district of the United States, the occurrence of the mineral being associated with the faulting.

Silt-filled Valleys.—All of the valleys below a certain level in this section and parts of adjacent sections have flat floors of silt ranging in width up to a maximum of over 10 miles.[2] It is plain that the valleys have been filled and that only the upper parts of the former hills are exposed. The flat strips may interlace, and in some cases hills or uplands form islands in the silt plain.[3] The depth of filling at the mouth of the Ohio is known to be 250 feet[4] and at least 175 feet in some of the smaller valleys of western Kentucky.[5] As the lower part of the filling is ordinary alluvium, it is inferred that the beginning of deposition came with a slackening of the current. In the last stage, when the silt was deposited, the streams were ponded.

Among other causes which may have worked together to cause valley filling, one which certainly was present and operative was the unusual load of detritus carried by streams which were fed

[1] ULRICH, E. O., and W. S. T. SMITH, The Lead, Zinc, and Fluorspar Deposits of Western Kentucky, U. S. Geol. Survey, *Prof. Paper* 36, p. 16, 1905.

[2] Indicated by the symbol for Pleistocene on the Kentucky Geological map, 1927.

[3] SHAW, E. W., Newly Discovered Beds of Extinct Lakes in Southern and Western Illinois and Adjacent States, Ill. State Geol. Survey, *Bull.* 20, pp. 139–157, 1915. On p. 146 Shaw proposes the term "Island Hills." See also, by the same author, Preliminary Statement Concerning a New System of Quaternary Lakes in the Mississippi Basin, *Jour. Geol.*, vol. 19, pp. 481–491, 1911.

[4] MALOTT, CLYDE A., The American Bottoms Region of Eastern Greene County, Indiana, *Ind. Univ. Studies*, vol. 6, no. 40, 1919. In this paper Malott recognizes the three possible reasons for aggradation given here.

[5] GLENN, L. C., Geology and Coals of Webster County, Ky., *Ky. Geol. Survey*, 1922; ref. to p. 32.

from the continental glaciers.   On this account the lower Ohio at a late glacial stage filled its valley with sand and gravel to a level at least 30 feet above its present highest floods.[1]   The waters which did this filling rose higher still, at least occasionally.   Tributary valleys were ponded, to some extent permanently, by the raising of their outlets, and to a greater extent by back water during floods.   In this condition they accumulated silt, which is now seen up to the level of the old fragmentary terrace which indicates the glacial aggradation of the Ohio.[2]

A second cause of aggradation is found in the lengthening of the Mississippi River by delta building in Pleistocene time.   At an earlier stage the Mississippi reached the Gulf shore more than 300 miles above its present mouth.   At that place, about at the mouth of the Red River, it is now 50 feet above the sea.   This would require its entire upper profile to be correspondingly raised, while at the same time increased load, caused by glaciation, required the profile to be steepened.

It may be, as assumed by Leverett,[3] that these two factors are sufficient to account for the valley filling along the Ohio and its lower tributaries.   It is nevertheless worthy of note that the region around the lower Ohio, in which such filling is exceptionally large, bears evidence of crustal disturbance both ancient and recent.   It is remarkable for its faults, which are older than the topography, and also for the New Madrid earthquake which came in the last century.   The hypothesis of local sinking to account for aggradation is thus suggested.   It is not without its difficulties, since it should at the same time have steepened the profiles upstream.   Abnormalities in the profile of the Mississippi between Cairo and Memphis are mentioned on page 87.

HISTORY OF THE PROVINCE

The oldest parts of this province are the two domes, which were dry land in late Paleozoic time.   The rest emerged in the Appalachian Revolution.   The domes must then have controlled the drainage but the physiography is unknown until Tertiary time.   The Cumberland peneplain must have developed

---

[1] *Cf.* the changes in the Mississippi River opposite Crowley's Ridge (p. 89).

[2] SHAW, E. W., *Jour. Geol.*, vol. 19, p. 486, 1911.

[3] LEVERETT, F., Outline of Pleistocene History of the Mississippi Valley, *Jour. Geol.*, vol. 29, pp. 615–626, 1921.

here as well as farther east. The uplift which followed was greatest, about 1000 feet, in the latitude of the Nashville dome. Everywhere the uplift diminished, and perhaps died out, toward the interior of the continent. It is not known how far in that direction the Cumberland peneplain ever was distinguished from its successor.

No doubt the drainage of the Cumberland peneplain was toward the northwest. After uplift a newer peneplain, nearly or quite coincident with the older surface at the west, began on the downstream side and spread eastward. This is the Lexington, or Highland Rim peneplain, provisionally correlated with the Harrisburg. No definite record of an intermediate "Allegheny" cycle (page 295) is preserved in this province.

The newer peneplain makes the horizon of the greater part of the Highland Rim and of the Bluegrass section. Where the rocks are unusually soft or soluble, the surface has been lowered, either by rainwash, or in one or more later cycles of normal or subterranean erosion. Such lowering may amount at places to several hundred feet, but the exact determination of the amount must await more definite knowledge with respect to crustal sinking. The frequent parallelism of surface and bedding planes is accounted for mainly by wasting of the mantle rock since the peneplains were raised. On any upraised peneplain, general wasting tends to reveal structural surfaces, much as the fabric of a cloth is revealed by wearing off the nap.

Apparently the Lexington peneplain extends indefinitely north of the Ohio River. An altitude of 900 to 1000 feet is common in southwestern Ohio. Its level declines to 900 feet on the Knobstone cuesta in Indiana and to 800 feet on the Shawneetown Ridge in southern Illinois (page 651).

Residual masses rising above the Lexington peneplain are almost limited to the cuestas. The Waverly cuesta (continuation of Muldraugh's Hill) south of the Bluegrass section reaches altitudes of 1200 to 1400 feet, which is to say, its crest is not much lower than the Cumberland peneplain to the east, with which it has sometimes been identified.[1] The same allowance must be made here for later lowering, partly by the wasting of the surface

---

[1] JILLSON, W. R., Peneplains in Kentucky, *Pan-Amer. Geol.*, vol. 50, pp. 333–338, 1928. Jillson's map, p. 335, indicates the "Cretaceous peneplain" on this cuesta and (probably too extensively) around the rim of the western coal basin.

and partly by the southward recession of the escarpment.   The cuesta survived in subdued form on the Lexington peneplain, as it probably did also on the Cumberland.   West of the Lexington dome the few hills or ridges which rise to 1000 feet or a little higher are merely culminating points in the undulating surface of Muldraugh's Hill.   They represent imperfections of the younger peneplain but their identification with the older is speculative.   The same applies to all the higher swells on the Dripping Springs and Pottsville cuestas, even where their general levels fall below 600 feet.   The westward convergence of the two former base levels, the subsequent lowering of the surface on soluble limestones, and the probability of local subsidence make correlations uncertain for the present.

Most of the topographic features in this province are due to erosion below the level of the Lexington peneplain.   Evidences of more than one subcycle are clear.[1]   At one or more stages incipient peneplains were developed on the softer shales or purer limestones.   Such, for example, are the Scottsburg lowland in Indiana (page 425) and the lower parts of the Pennyroyal in Kentucky.   These lowlands do not represent the present base level.   They are themselves being destroyed by the cutting of new valleys, as near the Ohio River, or by a new cavern cycle of erosion, as in the Mammoth Cave district.[2]

Other features younger than the Lexington cycle are the broad, in some cases abandoned, valleys mentioned on page 431.   These have been correlated in age with the Parker Strath, which indents the Worthington peneplain (page 301).   The latter appears to be a more or less local development in the Plateau province of the widespread Lexington peneplain farther west.

Correlation of Events in the Nashville Basin.—The Nashville Basin is correlative in time with the valleys of all ages cut in the Lexington plain.   The explanation of its vastly greater volume involves a greater post-Lexington uplift, and a renewal of doming instead of mere regional rise.   Here, as on the Lexington

[1] WELLER, J. M., The Geology of Edmonson County, *Ky. Geol. Survey,* 1927.   See also FLINT, R. F., Geomorphology around the Head of the Gulf Embayment (unpublished at the time of this writing).

[2] MALOTT, CLYDE A., Valley Trenching and Gradation Plains in Southern Indiana, *Science,* vol. 43, p. 398, 1916; The American Bottoms, *Ind. Univ. Studies,* vol. 6, no. 40, p. 25, 1919; "Handbook of Indiana Geology," p. 192, 1922.

dome, wide valleys were developed at intermediate depth, exemplified by the valley of Duck River in the upland west of the Nashville Basin. If the succession of events here was the same as farther north, it would appear that the local peneplain of the present basin floor is the equivalent in age of the narrow valleys cut below the Parker Strath in the plateau province. If so, this is a remarkable illustration of the different rates at which physiographic features develop under different conditions. Long-distance correlations of erosion cycles are hazardous at best, but even the conclusion just suggested would be scarcely more surprising than the undeniable fact that the Nashville Basin has been excavated in the same time occupied by the Cumberland River in cutting its narrow valley above Carthage, the point at which the basin abruptly opens out. The Parker Strath antedates the Kansan glacial stage, and the floor of the Nashville Basin, according to Galloway, is of mid-Pleistocene age (page 434).

Summary of Cycles.—In summary, it may be said that the Cumberland peneplain was uplifted so little at the west that identification of its remnants in western Kentucky is uncertain. Elsewhere in this province it is represented, if at all, only by some of the hills and ridges on the higher cuestas. The Lexington cycle was followed by uplift of 100 to 200 feet (probably more on the Nashville dome), after which straths of considerable width and probably some local peneplains were developed. A later and similar uplift resulted in trenching of valleys, and the development of the peneplain in the Nashville Basin and others on soft rocks near the Ohio River. A lower local base level along the Ohio was favored by the greater cutting power of the stream after its great accession of headwaters due to drainage changes in the Glacial Period. A final rise caused deeper entrenchment, especially of the larger streams. In the meantime, aggradation of the Mississippi and the lower Ohio, perhaps acting in conjunction with diastrophism, caused a cycle of aggradation in the western part of the province.

Drainage.—The general direction of the main streams has probably been northwestward ever since the province became dry land. There may well have been a struggle with the rising domes, but the compromise now seen was effected before the end of the Cumberland cycle. That streams in the Lexington cycle had about their present courses is indicated by the old shallow valleys in which the streams are now entrenched. A few peculiarities deserve mention.

The Cumberland River above the Nashville Basin follows the strike of the rocks southwestward on the eastern limb of the anticline between the two structural domes. There can be little doubt that in this part it is a subsequent stream whose position has gradually shifted eastward down the dip. Its headward growth has certainly limited that of the Green River headwaters, and some of them may even have been diverted in the two older cycles.[1]

The northerly course of the Tennessee River for 125 miles deviates a possible 45 degrees from the regional slope and dip. A straight northwest course (down the regional slope) from where the river enters Tennessee would reach the Mississippi about 70 miles (air line) from the present mouth of the Tennessee. The course chosen lies along the edge of the coastal plain sediments, not the exact edge of any one formation, for the sea came in repeatedly to about the same limit in Cretaceous and Eocene time. Moreover, all edges have been worn back. The Tennessee River is represented by Chamberlin and Salisbury[2] as flowing at one time southwestward across northern Mississippi, then captured by a north-flowing stream. No course across Mississippi is supported by collateral evidence.[3] The problem of its northward course to the Ohio is similar to that presented by the Delaware and the Potomac in following the inner edge of the Coastal Plain. The westward course of the Tennessee across Alabama and its northward course across Tennessee may both have been determined by the edge of coastal plain sediments.

The Falls of the Ohio at Louisville are interesting because they constitute the sole significant interruption of an otherwise graded stream. The river here drops 26 feet in less than 2 miles. Presumably the river was fairly graded before its valley was aggraded 150 feet by outwash from the ice sheet. On the low

[1] Sauer, C. O., Geography of the Pennyroyal, p. 26, *Ky. Geol. Survey*, 1927.

[2] "Geology," vol. 1, pp. 165–168.

[3] Shaw, E. W., U. S. Geol. Survey, *Prof. Paper*, 108, p. 158, 1918.

shale plains around Louisville the filling spread widely and the river flowed here and there, coming finally to a single fixed channel a few miles north of its old course. When filling ceased and downcutting began, a strong limestone was encountered at 400 feet A.T., whereas its old channel, discovered by drilling on the opposite (southeast) side of the city was only 360 feet above the sea.[1] The Ohio is therefore superposed on its own alluvium at this point.

Entrenched Meanders.—For meanders within rock walls, this province, with adjacent parts of the Allegheny Plateau, is unexcelled in North America, perhaps in the world. Any stream without this feature is exceptional. Such wholesale prevalence of entrenched meanders can only mean that at some time before entrenchment, both relief and gradients were low. It is not necessary to assume that every meander between rock walls existed first at the level of the upland; it is possible for a curve to change its form while the gorge is being cut, and afterward, but it is not believed that such an explanation can account for the perfection and universality of these forms in this region. It is quite possible that some well-rounded curves have developed during downcutting from more angular bends,[2] but the omnipresence of such forms, and the occurrence, not far away, of vertically incised, and surely inherited, meanders makes this explanation unnecessary.

It does not follow that all of the streams showing inherited meanders must have wandered on a common peneplain at the same time. Indeed, strictly speaking, no stream ever meandered on any peneplain, but rather on a flood plain. But the coexistence of a great number of wide flood plains, reaching far up the headwaters, strongly suggests low relief between them. In

[1] BUTTS, CHARLES, Geology and Mineral Resources of Jefferson County, *Ky. Geol. Survey*, 4th ser., vol. 3, p. 204, 1915.

[2] These have been called "ingrown" meanders by Rich (*Jour. Geol.*, vol. 22, pp. 469–497, 1914). *Cf.* R. C. Moore, Significance of Enclosed Meanders in the Physiographic History of the Colorado Plateau Country. *Jour. Geol.*, vol. 34, 1926. Rich would divide all incised meanders into entrenched and ingrown. It seems best to adhere to usage which makes "incised" and "entrenched" the same. This general class may then be divided into (1) inherited and (2) ingrown meanders. Actual forms are often partly the one origin, partly of the other.

FIG. 125.—Airplane view of Kentucky River at Highbridge, Ky. The river here traverses the Lexington peneplain in an entrenched meander, the height of the railroad above the water being 282 to 284 feet. (*Fairchild Aerial Surveys, Inc.*)

order to meet the conditions previously described for this province, it must be assumed that some of the streams were flowing in wide shallow valleys developed after the peneplain was

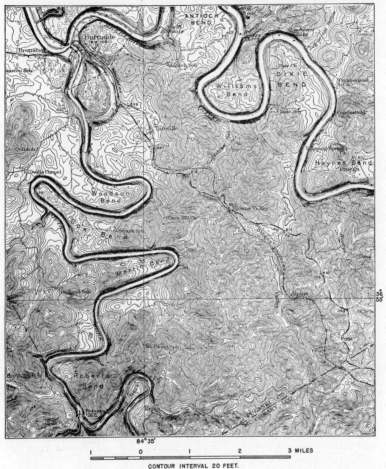

CONTOUR INTERVAL 20 FEET.

FIG. 126.—Entrenched meanders of the Cumberland River and South Fork in the Highland Rim. Slip-off slopes and some angular bends suggest substantial change in the form of some curves during entrenchment. Upstream from this area the two sides of the South Fork gorge are equally steep. (*U. S. Geol. Survey.*)

slightly raised. That the streams were meandering in these wide valleys is consistent with the advanced age of the valleys and also with some recent uplift at their heads (in the next province) by reason of which gravel was brought down and deposited.[1]

In the harder rocks of this region, mainly sandstone on the east and Highbridge limestone in the Bluegrass section, many well-rounded meanders have cut down almost vertically and have changed little since. The opposite bluffs are equally steep and there is little or no flood plain at the bottom. In the less resistant rocks the stream accomplished a good deal of lateral cutting during entrenchment, causing slipoff slopes on one side while undercutting a steep cliff on the other. There has also been some "sweeping" (downstream progression) by these meanders, producing a limited amount of bottomland by planing away the spurs. Patches of bottomland generally occur alternately on one side and the other. Southeast of Lexington, Ky., the Kentucky River repeatedly crosses a fault from the Highbridge to the softer limestones or the reverse. In each case the sudden change in valley form, narrow and steep in the former and wide open in the latter, strikingly illustrates the statements made above. The surface must have been smoothly planed when the original meanders overlapped the two types of rock.

A stream which meanders through most or all of its course may be entrenched in one part and not in another. At the foot of the Dripping Springs escarpment the Barren River meanders at a level which is near that of the plain, though it is deeply incised above and below that locality. The lower plain appears to be the work of a newer cycle, largely by subsurface waters, probably as good an example of the cavern cycle as can be found in America.

[1] MILLER, ARTHUR M., "Geology of Kentucky," p. 179. Miller here points out that the presence of the gravel in the Irvine formation is not consistent with the idea that streams were lazily meandering over a plain and that nothing happened except a general rise. He would have the meanders largely ingrown.

CHAPTER IX

CENTRAL LOWLAND EAST OF THE MISSISSIPPI

THE PROVINCE AS A WHOLE

Here, as elsewhere, the term "lowland" is necessarily a generalization. The province has its lower and its higher tracts which it is necessary at times to distinguish as local lowlands and uplands. At places the major rivers, like the Ohio, even have steep-sided valleys, adjacent to which the surface, though no higher than elsewhere, is being dissected in true plateau fashion. In absolute elevation this province ranges from 1500 or even 1800 feet on its western border down to 450 feet in southern Illinois and to less than 300 feet on the shores of Lake Ontario. The dominant regional slopes are toward the Mississippi and Ohio Rivers. The St. Lawrence basin is narrow.

The great size of physical provinces in central United States suggests widespread uniformity. The Central Lowland, 585,000 square miles in area, including water surface, wholly or partly covers 16 states. The area of the Great Plains in 10 states is 532,000 square miles. Within these large areas the variation in essential morphologic form is no greater than in the smaller provinces. Some parts are even monotonous in landscape, others show great variety among features which are inseparable in treatment and intimately interspersed. The lack of major distinctions in this great area is due in part to its nearly flat-lying rocks. Glaciation dominates most of the landscape, but it probably created as much variety as it destroyed.

Province Boundaries.—Throughout most of its length, the province boundary is marked by a visible contrast of topography on its two sides, and in many places by an inward-facing escarpment. East of Lake Ontario, the lacustrine plain of this province comes to an end against the dip slope of the Tug Hill cuesta belonging to the Mohawk section of the Appalachian Plateau.[1] South of Lake Ontario, the plain abuts against the northern

[1] See map of State of New York showing surface configuration and watersheds; 200-foot contour interval—N. Y. State Museum, 1910.

449

escarpment of the Allegheny Plateau which rises 600 to 1000 feet in 5 to 10 miles. This escarpment, continuing southwestward but becoming lower in Ohio, forms the boundary as far as Cleveland. From Cleveland to the southern third of Ohio there is no definite escarpment, but generally within a zone less than 10 miles wide the smooth glaciated plain on the west gives way to the slightly higher and more dissected Allegheny Plateau on the east.

From northern Ohio almost to St. Louis the province boundary is approximately at the edge of the glacial drift. For most of the distance, however, the drift thins out so gradually that its extreme limit is uncertain and topographically negligible. A marginal belt of ambiguous character, often 20 miles wide, while important from the standpoint of historical geology, is here assigned to the nonglaciated provinces. From the Allegheny Plateau to the Mississippi, the bordering province is the Interior Low Plateau, for the most part no higher than the Till Plains but characterized by a dissected plateau topography. Farther west the boundary is against the Ozark Plateau. For some distance the Mississippi and Missouri rivers agree so nearly with the edge of glacial drift that they are taken as the province boundary. On the west side of the Interior Highlands, the transition to the Osage (unglaciated) section of the Central Lowland is gradual. Farther south the boundary between the Central Lowland and the Coastal Plain province is described on page 100.

The Central Lowland is limited on the south by the Central Texas Section of the Great Plains province, an area in which remnants of a higher level remain as mesas and buttes, a landscape which is less advanced in its erosion cycle than the prairies of the Osage section. The distinction between the Central Lowland and the Great Plains on the west is a matter partly of altitude and partly of topography. The boundary line through the greater part of its length is marked by an east-facing escarpment which is mentioned more particularly below in connection with the several sections.[1]

On its northern side the Central Lowland ends against the Laurentian Upland, generally with a visible rise of the latter.

[1] See also the author's companion volume, "Physiography of Western United States," pp. 2–4, McGraw-Hill Book Company, Inc., New York, 1931.

The boundary lies in Canada except for the great southerly detour around the Superior Upland. At places it is poorly marked, especially in northeastern Minnesota where the drift is very thick. Where it follows the edge of the Wisconsin Drift-less Section the line adopted is at the limit of the younger drift.

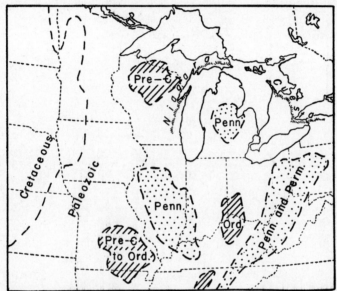

Fig. 127.—Sketch map showing three centers of uplift indicated by the old rocks exposed. These are the Superior Upland, the Ozark dome, and the Cincin-nati anticline. Also, three centers of depression indicated by the presence of younger rocks, the Allegheny Plateau, the Michigan coal basin, and the Illinois coal basin. Cretaceous rocks at the west occupy the syncline of the Great Plains. Within the limits of this map it may safely be assumed that all beds dip slightly from the older outcrops to the younger.

This leaves in the "driftless" section a belt of older drift in which the characteristics of glacial topography are all but lost.[1]

Geologic Structure.—The rocks of the Central Lowland dip very gently from three localities: (1) The Cincinnati anticline which exposes Ordovician beds, (2) the Ozark dome which brings

[1] FENNEMAN, N. M., Physiographic Divisions of the United States, *Ann. Assoc. Amer. Geogr.*, vol. 18, pp. 264–353, 1928; ref. to p. 289. This is one of the cases in which, after specifying the prominent criteria by which two adjacent divisions are defined, it is found either that they overlap or that they fail to meet. Where odds and ends occur they are thrown into adjacent areas.

the Pre-Cambrian to the surface, and (3) the Canadian Shield of
Pre-Cambrian rocks, more especially its domelike outlier in
northern Wisconsin and Michigan. These are centers of uplift
around which rocks of younger age outcrop in successive belts.
Conversely, all dips are toward three synclines, (1) the great
Appalachian coal basin in which lie buried all the Paleozoic
systems from the Permian down, (2) the Michigan basin, deep
enough to have preserved the coal measures from erosion, and
(3) the long, wide syncline of the Great Plains under which the
Paleozoic rocks of the Central Lowland pass beneath the Cretaceous. An eastward extension of this great structural trough
reaches to Indiana and western Kentucky and is recognized on
the geologic map by the Carboniferous rocks which have been
preserved within it. Given these centers or axes of uplift and
depression, the essentials of the geologic map may be brought to
mind at will.

Despite the faintness of all dips the structure is important,
since it determines which formation shall constitute the substratum in any one locality. Moreover, erosion on gently dipping
strata is apt to result in escarpments, as it has done in parts of
this province. Physical properties of particular formations are
given below as needed. Doubtless the whole province has been
well peneplaned at least once, and it is certain that the softer
rocks were cut down later to smoother forms and lower levels.

Outline of Glaciation.—Topographic distinctions in this
province depend more on glacial history than on underlying rocks.
It is necessary to recognize that the drift cover is quite unlike
in its different parts, partly because of difference in age and
partly for other reasons. The ice advanced at least half a
dozen times, between which times were stages of deglaciation,
most of them much longer than the time elapsed since the last
invasion. Each ice sheet (except the Nebraskan which came
first) covered some territory not reached by its successors. So
the entire glacial cover in the United States may be divided up
into parts distinguished according to age.

The classification and chronology of American ice sheets has
been variously given.[1] A long-used classification recognized five
glacial epochs, the Nebraskan (at bottom), Kansan, Illinoian,

[1] KAY, GEORGE F., Classification and Duration of the Pleistocene Period,
Bull. Geol. Soc. Amer., vol. 42, pp. 425–466, 1931.

Iowan, and Wisconsin, each followed by an epoch of warm climate and deglaciation. As the Nebraskan drift was covered by later sheets, it enters little into the study of physiography. There is some question as to the place and rank of the Iowan. By some students it is now thought to be, in part at least, a close correlative of the Illinoian, while others are disposed to

Fig. 128.—Map of North America showing the area covered by Pleistocene ice sheets at their maximum extension; also the main centers of accumulation. (*U. S. Geol. Survey.*)

include it in the Wisconsin. It is not certain that all of the so-called Iowan is of the same age. In any case it is convenient to the physiographer to combine in one physiographic section the most important area of Iowan drift (mainly northeastern Iowa) with the adjacent Wisconsin drift.

The Wisconsin drift sheet is not only double, but triple or multiple. It has long been known to have been deposited in at least two advances of the ice. More recently it has been separated into as many as five sheets, distinguished partly on the basis of age, partly by the direction from which they came.[1] Thus the present drift cover falls into three main divisions, Kansan, Illinoian, and an assemblage of more recent sheets.[2] Much the largest part of the drift now exposed belongs to the last division, the others appearing only where the limits of later ice sheets fell short of the earlier advances.

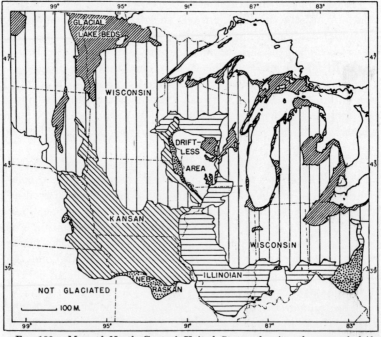

Fig. 129.—Map of North Central United States showing the several drift sheets, also areas of lacustrine plain. The southern areas indicated as Nebraskan are designated by Leverett as containing only scattered boulders. (*F. T. Thwaites, Glacial Geology. Edwards Brothers, Inc.,* 1937.)

Basis of Sections.—Had glaciation not occurred, it is probable that large parts of this area would now be topographically distinguished from other parts by reason of differences in their underlying rocks. There would be cuestas and uplands and

[1] Leverett, F., U. S. Geol. Survey, *Prof. Paper 154-A*, Fig. 5, p. 19, 1929.

[2] The most significant grouping from the standpoint of historical geology would probably be a twofold one, treating the Nebraskan and Kansan stages as relatively old, and the Illinoian with all that follow as relatively young.

lowlands, rough and smooth surfaces, remains of older and the beginnings of newer peneplains. Sections would have been outlined on this basis just as they have been in the Interior Low Plateau.[1] As it is, wherever the glacier went, the landscape is in large part the product of ice work or of water working under conditions imposed by glaciation.

The province is thus divided into six sections, based upon the relations of the present surface to glaciation. Two widely separated parts were not covered by the ice. One of these, the *Osage section*, stretching from Missouri and Kansas to Texas, lay south of the limit of glaciation. The other, the *Wisconsin Driftless section*, lies far within the glaciated area, but most of it was untouched except by outwash. On its north and west sides, this section is arbitrarily made to include narrow strips of land which were glaciated so long ago that an erosion topography has been reestablished.

Two other sections, the *Till Plains* on the east and the *Dissected Till Plains* on the west, owe their characters to the complete burial of preglacial features in such a manner as to produce a surface of small relief. In the eastern one of these sections, extending from central Ohio to the Mississippi, glaciation was sufficiently recent (Illinoian and Wisconsin), so that the plains are in large part preserved. The western section, beyond the Mississippi, was glaciated in an earlier stage (Kansan) and is now submaturely dissected.

There remain the *Great Lake section* and the *Western Young Drift section*, both lying on the north and separated by the Wisconsin Driftless section. These are characterized by an association of varied features due to recent glaciation, in which nearly level till plains are much less important than farther south. The Great Lake section is separated empirically rather than logically from the Till Plains on the south. Glacial deposits of the same age extend from one to the other, but the conditions of deposition were different. North of the dividing line, marginal moraines are more numerous and have a more characteristic expression. With them are abundant outwash plains, some of

[1] Attempts to differentiate the several parts of the Central Lowland on the basis of preglacial erosion cycles appear in some of the U. S. Geol. Survey folios, *e.g.*, Columbus (No. 197) and Detroit (No. 205). The results, while interesting, afford no adequate basis for areal discussion.

them profusely pitted. Lake basins are numbered by the thousand while other basins retain swamps. Another type of landscape characteristic of these northern sections is the lacustrine plain, notably those bordering the Great Lakes. The aggregate area of such plains is large but much dispersed. Till plains are not absent from these sections, but they are much less continuous and less flat than in the Till Plains sections. On the other hand, there is neither lake, swamp nor lacustrine plain in the Till Plains sections, while outwash plains and distinctly morainic ridges are rare.

THE GREAT LAKE SECTION

Distinguishing Features

The distinguishing characteristic of the northeastern part of the Central Lowland is the dominance and variety of features of recent glacial origin. Lakes are so abundant as to characterize the region, but they are very unequally distributed. Large areas are without them and they afford no criterion by which to draw a boundary. Four of the Great (Laurentian) Lakes are included, and perhaps ten thousand smaller ones. Swamps, large and small, represent the intermediate stages between lakes and dry land. The number of basins, large and small, with and without water, is vastly greater than is shown, even on the best maps. The Great Lakes are bordered locally by flat plains which were portions of their bottoms when the continental ice formed their northern or northeastern shores (Fig. 129, page 454). All of these features are evidences of recent glaciation; in addition there are marginal moraines and outwash plains, and between them large areas of rolling ground moraine. These superficial features are more or less interrelated, but all are ultimately related to an uneven rock floor in which were great master valleys which cast the moving ice into distinct lobes. It is not only the typical assemblage of topographic forms but the group of associated problems, largely connected with the Great Lakes, that makes it desirable to treat this region by itself, although geologically its limits are arbitrary. From a popular standpoint it is unfortunate that the southern boundary of this section from Fort Wayne to Cleveland should lie between two landscapes so much alike superficially as lake plains and till plains; but lake plains constitute a large and essential part of the section on the north and are wholly absent from the section on the south.

FEATURES DUE TO BED ROCK

Rocks and Structure.—The rocks underlying this section range from Cambrian to the Carboniferous coal measures. The masking effect of thick glacial drift makes it unnecessary to consider small alternations of hard and soft, but the effect of three massive strong formations (or groups) is too prominent to hide. These are the Prairie du Chien dolomite (Lower Magnesian limestone) of Ordovician age, the Niagara limestone and dolomite (Silurian), and the Marshall (Mississippian) sandstone. Locally in Wisconsin the Platteville and Galena limestones belong in the same class. Also, two Devonian limestones in Michigan, the Helderberg in the south and the Traverse in the north, are locally resistant. None of the other beds make cuestas or uplands. The Niagara limestone is the most outstanding of the strong formations. Everywhere it is underlain by weak beds, the Maquoketa (topmost Ordovician) shale in the west, and the Medina and Clinton, weak sandstone and shale, in the east. The beds above are also weak, including the rest of the Silurian and all of the Devonian. The Marshall sandstone, second in importance to the Niagara limestone, is likewise enclosed between weak beds, Devonian and basal Mississippian below, and all the younger rocks of the region above. In the following generalized column, the rocks are grouped with reference to their resistance:

GENERALIZED COLUMN OF PALEOZOIC ROCKS IN THE GREAT LAKE SECTION OF THE CENTRAL LOWLAND

Pennsylvanian:
    Shales and sandstones with coal, preserved in the synclinal basin of Michigan.

Mississippian:
    Limestone with minor constituents (Grand Rapids series of Michigan).
    Marshall sandstone, making the uplands of the Lower Peninsula of Michigan.
    Shale with a little sandstone (mainly in Michigan outside the ring of uplands).

Devonian:
    Shale and limestone, mainly beneath or near Lakes Michigan, Huron, and Erie, and extending east and west from Lake Erie. Only the Helderberg limestone at the bottom and the Traverse limestones in the middle (both of limited outcrop) are relatively resistant.

GENERALIZED COLUMN OF PALEOZOIC ROCKS IN THE GREAT LAKE SECTION
OF THE CENTRAL LOWLAND.—(*Continued*)

Silurian:

Dolomite, embracing some glass sand, rock salt, and gypsum (Monroe
formation at the extremities of the Lower Peninsula and around Lake
Erie).

Niagara limestone and dolomite, making a prominent cuesta.

Ordovician:

Upper Ordovician shales, beneath Lake Ontario, Georgian Bay, and Green
Bay, and the lowlands in line with these.

Platteville and Galena limestones, chiefly in the relatively low land west
of the Niagara cuesta in Wisconsin but making an independent cuesta
farther west.

Prairie du Chien dolomite, making a cuesta west of the Niagara in
Wisconsin.

Cambrian:

Generally weak sandstone in Central Wisconsin and the Northern Peninsula of Michigan.

All of these rocks are depressed in a basin whose deep center
is in the lower peninsula of Michigan. There the rocks which
outcrop at the west and north are buried to a depth of 8000 feet.
Around this center the formations outcrop in concentric rings
spreading west almost to central Wisconsin, south into Indiana
and Ohio, and north and east far into Ontario. Southeast of the
Michigan basin a low anticline is passed in the basin of Lake Erie
beyond which the dip leads down to the great Appalachian coal
basin. On the structure here described, erosion has produced a
series of lowlands and uplands. Among the latter the Niagara
cuesta is the most extensive and apparent.

Niagara Cuesta.—From the dips described here it is seen why
the strong Niagara limestone outcrops in a belt of sloping upland
stretching west through New York and making a half circle
around Lakes Huron and Michigan.[1] Everywhere west of Lake
Ontario this band of upland slopes inward toward the southern
peninsula of Michigan and presents a scarp on the outer side.
The steep slope is partially obscured by glacial drift, but here
and there bare rocks appear. This escarpment is well known
where crossed by the Niagara River at Lewiston. It forms the
northern front of the plateau in which the Niagara gorge is cut
250 feet deep, and overlooks the flat strip of lowland along Lake

[1] Well shown in the geological map of North America in such a manner
as to suggest the structure.

Ontario.   The escarpment diminishes in height eastward (being but 50 feet at Rochester) but continues west and northwest, dividing the Ontario peninsula into two distinct parts.   It forms the peninsula and islands between the main basin of Lake Huron and Georgian Bay, overlooking the latter with high, steep, sometimes rocky, slopes and declining gently to Lake Huron.   The same high belt stretches west 150 miles through the northern peninsula of Michigan with a scarp to the north 50 to 200 feet high, and a gentle southward slope to the lake.[1]   The escarpment might be much higher at places if its foot were not buried by glacial drift.

From the Northern Peninsula of Michigan the Niagara cuesta turns south into Wisconsin, first as a line of islands, then as the Green Bay Peninsula, then as the dominating ridge of eastern Wisconsin, deeply drift-covered for the most part, showing no detail of its own except the high rocky cliffs overlooking Green Bay, and local cliffs near Lake Winnebago farther south; but always the slope away from Lake Michigan (ignoring the drift cover) is steep, and toward the lake it is a gently inclined plane. The escarpment is 175 to 200 feet high on the shore of Green Bay and nearly 300 feet high on Lake Winnebago and for some miles south of that.   Ignoring the drift at its base and the waters of Lake Winnebago, the height is 400 feet at places in Eastern Wisconsin.   Where the escarpment rises from a land surface instead of from water, its height and clearness both vary but, taken as a whole, it is the most significant topographic feature in Wisconsin.   Its absolute elevation is 750 to 1200 feet, the maximum being near the middle.   Throughout its extent in Wisconsin, the Maquoketa shale underlies the drift at the foot of the slope, its weakness being in part accountable for the steep westward slope.   The dip slope of the cuesta descends eastward beneath Lake Michigan, whose basin is carved in the weak Devonian rocks 1400 feet below the level of the Niagara upland.

The Marshall Cuesta.—In the lower peninsula of Michigan is another cuesta on the Marshall sandstone, circular in plan but broken down at several places where streams once ran in or out.

---

[1] RUSSELL, I. C., Geol. Reconnaissance along the North Shore of Lakes Michigan and Huron, Mich. Geol. Survey, *Ann. Rept.*, 1904; LEVERETT, F., Surface Geology of the Northern Peninsula of Michigan, Mich. Geol. Survey, *Pub.* 7, p. 20, 1911.

Thus it is deeply breached on the east by Saginaw Bay, and on the west by a broad, drift-filled valley whose rock bottom is near sea level. A wide depression in the surface of the bedrock

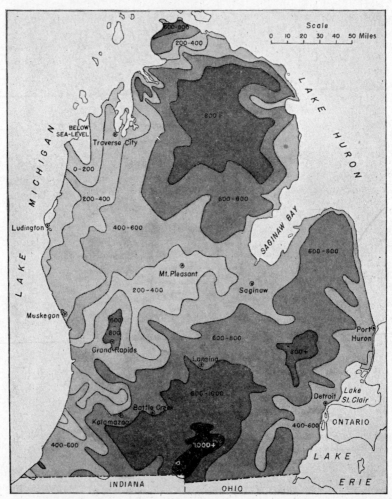

FIG. 130.—Relief map of the bedrock surface of the Southern Peninsula of Michigan. Contour interval 200 feet. (*Michigan Geol. Survey.*)

connects these two gaps, crossing the peninsula from Saginaw Bay on the east to Lake Michigan. If the thick drift were removed the remnants of this cuesta would appear as local uplands on the north, south, and southeast, rising at places 1000 feet above the lowland. The inward dip slope and the outward scarp slope are obscured by glacial deposits whose average thickness is several hundred feet. All of these high and low areas of the rock surface correspond in a general way with high and low parts of the present surface, but the agreement is only approximate, for the drift varies greatly in thickness.

Prairie du Chien Cuesta.—Twenty to 30 miles west of the Niagara escarpment in Eastern Wisconsin, the Prairie du Chien dolomite (Lower Magnesian limestone) makes another west-facing escarpment, limiting a cuesta which is second only to the Niagara in prominence. In southern Wisconsin the dip flattens and the cuesta turns off to the west into the Driftless section (page 525). In northern Wisconsin and the Upper Peninsula of Michigan the Niagara is the only distinct cuesta. The rest of the surface is a drift plain which abuts against the Superior Upland on the west, and ends in a 100 to 200-foot drop to Lake Superior on the north.[1]

The height of the Prairie du Chien cuesta increases from zero opposite Green Bay to 300 feet near Madison. Its outliers and crenulations are generally rounded by the drift cover, but occasionally exposed in ledges. Its absolute elevation is 700 to 800 feet near Green Bay and more than 1200 feet at the south and southwest. This strong dolomite is overlain by the weak St. Peter sandstone, the Platteville and Galena limestones, and the Maquoketa shale, all weak or topographically inconspicuous in eastern Wisconsin, though in the Driftless section to the west the Platteville makes another distinct cuesta. It may be said to form a subordinate cuesta in Eastern Wisconsin, but in its larger relation it is part of the lowland between two important cuestas.[2] Generally the gentle eastward slope of the top of the Prairie du Chien cuesta bevels the overlying rocks.

Baraboo Range.—A feature of the rock surface unrelated to the cuestas is the Baraboo Range[3] which surmounts the plain of

[1] For greater detail see Leverett, Surface Geology of the Northern Peninsula of Michigan, cited above.

[2] *Cf.* MARTIN, L., The Physical Geography of Wisconsin, Wis. Geol. Survey, *Bull.* 36, pp. 219–220, 1932. Also his Fig. 86, p. 232.

[3] SALISBURY, R. D., and ATWOOD, W. W. The Geography of the Region about Devils Lake and the Dalles of Wisconsin, Wis. Geol. Nat. Hist. Survey, *Bull.* 5, 1900.

Cambrian sandstone and lies partly in the Great Lake section and partly in the Driftless Area to the west (see map, Pl. 4). It is what remains of a great syncline in Pre-Cambrian quartzite whose trend, east-northeast and west-southwest, is roughly parallel to the strike of the Prairie du Chien cuesta and to the edge of the Superior Upland. Both limbs of the syncline make ranges, the two coming together at the east end around a canoe-shaped valley. The southern range, 25 miles long, reaches an altitude of 1620 feet where the surrounding plain is about 900 feet high and the Wisconsin River 150 feet lower. Much of its crest is an upland with gentle slopes between 1200 and 1500 feet high which suggest one or more peneplains, destroyed on the surrounding weaker rocks (page 468). The Wisconsin River runs around these ridges to the east, but canyons, deep enough and wide enough to accommodate the river, cross both ranges and have long been recognized as marking the river's preglacial course.[1] Obviously, the same ranges were standing where they are when the Paleozoic sediments began to be laid down. With progressive deposition the mountains were buried and the Wisconsin River superposed. By later erosion the surrounding surface was lowered, the mountains exhumed (resurrected), and the transverse canyons cut (or cleaned out if cut before burial). No better examples of resurrected mountains are known.

Devonian Lowland.—There is no single geographic name for the important ring of lowland which lies outside the Marshall uplands, intervening between them and the semicircular Niagara cuesta. This broad ring of lowland is largely covered by the waters of Lakes Michigan, Huron, St. Clair, and Erie. The arc on the south connects the head of Lake Erie with that of Lake Michigan. Despite its deep drift cover it remains relatively low. Throughout its extent, this ring of lowland follows the strike of the weak Devonian and lowest Mississippian rocks, which dip inward beneath the stronger sandstone toward the central coal basin of Michigan. Almost throughout its circumference it lies at the foot of the Niagara dip slope.[2]

[1] CHAMBERLIN, T. C., "Geology of Wisconsin," vol. 1, p. 254, 1883.

[2] Russell (*op. cit.*, p. 53) credits James Hall with being the first to point out this relation for Lake Michigan, and gives to Charles Whittlesey credit for the corresponding interpretation of Lake Huron (no citations). A brief instructive and emphatic statement of this relation is made by J. W. Spencer,

Ontario-Green Bay Lowland.—In passing outward from the central basin of Michigan the next lowland is found at the base of the Niagara escarpment. It is a long trough made by effective erosion of the weak beds beneath the Niagara. In the west these are upper Ordovician shales.[1] In New York there is, in addition, some soft sandstone in the Silurian. The deeper parts of this trough are the basins of Lake Ontario, Georgian Bay, and Green Bay. Intervening or adjacent, and less deeply eroded, are the narrow plain south of Lake Ontario and the broader one north of it, the plain of low relief in the eastern half of the northern peninsula of Michigan, and the lowland of the lower Fox River and Lake Winnebago in Eastern Wisconsin.

The Green Bay Lowland is one of the most important of the region, very prominent in the early history of Wisconsin.[2] Its surface in eastern Wisconsin is 50 to 250 feet lower than the cuestas on either side. At the north it is the bottom of Green Bay; farther south it is the bottom of Lake Winnebago and the valley of the Lower Fox River. In southeastern Wisconsin it is the long valley of the south-flowing Rock River (West Branch). The same surface spreads widely over northern Illinois, where its lowland character is lost. In the main this valley is due to the sapping and retreat of the Niagara escarpment and the stripping of the shale from the underlying limestones.

Central Plain of Wisconsin.—The west-facing Prairie du Chien escarpment overlooks an extensive plain underlain by what is left of the Cambrian sandstone after prolonged degradation. Its altitude is generally between 800 and 1000 feet. Most of this plain lies in the Driftless Area to the west.

PREGLACIAL TOPOGRAPHY

Total Relief.—The high and low belts described above are the main features of the preglacial topography. The total

---

Relationship of the Great Lake Basins to the Niagara Limestone, *Bull. Geol. Soc. Amer.*, vol. 24, pp. 229–232, 1913.

For altitudes of the several plains and cuestas in the eastern part of this section see U. S. Geol. Survey, *Bull.* 818, 1931.

[1] Classed as Richmond on the geologic map of the United States, U. S. Geol. Survey, 1933.

[2] WHITBECK, R. H., Geography of the Fox-Winnebago Valley, Wis. Survey, *Bull.*, vol. 42, pp. 24ff., 1915.

relief in preglacial time is fairly well known, except for the principal lake basins. The cuestas in Eastern Wisconsin may have risen 400 feet, or even more, above adjacent lowlands. The corresponding relief in western New York was about the same, and in Michigan it was greater. Uncertainties arise from the possibilities of glacial erosion, especially in the Great Lake basins. Over considerable areas the surface on the harder rocks has now an altitude of about 1000 to 1200 feet, while the water in Lakes Michigan and Huron stands at 581 feet. It may be assumed with safety that the preglacial lowlands in these basins were not higher than the present water level, though some geologists would not allow that they were much lower.[1] The total relief was in any case well over 600 feet. On the other hand, some geologists believe that these basins had almost their present relative depth and even capacity before the Ice Age.[2] In that case the total preglacial relief would exceed 1500 feet. As these basins are located on the largest belt of weak rocks, it is reasonable to expect that the old river valleys which they represent were the deepest in the region. Hence the total relief was probably much in excess of 600 feet. But it seems necessary also to suspect that the basins were far from having their present depth, and that the relief was therefore much less than 1500 feet. (For further discussion see History, page 487.)

Local Relief.—From observations where the drift is thin, it appears that the Niagara cuesta rises to a fairly uniform altitude for long distances. The uniformity is too marked to admit the supposition that erosion was everywhere mature. It may have been submature. The same is true of the Prairie du Chien cuesta near Madison, Wis., where the forms of broad remnants of this formation are only partially obscured by the drift. In that vicinity the relief of the rock surface is 400 to 500 feet, measured from the tops of upland remnants to the bottoms of valleys in the lowland.[3] It is to be remembered that the lowlands themselves have been trenched and partly dissected. Data from wells reveal preglacial valleys of like depth, now

[1] MARTIN, L., see footnote, p. 488.

[2] TAYLOR, F. B., see footnote, p. 488.

[3] THWAITES, F. T., *Bull. Wis. Geol. Nat. Hist. Survey*, 8, 2d ed., p. 177, map, 1910.

wholly obscured by drift, in southeastern Wisconsin.[1] Wherever the drift is not too thick in the region around Green Bay and the upper lakes, the relief on the harder rocks is seen to be much the same both in style and in amount.

Relief on the weaker rocks which underlie the lower belts was naturally less. Locally they were peneplaned in a later cycle and again dissected. The best known of the lowlands is that on the Cambrian sandstone, much of which, in central Wisconsin, was never glaciated. It appears that this, while not peneplaned, was reduced to a gently undulating surface without steep slopes except on its rather numerous monadnocks (page 523). The lowland made by stripping the Maquoketa shales from the Galena limestone may have been quite as smooth. The lowlands on Devonian shales are largely covered by the lakes and probably much altered, but a large area in northwestern Ohio and northern Indiana, though covered by some 300 feet of drift, is believed to have a relatively smooth surface at about, or a little above, the level of Lake Erie[2] (573 feet A.T.) but rising southward and merging with a similarly smooth and deeply buried surface on the Niagara limestone.

In a general way the topography of the drift-covered area may be inferred from that of the adjacent nonglaciated areas. Southwestern Wisconsin, eastern Ohio, and southern Indiana differ among themselves in detail, as do also the several parts of the Great Lake section.

Possible Base Levels.—Ever since the recognition of peneplains in the Appalachian region, there has been a tendency to refer the rock surface of interior United States to the work of Appalachian cycles. Knowledge on this point has not made much advance in nearly half a century, partly because of the difficulties in long-distance correlation, partly because the interior is almost lacking in sediments of Cretaceous and Tertiary ages which might help to fix the age of its topographic features. Moreover, in a region of relatively small uplifts and nearly

---

[1] ALDEN, WM. C., The Delavan Lobe of the Lake Michigan Glacier, U. S. Geol. Survey, *Prof. Paper* 34, p. 15, 1904.

[2] LEVERETT, F., Water Resources of Indiana and Ohio, U. S. Geol. Survey, 18*th Ann. Rept.*, pt. 4, p. 433, 1896. As this is known only by data from wells, often far apart, the amount of local relief remains uncertain.

horizontal beds, where the surface over wide areas is cut on or in a single formation, it is often difficult to say how closely a given plain is related in its origin to base level, and how closely to the influence of a single, more resistant formation.

An examination of the structure and thickness of the different formations indicates that as much as several thousand feet of sediments may have been eroded from parts of the surface. In other parts, the lowering was very little. But the maximum present heights of the harder beds, *i.e.*, of the cuestas, are much the same whether the thickness of rock removed from above was great or small. Even in the absence of extensive plateaulike surfaces on the cuestas, the degree of uniformity in altitude is greater than could be expected from degradation that was never limited by a base level nearer the surface than at present.

All of the higher belts described above culminate at altitudes which differ but a few hundred feet. Some differences of altitude must be allowed on even the best peneplain. Unequal wasting of crests and divides must also be assumed during the long time occupied in carving out the cuestas since the peneplain was made at their tops. In addition, there has been unequal uplift, presumably greatest around the Pre-Cambrian upland in Wisconsin.

It is also true that the belts of outcrop of the several formations, though irregular in detail, have straighter boundaries than would be expected had there not been long halts near base level in the process of degradation. All of them have been shifted a long way down the dip, and the chances of any regularity at all must depend on some rough approach to a limit beyond which further shifting was impossible. It is true that these facts are only broad generalizations which do not impress all geologists equally. A few have been able to conceive of continuous downcutting since the Paleozoic time with sufficient uniformity to produce the observed results (page 530).

Whether the present topography shows the remains of peneplains well or poorly or not at all, it is reasonable to suppose that the area was peneplaned more than once in the millions of years since it rose above the sea. Any other supposition would imply a resistance to erosion quite out of proportion to what similar rocks have shown elsewhere.

The very hard Baraboo quartzite has its flattest surface at 1400–1480 feet, with suggestions of another level at 1200 feet, and one swell reaching above 1600 feet.[1] It is quite probable that when the region was reduced to its lowest level and least relief, the strong Baraboo quartzite stood a little higher than the rest; also that it has been less wasted since uplift. Tentatively, therefore, it may be assumed that the 1400- to 1480-foot level represents the old surface in the Baraboo region when the present tops of the Niagara and other cuestas were parts of a general peneplain whose present horizon is at about 1200 feet. If the small and rather ambiguous patches on the Baraboo Mountains at the 1200-foot level be regarded as incipient peneplains, it is possible that these should be substituted for the higher surface in the above statement.

Most of the surface of the Great Lake section is reduced well below these high levels, some of it to well-developed lowlands which suggest old age. Much of the rock surface does not suggest relationship to any base level, but rather to stratigraphic horizons. There are lowlands now, ranging in altitude from 600 to 900 feet, but whether they were all produced in the same cycle, or during and after a series of uplifts, has not been worked out. It is certain, however, that a late preglacial uplift inaugurated a cycle in which valleys were carved in the older surfaces.[2] Probably the succession of events was complex. It is also probable that the oldest and highest level has been deformed by mild warping, making the present altitude of the cuestas less uniform than it would otherwise be.

For aught that is known, the lowlands in Wisconsin may be contemporaneous with the one that borders Lake Erie and connects the Erie basin with the upper Wabash Valley. No doubt, the best lowlands, probably good peneplains, were on the Devonian rocks now cut out to make the basins of the Great Lakes.

---

[1] TROWBRIDGE, ARTHUR C., The History of Devils Lake, Wisconsin, *Jour. Geol.*, vol. 25, pp. 344–372, 1917. From a critical study of this region Trowbridge infers that the flat top of the Baraboo Range at 1400 to 1480 feet represents a widespread peneplain, the same as that represented by the crests of the cuestas. The beginning of a later peneplain at the 1200-foot level has also been suggested, but with less confidence. Then followed a rise of 600 feet.

[2] ALDEN, WM. C., The Quaternary Geology of Southeastern Wisconsin, U. S. Geol. Survey, *Prof. Paper* 106, p. 104, 1918. In this paper Alden recognizes the three cycles here suggested.

Age of Peneplains.—The geologic dates of these old surfaces and their correlation with peneplains farther east is uncertain. To all of the uncertainties of age in the Appalachian region (page 255) must be added those which distance introduces. LaForge[1] correlates the higher surfaces with the Highland Rim (Lexington) peneplain. It is not improbable that this peneplain, which may now be traced with considerable certainty from Tennessee to western Ohio, extended over the Great Lake section and is now represented in the uplands of Michigan. In that case the northern lowlands are in the morphologic position of the Nashville Basin. For the present all such correlations should remain tentative.

A single deposit of gravel on the Baraboo upland has led to oft-repeated suggestion that a peneplain at that level was made in Cretaceous time. This gravel is similar in character and in topographic relations to scattered deposits on other upland remnants farther west and south (not in this section). One of these in southeastern Minnesota rests, apparently conformably, on Cretaceous beds. Hence the gravel and the erosion surface on which it rests were pronounced Cretaceous. As this harmonized with contemporary theories about Eastern United States, the suggestion received some currency, though it was plain that both the erosion surface and the deposit might date from any later time.[2] If the old hypothetical peneplain proves to be the correlative of the Lexington, it was no doubt developed late, rather than early, in Tertiary time.

Preglacial Drainage.—In a region so deeply covered with drift, it is not to be expected that the preglacial drainage will be well known. Interesting details have come to light here and there, but as yet there is no general agreement on a plan by which they can all be fitted together. There can be no doubt that the master streams were on the belts of soft rock now occupied by the Great Lakes. It has even been commonly assumed that all these basins, including Lake Superior, belonged

[1] LaForge, L., Detroit folio (No. 205), U. S. Geol. Survey, 1917.

[2] Salisbury, R. D., Preglacial Gravels on the Quartzite Range near Baraboo, Wis., *Jour. Geol.*, vol. 3, pp. 655–667, 1895. In this paper Salisbury suggests the correlation of this gravel with the Lafayette gravels preserved in patches in the Mississippi Valley. Trowbridge (*op. cit.*, p. 353) would make them "late Tertiary." Trowbridge's citations on the same page are valuable.

to a single drainage system. At least they are known to be connected by deep drift-filled valleys. Yet it remains unknown whether this system was tributary to an ancestral St. Lawrence or to the Mississippi. Some of the deeply buried valleys (all commonly thought of as preglacial) may even be interglacial. There is no warrant for assuming that a single plan of preglacial drainage endured throughout the earlier glacial epochs and then gave way suddenly to the present plan. So long as buried valleys are not known to have been contemporaneous, any reconstruction of a former drainage pattern must be tentative.

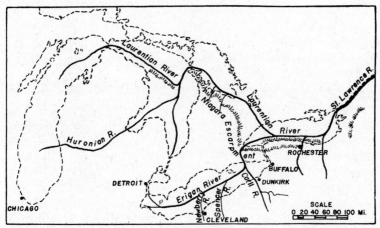

Fig. 131.—Preglacial drainage of the Great Lakes region as inferred by J. W. Spencer in 1891. (*Amer. Geologist, vol. 7.*)

It is easier to reconstruct such a single hypothetical drainage system by assuming an outlet to the Atlantic than by assuming drainage to the Mississippi. This was done long ago by J. W. Spencer (Fig. 131).[1] In favor of that plan it may be pointed out that all of the streams are made to follow lines adjusted to the structure, and that they do not come together at improbable angles. The Niagara cuesta, even more prominent then than now, is known to be crossed by deep transverse valleys wherever required by Spencer's plan.[2] Thus, 12 to 14 miles west of

[1] SPENCER, J. W., Origin of the Basins of the Great Lakes of America, *Amer. Geologist,* vol. 7, p. 87, 1891.

[2] SPENCER, J. W., Relationship of the Great Lakes Basins to the Niagara Limestone, *Bull. Geol. Soc. Amer.,* vol. 24, pp. 229–232, 1913.

Niagara Falls, there is a drift-filled valley, known to science as the Dundas Valley, connecting the Erie and Ontario basins. Its rock bottom, where it crosses the Niagara escarpment, is at least 375 feet below the surface of Lake Erie and more than 100 feet below its bottom. A similar old valley beneath the city of Cleveland, with its bed near sea level, may represent the upper course of the Dundas stream, or its lower course if the drainage was toward the Mississippi. The Niagara cuesta is also broken through by a deep passage between Lake Huron and Georgian Bay. Its depth in the rock is not known, as the bottom of the passage is no doubt on a filling of drift. Again, there is a drift-filled gorge transecting the Niagara cuesta from Lake Superior just above the Soo to Lake Huron just east of the Straits of Mackinac. A buried valley, whose rock bottom is far below lake level, connects Georgian Bay and Lake Ontario. Like these two basins themselves, this old valley is carved on the soft Ordovician shales at the foot of the Niagara escarpment.

Of these drift-filled valleys, only the Dundas is known to be as deep as the basin it is supposed to have drained, but there can be no question that all were carved by streams. However, there is no evidence in the gorges themselves of the direction of flow.

Another hypothetical system of preglacial drainage assumes flow in the opposite direction through most of these gorges and an ultimate escape to the southwest,[1] but the lower courses of the old valleys, which must in that case have led to the Mississippi, are assumed to be completely obliterated by the drift cover. Those who have given most study in the field to the Pleistocene history of the Great Lake region do not yet find the evidence sufficient to decide the direction of preglacial drainage.[2]

Valleys in the bedrock surface of Michigan (Fig. 130) suggest northward as well as southward drainage. However, Lake Michigan has two deep basins separated near the middle by a plateau about 350 feet below the water level, *i.e.*, more than 200

---

[1] GRABAU, A. W., Niagara Falls and Vicinity, *Bull. N. Y. State Museum*, 45, pp. 37–54, 1901. See especially Figs. 5 and 6, pp. 44–45.

[2] LEVERETT, F., Outline of the History of the Great Lakes, Mich. Acad. Sci., *12th Rept.*, pp. 21–22, 1910. While Leverett here leaves the question undecided, his cautious language implies at least an even chance that the drainage, or at least part of it, was toward the Mississippi. TAYLOR, F. B., Niagara folio (No. 190), p. 16, 1913.

feet above the southern basin and 500 feet above the northern. It is possible that the two halves of this long trough may have been drained in opposite directions from the middle. The bedrock surface south of the lake, in Indiana, is below the lake level at many places but no master valley leading south is demonstrable.[1] At the north end, Grand Traverse Bay and Green Bay represent north-flowing streams. Drillings around the former

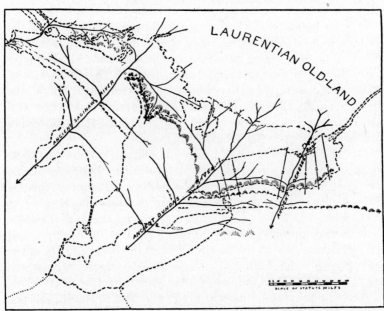

Fig. 132.—Drainage of the eastern Great Lake region in Tertiary time, as conceived by A. W. Grabau. (*Bull., Buffalo Soc. Nat. Sci.*)

show the rock surface to be 600 feet below the lake.[2] The preglacial stream in Green Bay probably came from far to the south and reached the trunk stream by a large gap in the Niagara cuesta.

The Wisconsin River has flowed for a very long time in its present general direction, but the Green Bay glacier spread westward across its old channel, compelling the river to take a

[1] *Cf.* LEVERETT, F., and F. B. TAYLOR, The Pleistocene of Indiana and Michigan, U. S. Geol. Survey, *Mon.* 53, p. 59, 1915. A suggestion of possible southward drainage is made here.

[2] SPENCER, *op. cit.*, 1913.

new and more westerly course.[1] In the latitude of the Baraboo
Range, however, all possible outlets farther west were so high
that an extensive lake was formed (page 523). When the ice
melted back, the lowest outlet uncovered was around the east
end of the range, the old gorges by which it had formerly crossed
the range being blocked by the terminal moraine.[2]

Behavior of the Glacial Ice

Older Ice Sheets.—Over the rock surface described above, the
last continental ice sheet moved in a general southwesterly
direction. At least one older sheet, the Illinoian, and probably
others, had moved over this territory. Their deposits are
occasionally reached by erosion[3] or distinguished in wells,[4]
but their influence on present topography must generally be
ignored for want of knowledge. However, it is a legitimate
supposition, supported by much evidence, that the older ice
sheets behaved much like the last, having similar lobes; also that
a substantial part of the drift was brought by them. The older
till, sufficiently compacted to be known as "hardpan," is reached
by drills in various localities ranging from northern Michigan to
Ohio and Illinois.

Influence of Major Features of Relief.—The last or Wisconsin
ice sheet was to some extent guided in its movement by the great
valleys, being deflected in some cases by a considerable angle.
As the ice was from 1000 to 2000 feet thicker in the great valleys,
it moved more freely and more rapidly there than on the divides
where friction was more effective. Also, melting was more

---

[1] ALDEN, WM. C., The Quaternary Geology of Southeastern Wisconsin,
U. S. Geol. Survey, *Prof. Paper* 106, pp. 110–111, 1918.

[2] For details and map, see R. D. Salisbury and W. W. Atwood, Wis.
Survey, *Bull.* 5.

[3] F. Leverett (Geology and Mineral Resources of the Cleveland District,
Ohio, U. S. Geol. Survey, *Bull.* 818, p. 59, 1931) states that Illinoian drift is
exposed at the lake edge.

[4] LEVERETT, F., Surface Geology and Agricultural Conditions of the
Southern Peninsula of Michigan, Mich. Geol. Survey, *Pub.* 9, p. 52, 1912.
It is here stated that the old drift is generally covered less than 50 feet, but
often 100 feet. Wm. C. Alden (Chicago folio No. 81, U. S. Geol. Survey,
p. 7, 1902) cites Leverett who states that Illinoian drift is generally encountered in wells at Chicago at depths around 150 feet.   For a general statement
of the evidences for older ice invasions in Michigan see F. Leverett, Surface
Geology of Michigan, Mich. Geol. Survey, *Pub.* 25, pp. 112–115, 1917.

effective where the movement was slower. The result was that each great trough came to be occupied by a lobe of ice which followed its course, somewhat as an independent glacier. The ice was moving toward the edge of the lobe at all points.[1] Doubtless, also, it was higher in the middle and sloped outward.

The effect here described was naturally greatest when the ice was not too thick and powerful, *i.e.*, during its oncoming and disappearance. When it was thickest and most extensive, reaching far toward the Ohio River, the effect of these valleys was largely lost and the ice cap spread over large parts of Ohio, Indiana, and Illinois with relatively little lobation (Fig. 133). The area covered only in this manner belongs to the Till Plains section. When the thickness of the ice became less, and its limit was not far south of the Great Lakes, the movement was so dominated by the great valleys that the sheet consisted entirely of distinct lobes. Their movements were not parallel and there was much crowding until melting and recession left bare strips or gaps between them. The lines along which lobes met bore some relation to the preglacial divides, but only in a most general way.

When the ice spread freely over Ohio, Indiana, and Illinois, its load of drift was largely disposed of by lodging as ground moraine beneath the broad ice sheet. Moraines built by the dumping of drift at the actual edge of the ice and not overridden may have a height of 75 to 100 feet at places in Illinois, but elsewhere they are relatively unimpressive. Marginal moraines built farther north, where the ice front was sharply looped, show a larger proportion of hummocky ridges. This is especially true of interlobate moraines as described below. Deposits of outwashed sediment also cover large areas[2] in the north, since the waters flowing from the ice were much impeded by morainic deposits and sometimes by old divides which had to be sur-

---

[1] This has not always been understood, and some wrong inferences have resulted. It was clearly stated and explained by T. C. Chamberlin in 1888, Rock Scorings of the Great Ice Invasion, U. S. Geol. Survey, *7th Ann. Rept.*, p. 184. Yet so careful and critical an observer as J. W. Spencer stressed the point that the striations are not parallel to the escarpments or to the lake shores in order to show that ice erosion had not deepened the lake basins. See J. W. Spencer, Origin of the Basins of the Great Lakes of America, *Am. Geologist*, vol. 7, pp. 86–97, 1891; ref. to p. 94.

[2] See map of Surface (Pleistocene) Geology of Michigan, *Mich. Geol. Survey*, 1907.

mounted.   When the ice front had retreated to the north or
northeast beyond the St. Lawrence-Mississippi divide, water
accumulated in the valleys between the ice and the divide, discharging to the south over the latter.   Such were the beginnings
of the Great Lakes whose history is recounted below.

Fig. 133.—Successive positions of the ice border.[1]   (*Leverett, Taylor and others.*)
As the movement of the ice at any one stage was toward the margins of the
several lobes, the direction at any one point necessarily changed as the sheet
contracted, the lobes developed, and their outlines constantly changed.   The
arrows must not be considered to indicate direction of movement when the ice
sheet covered the entire area.   They will be interpreted correctly if considered
as having their points at the edge of the shrinking ice.

[1] Leverett states that since this map was published in 1915 some of the stippled Illinoian
area in northwestern Illinois and southwestern Wisconsin has been found to carry a cover of
early Wisconsin drift.   Much of this was mapped as "Iowan" in *Mono.* 38, U. S. Geol.
Survey, 1899, Plate VI.

Lobes of the Wisconsin Ice Sheet.—The Niagara cuesta in Wisconsin is accountable for the separation of two of the most distinct units of the Wisconsin ice sheet, the Green Bay and Lake Michigan lobes. It was the most outstanding ridge in the area, having its trend in the direction of the ice movement; hence ideally calculated to cause lobation. On both sides of this great ridge, where the ice was deep, its movement was relatively free and rapid, being roughly comparable to the thread of a river. With more effective friction and retardation on the ridge, melting lowered the surface and caused the slope to be from the axis outward in each lobe. As the movement of ice in a sheet is in the direction of the surficial slope,[1] the ice approached the interlobate margin from both sides, at places nearly at right angles, always bearing its load of debris to be contributed to the interlobate moraine.

In this case the line along which the lobes met, except near its south end, lies 5 to 15 miles east of the Niagara escarpment, even where the latter is highest and steepest. As suggested above, the limits of lobes, while causally related to rock divides, show no close agreement, partly because a moving mass of such size must ignore details, but partly, perhaps, because one lobe may be better fed from the parent mass or from snow and may therefore spread more vigorously.

The Lake Michigan lobe owes its origin to the Devonian lowland, its separation from its western neighbor to the Niagara cuesta, and from its eastern neighbors to the Marshall sandstone upland in northern Michigan (Fig. 130). For 300 miles its axial movement was nearly south. Within its margins are several secondary lobes, or lobelets, illustrating the responsiveness of ice movement to local slopes. These are the Delavan lobe[2] developed in a valley indenting the Niagara escarpment in southeastern Wisconsin, and the Grand Traverse and Little Traverse lobes[3] developed in Grand Traverse Bay.

In the southern peninsula of Michigan the ice moved over the northern upland with difficulty. Movement was concentrated

---

[1] CHAMBERLIN, *op. cit.*, p. 184.

[2] ALDEN, WM. C., The Delavan Lobe of the Lake Michigan Glacier, U. S. Geol. Survey, *Prof. Paper* 34, 1904.

[3] CHAMBERLIN, T. C., Preliminary Paper on the Terminal Moraine of the Second Glacial Epoch, U. S. Geol. Survey, *3d Ann. Rept.*, p. 326, 1882.

in the Lake Michigan lobe on the west and the Huron-Saginaw lobe on the east. These masses, at first in contact, were later separated by a widening interlobate zone.

Advancing southward in the basin of Lake Huron, the ice moved as a single sheet until it reached the Marshall cuesta on the "Thumb"[1] whose rock surface is 1000 feet or more above the lake bottom. On this barrier the stream parted, one very important lobe advancing southwestward in the Saginaw lowland and another going south. While the ice sheet was still thick and extensive, this south-moving lobe merged with the ice in the Erie basin, the combined Huron-Erie lobe moving southwestward into Indiana. Before lobation was well begun, the ice advancing southwestward through the Erie basin formed a continuous sheet with that of the Saginaw lobe west of the Thumb and with that of the Lake Michigan lobe, and extended to central Illinois. With decrease in thickness and extent, and with more complete control by rock contours, the Saginaw lobe shrank far back, leaving a broad gap between the Lake Michigan and the Huron-Erie lobes. With the same changes carried further, the Erie and Huron lobes became distinct, each spreading within its own basin, while the two met and built a low interlobate moraine (probably under water)[2] in the Ontario peninsula. Most of these developments can be traced on Fig. 133, which shows successive positions of the ice border. A small secondary lobe, comparable to those mentioned above, branched off from the Erie lobe, moving south in the wide, low valley of the Grand River in eastern Ohio (page 316). In fact, the whole southern margin of the Erie lobe west of Pennsylvania was more or less scalloped,[3] but this margin lies outside of the section here considered.

The ice in the Ontario basin, once confluent with that of the Erie basin, gradually became an independent lobe north of the Niagara escarpment. During an important chapter of the late Pleistocene, this lobe survived while the Erie basin was filled with water (page 492).

[1] The Lower Peninsula of Michigan has the shape of a mitten, the thumb being east of Saginaw Bay.

[2] LEVERETT, F., U. S. Geol. Surv., *Mon.* 41, Pl. 2, p. 50, 1902.

[3] Best shown on Pls. 13 and 15 of Leverett's Monograph 41 of the U. S. Geol. Survey.

Glacial Deposits and Topography

The Kettle Moraine of Wisconsin.—The interlobate moraine between the Green Bay and Lake Michigan glaciers is among the most impressive of its kind. Along their common boundary for more than 150 miles both glaciers contributed to the moraine, at places more than 100 feet deep. It is familiarly known as the Kettle Moraine, being noteworthy for its topography of "knobs and kettles" which appear unique to those who are accustomed to the more orderly plan of continuous valleys in a water-carved surface.

Probably all of the factors which may be involved in making marginal moraines were active in this accumulation. Parts of it bear the appearance of merely falling in disorderly heaps as the ice that carried it melted. Chamberlin has classed this as "dump moraine."[1] Other parts with equally fortuitous hummocks and hollows may have been moved forward bodily by advancing, or readvancing, ice. This has been called "push moraine." Still other parts are water-laid or "kame moraine." Lastly, the back slope by which the terminal ridge merges into the ground moraine represents progressively increased lodgment under the ice as the sheet, melting at the bottom as well as at the top, grew thinner and lighter and less able to urge forward its basal load. This has been styled "lodge moraine." All of these processes together built at places a single ridge, elsewhere a series whose number changes as ridges merge or divide.

The belt of Kettle Moraine ranges in width from 2 or 3 to 10 or 12 miles, if attendant belts of kames be included. At places it is possible to distinguish a median ridge or zone, which received deposits from both sides, from the lateral ridges which were the work of one lobe or the other. While the two ice fronts stood near together, the narrow aisle between them was necessarily the site of many ponds, and subject to deposition as well as to local erosion by melt water which escaped mainly along this line. Many kames were built at the edge of the ice, and large areas of hills resembling kames (and often so called) are really outwash plains so deeply and closely pitted with ice-block molds that no

[1] Chamberlin, T. C., Proposed Genetic Classification of Pleistocene Glacial Formations, *Jour. Geol.*, vol. 2, pp. 517–538, 1894.

plain surface is left between the hollows.[1]   Belts of such topography, at places 5 or 6 miles wide, are common on both sides of the interlobate moraine.

Marginal Moraines of the Green Bay Glacier.—During the growth of the Kettle Moraine the Green Bay and Michigan lobes were in contact to a point about 8 miles south of Whitewater,

FIG. 134.—Kames near Oconomowoc, Wis.   In this locality between the Kettle Moraine and the wasting Green Bay glacial lobe, abundant deposits of water-laid drift were made.   (*Wis. Geol. and Nat. Hist. Survey.*)

Wisconsin.[2]   At this point the moraine of the Green Bay glacier curves off to the west, then to the north, forming the boundary between the Great Lake section and the Driftless Area.   Its topography is not everywhere so distinctive as that of the Kettle Moraine, but it is, on the whole, a remarkably strong and continuous ridge.   Between the two Baraboo ranges, where the

[1] THWAITES, F. T., The Origin and Significance of Pitted Outwash, *Jour. Geol.*, vol. 34, pp. 308–319, 1926.

[2] It is worthy of note that T. C. Chamberlin, when a young man, was a professor of natural science in the State Normal School at Whitewater, and that this locality, in which features of glacial deposition are crowded in such great profusion, engaged his attention and stimulated his interest in glaciology, a line in which he was to become the world's leading authority.

thickness of the drift reaches several hundred feet, the width of the terminal ridge contracts to $\frac{1}{2}$ mile. At other places the ridge may be double or multiple. Beyond it to the west and south is a plain of glacial outwash, irregular in width and interrupted. Parts of this plain are conspicuously pitted. Within the area covered by the Green Bay lobe are also recessional moraines,[1] at least seven being noted south of Lake Winnebago. These are not continuous ridges, but are composed rather of patches of morainic topography, showing less local relief than the outer terminals.

Ground Moraine of the Green Bay Glacier.—Most of the area covered by the Green Bay glacier is ground moraine with a local relief of 50 to 150 feet. This is much more than the average thickness of the drift, but bare rocks are exceedingly rare. The present surface reflects the form of the under surface of the ice, which was obliged to fit itself to a rough surface, but at the same time was moving and constantly compelled to change its form. It was separated from that surface by a sheet of till which, though insufficient to level up the floor, lodged in such a manner as to bury the steepest slopes and produce a surface of flowing curves. Some undrained hollows were left which are now lakes or swamps.

Commonly ground moraine accumulates more deeply in valleys than on hills and tends to reduce the relief. Under exceptional conditions, for reasons not yet fully understood, it piles up in oval hills or drumlins. An area east and northeast of Madison, Wis., is one of the foremost drumlin districts in the United States. At least 1400 such hills have been identified in 1325 square miles, only 74 of these being beyond the limits of the Green Bay lobe.[2] An occasional square mile contains a half dozen or more. A common height is 30 to 60 feet but they vary widely beyond these limits. All are elongated in the direction of ice movement. Many of them rise from marshy plains. Some have

---

[1] ALDEN, U. S. Geol. Survey, *Prof. Paper* 106, p. 134; also Pls. 3 and 4, 1918. Plate 23 shows the moraines of the Wisconsin stage from central Wisconsin to central Michigan and southern Indiana.

[2] ALDEN, W. C., The Drumlins of Southeastern Wisconsin, U. S. Geol. Survey, *Bull.* 273, p. 9; also Pl. 1, 1905. *Cf.* also Pl. 3 in U. S. Geol. Survey, *Prof. Paper* 106, 1918. The origin and explanation of drumlins is discussed by Alden in both of these papers, also by Chamberlin and Salisbury, *Geology*, vol. 3, pp. 360–361, 1906; also by H. L. Fairchild, *Bull. N. Y. State Museum*, 111, pp. 429–430, 1907.

rock cores, but whether this is more than a coincidence is not known.

Terminal Moraine of the Lake Michigan Lobe.—From the end of the interlobate Kettle Moraine, the moraines of the Lake Michigan glacier, which includes the small Delavan lobe, extend southward. The outer and older ridges go far beyond the limits of the Great Lake section into the Till Plains section. The late Wisconsin (Valparaiso) moraine, contemporaneous with that of the Green Bay glacier, is concentric with the shores of Lake Michigan, its outer edge being about 40 miles south of Chicago. The limits of the area treated here as the Great Lake section are, however, empirical, as described on page 455 and do not agree everywhere with those of the ice at any one time. From southern Wisconsin to the Wabash River, this arbitrary boundary agrees fairly well with that of the "Late Wisconsin" drift as formerly mapped by Leverett.[1] Beyond that it follows the Wabash River and the shores of the Pleistocene Great Lakes.

In Illinois, most of the area comprised in the Great Lake section is occupied by the Valparaiso and similar moraines. In a sense these are ridges, but at most places that fact is not recognized in a casual view. They may rise with gentle slope several hundred feet on the lakeward side but, as a single ridge may be miles in width, and there is in any case a regional slope toward the lake, the larger relations are not seen. The local relief is considerable, but generally it is characterized by the flowing curves of an overridden surface and is rarely hummocky. These and earlier moraines in Illinois owe their mass mainly to the lodgment of the load beneath the ice as it thinned toward its edge and lost its power. Most of the drift was therefore overridden by the ice, and the style of topography was thus controlled. Only locally was debris dumped at the extreme edge and not subsequently passed over by the ice. Toward the north, however, and also toward the east in Indiana, these same ridges merge into forms which agree better with the ordinary conception of terminal moraine. In the vicinity of Valparaiso,

---

[1] LEVERETT, F., The Illinois Glacial Lobe, U. S. Geol. Survey, *Mon.* 38, Pl. 6, 1899. In a later work (U. S. Geol. Survey, *Mon.* 53, 1915), Leverett separates the "Late Wisconsin" into Middle and Late Wisconsin, and puts the Kettle Moraine in the Middle Wisconsin. The Late Wisconsin is bounded by the Port Huron morainic system, and correlatives.

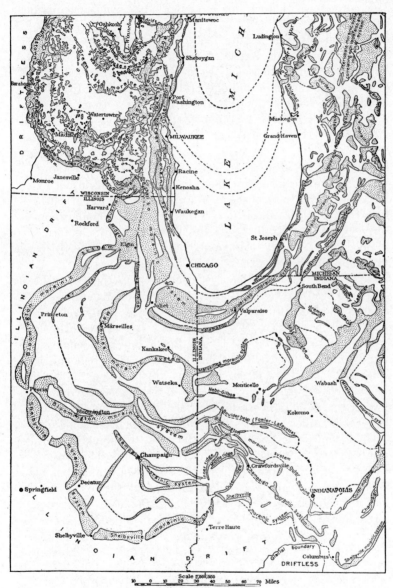

Fig. 135.—Moraines of the Lake Michigan and Green Bay glaciers of the Wisconsin stage of glaciation. (*Alden U. S. Geol. Survey Prof. Pap.* 106.)

Ind., and from there east and north, the moraine is a typical hummocky terminal ridge.   Much of the area covered by this lobe in Michigan has the hummocky character of end moraines, but the distribution is irregular, not in long ridges of consistent trend.   Between these morainic tracts are till plains, and a considerable belt is lacustrine plain (Fig. 136).

Ground Moraine and Lake Border Moraines.—The topography of the ground moraine of the Lake Michigan lobe in Wisconsin is much like that of the Green Bay lobe except for the lack of drumlins.   A zone 10 to 20 miles wide along the lake shore and extending south to Chicago, is occupied by the so-called Lake Border Moraines.[1]   After a wide gap at the head of Lake Michigan, a very narrow corresponding belt appears on the south and east sides of the lake.   The surfaces of these ridges, one to four in number, have the undulating character of ground moraine.   As ridges they may escape the notice of the casual observer, but their influence is obvious on the map by reason of their control of drainage lines.   The North Fork of the Chicago River, the Desplaines, and the Milwaukee River are among those which follow the intervening troughs parallel to the lake shore. Above these troughs the ridges may rise with gentle slope 50 or more feet on their outer sides and decline twice or three times as much in the longer slope toward the lake, but the generalized slopes are still gentle.   All the dimensions are largest in Wisconsin.   The corresponding belt near the lake in Michigan is occupied by less smooth and less continuous ridges.

The undulating surfaces of these ridges were plainly formed beneath the ice, but in each case beneath its edge.   It was pointed out above (page 477) that the iceward slope of a marginal moraine is due to the lodgment of the load beneath the ice. In this case, as in that of the Valparaiso moraine in Illinois, the other ridge-making processes were almost, but not entirely, inoperative.   These broad smooth contiguous ridges have the position of recessional moraines, though one or more slight readvances of the ice may be involved.   In any case they are marginal, but they are strikingly different from the irregular,

[1] LEVERETT, F., The Illinois Glacial Lobe, U. S. Geol. Survey, *Mon.* 38, pp. 380–412, 1899; ALDEN, W. C., The Quaternary Geology of Southeastern Wisconsin, U. S. Geol. Survey, *Prof. Paper* 106, 301–307, 1918.

patchy, and dumplike deposits which often mark the position of a receding glacial front.

Interlobate Areas in Michigan and Indiana.—The ice pressed into the Southern Peninsula of Michigan from all sides. That of the Saginaw lobe crossed the entire state between competitors from either side. With the ice lobes thus converging, it is not surprising that the drift is very thick, averaging over 300 feet[1] and reaching more than 800 feet in thickness under the highest point of the peninsula. The high and low points on the surface of such accumulations cannot be expected to agree closely with those of the buried rock surface. There is a suggestion of crowding, or at least of closing all gaps between the lobes. No doubt, this was true even after the front of the ice had melted back far from its outermost position, but at a later stage there were gaps of increasing width between the shrinking lobes.

A strict use of the word "interlobate moraine" would limit it to a very narrow strip which received accretions of drift from both sides. All deposits on either side of this strip would then be allotted to one lobe or the other. But it is not always easy to identify a line along which the two ice masses may have been in contact. Moreover, some features of an interlobate strip are much the same whether the strip be wide or narrow; for example, those which are due to the abundance of water and its inability to escape except by following the ice front. In practice the term "interlobate" is not so narrowly used. Belts, sometimes many miles wide, are marked by irregular morainic patches or short ridges of varying trend, among which are more or less fortuitous depressions and much evidence of glacial waters.

The largest continuous area of this description lies in southern Michigan and northern Indiana between the Valparaiso moraine and the contemporaneous moraine of the Huron-Erie lobe (Fig. 136). It is interlobate in a geographical rather than a strict technical sense, for the Saginaw lobe once covered the area. The retreat of the Saginaw front was relatively so rapid that this long rectangular area was left bordered by ice on its two long sides, and closed in at the north by the retreating Saginaw ice.

[1] LEVERETT, F., Surface Geology and Agricultural Conditions of the Southern Peninsula of Michigan, Mich. Geol. Survey, *Pub.* 9, pp. 20, 24, 1912.

That lobe in its retreat left hummocky terminal ridges, scattered, patchy, and irregular, but generally transverse to the trend of the more continuous terminals of the bordering lobes.   The entire area contains only minor tracts of ground moraine or till plains. Its nonmorainic parts (most of the area) are covered with sand and gravel[1] carried in by the abundant outwash from the surrounding ice.   Some of this represents the channels, flood plains, and alluvial fans of the streams of that time.   Much of it was laid down in shallow lakes and has a surface of small relief.   The broad, flat, swampy basin of the Kankakee River in northwestern Indiana and northeastern Illinois, much of it now reclaimed, is underlain by such lacustrine and fluvial sand and gravel.   In its southern part dunes are rather common.

The northwest corner of the rectangle described above is near Kalamazoo.   From that locality a great belt of interlobate character extends north and then northeast to the highland of Marshall sandstone which the ice tried to evade by going around on both sides (*cf*. Figs. 133 and 136).   The tendency of the ice to spread after the barrier was passed caused it to move from both sides into the belt here outlined.   This belt is characterized by irregular tracts or ridges of strongly morainic expression, and bordered at most places by more continuous and linear moraines built by the Saginaw and Lake Michigan lobes after considerable recession of their fronts.   Its northeastward extension, covering much of the preglacial highland, has fragmentary ridges, some of which are parallel to the retreating ice fronts, which were shifting toward the Michigan and Huron basins.   Throughout this northern interlobate belt, as in the area south of Kalamazoo, abundant water from the ice on three sides spread much sand and gravel along streams and in temporary lakes.   It is in this part that the converging ice left the deepest cover or drift, a possible 1000 feet in at least one place, in northern Michigan, or twice the thickness found in northern Indiana.   Between the strong moraines bordering this northern interlobate belt and the shore to the east, north and west, the plan or system of morainic ridges, if not confused, is at least made complex by the tendency of the ice margin to break up into minor lobes or scallops.

[1] See Leverett, F., and Taylor, F. B., U. S. Geol. Survey, *Mon.* 53, Pls. 6 and 7.

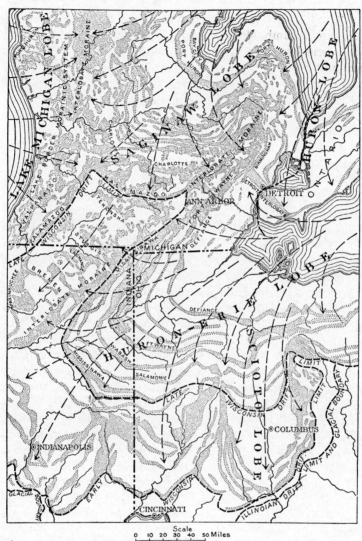

FIG. 136.—Moraines of southern Michigan and parts of adjacent states, showing the Late Wisconsin ice front and the direction of ice movement. Broken lines indicate the greatest extent of the ice in the Early Wisconsin and Late Wisconsin stages. [*U. S. Geol. Survey, folio* (*No.* 205).]

An interlobate belt similar to the one just described lies on the axis of the Thumb, along the line of contact of the Saginaw and Huron-Erie lobes. From near the end of that peninsula to a point west of Ann Arbor, it follows the crest of the Marshall sandstone cuesta, but at intervals the recessional moraines of the Saginaw lobe turn off to the west. The main belt continues southwest to the Wabash River, marking the limit of the well-developed Erie lobe.

Area Covered by the Saginaw Lobe.—Outside of the areas described here as interlobate, the marginal moraines of the Saginaw and Huron-Erie lobes are more linear and continuous, marking somewhat clearly the successive positions of the ice front, between which are strips of till plain. This is specially true in the case of the Saginaw lobe. In its orderly contraction this glacier built as many as ten concentric crescentic moraines (Fig. 136). South of the Grand River (city of Lansing) a large part of the area is occupied by broad strong moraines with hummocky surface. All of the rest (including at least one south of Lansing) are relatively smooth and narrow. Between them are wider belts (but generally only 1 to 5 miles) of still smoother till plain. Behind this series of slender crescentic moraines, around the head of Saginaw Bay and for 40 to 50 miles southwest of it, the surface is almost flat except for one or two smooth, inconspicuous moraines laid down under water. The flatness of this area is due in part to deposits of clay and sand in Pleistocene lakes which once covered it, but the underlying till plain was itself very smooth. This is much the broadest expanse of smooth surface in Michigan, all of which lies on the border, mainly on the east side.

Area Covered by the Huron-Erie Lobe.—As the front of the Huron-Erie lobe fell back to the southeast from the ridge that makes the Thumb, it also left a series of parallel moraines, the first ones strong, the later ones weaker and smoother. North of the Wabash, the parallelism of this series is less distinct, but south of that line (in the Till Plains section) it is very striking (page 515 and Fig. 136).

A continuous strip of lacustrine plain extends from Saginaw Bay around the Thumb along the western shores of Lakes Huron, St. Clair, and Erie. From Lake Erie it extends 100 miles southwest to Fort Wayne, Indiana. The southern limit of this plain is also the limit of the Great Lake section.

History of the Great Lakes

Origin of the Basins.—There is no evidence that the Great Lakes existed in any form prior to the glacial epoch. Other factors have been very important in determining their outlines and depths, but it is more than doubtful that closed basins would have come into existence in these valleys except for glaciation.[1] There is no reason to doubt that lakes were occasioned by the earlier ice invasions, but there is no known connection between them and the present system. Four factors must be taken into consideration in all speculations regarding their origin. These are (1) preglacial stream erosion, (2) crustal warping, (3) glacial scour, (4) filling and obstruction by drift.

The most important known facts concerning preglacial drainage have already been mentioned (page 468). Hypotheses on this subject depend in part on what is believed with regard to past altitudes and tilting of the continent. On this subject, the main facts known with certainty are that during postglacial time the surface has been tilting toward the southwest. This has been accomplished mainly by a rise at the northeast. It is also known that at an earlier, but still not remote, time (perhaps late Pliocene) the northern part of our continent was for a while much higher than at present, and that deep valleys were cut in what is now the Continental Shelf. To what extent the interior of the continent stood high at the same time is poorly known; hence it remains in doubt whether the high level at the northeast indicates a southwesterly slope. Considerable altitude in the interior seems to be indicated by certain deep buried valleys (page 505). It is apparent that the relative weight given to these facts will determine one's conclusion as to the general direction of preglacial drainage.

Regardless of the general direction of drainage, it is known that the ice sheet cast itself into lobes, each lobe occupying one of the major lowlands, and that the ice was thickest and heaviest, and its movement most rapid, along the axis of each lowland. On the question, whether the depth of the basins was substantially increased by glacial scour, geologists still differ. The bottoms of all the basins, except that of Lake Erie, are far below sea level, and this depth must be accounted for either by glacial

---

[1] *Cf.* Spencer, J. W., Origin of the Basins of the Great Lakes of America, *Amer. Geologist*, vol. 7, pp. 86–97, 1891.

erosion or by crustal warp.   It has been believed by some that
the latter is sufficient by itself to produce the results and that the
former is only incidental.[1]   Others ascribe a part or most of the
depth to ice erosion.[2]   Aside from the inference to be drawn from

Fig. 137.—Glacial grooves on Kelly's Island, Lake Erie.   Striking features
due to abrasion by debris-laden ice are here preserved in a park set aside by the
State of Ohio.   (*Ver Steeg, Ohio Jour. Sci., vol.* 35.)

present altitudes of the rock surface and from the forms of the
valleys, there remains the fact that the enormous volume of
drift, averaging more than 300 feet in thickness in Michigan and
northern Indiana, necessarily came from somewhere.   Most of it

---

[1] SPENCER, *loc. cit.   Cf.* GRABAU, A. W., Preglacial Drainage in Central
Western New York, *Science*, vol. 28, pp. 527–534, 1908.   TAYLOR, F. B.,
Study of Ice-sheet Erosion and Deposition in the Region of the Great Lakes,
Bull. Geol. Soc. Amer., vol. 22, p. 727, abs., 1911.   Taylor thinks that ice
erosion was extremely small except on weathered material.   In discussion,
Salisbury cites the great amount of fresh rock material in the drift as evi-
dence of glacial erosion.

[2] CHAMBERLIN, T. C., "Geology of Wisconsin," vol. 1, pp. 253–257, 1883.
R. D. Salisbury ("Physiography," p. 246, 1919) regards glacial erosion as a
major factor.   Martin (*op. cit.*, pp. 237–238) expresses the belief that the
basin of Lake Michigan was drained in preglacial time by a stream which
flowed south "no more than one to two hundred feet below the present
surface of Lake Michigan, or 581 feet, if indeed it was below 581 feet at all."

is from the same formations that underlie the lake region, not from farther north. Most of it is also from fresh rock, not from the ancient soil mantle. Analogies with alpine glaciers and fiords cannot be pressed far, but it is probable that the facts taken to indicate substantial deepening by ice erosion have been correctly interpreted.

The importance of drift accumulations as dams at the south or southwest ends of the basins depends on whether these basins would otherwise be drained in that direction. The rock surface south of Lake Michigan is so near the lake level that buried valleys may yet be discovered, not only lower than the lake level but lower than the rock bed of the Niagara River. In that case the drift accumulation determines the present eastward discharge. But even should such valleys be found, most of the depth of the basins would remain to be accounted for.

Growth and Changes of Glacial Lakes in General.—Whatever direction the earlier drainage may have had, it is certain that during the last or Wisconsin glaciation the northeastern part of the continent was so low that the presence of the ice over the St. Lawrence basin was the only thing that prevented drainage in that direction. The glacier at its greatest extent went far beyond that drainage basin and reached its limit on slopes leading to the Mississippi. The first critical point in the history of the Great Lakes was reached when the retreating front began to descend the slopes north and east of the Mississippi-St. Lawrence divide. Water then began to be ponded between the divide and the ice. There were many such ponds, each occupying a tributary valley in the St. Lawrence basin. Each basin filled to the level of the lowest available notch or sag, over which it spilled to the Mississippi or to another lake. The level of each pond was independent of all others. The several ponds were separated by the minor divides in the St. Lawrence basin. With further retreat the smaller tributary valleys united, or sags were uncovered in the uplands between them. Then two or more lakes having different levels merged into one body of water at a common level with a single outlet, the others being abandoned. Such fossil channels, crossing either the main or minor divides are numerous.[1] Pro-

[1] FAIRCHILD, H. L., *Glacial Waters in Central New York, Bull. N. Y. State Museum*, 127, 1909; also many other bulletins of the New York State Museum.

gressive union in the manner described resulted in larger and fewer lakes until a single one, Lake Algonquin (page 495) was larger than any three of the present lakes. It was again subdivided when lower outlets were uncovered and the level fell. These changes of outline were complicated with others resulting from tilting and from temporary readvances of the ice front.

Until the Great Lakes reached almost their present forms, their levels were determined by the ice barrier. Parts of the region not now under water were submerged most of the time and are now typical lacustrine plains. Other parts were covered by water for such short times that submergence is only inferred from the altitude of fossil shore lines. These old shores have all grades of distinctness from thick belts of beach gravel and sand, extending hundreds of miles with only an occasional break, to faint indications widely spaced. Some of the beaches were again temporarily submerged and partly defaced. Their order of succession from the outermost beach to the present shore is not in every case the order of age. The old outlets are also variously preserved, some still showing rocky beds, others having thick accumulations of peat. It is by studying the old shore lines, their altitudes, their correlation, their tilt, and their relations to the old outlets that the history of the lakes is deciphered. The details of this history belong to the specialized science of glaciology and to historical geology.[1] Only a summary is necessary here. With the help of Figs. 138 and 139 and the accompanying table, page 496, the following brief statement should be clear.

Lake Chicago and Its Correlatives.[2]—Immediately after the ice-cap became limited to the St. Lawrence basin, standing water began to cover the valleys which were being evacuated by the

[1] For a complete history see F. Leverett and F. B. Taylor, The Pleistocene of Indiana and Michigan and the History of the Great Lakes, U. S. Geol. Survey, *Mon.* 53, 1915. Leverett has published an excellent "Outline of History of the Great Lakes" in the 12*th Rept. Mich. Acad. Sci.*, pp. 19–42, 1910, which was revised in *Mon.* 53, U. S. Geol. Survey. Taylor had published a summary of slightly different scope, "The Glacial and Post-glacial Lakes of the Great Lake Region," Smithsonian Report for 1912, pp. 291–327, 1913, which was reprinted as Chap. XII of *Mon.* 53, U. S. Geol. Survey.

[2] The glacial lakes here grouped together are *correlative* rather than strictly contemporaneous.

five main lobes.　Thus originated Lakes Duluth,[1] Jean Nicolet, Chicago, Saginaw, and Maumee.　Lakes Duluth and Chicago expanded almost to the dimensions of Lakes Superior and Michigan, respectively, before their identity was lost by merging into Lake Algonquin at a late stage in the evolution of the group. The others soon merged into bodies of different names.　The one which began as Lake Maumee had the most complex history. A change of name indicates, in most cases, that the outlet was shifted, though it will be observed that this rule does not always work both ways.

Lake Chicago originated as a string of ponds at the edge of the ice when the inner slope of the Valparaiso moraine began to be laid bare.　As the slope near Chicago was relatively smooth, these ponds quickly coalesced into a narrow crescent-shaped lake which overflowed to the Desplaines Valley and thus to the Illinois River and the Mississippi.　At the beginning this outlet was 60 feet above the present Lake Michigan, but when finally abandoned it had been cut down to less than 10 feet above the present lake level.　Good beaches mark the initial height and two intermediate heights at which the falling level halted.[2]

The original *Lake Maumee* in the Erie basin overflowed to the Wabash River at Fort Wayne.　When the ice front receded to a lower level on the Thumb of Michigan, Lake Maumee spilled over the divide, and its waters, abandoning the Fort Wayne outlet, escaped by way of the Grand River Valley, Lake Chicago, the Desplaines River, and the Illinois to the Mississippi.　A readvance of the ice shifted the outlet southward, up the slope of the Thumb to a position near Imlay.　This again raised the level of the lake but not quite high enough to reach the old spillway at Fort Wayne.　At each of these stages good beaches were built, the second in point of time, but lowest in position, being submerged later but not wholly effaced.　Then a temporary disappearance of the ice from the Thumb caused Lake Maumee to merge with Lake Saginaw, forming *Lake Arkona*.[3]

[1] For predecessors of Lakes Duluth and Jean Nicolet see papers of Leverett and Taylor referred to above.　Also *Prof. Paper* 154*A*, U. S. Geol. Survey, by Leverett, pp. 54–57.

[2] For complete description and explanations see Wm. C. Alden, Chicago folio (No. 81), U. S. Geol. Survey, 1902.

[3] Constant reference should be made to Figs. 138 and 139, and to the table on pp. 496 and 497.

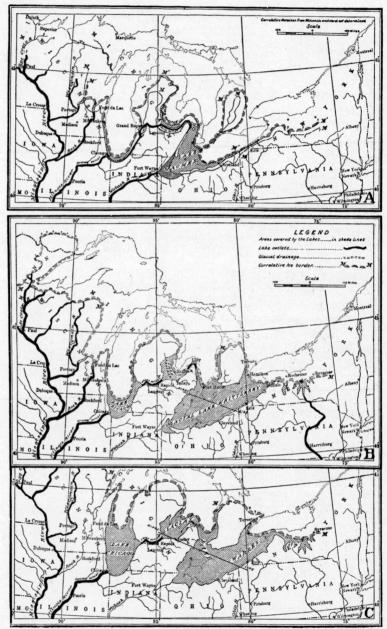

Fig. 138.—Three stages in the early history of the Glacial Great Lakes,
Heavy lines represent outlets. (*Taylor and Leverett, Wis. Geol. Survey Bull.*
36.)

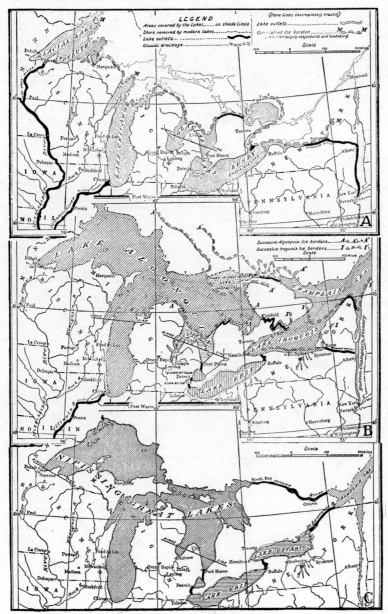

Fig. 139.—Three stages in the later history of the Glacial Great Lakes. Heavy lines represent outlets. (*Taylor and Leverett, Wis. Geol. Survey Bull. 36.*)

Lakes Whittlesey, Wayne, and Warren.—As the Thumb was again partly covered by ice, the waters on its two sides again became separate lakes at different levels. The one in the Erie-Huron basin, known as *Lake Whittlesey*, discharged over the divide, past Ubly, to the renewed Lake Saginaw. By this time the basin of Lake Erie was free from ice as far east as Dunkirk, N. Y., and Port Royal, Ontario. Lake Whittlesey covered fully twice its area. The beach of this large lake, more than 40 feet below the main Maumee beach, is among the most prominent of the series.

A beach 80 to 85 feet below the Whittlesey, much reduced and smoothed, as if by later submergence, seems to indicate a lower stage than that of Lake Warren which follows. The low intervening stage is called *Lake Wayne*. As the level indicated seems to have made the westward outlet impossible, it is surmized that the ice front at this time may have fallen back sufficiently from the face of the Allegheny Plateau to permit an eastward escape across New York.[1] Wherever the outlet was, it has not been identified with any of the stages described in New York. Later the westerly outlet was resumed, initiating *Lake Warren*.

Glacial Lakes of Central New York.—While the above described changes were going on in the Erie basin and farther west, an independent evolution was in progress in the Ontario drainage basin. The Allegheny Plateau north of the Ontario-Susquehanna divide embraces valleys large and small, with divides of north-south trend. Certainly as early as Lake Whittlesey, lakes in these valleys had been discharging southward across the divide to the Allegheny and Susquehanna rivers. A complicated series of changes was passed through before a dozen or more of these lakes united to make Lake Newberry, which overflowed to the Susquehanna, then Lake Hall, which drained westward to Lake Warren, then Lake Vanuxem, which was tributary to the Mohawk.[2] Then for a short time, the edge of the ice

---

[1] TAYLOR, *op. cit.*, p. 306. Also U. S. Geol. Survey, *Mon.* 53, pp. 389, 391.

[2] The nature of the development in New York is shown in Figs. 138 and 139 p. 492. For discussion see H. L. Fairchild, Glacial Waters in Central New York, *Bull. N. Y. State Museum*, 127, 1909, see especially the plates; also Glacial Waters in the Lake Erie Basin, *Bull.* 106, 1907. For an excellent summary description of the early eastward outlet see G. K. Gilbert, Old Tracks of Erian Drainage in Western New York, *Bull. Geol. Soc. Amer.*, vol. 8, pp. 285–286, 1897.

rested so low on the slope that the course of drainage to the east was almost free from lakes. During the latter part of this series Lake Warren was in existence but did not spread east of the Erie basin. When the ice again advanced, closing the eastward outlet, the waters in central New York rose until all were merged with Lake Warren, whose existence was later terminated by the renewal of the easterly outlet, allowing the water level to sink to that of Lake Lundy (Dana).

During the early stages of the outlet along the northern face of the Allegheny Plateau, the stream connected a series of lakes, cutting gorges, some of them with cascades and cataracts, across the divides, and building deltas in the lakes. Temporary spillways are numerous, their sites changing with the changing position of the ice front and the changing outlines of the lakes.[1]

Lakes Iroquois, Algonquin, and Nipissing.—Reverting to the history of the major lakes, the ice in the Ontario basin had now melted back beyond the Niagara escarpment. Lake Lundy (Lakes Dana and Dawson in New York) was one of the stages in the intermittent fall of the water as the eastward outlet, following the retreating ice front down the northward slope, fell to the level of the divide at Rome. The level at or near that stage was of longer duration and the old shores are well marked. The corresponding lake, called Iroquois, is among the best known of the glacial lakes. The water stood several hundred feet above the present level of Lake Ontario, hence the lake was much more extensive. The outlet at Rome continued until the ice in the St. Lawrence Valley shrank away from the Adirondacks and opened a lower course to the sea. The present land surface in the St. Lawrence valley was then below sea level as the bed of Lake Ontario is even now. Only the ice kept the lake up and the sea out. With the disappearance of the ice the "Champlain Sea" entered.

In the fall from the Lundy to the Iroquois level, the Niagara cuesta was left above the waters. Thus Lake Erie became a separate body, discharging by the Niagara River, and Niagara Falls came into being. The ice-free southern part of the Huron basin contained the beginning of *Lake Algonquin*, but this body was still barred off from Lakes Chicago and Duluth, which seem

[1] Well shown in Fairchild's reports. Note among others *Bull. N. Y. State Museum*, 106, Pl. 5.

SUCCESSION AND RELATIONS OF THE PLEISTOCENE GREAT LAKES

Glacial lakes and their successors	Contemporary with	Originated by	Outlet	Level[2]	How ended
Duluth[1]	Chicago, etc.	Retreat of Superior lobe	Brule-St. Croix divide	1066 ft.	Merged with Lake Algonquin
Jean Nicolet	Chicago, etc.	Retreat of Green Bay lobe	Rock River; then Fox-Wisconsin divide	800 ft.	Merged with Lake Chicago
Chicago	Duluth, Maumee, etc.	Retreat of Lake Michigan lobe	Desplaines River to Illinois River		
Glenwood stage				642 ft.	Merged with Lake Algonquin
Calumet stage				622 ft.	Merged with Lake Arkona
Tolleston stage				602 ft.	Merged with Lake Warren
Saginaw	Chicago, Maumee, etc.	Retreat of Saginaw lobe	Grand River		
Later stage (After Lake Arkona)	Chicago, Whittlesey	Readvance of ice on the Thumb	Grand River		
Maumee	Chicago, etc.	Retreat of Huron-Erie lobe			
First stage			Wabash River	790 ft.	
Second stage		Further retreat	Across the Thumb to Lake Saginaw	760 ft.	
Main stage		Readvance of ice on the Thumb	Across the Thumb	780 ft.	Union with Lake Saginaw
Arkona	Chicago, etc.	Retreat of ice from the Thumb	Grand River	710–694 ft.	Divided into Lake Whittlesey and 2d Lake Saginaw
Whittlesey	Chicago, 2d Saginaw	Readvance of ice on the Thumb	Across the Thumb to 2d Lake Saginaw	738 ft.	Merged with others at lower level
Wayne	Chicago, etc.	Retreat of ice everywhere	South of Syracuse to Mohawk River(?)	653–658 ft.	Level raised; outlet shifted to Grand River

			Outlet	Altitude[2]	
Warren	Chicago, Duluth, etc.	Readvance of ice in the east	Grand River	680–670 ft.	Level dropped; outlet shifted to east
Lundy (or Dana)	Duluth, Chicago, etc.	Recession of ice	Near Syracuse to Mohawk River	640 and 620 ft.	Separation of Lakes Iroquis and Erie
Iroquois	Erie, Algonquin	Fall of level to that of the divide at Rome	Mohawk River	....	Merged into the Champlain Sea
Algonquin First stage (Huron basin only)	Iroquois, Erie	Fall of level made Lake Erie independent	Port Huron	607 ft.	
Second stage (Superior, Michigan, and Huron)	....	Retreat of ice	Trent Valley		
Third stage	....	Southwestward tilt	Port Huron or Chicago or both	607 ft. at Port Huron and Chicago	Disappearance of ice barrier
Nipissing Great Lakes	Champlain Sea	Melting of ice from Ottawa Valley	Port Ottawa, then Huron	597 ft. at Port Huron and Chicago after closing of Ottawa outlet	Rise and closing of Ottawa outlet
Modern Great Lakes Superior	....	Fall of Lake Huron below the Sault Rapids	St. Marys River	601 ft.	
Michigan	Five lakes contemporary since closing of Ottawa outlet. Erie began much earlier	Change of Nipissing outlet	St. Clair River	582 ft.	
Huron		Change of Nipissing outlet	St. Clair River	582 ft.	
Erie	....	Fall of Lake Iroquois below Niagara escarpment	Niagara River	573 ft.	
Ontario	....	Rise of St. Lawrence Valley above sea level	St. Lawrence River	247 ft.	

[1] For predecessors of Lake Duluth see Leverett, *op. cit.,* p. 25.

[2] The levels given here are the present altitudes of beaches near the old outlets. Compare with levels of the present Great Lakes as given in the table.

to have coalesced even before the ice left the Soo and the Straits of Mackinac. With the withdrawal of the glacier from the straits, the three upper lakes and probably much land on the north and east became a single water body, Lake Algonquin, which probably divided its discharge between the Chicago and St. Clair outlets, the latter leading to Lake Erie. The level of Lake Algonquin was still held up by ice on the east, so that its waters covered the ice-free part of the lowland on Ordovician shales between Georgian Bay and Lake Iroquois. The final disappearance of the ice from this lowland opened a lower outlet by way of the present Simcoe and Kawartha Lakes and the Trent River Valley. By this time, with much of the glacial ice gone, the continent had begun to rise again at the northeast. Indeed, a large part of the well-attested tilting was during the life of Lake Algonquin.[1] The result was the abandonment of the Trent outlet and the reoccupation of one or both of the southern outlets.

There remained beneath the shrinking ice sheet at the northeast, one more valley of lower level than the outlets of Lake Algonquin. This was the depression marked by Lake Nipissing and the Ottawa River, leading to the St. Lawrence above Montreal. In due time this became the outlet of the *Nipissing Great Lakes*, no longer glacial, but postglacial, being independent of ice barriers. They lasted until the Ottawa outlet was in turn raised too high. For a time the discharge was divided, then the St. Clair River again became the only outlet. With this last change the modern Great Lakes began. Lake Erie was again brought into the chain, and at about the same time the rise at the northeast shut the sea from the Ontario basin. Then Lake Ontario and the St. Lawrence River came into existence together.

The tilting of the continent did not extend south of a line running west-northwest from near the northeastern corner of Ohio. All beaches below that line retain their horizontal position. Their approximate altitudes are given in the accompanying table. North of the hinge line[2] the old shores rise. Their vertical intervals also become greater toward the northeast since the older and higher shores were most affected.

[1] TAYLOR, *op. cit.*, p. 319.

[2] The hinge line itself shifted nearly 100 miles to the north before the time of Lake Algonquin.

Niagara Falls.—It was during the intermittent fall to the level of Lake Iroquois (Rome outlet) that the waters north and south of the Niagara escarpment first stood at different levels. Then the Niagara River and the Falls were born, the latter being located at the face of the escarpment 6½ miles north of their present position. As the strong Lockport limestone is limited to the upper part of the escarpment and is underlain by easily erodible shales and sandstones, recession of the cataract was inevitable.[1]

As the main cataract is now receding upstream between 4 and 5 feet per year, and the total length of the gorge made by recession is 34,300 feet, it was once thought that a simple calculation would determine the length of time since the ice front left that point. Then it was seen that the rate of recession must have varied with the volume of the river. This in turn was dependent on the area and other outlets of the Pleistocene lakes. The level of the water at the foot of the falls also varied with the tilting of the Ontario basin. At one time the level of the lake on the north was so high as to reduce the height of the falls by half and to interfere with undercutting. From a study of the changing outlines of the lakes it has been estimated that the water in this outlet has varied in amount from 15 to 110 per cent of the present discharge. By close study the whole length of the gorge has been divided into five sections, each cut during a known stage of lake history, for which the area and discharge can be estimated. Even if the discharge were known with precision, it is still necessary to estimate the rate of recession, for the two do not vary in identical manner. The evidence from Niagara suggests that the Falls have been at work not less than 20,000 nor more than 35,000 years (*cf.* St. Anthony Falls, page 585).

TILL PLAINS SECTION

Distinguishing Characteristics.—The recognition of a Till Plains section south of the Great Lake section is avowedly based

---

[1] Details are omitted here. Adequate descriptions and accounts of the changes in Niagara Falls are available in textbooks and public documents. See, among other sources, F. B. Taylor, Niagara folio (No. 190), U. S. Geol. Survey, 1913; G. K. Gilbert, Niagara Falls and Their History, Nat. Geog. Soc., *Mon.* vol. 1, no. 7, 1895; A. W. Grabau, Niagara Falls and Vicinity, *Bull. N. Y. State Museum*, 45, 1901. J. W. Spencer, The Falls of the Niagara, Their Evolution and Varying Relations to the Great Lakes, *Canad. Geol. Survey*, 1907.

on empirical distinctions, not on geological categories. The distinction between the two areas when considered as wholes is physiographically significant and humanly important. None the less, the line that separates them in Indiana and Illinois is an arbitrary generalization. The best that can be said of the division agreed upon is that it facilitates description and discussion of the two sections and makes possible some general statements about each.

If justification of the two sections be attempted in geologic terms, the Till Plains section may be distinguished as that portion of the glaciated area East of the Mississippi wherein the movement of the ice was less controlled and diverted by deep valleys. From this point of view the most basic distinction goes back to the dominant cuestas and lowlands of the lake section. There follow in logical sequence, or in more or less close association, a more marked lobation of the ice, a greater prevalence of morainic topography both interlobate and frontal, lakes and swamps, and abundant sandy outwash deposits not confined to stream valleys. All of these features, which claim a large share of space in the description of the northern section, become insignificant or at least relatively unimportant in the southern section. As a basis for the scientific division of an area, these features may be important or unimportant, but at least they are *real*. In the geography of the region they are very significant.

Preglacial Topography

Features Due to Underlying Rocks.—Distinctions in the underlying solid rock express themselves in the unequal altitudes of certain wide belts, but these vary little, where at all, in the forms of the landscape. Even in the southern and southwestern parts, where the glacial drift averages less than 30 feet in thickness, it generally filled the smaller valleys and now controls the surface forms, modified only by later erosion.

The dominant structural features here are the northern part of the Cincinnati anticline, which brings Ordovician rocks to the surface, and the southern Illinois syncline, which retains its Carboniferous coal measures even where the surface is very low. From southwestern Ohio the beds dip faintly, never visibly, to the east, north, and west beneath the coal measures in the Allegheny Plateau, the Michigan coal basin, and the Illinois coal basin. All Paleozoic systems above the Cambrian were thus exposed in the preglacial rock surface.

Ordovician limestones and shales underlie a surface 900 to 1000 feet high in southwestern Ohio and southeastern Indiana, no doubt a well-developed peneplain. The same surface spreads widely over the Silurian, which consists mainly of the Niagara and other limestones. Most of western Ohio and eastern Indiana are thus accounted for. Adjacent narrow strips of Devonian are also of limestone, but beyond them are the soft shales of the Upper Devonian.

The geologic map shows three belts of easily wasted Devonian shales, and all are low. One on the east extends from near Sandusky on Lake Erie almost due south to the Ohio River. One on the north connects the head of Lake Erie with that of Lake Michigan. The belt on the west extends northward from Louisville to Indianapolis, the latter city, though situated on a wide till plain, being several hundred feet lower than the surface 20 miles to the east or west. Where this trough lies at the foot of the Knobstone escarpment (page 426), it is little more than 500 feet in height. On its east side the surface rises with the dip of the middle Devonian limestone to the general level mentioned above.[1] The lower part of this slope is essentially the stripped upper surface of the limestone.

The corresponding broad north-south belt in central Ohio is, for much of its length, 200 to 300 feet deep. The dip slope of the Middle Devonian limestones descends eastward to this trough as the corresponding slope descends westward in Indiana. The axis of the trough near its middle is more than 800 feet high. It declines northward to near the level of Lake Erie and southward to a similar low level near the Ohio River. It may have been occupied at one time by longitudinal streams in headwater opposition.[2] The low belt between Toledo and Chicago is probably nowhere much above the level of the lakes.

Except for the weakness of the upper Devonian formations, the most noteworthy contrasts in resistance are found in the Carboniferous rocks. These have been described in discussing the cuestas of the Interior Low Plateau in southern Indiana.

[1] Clyde A. Malott ("Handbook of Indiana Geology," p. 86, 1922) treats this as the Muscatatuck Regional Slope.

[2] LEVERETT, F., U. S. Geol. Survey, *Mon.* 41, p. 75, 1902.

The ridges extend northward with diminishing prominence
beneath the Till Plains, but the surface is so smoothed by the
drift that ridges and lowlands can only be distinguished by exact
surveys.   On the west side of the Illinois coal basin all beds rise
toward the Ozark dome.   Here the strong Mississippian limestones emerge from beneath the weaker coal measures.   South
of St. Louis they form a cuesta whose west-facing escarpment
overlooks the Mississippi River, and whose crest, 650 to 750 feet
in altitude, rises several hundred feet above the plain on the east.

Fig. 140.—Limestone sinks 1 mile south of Stolle, Ill., near East St. Louis.
Sinks are not characteristic of the Till Plains but occur near the border.   (*Ill.
Geol. Survey.*)

The Mississippi here occupies a strike valley which contours the
Ozark dome.[1]

Preglacial Relief.—The local relief of the bedrock surface,
while not everywhere known, is probably less marked than that
of adjacent driftless areas in Wisconsin, Missouri, Kentucky, and
eastern Ohio.   The belts of Devonian shale certainly were in
part, and may have been everywhere, gently rolling lowlands,[2]

[1] LEVERETT, F., Water Resources of Illinois, U. S. Geol. Survey, 17th
Ann. Rept., pt. 2, p. 705, 1896; SHAW, E. W., and T. E. SAVAGE, Murphysboro-Herrin folio (No. 185), U. S. Geol. Survey, 1912; FLINT, R. F., "Geomorphology around the Head of the Gulf Embayment" (manuscript).

[2] HUBBARD, GEO. D., Geology of the Columbus Quadrangle, Geol. Survey
Ohio, 4th ser., *Bull.* 14, pp. 55–57, 1911.   Hubbard would allow a relief of
perhaps 100 feet with gentle slopes and wide flood plains.

probably trenched as the result of a rise not long before the glacial epoch, or (more probably) in an interglacial stage. The plane rock surface at about 600 feet A.T. beneath the Maumee basin spreads over Devonian shale and Silurian limestone alike. The latter may have been merely stripped, or perhaps peneplaned. At all events it rises southward, almost with the dip of the beds, until it merges with the extensive rock plateau mentioned above, 800 to 1000 feet high.[1] The wide expanse of Silurian limestone in Ohio and Indiana had, so far as known, a rather level surface. The Devonian had been stripped from this surface, but whether at base level or a little above is uncertain. This surface is known to be trenched by young valleys more than 350 feet deep.[2]

The surface of the extensive coal measures of Illinois and Indiana seem to have been carved to maturity. The relief in eastern Illinois was perhaps 100 to 150 feet and the slopes gentle.[3] The larger streams had broad flood plains, that of the lower Wabash being then, as now, 12 to 15 miles wide. The Illinois Valley was 8 to 10 miles wide from bluff to bluff in the coal measures, narrowing to 3 miles in the Mississippian limestone.[4]

Several tracts of high rock surface are explained by drainage relations rather than rock character. The most prominent is in Logan County in the middle of the western half of Ohio. Here the weak rocks of the late Devonian cap a group of hills which rise to more than 1400 feet without the drift cover, which adds another 100 feet. Even now rivers radiate from that point. Another high tract, with a rock surface rising to 1100 feet, is in Randolph County, Ind., just north of the 40th parallel and near the Ohio boundary.

Possible Erosion Cycles.—The problem of erosional history as stated on pages 465 to 468 is the same throughout the Central Lowland. The older rocks in the Till Plains section have been worn down, to say the least, many hundreds of feet. Yet there are very few places in the area at which an extensive view would not present a nearly flat horizon. Reasoning from this fact, and

---

[1] LEVERETT, F., U. S. Geol. Survey, 17*th Ann. Rept.*, pt. 2, p. 433, 1896.

[2] BOWNOCKER, J. A., A Deep Preglacial Channel in Western Ohio and Eastern Indiana, *Amer. Geologist*, vol. 23, pp. 178–182, 1899.

[3] CAMPBELL, M. R., and LEVERETT, F., Danville folio (No. 67), U. S. Geol. Survey, 1900.

[4] LEVERETT, F., U. S. Geol. Survey, *Mon.* 38, p. 17, 1899.

from analogy with the Appalachian region, leads to the inference that the Till Plains section was reduced to a peneplain at least once, and parts of it several times. As the general level is at some places 500 to 600 feet and elsewhere 900 to 1000 feet, it is inferred that at least the higher parts are well above their present base level. This is attested by the depth of valley cutting. The Ohio and Mississippi flow in trenches 400 to 500 feet deep where the adjacent upland is 900 to 1000 feet high. Even the shale lowlands are higher than necessary to give the requisite gradient for drainage to the sea. Lake Erie is the local base level for some of these lowlands, and the existence of the Niagara Falls and rapids, to say nothing of the rapids in the St. Lawrence, shows that temporary barriers are holding up the local base level at least 200 feet.

The Higher Level.—The most typical part of the higher rock surface, namely, the limestone upland, 900 to 1000 feet high in western Ohio and eastern Indiana, is plainly a part of the same peneplain which appears on the Knobstone and Pottsville formations of southern Indiana and in the Bluegrass district of Kentucky.[1] The Shawneetown Ridge of southern Illinois (page 651), much of whose surface is near 800 feet, may well be a part of the same surface. The high rock masses centering in Logan County, Ohio, and Randolph County, Ind., are monadnocks.

Probably the rock surface in western Ohio (Lexington peneplain) is genetically the same as that of northwestern Illinois and adjacent parts of other states, where it is called the Lancaster peneplain[2] (page 531). This surface reaches an altitude of 1200 feet in southwestern Wisconsin, where it may have suffered uplift. Toward the south it declines to a lowland of later origin, but toward the southeast, from Wisconsin to Ohio, there is no sharp break in the altitude or character of the rock surface, though it is lower in the longitude of Lake Michigan.

Devonian Lowlands.—The lower parts of the rock surface are mainly (1) the lowlands on Devonian shale and (2) the extensive

---

[1] This assumption is made in various publications of the U. S. Geological Survey, *e.g.*, the Columbus folio (No. 197) and the Detroit folio (No. 205).

[2] GRANT, U. S., and E. F. BURCHARD, Lancaster-Mineral Point folio (No. 145), U. S. Geol. Survey, 1907. The difference between the Lancaster and a possible Dodgeville peneplain (p. 533) may be ignored in long-distance correlation.

low surface on the coal measures in southern Illinois. As the former may have been occupied by streams at some time in the Tertiary, the question may be raised whether it is necessary to differentiate them in age from the limestone uplands. The suggestion has been made that these low strips were merely the major valleys in the Lexington peneplain, but such an explanation seems inadequate. In favor of the hypothesis that they are local peneplains of later age it may be noted that (1) several of these lowlands, notably the one which stretches westward from Lake Erie, are too broad and too nearly level for river valleys; (2) the limestone uplands are apparently more tabular and more uniform in height than would be expected if important valleys existed at their edges during their development; (3) some large valleys in the limestone, like the deep one noted in western Ohio,[1] are topographically young. In northern Illinois two local peneplains or straths have been discriminated at intervals of 80 to 100 feet, the last one being trenched by preglacial streams.[2]

That the low level of the surface on Devonian shales is due to the softness of the rocks will scarcely be questioned, but this fact alone does not make it certain that these areas passed through an additional cycle of youth, maturity, and old age since the limestones were peneplaned. The more exact the correlation between elevation and rock resistance, the more impressive is the suggestion that general wasting of an old surface has lowered soft rocks more than hard rocks without substantially altering the style of topography. On this hypothesis, the flatness of the entire area might be the result of a single erosion cycle, the lower areas having passed through the same history as the higher, and differing only in the rate of general wasting since the peneplain was made and moderately raised. Such an explanation is

---

[1] BOWNOCKER, *loc. cit.* The valley here described is commented on by Leverett, U. S. Geol. Survey, *Mon.* 41, p. 183.

[2] HERSHEY, O. H., Preglacial Erosion Cycles in Northwestern Illinois, *Amer. Geologist,* vol. 18, 1896, see pp. 76–84. Hershey recognizes five cycles in this district represented by (1) the tops of the Niagara remnants, (2) the Lancaster peneplain, (3) dissected plains up to 3 miles in width along certain streams, (4) floors of sharply incised valleys, locally several miles wide, (5) gorges cut in the rock below the last-named plains, some of them being cut several hundred feet below the present streams and filled with glacial material. The reality of the first is uncertain (see p. 532), as is also the significance of several of the others beyond the immediate district discussed.

favored by the dip slopes leading down from the limestone uplands to the shale lowlands. However, it remains true that there are places in which the assumption of a distinct cycle later than the Lexington is imperative. The Nashville Basin is among the best examples.

Lowlands of Southern Illinois.—In southern Illinois and southwestern Indiana the surface on the coal measures beneath the glacial drift for more than 150 miles east and west, and 100 miles north and south, is only 400 to 500 feet high. Toward the north it rises gradually and merges into the Lancaster peneplain. Toward the east it rises more rapidly with the dip of the beds to the level of the Indiana cuestas.[1] On its west side this low tract meets the dip slope of the noteworthy cuesta of Mississippian limestone which borders the trench of the great river. On its south side, for 60 miles only, it abuts against the Shawneetown Ridge (page 651), generally 700 to 800 feet high. On the west and south, therefore, the low level ends where soft rocks give way to hard, while on the east and north the gradual rise is related in a much less exact way to the nature of the rocks.

The low level of southern Illinois has been variously explained. Two main lines of argument have been based on (1) a possible smaller uplift or a subsequent downwarp, (2) greater reduction since the general uplift, either by general lowering of divides after mature dissection or by the development of a new peneplain which was dissected later. Either a sinking of this district or a rise on the southwest[2] is strongly indicated by the valleys of streams flowing southwest to the Mississippi (page 517). Differential erosion seems to be equally well attested by observation, beside being inherently probable. However large or small the

[1] The most expressive map to show altitudes in Illinois is Pl. 4 following p. 8 in Leverett's monograph on the Illinoian lobe, U. S. Geol. Survey, *Mon.* 38, 1898. It must be remembered, however, that the drift is thick in the northern part of the state.

[2] SHAW, E. W., Quaternary Deformation in Southern Illinois and Southeastern Missouri, abs., *Bull. Geol. Soc. Amer.*, vol. 26, pp. 67–68, 1915. This abstract gives the reasons for assuming a northeastward tilt since middle or late Tertiary time. In U. S. Geol. Survey folios (Nos. 185 and 195), Shaw treats the surface of southern Illinois as a peneplain of the "third cycle," counting the Lancaster in the north as the second. Presumably the general level of the Shawneetown ridge (omitting its exceptional swells) is his second peneplain. Hershey (*op. cit.*, p. 90) speaks of the coal basin as an area of depression.

factor of diastrophism may have been, the low surface in southern Illinois is probably to be classed with that of the Devonian shales in Indiana and Ohio. The relation between the low surface on the easily eroded coal measures and the higher surface on harder rocks that dip beneath the basin, especially on the west and south, strongly suggests the relation between the surface of the Allegheny Plateau around Pittsburgh and the higher rim of Pottsville sandstone to the north and east (page 293).

Topography Due to Glaciation

Behavior of the Ice.—The Illinoian ice sheet came from the northeast and reached the southern limit of this section. The Wisconsin ice sheet came from the same direction and covered at least half of the area, leaving western and southern Illinois and a narrow strip farther east uncovered (Fig. 129). The plan on which the two ice sheets were cast into lobes was the same. The Wisconsin ice as shown above, embraced half a dozen or more lobes, large and small, while confined to the Great Lakes region, and the Illinoian sheet at the same stage of advancement may have shown a similar number. At its greatest extension the effect of minor divides and valleys in the north was lost, and only the lowland of Lake Michigan and the one which embraces Lakes Huron and Erie affected the ice movements and the ice border. The north-south ridges of southern Indiana were strong enough to hold back the edge of the earlier ice and thus divide the Illinois from the Erie lobe.

The Illinoian Drift Sheet.—The surface of the Illinoian drift sheet is remarkably level except for some postglacial erosion which does not affect the flatness of the horizon between streams. Even its edge is not generally marked by a terminal moraine, though there are some knobs at places in eastern Iowa and western Illinois where the margin of this ice sheet rested on still older (Kansan) drift.[1] South of St. Louis the ice climbed the dip slope of the Mississippian cuesta to its crest. Similarly it

[1] Many of the facts and interpretations concerning the Till Plains section are taken from three monographs by Frank Leverett, published by the U. S. Geological Survey. These are *Mon.* 38, "The Illinois Glacial Lobe," 1899, *Mon.* 41, "Glacial Formations and Drainage Features of the Erie and Ohio Basins," 1902, and *Mon.* 53, "The Pleistocene of Indiana and Michigan and the History of the Great Lakes," 1915. References to these monographs will be made by number only.

stopped on the crest of the Shawneetown ridge, but at neither place did it build a moraine. From the latter place eastward to southern Ohio, where its edge is lost beneath the younger drift, the Illinoian till generally (though not everywhere) thins gradually to an indefinite edge (*cf.* page 413). Morainic ridges back from the edge are also rare. The glacier seems to have moved forward and melted back with no significant halts in the shifting front. It filled valleys with till and outwash several hundred feet deep and smoothed the landscape with a general cover whose surface is 10, 20, or 30 feet above the old divides. The average thickness in southern Illinois is not more than 30 feet.

Loess and "White Clay."—The Illinoian drift sheet, where not covered by the Wisconsin, is everywhere mantled by loess or by a denser, more clayey substance believed to be its equivalent. Near the larger rivers this mantle is typical loess. For long distances on their bluffs its thickness may exceed 30 feet. At places on the east bluff of the Mississippi and on both sides of the Illinois River, it reaches 50 feet or even more. Generally, within a belt of 10 miles, these great thicknesses decrease to 10 feet, and farther away to half that amount. At places this thinning causes a distinct slope of the upland away from the stream.[1] As the distance from the stream increases, the very porous, mealy character of the loess gradually gives way to finer texture, greater density, and a higher clay content. This is its character over much of southeastern Illinois. It is intensified in southern Indiana and Ohio where soil of this origin on poorly drained uplands or "crawfish lands" is colloquially called "white clay."

The mantle of loess or other surficial loam here described was spread over the older drift and to some extent over the adjacent driftless landscape without regard to altitude. Hills and valleys, the low coal basin of southern Illinois and the high ridges of southern Indiana, were alike mantled. It is now well known that the typical loess of central United States is a deposit of dust[2] brought by the wind. In view of the continuity of the sheet and

---

[1] FENNEMAN, N. M., Physiography of the St. Louis Area, Ill. State Geol. Survey, *Bull.* 12, p. 59 and Pl. 8, 1909.

[2] CHAMBERLIN, T. C., Supplementary Hypotheses respecting the Origin of the Loess of the Mississippi Valley, *Jour. Geol.*, vol. 5, pp. 795–802, 1897. In the earlier stages of American geology, there was a long controversy over

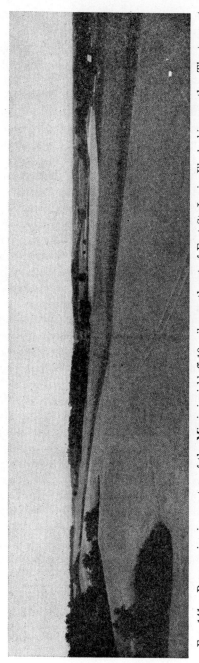

FIG. 141.—Panoramic view on top of the Mississippi bluff 10 miles northeast of East St. Louis, Ill., looking north. The trees at the left are in ravines indenting the bluff. The great local thickness of the loess is accountable for the eastward slope. (Ill. Geol. Survey.)

its perfect gradation from typical loess to "white clay," the latter is classified as loess, the physical difference being ascribed in part to assortment during its flight. The close relation of the thickness and character of the loess mantle to the proximity of large, south-flowing streams points to the flood plains of these streams as one of the immediate sources of the dust. As the prevailing winds in this latitude are from the west, the deposit is always more abundant on the east side. The ultimate source of the greatest body of loess was in some way connected with the Iowan ice sheet (page 598). Size of grain and thickness of the deposit decrease with distance from the limits of the Iowan ice as they do with distance from the streams.

In western Illinois and parts of Iowa and Missouri the loess is the parent material of a very rich dark soil, but its virtues decrease toward the south and east. The "white clay" of southern Illinois, Indiana, and Ohio, especially on flat, poorly drained remnants of the original plain, the "crawfish lands," is inferior. Even in Illinois the greatest productivity is more generally on the younger drift, not on the loess.[1]

Postglacial Erosion.—Probably more than half of the Illinoian drift retains the flat form imparted by the ice. The other half, or a little less, is more recent valley side or, along the larger streams, valley bottom. The major valleys were not wholly obliterated by glaciation. For example, the Illinois River follows its old valley below Hennepin, where it makes its abrupt turn to the south. It has already cut a postglacial trench 150 to 250 feet deep and, for long distances, 5 to 7 miles wide. At places the preglacial valley has been cleaned out to its full width, thought not to its full depth. Tributary streams, quite independent of preglacial valleys, are branching out in dendritic pattern and dissecting the plain (Fig. 142).

Aside from the Mississippi, the Illinois below Hennepin is the only river in the northern two thirds of the state that follows its

---

the possible aqueous origin of the loess. (See CABLE, E. J., Bibliography of the Loess, *Proc. Iowa Acad. Sci.*, vol. 23, pp. 159–162, 1916.) So far as the widespread mantle is concerned, the aeolian hypothesis is now established. It is recognized, however, that there are local deposits of water-laid silt which are discriminated from aeolian loess with great difficulty.

[1] For value of land per acre see "Statistical Atlas of the United States," Pl. 248, Department of Commerce, 1924.

preglacial valley consistently. Others, while having some regard for old divides, have only here and there cut their new channels between the old bluffs. In the southern third of Illinois and the corresponding parts of Indiana and Ohio where the drift is thinner, all of the larger streams, the Kaskaskia, the Wabash,

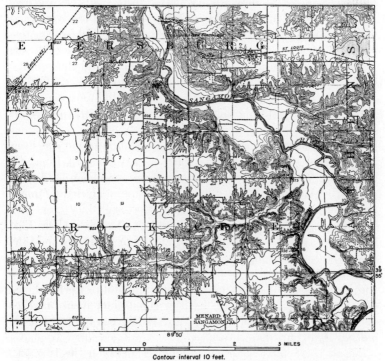

Contour interval 10 feet.

FIG. 142.—Youthful dissection of the loess-covered Illinoian till plain by tributaries of the Sangamon River northwest of Springfield, Ill. (*U. S. Geol. Survey.*)

the two branches of the White River, the two Miamis, and many smaller streams have reoccupied their old valleys.[1] Already there are many flood plains whose width is measured in miles, that of the lower Wabash being 12 to 15 miles wide. Dendritic tributaries have made much headway, but not enough to leave any large area without remnants of the flat plain.

[1] For the relations of present to preglacial drainage in various parts of Illinois see F. Leverett, Water Resources of Illinois, U. S. Geol. Survey, 17*th Ann. Rept.*, pt. 2, p. 706, 1896.

The Area of the Wisconsin Drift

Comparison of the Older and Newer Drift Sheets.—The younger drift sheet differs from the older in several ways, the most obvious being that it is less extensive. There is here only a limited covering of loess on its southern and western borders. The combined thickness of the younger and the underlying older drift sheets, Illinoian and pre-Illinoian, is 100 to 150 feet, instead of the 30 feet of the exposed Illinoian. For considerable distances, notably in central Illinois, the margin of the younger drift is thus raised 100 feet above the older. A further difference is found in the presence of prominent recessional moraines in the younger drift. Still another difference is seen in the occurrence of minor lobes.

The Wisconsin ice, like the Illinoian, embraced but one great lobe west of central Indiana. Farther east the Erie lobe split on certain divides into minor lobes corresponding in a general way with the present larger drainage basins. Thus the monadnock ridges in eastern Indiana and western Ohio (page 503) initiated the East White, Miami, and Scioto lobes (Fig. 133). The ice was also held back by relatively high ground near Mansfield, Ohio, and again by an old divide between Canton and Akron. The small but well-developed Grand River lobe east of the last named line was entirely outside of this section. No doubt the Illinoian ice sheet had the same minor lobes but their effect on moraines was confined to the territory in which the older drift is buried.

To all these constructional differences between the two drift sheets must be added the fact that the newer surface is less eroded. Yet, despite these things, the prevailing aspect of the newer surface, as of the older, is that of the till plain uninfluenced by the forms of the buried rock surface. On both surfaces, outwash is confined to valleys instead of making extensive sheets and pitted plains as in the Great Lake section to the north. Lakes and lacustrine plains are absent, and swamps all but absent, throughout the Till Plains section. If the water table at places is so near the surface as to make artificial drainage necessary, that fact merely emphasizes the flatness; it is not because of basins.

Marginal Moraines in General.—The moraines of this section are much more prominent on a map (Fig. 136) than in the field.

Some of them are, indeed, massive, not only miles in width but deep.   In rare cases they rise as much as 100 feet above the surface in front, though half of that height is a much commoner maximum.   There are even some hummocky tracts of the knob and kettle type, but sag and swell is much more common.   Anyone not interested in drainage might cross many of the moraines shown on the map without noting any ascent or descent, or any difference in topography.   Except in the angles between lobes, tracts of sharp relief are apt to be limited to the narrow outer slope of a moraine.   Thus the Shelbyville moraine, the outer-most of the series in central Illinois, one of the strongest ridges of the group, with occasional points 150 feet high, is distinctly seen from the west or south.   From the plain at its foot it rises 75 to 100 feet within 1 or 2 miles but then slopes north or east with a gradient so small, and with a surface so smooth, that its inner base is indefinite.[1]   The so-called ridge, except for its narrow outer slope, is best described as "only the thickened edge of the drift sheet."   This description, which minimizes the topographic effect of moraines, is not applicable to all parts of all the marginal moraines, but it leaves the correct impression that the general character of the moraines in this section is different from that of the more abundant moraines in the Great Lake section.[2]

A correct conception of the character of these moraines is favored by remembering that the more important ones represent small readvances of the ice.[3]   In its last few miles the typical ice sheet thins rapidly, losing weight and power to urge forward the material at its base.   This favors excessive lodgment and a thickening of ground moraine near the edge whenever the ice front remains long on a single line.   All of the drift thus deposited

[1] For description see F. Leverett, U. S. Geol. Survey, *Mon.* 38, pp. 192*ff.* On p. 195 Leverett states, "Were one not aware of the great relief above the outer border district, and certain that it is due entirely to the presence of a sheet of drift not found there, one might well question the propriety of calling this a moraine belt."   His description of the complex and important Bloomington moraine (pp. 240–251) includes a number of districts of sharper relief.   For the character of moraines in Indiana see Leverett, U. S. Geol. Survey, *Mon.* 53, p. 56, 1915.

[2] *Cf.* also G. D. Hubbard's description of the important Powell moraine (30 to 40 ft. high) north of Columbus, Ohio.   Geol. Survey of Ohio, 4th series, *Bull.* 14, p. 82, 1911.

[3] LEVERETT, F., and F. B. TAYLOR, U. S. Geol. Survey, *Mon.* 53, p. 31, 1915.

is overridden by the moving ice, and its surface is smoothed accordingly. Only in a narrow zone in front of the ice does the drift retain the forms imparted to it by dumping, pushing, or deposition from water. All that lies farther back has been smoothed by the overpassing ice. A readvance of a few miles, lasting for a short time only, may do much to smooth even this outer zone. In that case the terminal (recessional) moraine will be known by its thickness rather than by any distinctive topography.

Interlobate Areas.—On the high rough divides already mentioned, the edge of the ice was disrupted. Its advance was so impeded that the moraines appear as if festooned from a few impassable points (Fig. 136). In the lee of those points the lateral edges of the resulting lobes were more or less parallel, but it does not appear that they actually met or participated in the building of a single morainic ridge, as was done at places in the Kettle Moraine in Wisconsin.

On the Miami-White divide in eastern Indiana, the bedrock surface itself rises to 1100 feet A.T. The ice climbed the northern slope to the summit and there deposited more than 100 feet of drift. In an east-west belt 30 miles long and 6 to 10 miles wide the morainic topography is marked by sharp knolls and deep basins like the moraines north of the Wabash in the Great Lake section. Toward the south, in the lee of the rock hills, the morainic character is less marked. The terminal moraines of the White and Miami lobes face each other across the upper valley of the Whitewater River.

The high divide near Bellefontaine, Ohio, is similarly covered by deep drift with a very hummocky surface, rising in one hill to 1540 feet, the highest point in Ohio. Parallel moraines of the Miami and Scioto lobes extend to the south, facing each other across a valley, now streamless, but once carrying a stream between the lobes. As in Indiana, the most pronounced morainic topography is found on the highland rather than in its lee. The high, rough surface of bedrock north and south of Mansfield, marking the Scioto-Muskingum divide, caused the glacial drift to be disposed in a manner similar to that just described.

Moraines of the Erie Lobe.—Among the striking features of the glacial map is the series of six or more semielliptical moraines southwest of Lake Erie and roughly parallel to its shore. Their relation to the diminishing Erie lobe is obvious. All of these recessional moraines are of small or moderate height; their slopes are gentle when not faint, and their surfaces generally smooth. Their minor role in topography is in strange contrast with their absolute control of drainage (Fig. 136). In the shallow troughs in front of successive moraines are the Mississinewa, Salamonie, and upper Wabash rivers, flowing northwest to join the Wabash. Then follow the St. Marys and the Auglaize, tributary to the Maumee. This simple arrangement would scarcely have been possible had the preglacial surface been less simple. North of the Wabash, in the Great Lake section, these ridges are less smooth, and the outer members of the series merge into the great interlobate belt stretching from the Wabash to the Thumb of Michigan (page 482).

DRAINAGE

Preglacial Drainage.—It is only in the southern and western parts of this section that even the major lines of preglacial drainage are known. There the drift is relatively thin and some streams are seen to be in old rock valleys. Where this is the case the direction of the older drainage was generally the same as at present, but some of the rock valleys may be interglacial, not preglacial. The Miami River below Dayton, the Wabash below Covington, Indiana, and the Illinois River below Peoria are all in preglacial rock valleys, from which the drift is now being cleaned out. The same is true of some intervening streams for shorter distances, and some of the larger tributaries near the main valleys.

Farther from the edge, where the drift is very thick, drilling has revealed preglacial valleys here and there, but knowledge is too fragmentary to make possible the reconstruction of a drainage system. Probably the shale lowlands were drained longitudinally. There must have been a large stream somewhere between western Indiana and the Allegheny Plateau which received the water of the Kanawha (page 303), but whether it led to the Erie basin or to the Wabash, or possibly even by a shorter course to the Ohio, is not known.[1]

[1] LEVERETT, F., U. S. Geol. Survey, *Mon.* 41, pp. 101–104, 1901.

Postglacial Streams.—In northern Ohio, Indiana, and Illinois, even the general plan and direction of the preglacial valleys is unknown. Even the larger streams are in postglacial valleys. The Illinois in its westward course across the younger drift has cut a valley about a mile wide, but it was long aided by overflow from the Pleistocene Great Lakes (page 491). The Wabash was similarly aided for a shorter time and its valley is of similar size. In its southwestward course to near the Illinois line, its possible relationship to older drainage lines is not known. The same is

Fig. 143.—Till Plains near Columbus, Ohio.   (*From a lantern slide by Howell's Microcosm.*)

true of the Miami above Dayton. The relation of the Scioto to a possible ancestor is only conjectured from the fact that its course follows a lowland on the Devonian shale. Thus far the postglacial erosion cycle is in its youth. Tributaries, where not guided by slopes on the surface of the drift, are working headward dendritically. Only a minor part of the original surface has been converted into valley side by the work of streams.

From a point near Clinton, Iowa, to the southeast corner of the state, the Mississippi River flows through the section, not at its edge, which is a few miles (maximum 20) farther west. Although this part of the river is in the Till Plains section, its course can better be explained after discussion of the other sections concerned (page 601).

Tilting Indicated by Streams.—The valley of the Illinois below the bend at Hennepin is peculiar by reason of its extremely low gradient, less then 2 inches per mile for more than 200 miles.[1] At least in its flatter stretches the stream is aggrading and building natural levees. Its wide flood plain is in large part swampy and threaded by sloughs. Locally it is protected by dikes 12 feet high above the natural levees, but much of it is not reclaimed.[2] As the gradient is less than a third of what is required by the much larger Mississippi, it is highly probable that

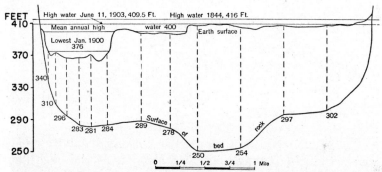

Fig. 144.—Cross section of the Mississippi trough, now largely filled with sand and gravel, 13 miles south of the Eads bridge, St. Louis, Mo. Vertical lines indicate exploratory borings made by United States Engineers. (*Ill. Geol. Survey.*)

northeastward tilting from the Ozarks has taken place since the old valley was partly cleaned out. Indeed the rock floor at Princeton near the bend of the river at Hennepin is now 14 feet lower than at any known point in the latitude of St. Louis.[3]

The valleys of tributaries of the Mississippi in southern Illinois were extensively ponded after glaciation.[4] This was not directly due to tilting, although the extent of it was no doubt due

[1] See LEVERETT, F., Preglacial Valleys of the Mississippi and its Tributaries, *Jour. Geol.*, vol. 3, p. 752, 1895.

[2] BARROWS, H. H., Geography of the Middle Illinois Valley, Ill. Geol. Survey, *Bull.* 15, p. 4, 1910.

[3] LEVERETT, *op. cit.*, p. 754.

[4] SHAW, E. W., Preliminary Statement Concerning a New System of Quaternary Lakes in the Mississippi Basin, *Jour. Geol.*, vol. 19, pp. 481–491, 1911; Newly Discovered Beds of Extinct Lakes in Southern and Western Illinois and Adjacent States, State Geol. Survey Ill., *Bull.* 20, pp. 139–157, 1915; SHAW, E. W., and T. E. SAVAGE, Murphysboro-Herrin folio (No. 185), U. S. Geol. Survey, 1912.

to low gradients which in turn came about by downwarping. Similar ponding has already been mentioned on tributaries of the lower Ohio (page 439). Its immediate cause seems to have been the aggradation of the main streams, either by outwash from the ice or by the excessive load brought down by streams from the newly exposed drift cover. The sites of these old lakes are now extensive terraces of sandy clay bordering the streams of southern Illinois and adjacent states. Some of the older terraces rise in a downstream direction, indicating that some of the tilting was quite recent.

THE DRIFTLESS SECTION OF THE UPPER MISSISSIPPI VALLEY
The Section as a Whole

General Relations.—In southwestern Wisconsin and parts of adjacent states is an area of about 15,000 square miles which was never covered by the continental ice cap, despite the fact that the ice several times advanced far south of it; in the Illinoian stage, more than 300 miles. The southeastward-moving ice on its west side and the southwestward-moving ice on its east side were not exactly contemporaneous and it is not certain that they ever actually met and enclosed the area, but their several drift sheets meet and overlap.[1]

The larger part of this section is a typical low plateau submaturely dissected, resembling large areas in Kentucky and Tennessee. A considerable part is "driftless" only in the sense of being free from ice-laid drift. Stream and lake deposits, including some glacial outwash, are important in this part, as loess is in others. For geographic purposes it is found best to include in this section a small area once glaciated and thinly covered by till, but so long ago that the topographic effect has been lost (see description of boundaries below). The total area of the section is thus about 20,000 square miles. The use of the name "Driftless section" can only be justified on the principle that it is desirable to include in the name of an area a suggestion of its most prominent (even though not universal) characteristic.[2]

[1] CHAMBERLIN, T. C., and R. D. SALISBURY, The Driftless Area of the Upper Mississippi, U. S. Geol. Survey, 6th *Ann. Rept.*, pp. 199–322, 1885. On p. 322 it is stated that the ice "seems to have completely surrounded it," but this is now doubted.

[2] When used in this conventional sense, the word "Driftless" is capitalized.

The reason why the ice failed to cover this area is found in the larger hypsometric features, not of this area, but of the surface over which the ice must have passed to reach it. The northern part of the section is lower than any adjacent surface, but it lies in the lee (southwest) of a wedge-shaped upland pointing northeast, *i.e.*, toward the oncoming ice from the Labrador center. This wedge, in northern Wisconsin and the northern peninsula of Michigan, is a full 2000 feet higher than the lake basins, Michigan and Superior, on either side. Most of the moving ice was thus shunted off to the south or west. The Chippewa and other small lobes, which climbed the upland, gave out in central Wisconsin. The Illinoian ice on the east side spread southwestward beyond the Mississippi into Iowa. In similar manner, but guided by much smaller differences in elevation, the several ice sheets on the west side, *i.e.*, from the Keewatin center, spread southeastward toward, to, or beyond the Mississippi. In the language of Chamberlin:

Diverted by highlands, led away by valleys, consumed by wastage where weak, self-perpetuated where strong, the fingers of the mer de glace closed around the ancient Jardin of the Upper Mississippi Valley, but failed to close upon it.[1]

Boundaries.—The contrast between this section and the Great Lake section on the east is sharp, the edge of the latter being marked by the strong Late Wisconsin terminal moraine. A zone of outwash plains and terraces at its western foot, ranging in width from zero to 6 miles, is assigned to the Driftless section. From the 43d parallel southwestward to the Mississippi River, this section borders the Till Plains. Here the contrast is much less obvious, the Illinoian[2] (or later) drift at this place being generally less than 10 feet thick and considerably eroded.

The delimitation of the Driftless Area from the Western Young Drift section and the Superior Upland involves some concessions

---

[1] U. S. Geol. Survey, 6*th Ann. Rept.*, p. 322, 1885. This explanation was probably given first by R. D. Irving, *Geol. Wis.*, vol. 2, pp. 632–634, 1877, and by N. H. Winchell, Geol. and Nat. Hist. Surv. Minn., 5*th Ann. Rept.*, p. 36, 1877.

[2] Leverett (U. S. Geol. Survey, *Mon.* 38) maps and describes this drift as "probable Illinoian," but finds later (personal communication) that much of the surface has an early Wisconsin cover. See also Alden (U. S. Geol. Survey, *Prof. Paper* 106, pp. 154–163).

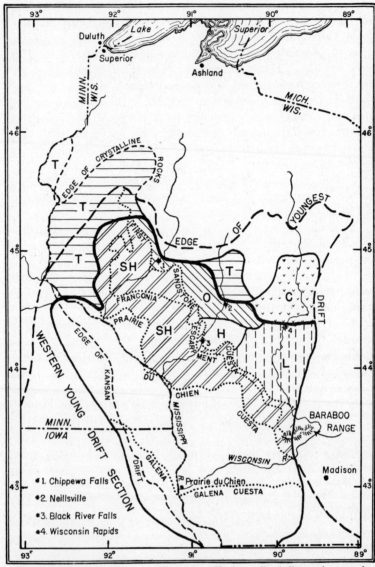

FIG. 145.—Sketch map of central Wisconsin. The heavy line indicates the somewhat arbitrary northern boundary of the Driftless section as treated here. The area marked *C*, underlain by crystalline rocks, is treated as a part of the Superior Upland despite the fact that it is driftless, or nearly so. Areas marked *T*, underlain by sandstone and thick drift, are included in the Superior Upland or Western Young Drift. The area marked *O*, included in the Driftless section, has very old, thin drift and outwash. *L* is the basin of Glacial Lake Wisconsin, containing monadnocks near the sandstone escarpment on the southwest. *H* is an expansion of the monadnock belt. *SH* is mainly sandstone hills, *i.e.*, dissected sandstone benches, thinly covered by old drift in its northern part. Dotted lines farther south show the much generalized Prairie du Chien and Galena escarpments. (*Generalized from Thwaites.*)

with respect to the literal use of the names and the strict application of the criteria by which the several divisions are defined. If the three names given above be used in a literal sense, the areas so designated will in some cases fail to meet and in other cases overlap. The boundary between the Driftless Area and the Western Young Drift is complicated by a fringe of old, and much eroded drift, which is here included in the Driftless section, thus extending it nearly 40 miles west of the Mississippi River on the Iowa-Minnesota boundary.[1] In northern Iowa the boundary thus located is not far from the northeast-facing escarpment of Silurian (Niagara) and Devonian limestone which, next to the Mississippi bluffs, is the most prominent topographic feature in northeastern Iowa.[2] The escarpment itself lies just within this section as thus defined.

The same principle is recognized in separating the Driftless Area from the Superior Upland. That province is so characteristically associated with the Pre-Cambrian rocks that it seems best to treat it somewhat liberally in order to cover the Pre-Cambrian terrane, especially where its topography is distinctive, even though the drift is thin and topographically negligible.[3] Areas of thick drift, whether young or old, are necessarily excluded from the Driftless section. The boundary here adopted is approximately that used by F. T. Thwaites.[4]

[1] For practical reasons it is better to include the narrow and ragged strip of Kansan drift in the section, which is like it topographically, than to show this strip as a slender and crooked peninsula of the Dissected Till Plains of southern Iowa. The latter plan might be more logical but would impair the geographic usefulness of such divisions. Fidelity to the facts is believed to be sufficiently observed by a plain statement of the difficulty.

[2] McGEE, W J, The Pleistocene History of Northeastern Iowa, U. S. Geol. Survey, 11*th Ann. Rept.*, pt. 1, pp. 199–577, 1889. McGee's statement that the Niagara escarpment for 100 miles forms the boundary of the Driftless Area, while not literally true, indicates the impression gained from the topography.

[3] This is one of the cases in which the effort to divide the country into physiographic units discovers odds and ends which are too small to be given coordinate rank in any workable scheme.

[4] THWAITES, F. T., personal communication. Roughly the same boundary is given in Thwaites' "Outline of Glacial Geology," Fig. 61, p. 97, 1935.

W. C. Alden is to be thanked for the use of unpublished data gathered by members of the U. S. Geology Survey, delineating the edge of the younger, presumably Wisconsin, drift. Samuel Weidman, the Geology of North Central Wisconsin, Wis. Geol. Nat. Hist. Survey, *Bull.* 16, 1907, gives

Underlying Rocks and Structure.—The surface of this area is carved on a substructure of hard and soft rocks dipping very gently to the southwest. The generalized column is as follows:

Rock Formations of the Driftless Area

Silurian:
  Niagara dolomite and limestone, at places very cherty. Maximum thickness in this section 220 feet.
Ordovician:
  Maquoketa (Richmond) shale, 200 feet, more or less.
  Galena dolomite, 200 to 250 feet.
  Platteville (Black River?) limestone and dolomite, 55 to 65 feet.
  St. Peter sandstone, very friable and variable in thickness, 30 to 175 feet.
  Prairie du Chien (Lower Magnesian) dolomite, generally siliceous, 150 to 250 feet thick.
Cambrian:
  Sandstones, generally weak but having at least two strong members. Maximum thickness, 1000 feet.
Pre-Cambrian:
  Crystalline rocks, igneous and metamorphic, all resistant.

Areal Description

Almost the entire section is a series of dissected cuestas whose trend is northwest-southeast. On its northeastern margin the Cambrian sandstone has been cut down to relatively low levels. The sandstone lowland is 50 miles wide in central Wisconsin, where it is traversed from north to south by the Wisconsin River. Its width decreases and its elevation increases toward the northwest. In central Wisconsin the northern limit of the sandstone plain is adopted as the boundary of the province. Toward the northwest, thick drift overlaps the Cambrian and is included in the Superior Upland. The rest of the sandstone plain is in part covered with thin, old, and much eroded drift, or with glacial outwash, and is here treated as part of the Driftless section.

At most places the flatness of the Cambrian lowland is enhanced by a mantle of unconsolidated, water-laid sediment which covers the sandstone except for isolated tracts and some steep hills. The material of this cover is lacustrine sediment and alluvium,

descriptions of the older drift which are still valuable though his classification and boundary lines must be altered.

some of it being glacial outwash. Swamp deposits cover a part of the surface.

Direct outwash of sand and gravel from the Wisconsin terminal moraine on the east is limited to a zone nowhere more than 6 miles wide, extending about 100 miles north from the Wisconsin River.[1] It consists in part of valley trains, but largely of outwash aprons, once smooth, now beginning to be dissected. The material of its surfaces ranges from barren sand to fertile loam. Outwash from the corresponding moraine farther north seems to have been carried away by streams instead of accumulating in aprons.

Glacial Lake Wisconsin.—A study of drainage and divides leads to the conclusion that the lowland for nearly 50 miles west of the Wisconsin terminal moraine was largely covered by a lake in the last glacial epoch. The preglacial Wisconsin River is believed to have been east of its present course[2] except near the Baraboo ranges, which it crossed in deep canyons (page 462). When these were closed by the Wisconsin glacier, the river must have flooded nearly 2000 square miles of lowland, giving rise to Glacial Lake Wisconsin.[3] The water rose until the lake overflowed to the Black River on the west, though its best known beaches were made later when the outlet was over the sandstone ridge at the Dalles of the Wisconsin.[4]

Sandstone Cuestas.—The lowlands described above are developed on the lower formations of the Cambrian sandstone, which have few resistant beds capable of protecting residual hills. There are, however, a few such beds, and remnants of these, either surviving to the present or having but recently disappeared, have caused very steep-sided, often flat-topped, hills to be preserved, some of them several hundred feet high (Fig. 146). In Western United States these would be called buttes or mesas. They now stand, isolated, on the gently rolling sandstone plain or rise above the flat surface of recent sediments. Throughout most of the plain they are widely scattered or absent, but toward the southwestern border of the plain, where higher Cambrian beds

[1] U. S. Geol. Survey, *Prof. Paper* 106, Pl. 3.

[2] ALDEN, *op. cit.*, pp. 110–111.

[3] CHAMBERLIN, T. C., "Geology of Wisconsin," vol. 1, p. 285, 1883. Chamberlin and Salisbury (*op. cit.*, 1885, p. 263) ascribe the smooth plain of aggradation to sediments in this lake.

[4] THWAITES, F. T., personal communication.

begin to form cuestas, such sharply defined outliers become increasingly abundant. The landscape here is unique in Eastern United States, the more so because of the prevalence of a soil that supports scattered jack pine and scrub oak instead of grass.

It might be supposed that isolated angular hills of the type described would constitute final evidence that a locality had not been overridden by glacial ice, yet such forms occur in the area of older drift where subaerial weathering has again become the dominant factor in shaping the hills. It is on this account that

Fig. 146.—A butte of Cambrian sandstone rising above Pleistocene deposits in the Driftless section.   (*Photograph by W. W. Atwood.*)

the margin of very old, thin drift is treated here as part of the Driftless section.

A detailed study of the dissected cuestas or "Hill Country" on the higher Cambrian formations southwest of the sandstone plain requires the recognition of the following formations, named in order from top to bottom:[1] Madison, Trempeleau, Mazomanie, Franconia, Dresbach, Eau Claire, Mt. Simon. Of these the fairly resistant Mazomanie or Upper Franconia makes a somewhat interrupted escarpment for nearly 200 miles (Fig. 145). It limited Glacial Lake Wisconsin on the west. In that latitude, lower benches are narrow, and represented mainly by outlying

[1] Martin, L., Wis. Geol. Nat. Hist. Survey, *Bull.* 36, p. 4, 1932.

hills. Farther north the Dresbach sandstone makes an intermediate, sharply dissected bench between the Franconia escarpment and the narrower lowland.[1] The similar Jordan (Upper Trempeleau) escarpment lies some miles back of the Franconia.

Dolomite Cuestas.—South and southwest of the Cambrian area is a series of three dolomite cuestas, ending with the Niagara at or near the section boundary. All three escarpments are prominent. Each cuesta has its dip slope, but it is important to note that these slopes are by no means as steep as the dips. Even in direction, the slope of the surface may deviate from the dip.[2]

The first cuesta is made by the Prairie du Chien dolomite, 150 to 250 feet thick where it passes beneath younger formations, but preserving only a fraction of that thickness in the escarpment. All beds are beveled by an undulating plateau surface, now youthfully to submaturely dissected. The larger creeks cut through the dolomite, even where it is thickest; so the relief is at least 200 to 300 feet, and reaches 500 feet near the great rivers. Valleys confined to the dolomite are narrow. Those that cut into the soft underlying sandstone tend to be rounded or flat-bottomed, while their sides are steep and the hills tabular unless narrowed to sharp ridges or points. Where the cutting is deep enough below the dolomite, valley walls are often terraced by the stronger members in the sandstone.

Elevations at the northern (or northeastern) edge of the rugged Prairie du Chien plateau are generally between 1250 and 1350 feet. There is a gradual decline of the summit level to the south and southwest amounting to 200 feet, more or less, before the base of the Galena escarpment is reached. Between these two boundaries the upland surface, the so-called dip slope, cuts across beds having a thickness of 100 to 200 feet.

A few miles south of the Wisconsin River, and at varying distances up to more than 30 miles west of the Mississippi, this rough plateau surface abuts against the escarpment that fronts the upland on the Galena dolomite. The thin and friable St. Peter sandstone and the soluble Platteville limestone generally

---

[1] For additional data see L. Martin, Rock Terraces in the Driftless Area of Wisconsin, abst., *Bull. Geol. Soc. Amer.*, vol. 28, pp. 148–149, 1917.

[2] TROWBRIDGE, A. C., The Erosional History of the Driftless Area, *Univ. Ia. Studies*, vol. 9, no. 3, p. 64, 1921.

appear in the slope, which is, at most places, a roughly dissected zone several miles wide. In Wisconsin the crest of this escarpment maintains a constant east-west direction 10 to 12 miles south of the Wisconsin River; also a fairly constant altitude between 1200 and 1300 feet. As it forms an important divide, the smooth crest, known as Military Ridge, has long been followed by highways and a railroad. Beyond the gorge of the Mississippi, the edge of the Galena bends to the northwest in Iowa and Minnesota, maintaining the same altitude.

The Galena upland is decidedly smoother than the Prairie du Chien. Some patches extending for miles are only mildly rolling. In general the surface is submaturely dissected, only the larger valleys being 300 feet deep in the north and 200 feet deep farther south. Tributaries head in the shallow, wide-open valleys of a former cycle. A little lower down, their courses are in narrow valleys with convex slopes, typical of rejuvenation. These forms are succeeded down stream by rounded bottoms and then by valley flats between bluffs. The Galena upland slopes southward for 50 miles, falling to an altitude of 900 feet at the foot of the Niagara escarpment in northern Illinois. The surface is not generally at the top of the Galena. That formation is partly cut away at the north, and is covered at the south and west by the Maquoketa shale. The dip is steeper than the slope, hence the surface bevels both formations. In Iowa and Minnesota the Galena cuesta is narrow and much dissected by tributaries to the Mississippi.[1]

Here and there on the Galena plain are small remnants of Niagara dolomite, which rise more or less abruptly 200 feet or more and are known as "mounds." Several of them are 300 feet high, and one of the Blue Mounds, near the east end of the Military Ridge, rises 1716 feet above sea level where the general level is 1300 feet. Some of the mounds, like the last-named, are capped by exceedingly siliceous beds of the Niagara formation. Their presence (along with other evidence) indicates that erosion in this entire region began its work at least as high as the top of the Niagara. The Niagara escarpment, in its retreat to the south, east, and west, has swept over the entire section, followed by its companions. There is no evidence that their movement

---

[1] For excellent descriptions see W J McGee, The Pleistocene History of Northeastern Iowa, U. S. Geol. Survey, 11*th Ann. Rept.*, pp. 199–577, 1889.

was ever faster than just now. This escarpment, with its northwestward extension of Devonian limestone in Minnesota, now stands approximately at the edge of the Driftless Area. Its height ranges from 60 to 150 feet, making the altitude of its crest 1000 feet or more, east of the Mississippi, and greater toward the northwest. The topography of its long back slope is rendered relatively smooth by a mantle of drift.

The Trench of the Mississippi.—The Mississippi River flows in an abrupt trench 200 to 600 feet deep, steep-walled and flat-floored, the flood plain being $1\frac{1}{4}$ to 7 miles wide. This plain declines from a level a little above 700 feet at the north to a little above 600 feet at the south. Its depth below the cuesta summits is therefore about 600 feet. North of the Wisconsin River, except for short stretches, the upland level of 1200 feet or more comes close to the bluffs. South of that, where the upland itself slopes south and the depth is less, the summits near the river are a little lower. There is some indication here that the gorge was cut in an old, shallow valley.

The real gorge in the rock is 150 to 210 feet deeper than it now appears, being filled to that depth with sand and gravel.[1] The Mississippi is like some other rivers of the region in having once cut a deep rock gorge, the bottom of which lies below its present grade.[2] Probably the region stood at a higher level during the cutting. This may or may not have been in preglacial time.[3] The Mississippi gorge was filled by outwash from the Wisconsin ice sheet to a depth 100 feet above the river near St. Paul, diminishing to 50 feet in northwestern Illinois. The terraces, 50 to 100 feet above the river, are what remains of the filling above the grade of the present river. They constitute only a minor part, but much the most valuable part, of the valley floor, and furnish the sites of its cities. Much the larger part of the valley floor is bottomland traversed by a maze of sloughs, among

---

[1] Figures taken from L. Martin, Gravel Terraces of the Mississippi River in Wisconsin, *Ann. Assoc. Amer. Geog.*, vol. 7, abs., p. 79, 1917. See also Martin's "Physical Geography of Wisconsin," p. 169, 1932.

[2] Valuable data on this subject are given by Leverett, Preglacial Valleys of the Mississippi and Its Tributaries, *Jour. Geol.*, vol. 3, pp. 740–763, 1895; also by H. M. Clem, The Preglacial Valleys of the Upper Mississippi and Its Eastern Tributaries, *Proc. Ind. Acad. Sci.*, 1910, pp. 335–352, 1911.

[3] The epoch of elevation is sometimes called Ozarkian and placed at the close of the Pliocene.

which the surface is largely swamp. Evidently the stream, embarrassed by its load, has from time to time shifted to the side of its trench, undercutting its bluffs and increasing their steepness.

Although the terraces indicate downcutting, there has been some later aggradation, which may still be in progress. This is indicated by low natural levees. At places the slope of the flood plain from the stream toward the bluffs is indicated by the fact that tributaries follow the foot of the bluff. The fall of the river for 150 miles north of Dubuque is only 4 inches per mile. Probably this gradient is too small to enable a stream of such moderate size to transport its load.

A little south of the Wisconsin-Illinois boundary, the bluffs are barely 1 mile apart. This is in or near the high edge of the Niagara cuesta. The trench widens downstream, also a little upstream, but not much within the limits of the Galena cuesta. From the mouth of the Wisconsin northward beyond La Crosse, the width increases to a maximum of 7 miles. This widening is related to the fact that the Cambrian sandstone at the south is not exposed above the river. The rise of the beds toward the north exposes more and more of the sandstone, making undercutting correspondingly easier.

Course of the Upper Mississippi.—The time and manner in which the Mississippi took its present course have not been finally determined. For the present, the course of the river below St. Paul may provisionally be treated merely as preglacial. The variation in width of the gorge has suggested various hypotheses of former divides,[1] the implication being that the drainage, crowded out of its old courses by the ice, followed older valleys, some down stream, some upstream, crossing divides where necessary. Variations in width and character of the gorge probably find sufficient explanation in the nature of the rocks crossed.[2] Assumptions of former northward flow along parts of the river's course remain unproved.

---

[1] HERSHEY, OSCAR H., The Physiographic Development of the Upper Mississippi Valley, *Amer. Geologist*, vol. 20, pp. 264–268, 1897. A. C. Trowbridge (The Erosional History of the Driftless Area, *Univ. Ia. Studies*, 1st ser., no. 40, 1921) outlines a possible evolution of the Mississippi, beginning with two streams in headwater opposition on an anticline running approximately east and west between La Crosse, Wis., and Winona, Minn.

[2] MARTIN, *op. cit.*, p. 145*ff*.

Trench of the Wisconsin.—The Wisconsin River flows west across this section, mainly through the Prairie du Chien upland, in a trench much like that of the Mississippi, averaging in depth 375 feet below the upland and 500 feet below the Military Ridge. The 12 mile slope from the latter to the river is one of the ruggedest tracts in Wisconsin. A striking feature of this trench is its regular decrease in width from nearly 5 miles at the east, where its old channel was deep in the Cambrian sandstone, to less than a mile at the west where the Prairie du Chien dolomite was never cut through. The narrowing of the valley toward its mouth is thus adequately explained. If the river ever flowed east, it was only for a short time when a very early ice sheet from the west may have obstructed its lower course (page 452). If the Wisconsin River in preglacial time followed its present course, it is highly probable that it joined a south-flowing Mississippi, and that its waters did not again turn north and return to the region from whence they came.

Like the Mississippi River, the Wisconsin cut a channel in the rock much below its present grade. Both trenches were, and still are, partly filled by late glacial outwash, but the Wisconsin has accomplished less in the removal of its filling than the Mississippi. Its valley floor has therefore a much larger proportion of terrace lands.[1]

Many tributary valleys of the Wisconsin and of the Mississippi have wide flats near the points where they enter the main valleys. These are at the same level, and continuous with, the late glacial terraces mentioned above. Those in the side valleys, however, are constructed, not of sand and gravel but of silt, often beautifully laminated.[2] The effect of aggradation by glacial outwash in the main valleys was to elevate the mouths of tributaries, reducing their gradient or even ponding the streams, thus inducing deposition of silt collected from their own basins.

Conditions were reversed in the making of Lake Pepin, a local widening of the Mississippi River, beginning 40 miles below St. Paul. For a distance of 22 miles the river is ponded, spread-

---

[1] MacClintock, Paul, The Pleistocene History of the Lower Wisconsin River, *Jour. Geol.*, vol. 30, pp. 673–689, 1922. This paper includes a valuable map and an interpretation of the order of events, but the interest is more in glacial history than in physiography.

[2] Chamberlin and Salisbury, *op. cit.*, p. 227.

ing to a maximum width of 2½ miles and having a maximum depth of 56 feet. The dam responsible for this ponding is a delta built by the Chippewa River when loaded with coarse gravel from the glacier at the northeast. This load could be carried on the relatively steep gradient of the tributary, but not by the less rapid waters of the main stream. The latter was aggrading its channel here as elsewhere, but not to the excessive height of the delta.

Interpretation of Topography

Cuestas or Peneplains.—An effort to interpret the geomorphology of the Driftless Area runs at once into the question of structural control *versus* erosional control. Those who emphasize the former call attention to the cuestas, each one obviously due to a strong formation; also to the difficulty of believing that there are just as many peneplains as strong formations, and similarly spaced. Both contentions must be admitted. Those who emphasize the control of base levels, rather than of hard rocks, point to the horizontal sky lines, the beveling of beds by the surface, and the unmistakable features of an old-age topography and rejuvenation; also the fact that surfaces so described are found at different levels within short distances. The truth of these observations cannot be questioned.

Emphasis on structural control has been pressed to the point of affirming that there is no proof of any former peneplain since the Pre-Cambrian, or that erosion has ever been halted since the land surface was first exposed.[1] Evidence of peneplains must of course be sought in facts, not in argument. Yet the probabilities are worth considering. It is commonly assumed that this area has been dry land ever since Niagaran time, perhaps 350 million years. Estimates of the total depth of erosion[2] are well within 1000 feet, being only a minor fraction of that amount in the southern part. The time allowance is at least ten times what has ever been allotted to the best post-Schooley peneplain. It is nearly twice as long as can possibly be allowed

---

[1] MARTIN, L., "The Physical Geography of Wisconsin," p. 72, 1932.

[2] TROWBRIDGE, A. C., *Univ. Ia. Studies*, vol. 9, p. 74, 1921. The paleographic maps in Chamberlin and Salisbury's "Geology," vol. 2, indicate the belief that no rocks younger than Silurian were ever deposited in this area.

for the Schooley itself, in which mountains were reduced to the best peneplain in Eastern United States. As for the region here considered, it would seem that, for much the greater part of 350 million years, the agents of erosion found little above base level to work on. It should be unnecessary to argue the case for past peneplanation in a region where the real problem is how it could escape being peneplaned 10 times over.

Relation of Prairie du Chien and Galena Cuestas.—The most prominent level is seen best on the Galena cuesta where considerable upland tracts, commonly called Lancaster peneplain, have very small relief. (The possibility of two peneplains is mentioned later.) Were the capacious Wisconsin valley filled, one might follow the same surface northward, as a state highway now does, on the rolling divide between the Mississippi and Kickapoo rivers almost to Sparta, a distance of more than 50 miles, never rising or falling more than 50 feet from the general level. The northern end of this strip, at an altitude of 1300 feet, is typical of the Prairie du Chien cuesta, as the southern end at 1200 feet is typical of the Galena cuesta. The stratigraphic horizon which is at the surface at the north is 580 feet below the surface at the southern end.[1] This strip is exceptional in that the softer formations between the Prairie du Chien and Galena here rise to the upland level, which bevels all impartially. Elsewhere these have been stripped away from the Prairie du Chien. Their edges are seen now at the foot of the Galena escarpment, and all are retreating together toward the south. A former peneplain is indicated by the higher, northeastern, margin of the Prairie du Chien, the similar Galena surface on the Military Ridge, and the crest of the Mississippi-Kickapoo divide. The sloping and dissected upland between the escarpments has been stripped.

Relation of Niagara and Galena Cuestas.—The southerly and southwesterly slope of the Galena cuesta has probably had much the same history as that of the Prairie du Chien, though being less high it is less deeply carved. Its forms are also less angular because of the nature of the rock and the absence of sapping. This surface declines southward to about 900 feet in northern Illinois where it begins to be lost among outlying patches of the Niagara escarpment, all flat-topped and, at this place, a little more than 1000 feet high. Altitudes here suggest a relation

[1] TROWBRIDGE, *op. cit.*, p. 72.

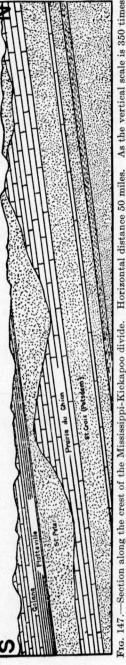

FIG. 147.—Section along the crest of the Mississippi-Kickapoo divide. Horizontal distance 50 miles. As the vertical scale is 350 times the horizontal it will be seen that the surface is a good peneplain.   (A. C. Troubridge, Univ. of Iowa Studies.)

between the Galena and Niagara cuestas similar to that between the Prairie du Chien and Galena, the same erosion surface covering both, and the weak Maquoketa shale being lowered or carried away by later erosion, just as the St. Peter sandstone and Platteville limestone were in the other case. There is no actual remnant of peneplain connecting the tops of the Galena and Niagara cuestas east of the Mississippi, as there is on the Kickapoo-Mississippi divide, almost connecting the Prairie du Chien and Galena cuestas. However, if the study is transferred to northeastern Iowa and southeastern Minnesota, an unbroken upland is seen to bevel the Galena and all higher formations. Its altitude here is 1300 feet, the east-facing Galena escarpment being about 100 feet high.[1] There can be no doubt of a peneplain on the Niagara in both of these localities.

The relatively low surface north of the Niagara cuesta is treated here as caused by later lowering of the peneplain which remains at the top of the cuestas. The fact that the sloping surface between Military Ridge and the Niagara cuesta bevels the beds from Middle Galena to upper Maquoketa has caused some to identify this surface with the peneplain and to assign the crest of the Niagara escarpment to an earlier cycle.[2] The view here

[1] Data taken from Oscar H. Hershey, The Physiographic Development of the Upper Mississippi Valley, *Amer. Geologist*, vol. 20, p. 253*ff*., 1897.

[2] HERSHEY, OSCAR H., Preglacial Erosion Cycles in Northwestern Illinois, *Amer.*

taken is that a strip of undetermined width south of Military Ridge does represent the Lancaster peneplain, eroded and somewhat lowered. South of that the Galena limestone was stripped of the overlying Maquoketa, but the stripping process was gradual and the part first exposed is cut down more. Beveling does not necessarily imply a surface that is contemporaneous throughout. Where stripping stops, the Maquoketa shale begins with a thin edge but thickens southward, as its dip carries it below the level of the present streams (Fig. 148).

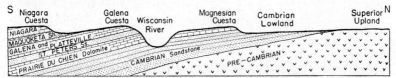

Fig. 148.—Diagram showing the relation of surface to bedding in the Driftless Area. A widespread peneplain, *S N*, truncated all beds. The present surface (heavy line) has been lowered a little on the strong beds and much on the weak beds since the peneplain was uplifted. Nowhere is the surface parallel to the bedding. The strong beds have been stripped for a longer time, and therefore more degraded, at points near the summit level than lower down. This causes the back slope of each cuesta to cut across the beds and thus to have a deceptive resemblance to an ordinary peneplain, tilted. (*Cf. Allegheny Plateau, Fig.* 81.)

Multiple Cycles.—If the above descriptions are essentially correct, it is a fair inference that all of the dolomite cuestas have been carved from a single peneplain of which the cuesta uplands are slightly altered remnants. The case is not seriously altered if these uplands themselves be regarded as a composite of two peneplains differing in elevation by about 200 feet.[1] The case is seriously altered, however, by regarding the back slopes of successive cuestas as successive peneplains. On the hypothesis of two peneplains the upper is called the Dodgeville and the lower surface the Lancaster. The Dodgeville peneplain is then correlated with the rather well-developed 1400-foot level on the Baraboo Mountains[2] and the Lancaster with the 1200-foot level

Geologist, vol. 18, p. 76, 1896. Hershey would project this Niagara peneplain northward over the tops of the mounds.

[1] TROWBRIDGE, A. C., The Erosional History of the Driftless Area, *Ia. Univ. Studies,* vol. 9, no. 3, 1921.

[2] Account must be taken of the possibility that the relatively flat benches on the Baraboo Range are due to wave erosion during burial by Paleozoic sediments. See F. T. Thwaites, Buried Pre-Cambrian of Wisconsin, *Bull., Geol. Soc. Amer.,* vol. 42, p. 745, 1931.

(page 466).   Those who recognize but one peneplain call it Lancaster and allow to it several hundred feet of residual relief.[1] This is the hypothesis provisionally adopted here.

Whether the differential erosion that made the relative lowlands and left the cuestas standing in relief should be regarded as the work of a separate cycle depends partly on how the word cycle is defined and partly on the illustration chosen.   It is not necessary to assume a succession of youth, maturity and old age in the degradation of the Maquoketa shales and the stripped Galena dolomite.   With a suitable rate of uplift the features of old age may never have been lost.   The same might be true of the lowland on Cambrian sandstone where it underlay the old peneplain.   In that case, however, the development of the Franconia, Prairie du Chien, and other cuestas was accompanied by extensive dissection which has now reached maturity.   That part of the lowland over which the innermost escarpment has retreated has necessarily passed through all the stages of an additional cycle.

The nature of the sloping surface between the crest of one escarpment and the foot of the next needs exact statement.   It is spoken of in one connection as a stripped surface, in another as beveling the beds.   The latter suggests a peneplain as the former suggests a structural bench.   The actual surface is neither of these in its simplest form, though having much in common with both.   These relations are pointed out in the explanation of Fig. 148.

HISTORICAL SUMMARY

Recorded physiographic history begins with general reduction to a surface of very low relief surmounted only by what is now the upper part of the Baraboo quartzite range, and by scattered mounds of resistant dolomite, some of them protected by chert. The outcropping edge of the main mass of Niagara dolomite (in Iowa) may have remained a little above the widespread level. If so, neither it nor the tops of the mounds are known to represent an older plain.   There may well have been repeated small uplifts, resulting in local peneplains at such small vertical intervals,

---

[1] GRANT, U. S., and E. F. BURCHARD, Lancaster-Mineral Point folio (No. 145), U. S. Geol. Survey, 1907.   The interpretation given in this folio is followed by W. C. Alden, U. S. Geol. Survey, *Prof. Paper* 106.

their remnants connected by such faint intervening slopes, that careful workers disagree on the number and extent of the surfaces and on the correlation of their remnants.

Following one or more uplifts of the surface thus described, a new cycle of erosion (with the reservations stated above) resulted in alternate lowlands and cuestas. A late preglacial uplift of 500 to 700 feet caused gorges to be cut in all larger valleys. The aggregate of all the erosion here described, following the general peneplain, developed the cuestas in their present form. Most of the work was accomplished before the first ice epoch, but there is some reason to think that tributary gorges were substantially increased later (*cf.* page 595, Leverett *vs.* Trowbridge).

The first glacier (Nebraskan?) covered much or most of this section west of the Mississippi. The age of the oldest drift on its northern border is in doubt. Its topographic effect has since been destroyed by erosion. The Wisconsin River was in its present course and aggraded its valley with outwash. A tongue of ice from a later glacier (probably Kansan) entered the Wisconsin Valley from the west. If the two great rivers were effectually dammed their combined waters must have been directed eastward in some unknown course. No records have been left of effectual damming, either here or farther down the Mississippi.

In one or more stages, glacial or interglacial, abundant alluvium was laid down on the lower parts of the Cambrian sandstone surface. During the Iowan stage a thick deposit of loess covered the area west of the Mississippi; also a strip east of the river, generally less than 10 miles wide. Farther east, the loess is thin or absent.

Down to the time of the Wisconsin ice invasion, stream gorges were probably deepening, at least intermittently. With the arrival of that ice sheet, carrying its great load of rock waste, the streams flowing from it were overloaded and proceeded to aggrade their channels to a maximum depth of about 300 feet, blocking the tributary valleys, which thereupon filled with sediment. During a part of the same time the ice in the Baraboo district stopped the flow of the Wisconsin River, giving rise to Glacial Lake Wisconsin.

With the disappearance of the ice and the excess load, there came to the streams renewed cutting power. The Mississippi has cleaned out most of the filling above its present level, leaving only a minor fraction as terraces. The Wisconsin has accomplished barely half as much. In both cases there remains a filling of several hundred feet below stream level. The fact that in these cases the gradient of the terraces is steeper than that of the stream is partly, if not wholly, explained by the ratio of water to sediment.

CHAPTER X

THE SUPERIOR UPLAND

Laurentian Upland.—This province is a part of the Laurentian Upland, one of the major divisions of the continent, essentially coextensive with the "Canadian Shield," an area of Pre-Cambrian rocks of all origins and histories, mainly crystalline and resistant, affected by great complexities of structure. Having become stable, it was worn down to a peneplain,[1] perfect in some parts, elsewhere approximate or very imperfect. A moderate rise of the surface occasioned some erosion, after which severe and repeated glaciation removed the mantle rock, destroyed drainage lines, and left the landscape with almost its present aspect except for vegetation, streams few and ungraded, lakes and swamps abundant. The most exceptional detail in this very general picture is a range of residual mountains on the northeast coast of Labrador.[2] There are other exceptional features, but the sameness throughout this vast area is far more impressive than the variation.

Boundaries.—When this vast Laurentian Upland becomes better known, it will no doubt be divided into provinces, one of which will be the Superior Upland. The term Superior Upland is applied here to that part of the Laurentian Upland which lies within the United States. How far it may extend in Canada is as yet undetermined. Its boundaries in the United States are necessarily conventionalized. Ideally the province should be restricted to Pre-Cambrian rocks, and its boundaries drawn accordingly. On its eastern side this criterion is followed so far as geologic boundaries can be determined where glacial drift is thick.

[1] WILSON, A. W. G., The Laurentian Peneplain, *Jour. Geol.*, vol. 11, pp. 615–667, 1903.

[2] DALY, R. A., The Geology of the Northeast Coast of Labrador, *Bull. Mus. Comp. Zool.*, vol. 38, pp. 205–270, 1902. Also, COLEMAN, A. P., Northeastern Peninsula of Labrador, Can. Geol. Survey, *Sum. Rept.*, 1916, 245–247.

In the northern peninsula of Michigan the line is made fairly clear by the greater altitude and relief of the crystalline surface. In Wisconsin the contrast is less, and the contact is so obscured by the drift cover that the line is indefinite.[1]

On the south the Superior Upland borders the Driftless Area. The impossibility of following any one criterion consistently in drawing the province boundary is explained on page 519. Glacial drift that is topographically significant is thrown into the Superior Upland, even where it rests on Cambrian rocks. A considerable area on Pre-Cambrian rocks is allotted to the same province despite the fact that the drift is so thin that the area has generally been believed to be unglaciated (see page 521). West of the meridian of St. Paul the glacial drift becomes so thick that the character of the underlying rock and the form of its surface lose their significance. Here the boundary between the Superior Upland and the Western Young Drift section is drawn arbitrarily (though still tentatively) along or near the 93d meridian.

Rocks.—The rocks which characterize this province are Pre-Cambrian, hence generally igneous or metamorphosed; hence also resistant, but by no means equally so. Interest in the rocks centers in their effect on topography. This in turn is dependent on two main characteristics, resistance to erosion and uniformity. With reference to the latter, the main distinction is between massive rocks and those which consist of beds, sills, and flows. In the main the massive rocks (or very thick and uniform sediments) underlie plateaus or local lowlands. Formations of diverse hardness make ridges and valleys. In the following table the rocks are grouped and characterized with respect to their effects on topography. The much generalized classification is consistent (not identical) with that shown on the new geologic map of the United States.[2]

---

[1] A comparison of older geologic maps with that of Wisconsin issued by the state in 1928 or with the new geologic map of the United States (1933) shows that the crystalline area has been greatly extended at the expense of the Cambrian. This indicates that the line of contact is not obvious. The map of Physical Divisions of the United States (U. S. Geol. Survey, 1930) is based on the older geologic maps. The line on Pl. 4 of this book follows the recent work of Thwaites. Where there is any contrast in the aspect of the surface on the two sides, it is probably nearer the old line than the new.

[2] U. S. Geol. Survey, 1933. This map is readily available and referenc.

Rocks Underlying the Superior Upland

Upper Cambrian: Sandstone with some thin shales; relatively soft and uniform.

Keweenawan sediments: Sandstone and conglomerate, less resistant than most of the formations but not uniformly soft.

Keweenawan intrusives: Mainly the great Duluth batholith of homogeneous gabbro; also acid intrusives which are harder.

Keweenawan extrusives: Often called trap rock, extensive flows of basic (and acid) lavas constituting a very thick mass.

Upper Huronian: Great masses of slate without much difference in hardness; some quartzites, iron formation, and volcanic rocks.

Middle and Lower Huronian: Metamorphosed sediments of varied character and resistance, including the greatest of the iron-bearing formations; also extensive granite intrusives.

Laurentian: Intrusive granite and gneiss. Subequal resistance is characteristic but not universal.

Keewatin: Basic extrusives commonly called "greenstone"; highly metamorphosed, largely schistose; unequally resistant.

The older members of this assemblage are very greatly deformed. Folds which must have reached mountain heights were peneplaned, probably more than once, before the unfolded sandstones were laid down. Some of the metamorphism could only be accomplished at depths of many thousand feet. The texture of the intrusive rocks also shows that it came to its present state under deep burial. The volume of rock eroded away since Paleozoic time began is vast indeed, but probably not large in proportion to that which was lost in periods represented by unconformities before Cambrian time. The geologic history of this region is, in truth, ancient history.

TOPOGRAPHY OF THE ROCK SURFACE

General Statement.—The present surface is a peneplain, varying in degree of perfection, but generally such that a hill or a group of hills, 200 or 300 feet high, is conspicuous and, if the district is inhabited, receives a name. Monadnocks above 400 feet are exceptional. Over the larger part of the area, postpeneplain valleys are (or were before glaciation) less than 200 feet deep, and dissection in this cycle was not complete. Some dis-

---

to it is essential to a clear understanding of this chapter. Some of the distinctions made here are based on the more detailed geologic map published as Pl. 1 in U. S. Geol. Survey, *Mon.* 52.

tricts are a little rougher, but in most places the combined relief, above and below the old base level, would probably range between 100 and 300 feet.[1] In the following descriptions the area referred to in each case can be identified by reference to the general geologic map of the United States.[2]

Northern Wisconsin.—The general description given above almost suffices for north Wisconsin. The rocks are mainly of the massive type, mostly granitic. Hence in most of the area the surface is plateaulike, its low, rounded hills and shallow valleys being without structural control. The horizon at the north is 1400 to 1500 feet high, but it declines toward the eastern and southern margins. A strip 20 miles wide and 40 miles long, bordering the Wisconsin River from Wausau to the southern boundary of the province, is exceptional in being almost free (where not wholly free) from glacial drift.[3] Its altitude declines from 1400 feet at Wausau to 1000 feet at Wisconsin Rapids at the south end, where its nearly flat surface is barely trenched by the Wisconsin River. At Wausau the river is entrenched more than 200 feet and the surface is dissected. Here Rib Hill, a quartzite monadnock, rises 550 feet above the general level. Its summit, 1950 feet above sea level, is approximately the highest point in Wisconsin. West of the Chippewa River is a hilly upland of Huronian quartzite, the Barron Hills, 25 miles long, reaching a height of 1770 feet.

Northern Michigan.—West of Marquette, Mich., are smaller districts underlain by massive rocks.[4] The surface of the

---

[1] MARTIN, L., The Geology of the Lake Superior Region, U. S. Geol. Survey, *Mon.* 52, pp. 85–116, 1911. On p. 89 Martin gives the local relief along certain lines, several of them in relatively rough districts.

[2] U. S. Geol. Survey, 1933. The map in U. S. Geol. Survey, *Mon.* 52, is desirable but not essential if the U. S. map is at hand. A more recent and authoritative map is published in U. S. Geol. Survey, *Prof. Paper* 184, 1935.

[3] See footnote, p. 521. The strip referred to is generally treated as belonging to the Driftless Area. A literal use of terms may require this, but its relation to the Superior Upland also needs to be recognized. The author follows F. T. Thwaites in choosing the latter course.

[4] The reader of this chapter should refer constantly to the geologic map of the United States. For descriptions of northern Michigan see F. Leverett, Surface Geology of the Northern Peninsula of Michigan, Mich. Geol. Survey, *Pub.* 7, 1911. While dealing mainly with the drift cover and largely with the Lake section, this bulletin gives data on general character of the upland. See also I. C. Russell, Surface Geology of Portions of Menominee,

upland here is 1400 to 1600 feet high, and its topography, as elsewhere on similar rocks, is much like that of northern Wisconsin except for local conditions of erosion. The granite near the shore of Lake Superior is sufficiently resistant to account for a group of once rounded or subdued hills, now dissected and called the Huron Mountains, whose highest summits are 1950 feet above the sea. The surface of the lake (local base level) is only 602 feet above the sea, hence the cutting power of streams is great, and the upland near the shore is carved into actual mountains. At no great distance inland sharp valleys disappear, and the surface on granite and slates alike is deeply drift-covered and of moderate relief. The tilted Huronian rocks of the great mining districts generally caused a ridge and valley topography.[1]

Northwestern Wisconsin.—The surface of northwestern Wisconsin and adjacent Minnesota must be considered in relation to its structure. Essentially, it is a northeast-southwest depression, a continuation of the western part of the Lake Superior basin. This depression is in part filled by what remains of an enormous series of Keweenawan lava flows. The remnant of this formation is a wide open trough, 40 or more miles in width, most dips being toward the northeast-southwest axis, marked approximately, but not accurately, by the St. Croix River.[2] Both edges of the trough are cuestas with outfacing scarps, the so-called "Douglas Range" on the northwest and the "Copper Range" on the southeast. In part these edges are known to represent fault scarps, but the drift is very thick and actual tracing is impossible. In the St. Croix quadrangle where the western limit is well known,[3] the general level is 1200 feet on the Keweenawan trap rock and 900 feet on the Cambrian sandstone. Over much of the upland

---

Dickinson and Iron Counties, Michigan, Mich. Geol. Survey, *Ann. Rept.*, 1906.

[1] Clements, J. M., H. L. Smyth, and W. S. Bayley, The Crystal Falls Iron-bearing District of Michigan, U. S. Geol. Survey, *Mon.* 36, 1899. See sections on Physiography, also on the Archean. Bayley, W. S., The Menominee Iron-bearing District of Michigan, U. S. Geol. Survey, *Mon.* 46, pp. 125*ff.*, 1904.

[2] Strong, Moses (ed. by T. C. Chamberlin), "Geology of Wisconsin," vol. 3, pp. 368–369, 1880. Discusses structural relations and history of the St. Croix River.

[3] Berkey, C. P., Geology of the St. Croix Dalles, *Amer. Geologist*, vol. 20, pp. 245–283, 1897; vol. 21, pp. 139–155 and 270–294, 1898.

on the tilted Keweenawan lavas, monoclinal ridges may be traced despite the covering of drift.[1]

For many miles both west and east of the Minnesota-Wisconsin boundary, the Douglas range[2] has a prominent northwest front, rising from 100 to 300 feet above a sandstone lowland that stretches southwestward from Duluth. Generally its dissected escarpment is a belt several miles wide. At its crest, 900 to 1000 feet A.T., and there only, are occasional severely glaciated outcrops of the Keweenawan rocks. South of Superior, Wis., it is a distinct cuesta with a smooth slope extending a few miles down the dip. Near the St. Croix River and parallel to it, several of the stronger beds (melaphyre) in the igneous mass make the so-called St. Croix Copper Range.[3]

Except for a few miles near the meridian of 92°30' the axis of the syncline is occupied by flat-lying sandstone or conglomerate of later age, Cambrian at the southwest, Keweenawan in the remainder. The latter includes much conglomerate and is by no means all weak. It makes the Bayfield Peninsula[4] (long. 91°) and the Apostle Islands which represent its drowned extension. The center of this peninsula is an upland 400 to 600 feet above the lake, the underlying rock being deeply buried beneath an interlobate moraine. Older maps show that it was long assumed to be trap rock, no doubt because of its altitude and because the escarpment of the Douglas Range is continuous around it and very near the shore.

From the St. Croix River northeastward to Keweenaw Point in Lake Superior, a distance of nearly 300 miles, the high south-eastern edge of the Keweenawan trap rock is known as the Copper Range. For 80 miles on and near the Wisconsin-Michigan boundary it is north of and parallel to the Penokee-Gogebic Range, a monoclinal ridge between monoclinal valleys, one of the great iron-mining districts of the province. The drainage in this ridge and valley zone suggests the Folded Appalachians. Transverse streams like the Montreal and the Bad River and Tylers Fork make rectangular turns, changing from transverse

[1] MARTIN, op. cit., p. 374.

[2] GRANT, U. S., Copper-bearing Rocks of Douglas County, Wisconsin, Wis. Geol. Nat. Hist. Survey, Bull. 6, pp. 6–8, 1901.

[3] GRANT, op. cit., Chap. 2 and Pl. 7.

[4] IRVING, R. D., "Geology of Wisconsin," vol. 3, pp. 69–70, 1880.

to longitudinal and back again after the manner of the Potomac and other Appalachian streams.[1]

Keweenaw Peninsula.—The synclinal trough described above broadens and deepens toward the northeast, where it is submerged, except for its upturned edges, beneath Lake Superior. The southeastern edge is the axis of the Keweenaw Peninsula, a continuation of the Copper Range, made by the same rocks, in the same structural relations as described above,[2] except that northwest dips here are very steep. Generally they exceed 45 degrees except at the ends of the peninsula. The overlying resistant sandstone and conglomerate help to make the range. The surface on the truncated edges of these hard rocks is a smooth plateau about 1350 feet high, barely notched by streams, except the few that flow across it from the lowland on the southeast. The broad passage occupied by a branch of Portage Lake, and containing the cities of Houghton and Hancock, probably carried a similar transverse stream until displaced by the glacier.

The escarpment of the Copper Range divides the Keweenaw Peninsula into an upland on the northwest and a lowland on the southeast, the latter being underlain by sandstone.[3] The narrow northern part of this lower plain, abutting against the escarpment, slopes down to Keweenaw Bay, southwest of which it extends for 60 miles with a width of nearly 20 miles. In this direction the plain rises, approaching, but not attaining, the altitude of the neighboring upland. The sandstone, being a younger formation, is preserved only by reason of down-warping and down-faulting. Keweenaw Bay is part of the evidence.

With an adjusted drainage system it might be expected that this lower surface on softer rock would be drained northeastward by a longitudinal stream. On the contrary, streams in its western half head directly into the escarpment and cross the highland

[1] IRVING, R. D., "Geology of Wisconsin," vol. 3, pp. 62–64, 1880. In this chapter Irving gives a valuable physiographic description of a rectangle 42 miles wide extending south from Lake Superior well into the "elevated interior" (1500 feet) of Northern Wisconsin.

[2] IRVING, R. D., and T. C. CHAMBERLIN, Observations on the Junction between the Eastern Sandstone and the Keweenawan Series, U. S. Geol. Survey, *Bull.* 23, 1885. See especially pp. 98*ff.* and Summary, p. 118.

[3] Shown on the geologic map of the United States (1932) as Cambrian. F. T. Thwaites (personal communication) states that most stratigraphers now agree that it is Upper Keweenawan.

of hard rock.   This of itself would indicate superposition, presumably on Paleozoic beds.   Remnants of formations as high as the Platteville have been found, and younger rocks may well have been present when the region last rose above the sea.

The Superior Lowland.—Extending southwest from Lake Superior is a noteworthy lowland, less than 20 miles wide, between the Douglas Range on the southeast and a similar escarpment on the northwest.   The latter is a continuation of the steep north shore of Lake Superior.   Between the opposing fault scarps is a downfaulted block of sandstone.   Between the head of the lake and the Bayfield Peninsula, the sandstone underlies a plain 5 to 10 miles wide, apparently flat, but actually rising from low cliffs at the water's edge to an altitude of 100 to 250 feet above the lake at the foot of the Douglas escarpment.   The flatness of this plain, as of all others around the western end of the lake, is enhanced by lake sediments (page 454) deposited when the adjacent escarpments were lake cliffs.   Streams crossing from the uplands have cut young, often terraced, valleys in this plain almost to the local base level.   From the head of the lake this same plain on a down-faulted block between hard rocks, extends with a width of 12 to 20 miles, far to the southwest, gradually rising until it reaches the general level.

Plateau North and West of Lake Superior.—West of the head of Lake Superior, northwest of the sandstone belt, is an area of 10,000 square miles underlain by very thick and fairly homogeneous Upper Huronian sediments, mainly the Virginia slate. Only the eastern third of this area, sometimes called the St. Louis Plain, is treated here as belonging to the Superior Upland, the remainder being so deeply covered by drift that the rock beneath is scarcely a factor in the topography.   Even in the eastern part, where there are occasional outcrops, the surface features are mainly glacial.   The same poorly drained upland, 1300 to 1400 feet high and of very moderate relief, an evident peneplain, extends from the escarpment on the south to the Giants (Mesabi) Range of the north.

East of the St. Louis Plain, extending north from the head of the lake, curving to the northeast and almost reaching the international boundary, is a strip 12 to 25 miles wide, underlain by the Duluth gabbro, a great homogeneous intrusive mass. Its peneplaned surface is a little higher (generally above 1500 feet) than that of the slates on the west, and probably a little less flat, but the southern half of this gabbro plateau differs little in quality from the St. Louis plain. However, the drift thins toward the northeast, and low rock hills and swells gradually become more numerous until, near the Canadian border, drift is almost wanting.[1] The relief, perhaps reduced by glacial erosion, is rarely more than 100 feet.

At its northeast end, near the Canadian boundary (Pigeon River) between the 90th and 91st meridians, the surface on the gabbro shares the extraordinary drainage pattern of the neighboring Gunflint district on Upper Huronian slates and dolerite sills.[2] Here is a most striking development of east-west monoclinal ridges and valleys, the latter marked by long narrow lakes. This was at one time ascribed to faults. In the area of sediments and included sills, all dipping strongly to the south, the fault hypothesis is unnecessary, since each monoclinal ridge is made by an outcropping sill, and the valleys are on slates. Yet the remarkable parallelism of lakes is just as well developed in the gabbro, though without the escarpments. Without faulting sufficient to produce lines of weakness the plan here is mysterious.[3]

South of the Gunflint district, between it and Lake Superior, are the Misquah Hills (2230 feet), perhaps the largest and highest group of monadnocks in the province. These and some ridges farther south are on a granitic belt bordering the gabbro on the southeast.[4] The 10- to 15-mile strip of southeast-dipping Keweenawan traps between the granites and the lake merges with the gabbro plateau at the south, and is distinguished from it only by a tendency to develop monoclinal ridges, several of which are pronounced. This district breaks off to the lake basin by the bold Duluth escarpment 400 to 800 feet high, no doubt a

---

[1] GRANT, U. S., Geol. Nat. Hist. Survey Minn., *Final Rept.*, vol. 4, pp. 434–435, 482, 492. The descriptions here cited begin at about long. 91°30′ and proceed eastward.

[2] CLEMENTS, J. M., The Vermilion Iron-bearing District of Minnesota, U. S. Geol. Survey, *Mon.* 45, p. 38, 1903.

[3] GRANT, *op. cit.*, p. 483. Grant here suggests that the "indistinct sheeted structure" of the gabbro with its low-angle southwest dip might possibly offer an explanation.

[4] Not distinguished on the U. S. geologic map but shown on Pl. 1 of U. S. Geol. Survey, *Mon.* 52.

fault scarp. It continues southwestward beyond the head of the lake, between the St. Louis plain and the sandstone lowland.

Mesabi and Vermilion Iron Districts.—The Mesabi, or Giants Range, the largest in the province and the site of the greatest iron mines in the world, is a more or less continuous ridge 100 miles long but varying in altitude, on the northwestern boundary of the slate and gabbro plateaus.[1] At its highest it rises 500 feet above the plains on either side, *i.e.*, to 1900 feet. Its location on the geologic map is indicated by the contact of the Upper Huronian and the intrusive granite on the north. Generally its broadly rounded crest (locally a level upland) is on the granite. At places a quartzitic bed of the iron formation makes the main crest. The structural reason for the existence of this range is not wholly clear, except that the Huronian iron formation dips gently south from the granite. This is sufficient to account for monoclinal ridges on its hard members.[2]

Like other ranges of the province, the Mesabi is crossed by both water gaps and wind gaps, suggesting superposition of streams on former Paleozoic sediments. Martin finds the wind gaps to be produced by capture in the course of adjustment, just as in the Appalachian Ridge and Valley province.

The eastern part of the Mesabi range is the southern border of the Vermilion iron-bearing district.[3] This is a belt of folded rocks 5 to 10 miles wide, stretching from west of Vermilion Lake (long. 92°30′) east-northeast to the Canadian boundary, 80 miles within the United States. Uplands on massive granites bound it on the north and extend to Rainy Lake and Rainy River on the international boundary. The rocks of the belt itself are stratified, mainly metamorphosed Huronian sediments and Ely greenstone, *i.e.*, Keewatin lavas. Close folding (no doubt, mak-

[1] For data and discussion see C. K. Leith, The Mesabi Iron-bearing District of Minnesota, U. S. Geol. Survey, *Mon.* 43, 1903; J. M. Clements, The Vermilion Iron-bearing District of Minnesota, U. S. Geol. Survey, *Mon.* 45, 1903.

[2] L. Martin (U. S. Geol. Survey, *Mon.* 52, pp. 103–105) discusses the question whether the structure as a whole is to be accounted for by folding or by upfaulting of the granite on the north, or by the intrusion of a distinct younger sill of stronger granite whose outcropping edge forms the main range.

[3] For maps and description of topography see J. M. Clements, *op. cit.*, pp. 34–46 and 431–436

ing mountains) and later base-leveling, followed by uplift and subsequent erosion, have made this belt one of ridges and valleys, the former 1600 to 1700 feet high and surmounted by a few monadnocks. The broader valleys, 250 to 350 feet below the hilltops, are local lowlands in which lakes are numerous and extensive.

The description of districts of deformed strata in terms of ridges and valleys, the product of two cycles of erosion, should not convey the idea that those features are as straight, continuous, or clean-cut as in the Appalachians. Generally they are short, and some are knobs rather than ridges. Their average trend is that of the belt, but continuity and parallelism must not be taken too strictly. Still, the elongation of the lakes in such districts is in strong contrast with the apparently fortuitous outlines on the neighboring granites and on the gabbro plateaus.

GLACIATION AND ITS EFFECTS

Lobes and Their Movements.—The Superior Upland has been repeatedly glaciated but the obvious work of ice is that of the last or Wisconsin glacial stage. Even this is not the work of a single sheet. The ice of that stage came from three distinct centers, advancing at different times and in different directions, and developing lobes of different pattern. Some of the lobes may be inferred from Fig. 155, page 571. The three centers of accumulation were respectively east, south, and west of Hudson Bay. The ice moved southwestward to this region from Labrador, south from Patricia, and southeast from the Keewatin district. The accumulation of continental ice progressed from east to west; at least the maximum extent of ice from the several centers followed that order. In the first two of five Wisconsin substages[1] Labrador contributed ice to central Illinois and southern Ohio. Subsequent advances of the ice from the several centers are indicated on Fig. 133.

Much the larger part of this province belongs to the domain of the Labrador ice cap. In its southwestward advance it parted in northern Michigan into two main streams. One moving south embraced the Green Bay and Lake Michigan lobes.

[1] LEVERETT, F., Moraines and Shorelines of the Lake Superior Region, U. S. Geol. Survey, *Prof. Paper* 154, pp. 1–72, 1928. See especially Fig. 5, p. 19.

The other moving westward through the Superior basin over-spread its southern rim, subdividing into minor lobes separated by the Keweenaw and Bayfield peninsulas.

In the matter of ice movements the most important topo-graphic feature south of Lake Superior was the eastern edge of the highland. Next in effectiveness was the Bayfield peninsula. Between these the ice spread southward to near the 45th parallel not far from the limit of the province, where it built a complex terminal moraine known as the St. Croix morainic system.[1] The ice between the limits named has generally been known as the Chippewa lobe, but its eastern part, *i.e.*, southeast of the Keweenaw peninsula, was the more or less independent Keweenaw lobe.

At a late stage a decided southeastward advance from the Keewatin center brought the ice to central Iowa (page 570). In the Superior Upland it overlapped the drift of earlier stages, generally leaving a thin veneer of gray drift on the thick red drift which had come mainly from the Superior basin (Fig. 155, page 571). At places the older terminal moraines composed of drift from the northeast were overridden by the western ice and covered with the thin newer drift without losing their relief.

Thickness of Drift.—In most of the province the glacial and glaciofluvial deposits are so thick as to control the details of topography and to give character to the drainage. Some of the higher hills or groups of hills owe their relief to the rock surface, but even among them the drift at places is deep. So also the ridges on Keweenawan trap and other bedded rocks represent preglacial forms, only partially (or not at all) obscured. An exceptional and remarkable area in northeastern Minnesota, north of the Vermilion Range, though strongly glaciated, was left almost driftless when the ice melted. This statement applies to the basin of Rainy River on both sides of the international boundary. Toward the west the bare rock district broadens and includes most of the granite area north and northwest of Vermilion Lake.[2]

Moraines.—The location of major belts of terminal moraine may be inferred from the above description of lobes. There are

[1] U. S. Geol. Survey, *Prof. Paper* 154, Pl. 1.

[2] WINCHELL, N. H., "Geology of Minnesota," vol. 1, pp. 116, 131, 134, 1884.

also many recessional moraines, but the distribution of marginal ridges is often irregular and patchy.[1] Their characteristic topography is at places remarkably developed, as for example in the interlobate area on the Bayfield peninsula. Here, and on the upland southwest of it, knobs and kettles may cause a relief of 100 feet. Large areas of outwash are interspersed.

Drainage.—The drainage, no doubt perfect and approximately adjusted in preglacial time, is typically that of a thick young drift sheet on a plain of no great relief. The narrow zone of old drift on the southern margin and the two districts of extremely thin and scattered drift are excluded from this generalization. Streams are consequent on the surface left by the ice. In pattern they seem to be entirely fortuitous, making unaccountable and unpredictable turns. In profile they are wholly ungraded. In number, they are few, since tributaries have had little time to develop. Lakes in a single county may be numbered by the hundred, and swamps measured by the mile if not by the township. Between these areas of stagnation, streams may flow in rapids and cascades, revealing their lack of adjustment to the rock surface on which they have been superposed. A few of the larger streams, like the Wisconsin, the St. Croix, and the upper part of the St. Louis, may correspond roughly to preglacial streams in the same general territory. In a sense they may have found their old valleys but not their old courses, and still less their old channels.

Lake Districts.—Lakes, while not wanting in any considerable area, are closely crowded in three districts. One of these includes the upper basin of the Wisconsin River, centering in Vilas and Oneida Counties, Wisconsin.[2] The northern part of this district lies in the broad rough terminal moraine of the latest Superior lobe.[3] Its eastern part, and perhaps the whole district, is in the lee of the Keweenaw peninsula, in a belt where the Keweenaw and Chippewa lobes built their marginal moraines.[4] Most of the

---

[1] All surface deposits in the northern part of the province are shown on Leverett's map. U. S. Geol. Survey, *Prof. Paper* 154, Pl. 1.

[2] THWAITES, F. T., Glacial Geology of Part of Vilas County, Wisconsin, *Trans. Wis. Acad. Sci. Art and Letters*, vol. 24, pp. 109–125, 1929.

[3] U. S. Geol. Survey, *Prof. Paper* 154, pl. 1.

[4] WHITSON, A. R., and T. J. DUNNEWALD, Soil Survey of Vilas and Portions of Adjoining Counties, Wisconsin, Wis. Geol. Nat. Hist. Survey, *Bull.* 43, 1915. See also Soil Maps accompanying *Bulls.* 47–50, North Part of

lakes, however, occupy basins in extensive outwash plains, made
by the burial and later melting of ice blocks.

Another district abounding in small lakes is in western Wisconsin between the St. Croix moraine and the St. Croix River,
extending west and southwest of the latter into Minnesota.
There is ample opportunity here for small lakes in the hollows of

Fig. 149.—Whitefish Bay, Lake of the Woods. The horizon indicates a
peneplain on strong Pre-Cambrian rocks of complex structure and, no doubt,
former strong relief.   The lake is in a preglacial valley, obstructed but not filled
by drift.   (*U. S. Geol. Survey.*)

the main moraine and the recessionals.   Here again many, if not
most, of the basins are found in outwash plains, generally in
front of recessional moraines.   The several types are well illustrated in the St. Croix Dalles quadrangle.[1]   The eastern part of
this district is in the belt where the Chippewa and Superior
lobes came together, and across which they faced each other in
melting away.

The third conspicuous lake district is in northeastern Minnesota, strangely enough in that part where drift is almost
wanting.   The remarkable assemblage of rock basins, elongated
in an east-west direction, has already been mentioned on page

North Central Wisconsin.

[1] CHAMBERLIN, R. T., Glacial Features of the St. Croix Dalles, *Jour. Geol.*,
vol. 13, pp. 238–256, 1905.

545. The presence of the lakes shows that enough drift is present to obstruct the preglacial valleys at intervals and to force the drainage into new channels.

HISTORY OF LAKE SUPERIOR

The manner in which the great Pleistocene lakes came into being is explained on page 487. When the last Superior lobe had its maximum extent, 60 miles southwest from Duluth, its front was on ground sloping toward the Mississippi. A retreat of 25 miles uncovered the Mississippi-St. Lawrence divide. Then water began to stand between the divide and the ice, rising to the level of the former and overflowing to the Kettle River, a tributary of the St. Croix, and thus to the Mississippi. Even before the disappearance of the ice from the western end of the basin, streams entering the trough from the highlands were ponded. Thus the valleys of the St. Louis River from the north and the Nemadji, Brule, and Ontonagon from the south became the sites of temporary lakes at independent levels.[1] The St. Louis Lake must have been in large part obliterated by the encroachment of the Keewatin ice from the northwest which forced it to discharge southeastward along the present course of the river.

The drainage pattern of the St. Louis basin is peculiar. Its long tributaries from the northeast are in line with the Mississippi to the southwest. The transverse direction of the main stream and its steep descent to the Superior trough strongly suggest capture.[2] If this ever occurred, it must have been in preglacial time. Leverett believes that no evidence of such capture has yet been found. Though the preglacial course was probably to the Mississippi, the only change thus far positively demonstrated was incident to glaciation.

The lake which formed in the main trough and gradually replaced the shrinking Superior lobe is known as Lake Duluth. As the ice melted back from headlands, all of the marginal lakes merged and covered the present shores to a point east of Keweenaw Point. The highest shore line is 425 feet above the

[1] U. S. Geol. Survey, *Prof. Paper* 154, pp. 54–57; also references on p. 490 of this book.

[2] MARTIN, L., Physical Geography of Wisconsin, Wis. Geol. Nat. Hist. Survey, *Bull.* 36, p. 438, 1932.

present lake at the west end, but later rising of the continent at the northeast has caused the old shores to rise in that direction. Where these beaches run at right angles to the isobases their tilt is a little more than 2 feet per mile.[1]

The outlet of Lake Duluth was always to the St. Croix River, first by way of the Kettle River at the extreme end of the lake, then over the divide between the heads of the Brule and St. Croix rivers (Pl. 4). When the ice front in its retreat reached the 88th meridian, water began to spill from Lake Duluth to Lake Chicago along the edge of the ice. By degrees (marked by repeated shore lines) the level of the former fell to that of the latter and the two were merged. It was probably later that the Straits of Mackinac were cleared of ice and these waters joined Lake Algonquin (page 498).

RÉSUMÉ OF HISTORY

Pre-Cambrian Peneplain.—That the Superior Upland is essentially a peneplain is beyond doubt. The surface that it now presents may have been developed in Pre-Cambrian time, buried and exhumed, but so sweeping a generalization is uncertain. It may be affirmed with certainty that the flat southern margin described on page 540 was peneplaned before Upper Cambrian time.[2] No doubt its relief was still further reduced by wave erosion during the incursion of the Upper Cambrian sea. So far as the crystalline surface at this place is not yet maturely dissected, it may be regarded as the denuded part of a peneplain that underlies the Cambrian. Its southward slope of 10 feet per mile is uninterrupted as it passes beneath the Cambrian sediments. The same is true on the east side, though in both cases the gradient increases with distance.[3] Remnants of Cambrian sandstone are found resting on the plain as far as 35 miles from

---

[1] LEVERETT, F., U. S. Geol. Survey, *Prof. Paper* 154, pp. 61–63.

[2] WEIDMAN, S., The Pre-Potsdam Peneplain of the Pre-Cambrian of North-central Wisconsin, *Jour. Geol.*, vol. 11, pp. 289–313, 1903; also Wis. Survey, *Bull.* 16, 1907.

[3] For more accurate data see F. T. Thwaites, Buried Pre-Cambrian of Wisconsin, *Bull. Geol. Soc. Amer.*, vol. 42, pp. 719–750, 1931. His Fig. 1 on p. 729 is a contour map showing steeper slopes south and west of Madison and very much steeper slopes toward the east. See also "Guide Book," 9th Ann. Conf., Kans. Geol. Soc., map opp. p. 354, 1935.

the southern edge and 20 miles from the eastern edge in Michigan.[1]

Conditions nearer the center of the province at the time that the marginal peneplain was being submerged and buried are

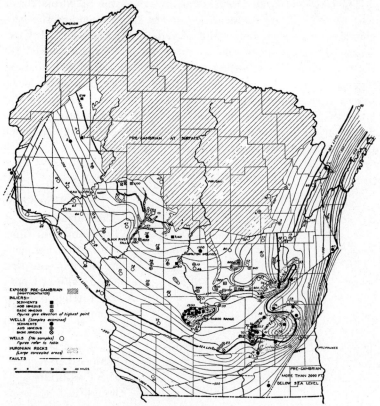

Fig. 150.—Depth of buried Pre-Cambrian peneplain (one or more) in Wisconsin, shown by 100-foot contours. Contours at sea level and 1000 feet above and below sea level are heavy. (*Thwaites, Geol. Soc. Amer. Bull., vol.* 42.)

poorly known. With the probability that the sandstone around Keweenaw Bay is Pre-Cambrian (page 543), the Paleozoic sea is not known to have reached the central part of the province until Middle Ordovician time. Quite probably it then submerged a peneplain, the age of which can only be said to be pre-Platteville. Hence, if the assumption is made that the entire

[1] BAYLEY, W. S., U. S. Geol. Survey, *Mon.* 46, pp. 125–129, 1904; also map in Menominee special folio (No. 62).

province is ancient peneplain stripped of later sediments, it is not to be understood that events throughout the entire area were necessarily simultaneous.

Burial and Stripping.—After submergence, the Superior Upland was covered to an unknown extent by Paleozoic rocks. The total possible covering is limited to formations which in southern Wisconsin have an aggregate thickness of not over 1000 feet, but the lower ones of these formations are known not to have covered (at least not entirely) the flanks of the Lake Superior trough. The Niagara formation at the top of the series certainly extended much farther than at present, but how far is not known. Apparently no part of this province has been denuded of more than 1000 feet of sedimentary rocks, and some parts have lost only a fraction of that amount.

On any credible supposition at least 300 million years have been available for the wearing away of the very moderate sedimentary cover described above. Obviously erosion must have been slowed down or resting for a large part of the time (*cf.* page 530) unless the Pre-Cambrian rocks themselves were decidedly elevated and worn down again.

To speak of the present surface as a Pre-Cambrian peneplain (with the reservations mentioned above) implies that the later erosion which carried away the Paleozoic rocks stopped when the older surface was reached. That rocks of Middle Ordovician age are preserved in fragments near Lake Superior might seem to indicate that such was the case, but it is known that warping and settling of the Superior basin was going on during and after the deposition of the Paleozoic rocks;[1] hence other parts may have been raised higher and lost more by erosion. That the southward slope of the well preserved Pre-Cambrian peneplain on the southern margin gives way to a gentler slope farther north may indicate that the upraised dome in the Pre-Cambrian surface was truncated by a later peneplain.

Possible Later Peneplain.—In 1896 Van Hise[2] discussed the Superior peneplain and tentatively assigned its development to the Cretaceous period. This seems to have been suggested by

[1] THWAITES, F. T., "Guide Book," 9th Ann. Conf., Kans. Geol. Soc., p. 225, 1935.

[2] VAN HISE, C. R., A Central Wisconsin Base-level, *Science*, vol. 4, pp. 57–59, 1896; A Northern Michigan Base-level, *ibid.*, pp. 217–220.

the fact that Upper Cretaceous sediments in Minnesota rest on what seems to be an extension of this same surface; probably also by the custom prevalent at that time of calling the Schooley peneplain Cretaceous.

No doubt the domed surface was always flatter on the top than around the edges, but it is also true that its higher interior has had abundant time to be reduced a second time if it was ever raised higher than the margin. A supposition in favor of such truncation is created by the gradation from youth on the recently stripped margin to greater advancement in the cycle farther north; also by the flattening of the slope remote from the margin. It is but natural to expect that, if there was a domed uplift, followed by stripping (the common assumption), the center has been exposed longer than the margins and should have made still further advancement in the post-stripping cycle.

It may well be that the larger part of the surface has been cut down considerably below the level of the once buried peneplain. This may have been accomplished in a clearly defined cycle ending in a new peneplain in Cretaceous or Tertiary time. On the other hand, the uplift may have been so slow or by such small increments that the old-age topography of the ancient surface was never lost.[1] In that case, some would prefer to call the present peneplain Pre-Cambrian, while others would give it a new name. Probably it is best designated merely as the Superior peneplain, a name that is noncommital as to age. However close the relation of the Superior peneplain to an older surface may be, it is safe to assume that the present upland surface was an integral part of a vast peneplain which in Tertiary time covered most of the interior of the United States.

Basin of Lake Superior.—While peneplains, either ancient or modern, were being made, the basin of Lake Superior (unless filled with water) must have been so shallow that streams entering it had no cutting power. As lakes are not known to have existed before the Pleistocene, the Superior basin in Tertiary time was probably near the general level, being in part graded down to the peneplain and in part graded up by the waste from higher parts. That the deep basin is very young is evident from the very limited extent to which the upland near its shores is dissected.

[1] *Cf.* Allegheny Plateau, p. 295, also the author's paper on Cyclic and Non-cyclic Aspects of Erosion, *Bull. Geol. Soc. Amer.*, vol. 47, 1936.

Its origin is due to relatively recent differential erosion, the conditions for which in the western half of the basin were as follows:

A Pre-Cambrian synclinal basin was partly or wholly filled with Keweenawan and Paleozoic rocks, largely nonresistant sediments. Owing to lateral pressure, the southeastern edge of

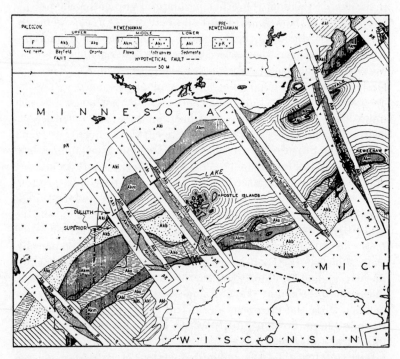

F<small>IG</small>. 151.—Structure of the Lake Superior Basin.   (*F. T. Thwaites, 9th Ann. Field Conference, Kans. Geol. Survey.*)

the trough was turned up along the great thrust fault that runs the length of the Copper Range (Fig. 151).   Either at the same time or later, the western end of the basin was dropped down as a graben between the Superior fault (Douglas Range) on the southeast and the Duluth fault (north shore) on the northwest.[1] Peneplaning, submergence, and burial ensued; then followed stripping, which resulted in a later peneplain which was not

[1] For origin of Lake Superior basin, see F. T. Thwaites, Sandstones of the Wisconsin Coast of Lake Superior, Wis. Geol. Nat. Hist. Survey, *Bull.* 25, 1912.

very different from the present upland surface, and which may (or may not) be essentially the same as the pre-Paleozoic peneplain. Soft rocks were thus left exposed in a zone stretching from east central Minnesota northeastward past Keweenaw Point. At the southwest this zone had two prongs, one of them in the main syncline, the other in a lateral graben on the northwest. East of Keweenaw Point the belt of soft rocks seems to have been bordered on the southeast by the retreating dolomite escarpments, just as the eastern end of the lake basin is today.

Uplift of the last peneplain at some time in the Tertiary (probably late) made possible the carving of preglacial valleys in the upland, the reduction of the soft rocks to lowlands, and the appearance of the present escarpments. It is not inconsistent with the picture here given to assume that a master stream followed the Superior basin throughout the long erosional history of the region. Flowing, as it must have done, on soft rocks, the valley cut by such a large stream in the last preglacial erosion cycle might well have been considerably deeper and certainly much wider than the late preglacial valleys now observed in the hard rocks of the upland. But the maximum depth attributable to stream erosion must have been far less than that of the present basin, which is 1290 feet below the lake level and 690 feet below sea level. The rest must be ascribed mainly to glacial erosion unless an improbable amount and kind of crustal warping be assumed.[1] If the preglacial basin had anything like its present depth, streams flowing into it would have carved valleys quite unlike those observed.

With reference to the mooted question of extensive glacial erosion, the case of Lake Superior is similar to that of the other Great Lakes (page 487). The argument for glacial erosion is, in part, based on the difficulties involved in accounting for the basin in any other way. Positive evidence is found in the great amount of red sandy drift deposited by the ice after moving over this area. The character of this drift has generally been accounted for by referring its origin to the red sandstone derived from the basin.

---

[1] The possibilities of crustal movements are discussed by F. T. Thwaites on pp. 226 and 227 of the "Guide Book" already cited. His Fig. 192 is a new topographic map of the bottom of Lake Superior, showing remarkable subdivision into minor basins.

Southwestward tilting of the shore of Lake Duluth in post-glacial time amounts to about 250 feet within the limits of Minnesota, but only a fraction of that amount has occurred since the ice ceased to hold up the lake level.   Only at or very near the shore does this tilting affect the topography.   At the head of the lake the water is rising on the shore and the lower course of the St. Louis River has become an estuary.[1]   This end of the lake, excluded from the sweep of shore currents, is now cut off by a superb bar, behind which are the harbors of Duluth and Superior.

[1] *Cf.* TAYLOR, F. B., Submerged Peat Beds among the Apostle Islands, *Science*, vol. 74, pp. 265–267, 1931.

CHAPTER XI

CENTRAL LOWLAND WEST OF THE MISSISSIPPI

WESTERN YOUNG DRIFT SECTION

Boundaries and Distinguishing Features.—A large area in Minnesota and the Dakotas, and extending south into Iowa, has much in common with the Great Lake section. Its distinguishing features are those of young glacial drift. This is the Western Young Drift section of the Central Lowland province. It extends west to the boundary of the province, which is located at the foot of a distinct rise of 300 to 600 feet.

Beyond this boundary lies the higher Missouri Plateau, embraced in the Great Plains province. The younger drift transcends this limit, extending about to the Missouri River in the southern part and to the Rocky Mountains farther north. South of the Young Drift section are the Dissected Till Plains, whose almost or quite mature drainage readily distinguishes them from the young surface to the north. The topography of the Superior Upland on the east is affected by the relief of the underlying rock surface. In the section here considered the contours of the bedrock-surface influence the forms of the landscape at only a few widely separated places, though the general slope and altitude are thus controlled.

Underlying Rocks.—The Pre-Cambrian rocks of this section are those of the Superior Upland, sufficiently described on page 538. At only a very few places do they require mention in connection with topography. Most of the Paleozoic rocks have been described (pages 522 to 526) in treating the Driftless Area of Wisconsin. Above the Niagara dolomite, the highest there described, come Devonian rocks, mainly limestone, then Mississippian limestones and a small area of Pennsylvanian shale and sandstone. All of these occur near the eastern margin only, and are well buried by glacial drift. Most of the area in the Dakotas, and a third of it in Minnesota and Iowa, is underlain by Cretaceous rocks, mainly shale. The important water-bearing

559

Dakota sandstone is found at the base of the Cretaceous.   The
Niobrara limestone underlies the drift in southeastern South
Dakota.   Fox Hills sandstone, near the top of the Cretaceous, is
preserved on a few old divides near the western boundary.   Overlying the Cretaceous beds in the Turtle Mountains is the Fort
Union (oldest Tertiary) formation, largely sandstone, decidedly
more resistant than the Cretaceous shales.   Over all is the glacial
drift, and over large areas are fine sediments deposited in
Pleistocene lakes, described below.

The Rock Surface in Minnesota and Iowa.—Comparative
altitudes in different parts of the section, hence also general
slopes, are, in the main, features of the preglacial topography.
An area around Itasca Lake (source of the Mississippi) northwest
of central Minnesota is 1500 to 1600 feet high, and a center from
which streams radiate.   The drift is very thick but, with little
doubt, this small area is part of a larger one extending south more
than 100 miles to the Leaf Hills, from which the rock floor
declines gently toward the north, west, and south; probably also
to the east.   Occasional exposures of granite or other rock in the
midst of deep drift show that the rock surface is not a perfect
plain.   Probably it is comparable with the smoother plateaus
of the Superior Upland (page 544).   Near the latter there is a
slow rise in the general level.

The southward decline of the rock floor extends to the Minnesota River.[1]   It is less than 800 feet above the sea at Mankato
on the 94th meridian, where the river turns sharply to the
north.   The river itself is entrenched approximately 200 feet
below the present land surface, and the channel in much of its
course is below the prevailing level of rock.   The level continues
low along the northeast course of the river to St. Paul, but
rises southeastward to 1200 or 1300 feet in southeastern Minnesota where the surface on the drift is at one place above 1400
feet.   Regional contours in southern Minnesota are roughly
parallel to the Minnesota River, bending sharply to the south as
they cross the valley of its southern tributary, the Blue Earth

[1] A good contour map (interval 100 feet) of southern Minnesota by O. E.
Meinzer is published as Plate 1 of U. S. Geol. Survey, *Water Supply Paper*
256, 1910.   A much generalized contour map of Minnesota (contour interval
250 feet) is found opposite page 8 of C. W. Hall's "Geography and Geology
of Minnesota," Minneapolis, 1903.

River. In this wide depression both the surface of the ground and that of bed rock rise southward, the latter probably to a maximum of about 1100 feet near the Minnesota-Iowa boundary. Farther south the rock surface takes the form of a wide trough declining southward. Its axis extends from the middle of the northern boundary to the southeast corner of Iowa[1] (see Drainage, page 601).

That the bedrock surface in these states is not flat is apparent from the occasional rapids where the Minnesota River encounters granite, or the Des Moines cuts into Carboniferous limestone. While the rock surface is not a perfect plain, and perhaps not a single peneplain, most of the relief is believed to have the form of broad swells or broad valleys. Angular valleys are also known[2] but do not give the rock surface its prevailing character. A relief of 250 to 300 feet is common. A range of 400 feet in altitude is probably the limit.

Rock in the Coteau des Prairies.—The Coteau des Prairies is a linear upland extending from the northeast corner of South Dakota a little east of south to the northwest corner of Iowa (page 564). Its top is 700 to 800 feet above the smooth drift plains, being more than 2000 feet high near the northern end. This upland mass has a rock core but its form is poorly known, for the drift is very thick, often 400 to 500 feet.[3] In the southern part, knobs of Sioux quartzite rise 1500 to 1700 feet above sea level, the Cretaceous surface around them being not above 1300 feet. Whatever rock core there is farther north must be of Cretaceous shale. That it is a mass of considerable dimensions may well be inferred from its ability to split the vigorous Wisconsin ice sheet as it did (page 573).

The Rock Surface in the Dakotas.—The rock surface, bearing occasional knobs of quartzite, rises from the Minnesota Valley southwestward to the Coteau and declines again to 1200 feet, more or less, in the James River Valley.[4] Abundant drilling in this valley shows that the rock surface is nowhere flat,[5] but the

[1] KAY, G. F., and E. T. APFEL, The Pre-Illinoian Pleistocene Geology of Iowa, *Ia. Geol. Survey*, vol. 34, pp. 26–29, 1928.

[2] KAY and APFEL, *op. cit.*, p. 30.

[3] LEVERETT, F., U. S. Geol. Survey, *Prof. Paper* 161, p. 11, 1932.

[4] TODD, J. E., *Science*, vol. 39, p. 268, 1914.

[5] Ten or more U. S. Geological Survey folios in the Dakotas include maps

broad swells and depressions, apparently smoothed by the ice, all come within a vertical range of several hundred feet. Bedrock is occasionally exposed where streams cut through the drift.

The most consistent regional slope in the section is the rise to its western boundary, beyond which in the next province, is a steeper and better known slope rising to the Missouri Plateau. As measured on the present surface of the drift, this steeper slope increases in amplitude from about 300 feet at the south, west of the lower James Valley, to 600 or 700 feet at the north, where it overlooks the basin of the Souris River. This slope is the front of the Missouri Plateau and is in the Great Plains province. It is mentioned here because of its bearing on the erosional history of the region (page 566). It is an "escarpment" only in the sense of being a relatively steep slope between two gentler ones. Where crossed by the Great Northern railroad, the slope is barely 10 feet per mile. Elsewhere the gradient rises to 100 or even 300 feet per mile. These, however, are surface slopes, due to immense accumulations of glacial drift on the edge of the Missouri Plateaus.[1] The corresponding westward rise of the rock surface may be either steeper or gentler. It is not necessarily located exactly beneath the surface slope, as the moraine is known at places to approach 500 feet in thickness and thus to build out and extend the plateau to the east. The foot of the steep slope, however made, is taken as the province boundary. The name Coteau du Missouri is applied to the broad divide, generally on morainic ridges, west of the steep slope.

The Turtle Mountains.—Surrounding the point where the 100th meridian crosses the International Boundary, is a compact area of 600 to 800 square miles covered by the same Tertiary rocks (Fort Union) which form the Missouri Plateau 50 miles away, indicating its once greater eastward extent. This outlier, called Turtle Mountains, is more than 2000 feet high, counting

---

showing thickness of the drift, which varies with the altitude of the surface and that of the underlying rock.

[1] CHAMBERLIN, T. C., Preliminary Paper on the Terminal Moraine of the Second Glacial Epoch, U. S. Geol. Survey, 3rd *Ann. Rept.*, pp. 291–406, 1882. See pp. 396–399. TODD, J. E., Moraines of the Missouri Coteau. U. S. Geol. Survey, *Bull.* 144, 1896. HARD, H. A., Geology and Water Resources of the Edgeley and LaMure Quadrangles, N. D., U. S. Geol. Survey, *Bull.* 801, pp. 22–23, 1929.

an estimated 100 feet of drift. Its slopes are not steep but the highland is none the less prominent. Its forests alone would make it conspicuous in a prairie country. Between this remnant and the plateau to the west is the flat valley of the Souris River, whose lowest level is 1100 feet above the sea. The Souris River circles round to the north side and enters the east-flowing Assiniboine. A faint swell 1500 to 1700 feet high, probably a divide of long preglacial standing, runs east from the Turtle Mountains to the Red River Valley.

Apparently, between the distinctly north-sloping valleys of the Red and Souris rivers, the country has a faint southward slope. Devils Lake at latitude 48° is 1465 feet high and seems to lie in the valley of a fairly large east-flowing preglacial stream.[1] The line of drift-mantled monadnocks between this lake and the Sheyenne River to the south are examples of what may be found at a number of places, presumably on preglacial divides, in the western part of this section. A few in South Dakota are made of Tertiary sandstone.

Rock in the Red River Valley.—The rock floor beneath the valley of the Red River of the North is about 800 feet high at its southern end, or 175 feet below the stream. It declines northward to 500 feet at the International Boundary where the valley floor is about 790 feet high. The rise of the rock surface on the west is at least 300 feet at the boundary between North and South Dakota, and increases northward to 1000 feet on the Canadian border, measured from the old channel to the top of the western escarpment. Except near the northern end the rise is not abrupt and is, in any case, masked by glacial drift. For the last 40 miles at the north the slope becomes a real escarpment, showing outcrops of Niobrara chalk beneath Pierre shale. This escarpment, exposed 300 to 500 feet above the glacial filling at its base, is the so-called Pembina Mountains. Its continuation in Canada is the Manitoba escarpment, known farther north as the Riding Mountains and Duck Mountains.

Preglacial Drainage.—With respect to lines of drainage before the ice epoch, the northward flow of the Red River to Hudson Bay is more certain than any other fact of equal mag-

[1] SIMPSON, H. E., The Physiography of the Devils-Stump Lake Region, N. Dak., *6th Biennial Rept.*, N. Dak. Geol. Survey, pp. 103–157, 1911. See p. 138.

nitude. Where that stream headed is less certain. The form of the Coteau des Prairies has suggested to some[1] a divide between streams converging northward to form the Red River, but Leverett[2] finds no reason to think that the drainage plan in Minnesota and northern Iowa was very different from the present, though the Mississippi River north of St. Paul did not find its old channel after glaciation. The St. Louis system, now discharging into Lake Superior (page 551) may well have been tributary to the Mississippi.

Concerning preglacial drainage in the Dakotas, it is generally agreed (1) that the present southward course of the Missouri is a relatively late device, having been adopted after one of the glacial invasions;[3] (2) that its tributaries from the west once extended farther east to one or more trunk streams whose courses are now obscured; (3) that the Missouri itself formerly flowed to Hudson Bay, whether leaving its present course at Fort Stevenson (long. 101°30′) as suggested by Todd[4] or near the mouth of the Yellowstone as stated by Alden,[5] or at some other point. Either of the suggested points is about half as far from Hudson Bay as from the Gulf of Mexico.

The exact southern limit of north-flowing waters has not been fixed beyond doubt. Todd[6] finds evidence that all western tributaries of the Missouri south of the Knife River, and as far south as the White, converged at a point in the James River Valley north of Aberdeen in northern South Dakota and flowed thence northeastward across the very low divide near the state line, through the oversized valley of the sluggish Wild Rice

---

[1] UPHAM, W., Tertiary and Early Quaternary Baseleveling in Minnesota, Manitoba and Northwestward, *Amer. Geologist*, vol. 14, pp. 235–246, 1894; ref. to p. 244.

[2] LEVERETT, F., U. S. Geol. Survey, *Prof. Paper* 161, p. 11.

[3] For evidence and opinions on the geologic date of this change see J. E. Todd, Pleistocene History of the Missouri River, *Science*, vol. 39, p. 273, 1914; W. C. Alden, Physiographic Development of the Northern Great Plains, *Bull. Geol. Soc. Amer.*, vol. 35, pp. 409–412, 1924; A. G. Leonard, Pleistocene Drainage Changes in Western North Dakota, *Bull. Geol. Soc. Amer.*, vol. 27, pp. 295–304, 1916; Leonard doubts that the Missouri River in late Tertiary time followed a course differing from that of the present in North Dakota.

[4] TODD, *op. cit.*, p. 266.

[5] ALDEN, *op. cit.*, p. 412.

[6] TODD, *op. cit.*, pp. 265–268.

River to the Red River Valley near its head.   At the same time
the James is believed to have flowed north in its present valley
from a divide at least as far south as Mitchell in latitude 43°40′.

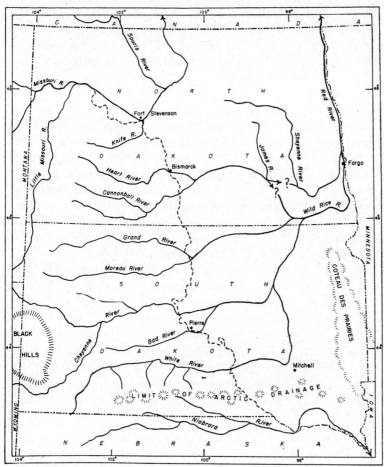

FIG. 152.—Sketch map of the Dakotas showing preglacial drainage to the north
as described by J. E. Todd.   The broken line shows the present course of the
Missouri River.   (*Science, vol.* 39.)

A line of monadnocks on the present divide between the White
River and the Niobrara, and extending east of the Missouri,
is interpreted as marking the preglacial divide separating drainage
to the Arctic from that to the Gulf of Mexico.   There are no
obvious impossibilities in this plan of drainage though for the

present it must be regarded as tentative rather than proved. It offers no adequate explanation of the great width, 6 to 10 miles, of the Missouri trench below the mouth of the James, in contrast with its narrowness, 1 to 3 miles, above that point.[1] The sudden widening below the mouth of the James suggests that during some part of Pleistocene time a large river must have flowed south through the James Valley.

Erosional History.—To state the history of this region in terms of erosion cycles known elsewhere would be a doubtful under-

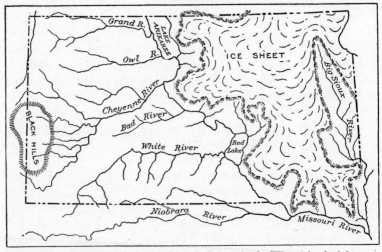

Fig. 153.—Outlines of drainage of South Dakota in the Wisconsin glacial stage. Except for proglacial lakes the Missouri River followed approximately its present course.   (*J. E. Todd.*)

taking. For aught that is known, the higher parts of the plateaulike rock surface in Iowa and Minnesota may represent the westward continuation of the Lancaster peneplain, or of the Dodgeville if the two are distinguished.[2] The altitude of the Lancaster-Dodgeville surface on Military Ridge in southwestern Wisconsin is about 1200 feet. The slightly higher rock surface in southeastern Minnesota may be interpreted as residual or attributed to postpeneplain diastrophism.[3] So much of Minnesota, northern Iowa, and the Dakotas lies at levels of 1200 to

---

[1] Well shown in U. S. Geol. Survey, *Water Supply Paper* 215, Pl. 2, map.

[2] No attempt is made here to distinguish between a Lancaster and a Dodgeville peneplain.

[3] MEINZER, O. E., U. S. Geol. Survey, *Water Supply Paper*, 256 p. 36, 1911.

1400 feet, or passes with imperceptible grade 100 feet above or below these limits, that the assumption of a once general peneplain is reasonable. The hypothesis may be complicated by assuming two or more base levels at small intervals. Probably in this deeply drift-covered region, poorly supplied with accurate topographic maps, the latter assumption can not at present be either proved or disproved.

The 400 feet of relief on the rock surface of Iowa is accounted for by Kay and Apfel[1] by allowing 200 feet of residual relief on the Dodgeville peneplain and regarding the Lancaster peneplain as consisting of wide valleys or local lowlands cut 200 feet below the Dodgeville. The use of these two names in the Western Young Drift section is questionable, though the facts are best explained by assuming a general peneplain, partly destroyed by very wide, shallow valleys. Most of the larger streams are now in such rock valleys, whose gentle slopes merge with the assumed peneplain in a way that makes delimitation impossible. The average slope toward the axis of the Minnesota valley is about 5 feet per mile on both sides. Slopes in the Des Moines and James valleys are still flatter.

Were it not for the valley of the Red River, cut deep in the rock, with steep slopes especially on the west, it might be questioned whether the broad valleys were not contemporary with the peneplain itself. In that case the surface of the section would never have had less relief than at the present day. However, the case of the Red River shows beyond doubt a relatively recent uplift of considerable magnitude. Probably all of the major valleys attained much of their relative depths after the same uplift. The Red River was most favored by its size and nearness to the sea, perhaps also by greater uplift at the place indicated. Following this uplift a wide lowland, later to become the basin of Lake Agassiz, was developed in northwestern Minnesota and Manitoba.

The fact that the relief of the rock surface is some 200 feet less than in the Driftless Area is explained in part by the presence of the largest river (the Mississippi) in the latter. In addition, the writers named believe that erosion of the rock in this area was interrupted by the earliest (Nebraskan) glaciation, and that before the streams could again begin to deepen their old valleys

[1] Kay and Apfel, *op. cit.*, p. 31.

in the rock, Kansan glaciation arrived and again set back the work. The excess of depth in the Driftless Area is thus accounted for by continued downcutting in the Pleistocene. It is true that in the Western Young Drift section some rock gorges were cut by streams which had been displaced by the early drift and superposed on divides, but the local gorges thus produced would not increase the total relief.

Prevailing levels in this section are lower than in the Missouri Plateau. It is possible to conceive of the plateau surface on the west as an older peneplain, preserved partly because of the superior resistance of the Cretaceous and Tertiary sandstones, and partly because of the arid climate. Such a conception is favored mainly by the eastern escarpment of the plateau. If the peneplains in the Great Plains and the section here considered be regarded as of the same age, as seems not improbable, the comparatively definite east front of the plateau is explained as incidental to the stream valleys at its foot. This seems to be the conception entertained by Upham.[1]

A peneplain represented by the horizon of view in this section (assuming the drift to be removed) would show quartzite monadnocks probably 300 feet high in the southern part of the Coteau des Prairies, and no doubt others of Pre-Cambrian or Cretaceous rocks, possibly a long ridge, in its northern part. Granite monadnocks might appear in western Minnesota in the hilly district stretching from the Leaf Hills to Lake Itasca. Still others capped by Fox Hills or even Tertiary sandstone would be seen on old divides near the plateau front.

GLACIATION AND ITS TOPOGRAPHY

Movements of the Ice.—The ice that covered this section in the early stages, as well as in the late Wisconsin, came mainly from the Keewatin center west of Hudson Bay. In middle Wisconsin time a relatively small area between central Minnesota and Lake Superior was last covered by ice from the Patrician

[1] UPHAM, W., The Glacial Lake Agassiz, U. S. Geol. Survey, *Mon.* 25, p. 103, 1896; also his paper in *Amer. Geologist,* cited on p. 564. Upham and those who follow him call attention to the geologic relation of the Turtle Mountains as an outlier of the Missouri Plateau, but they do not explain that if the surface of the Missouri Plateau and that of eastern North Dakota are parts of the same peneplain, the Turtle Mountains must be older.

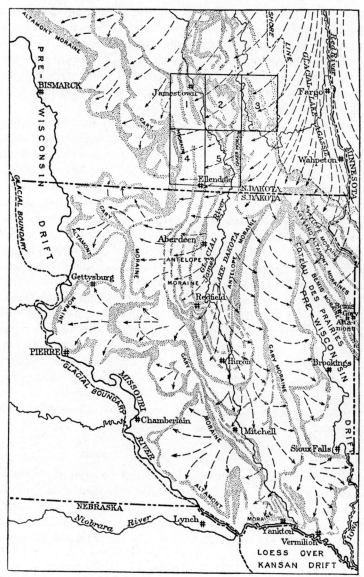

Fig. 154.—Sketch map of North and South Dakota showing moraines and directions of ice movement. (*U. S. Geol. Survey.*)

center a little east of north from Duluth (page 547). The Keewatin ice, moving south in the Red River Valley in late Wisconsin time, parted on the Coteau des Prairies into two main streams, following the wide, gently sloping rock troughs described above. The Dakota lobe west of the Coteau followed the James Valley. At the west it climbed the escarpment of the Missouri Plateau but was unable to proceed much farther.

East of the Coteau des Prairies, the Des Moines lobe in late Wisconsin time followed the wide lowland of the Minnesota and Blue Earth valleys, over the gentle rise between the latter and the Des Moines Valley, and down that valley to the site of Des Moines. This lobe was restricted on the west by the Coteau des Prairies and on the east by the relatively high surface (page 560) which extends west from the Military Ridge.

In west-central Minnesota the eastward spread of the late Keewatin ice carried it over the relatively high and hilly granite area (page 560) but its movement was impeded, and 50 miles farther east it reached its limit. Between the high district in west-central Minnesota and that in the southeast there is the broad sag followed by the Minnesota River, connecting with another lowland north of Minneapolis. Sensitive to even small differences in altitude, the ice pushed outward in this depression at right angles to the main current, advancing 60 or 70 miles to the northeast, to and beyond the St. Croix River. This is the Grantsburg sublobe[1] (Fig. 155).

Again 150 miles farther north, the eastward spread of the ice took advantage of a relatively low passage between the granite upland and the Mesabi Range (page 546) through which the Upper Mississippi passes. Advancing 40 miles beyond that wide passage, this St. Louis sublobe[2] pushed up the St. Louis Valley to the northeast and down the Mississippi to the southwest.

Features of the Drift.—All of these glacial lobes built strong terminal moraines and generally recessional moraines at frequent intervals. The outer terminals are noteworthy for their broad belts and long stretches of knob and kettle topography with local relief of 50 to 150 feet. Associated with this type are many morainic lakes, swamps, and boulder fields. Only occasionally do the recessional moraines have this character.

[1] SARDESON, F. W., U. S. Geol. Survey, *Prof. Paper* 161, pp. 78–89, 1932.
[2] LEVERETT, F., U. S. Geol. Survey, *Prof. Paper* 161, pp. 64–66, 1932.

A surface of sag and swell is much more common on them than hummock and kettle. Lakes and swamps are none the less

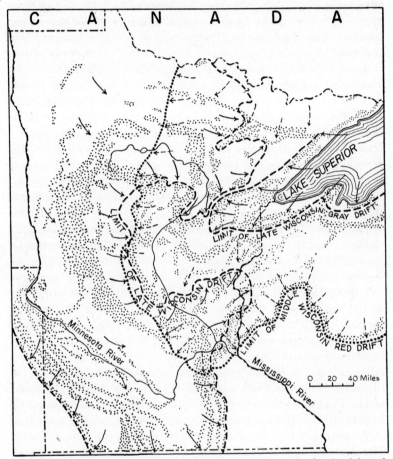

FIG. 155.—Sketch map of Minnesota and western Wisconsin showing lobes of the late Wisconsin gray drift from the northwest and the east, overlapping middle Wisconsin red drift from the north. The latter extends beneath the gray drift approximately to the dotted line. Late Wisconsin ice from the northwest came from the Keewatin center west of Hudson Bay; the Superior lobe came from the Labrador center. The Middle Wisconsin ice in this area came from the Patrician center south of Hudson Bay. Shaded areas are moraines. (*Data from Leverett, U. S. Geol. Survey, Prof. Pap. 161.*)

common, as they are even on the intervening ground moraine. Probably an eighth to a fourth of the total area would be mapped as marginal moraine. Between these ridges is ground moraine or till plain, generally smoothly rolling and constituting the larger part of the area. Gravelly, sandy, or swampy plains of glacial outwash are common and extensive. In addition to these are more than 20,000 square miles of lacustrine plain, most of it in the basin of Glacial Lake Agassiz, and much of it swampy.

Everywhere the drainage is young. Except near the larger rivers, which are consequent on the drift surface, streams are widely spaced. Few channels have been developed, except along lines of depression which were ready made when the ice vanished. Some whole counties in the Dakotas are without running water.[1] Partly on account of the young drift topography, and partly by reason of less rainfall, many small areas have only internal drainage. The brackish Devils Lake of North Dakota is the hydrographic center of an area of 3500 square miles.[2] On the other hand, much land needs artificial drainage even in the Dakotas and Iowa, while in Minnesota 14 per cent of the area is classed as swamp.[3] Of morainal lakes, Minnesota alone has at least 7000. The number of lakes in all these states has decreased and is destined to become much smaller within a century.

Till and Outwash Plains.—Despite the prominence of moraines, and the amount of space given to their description, the ground moraine (till plains) occupies much the larger part of the area. Aside from a few monadnocks and the larger features already mentioned, and except for local beginnings of postglacial erosion, relief is wholly depositional. The gentle swells and sags of the surface on the thick sheet of till give no clue to the form of the buried rock surface.[4] A wide belt near the Minnesota River is of this character, relatively free from recessional moraines but partly covered by outwash and lake deposits (page 584). The Des Moines Valley is much the same, though recessional moraines are not wanting.

---

[1] SIMPSON, H. E., and H. B. RIFFENBURG, Geology and Ground-water Resources of North Dakota, U. S. Geol. Survey, *Water Supply Paper* 598, p. 59, 1929.

[2] SIMPSON, H. E., The Physiography of the Devils-Stump Lake Region, North Dakota, *6th Biennial Rept.*, N. D. Geol. Survey, pp. 103–157, 1911.

[3] U. S. Geol. Survey, *Prof. Paper* 161, p. 9.

[4] The form of the rock surface in southern Minnesota is shown in U. S. Geol. Survey, *Water Supply Paper* 256. A. G. Leonard, (*Jour. Geol.*, vol. 27, p. 23) gives estimates of the thickness of the drift in North Dakota.

Terminal Moraines.—Moraines formed at or near the edges of the ice sheets described above are generally pronounced. The name Altamont is applied to the most prominent moraine of the Keewatin ice sheet.[1] It may be a narrow ridge or a belt a dozen miles wide. It may be single, double, or multiple; or it may merge with its successor, the Gary moraine, in still broader hummocky tracts where ridges are confused. Its height above the plain inside may be less than 50 feet; perhaps 50 to 150 feet is most common; but it may be 400 feet, as at places on the western edge and in the lower James Valley.[2] The thickness of the drift at places approaches 500 feet.[3]

Throughout the western border the Altamont moraine lies on the Missouri Plateau, hence outside the province here described.[4] Its east-west course on the southern edge of the Dakota lobe is shown in Fig. 154. Despite the vigor of an ice sheet that was capable of building such a massive moraine, it runs out into lobelets on both south and west sides.

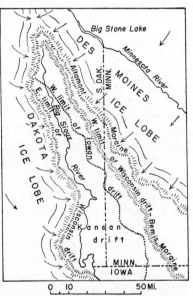

Fig. 156.—Relation of drift sheets to the Coteau des Prairies. (*Data from U. S. Geol. Survey.*)

At the head of the Coteau des Prairies the ice of this stage was exhausted 140 miles north of the limit reached in the James

---

[1] Leverett (*Bull. Geol. Soc. Amer.*, vol. 33, pp. 102–103, 1922) states that the Altamont moraine, though continuous and strong, does not lie at the edge of the Des Moines lobe, that position being occupied by the Bemis moraine, at least east of the Coteau des Prairies.

[2] Todd, J. E., Moraines of Southeastern South Dakota, U. S. Geol. Survey, *Bull.* 158, p. 38, 1899.

[3] Hard, H. A., Geology and Water Resources of the Edgeley and La Mure Quadrangles, N. Dak., U. S. Geol. Survey, *Bull.* 801, pp. 22, 27, also Maps, 1929.

[4] Described in the author's companion book, "Physiography of Western United States," p. 73, McGraw Hill Book Company, Inc., New York, 1931.

Valley and more than 300 miles in a direct line from the limit of the Des Moines lobe. The Altamont moraine was piled on the rock substructure to a height of 700 feet above the plain. Toward the south the edges of the ice on either side approximately followed the contours, separating at a small angle. The entire linear upland had been glaciated before. Indeed it consists largely of older drift. The acutely pointed area left bare at this time has a surface much like that of the broad area of Dissected Till Plains to the south, to which it logically belongs. So consistently does the Altamont moraine on the west (here combined with others) contour the flank of the older ridge that the Big Sioux River follows the trough between the two throughout its length.

Technically the above simple plan is modified by the fact that another moraine, the Bemis (called Altamont in all reports previous to 1922), lies in front of the Altamont at the edge of the Des Moines lobe. A more important modification is found in northwestern Iowa, in the presence of a slightly older (but still rather young) drift sheet just outside the Altamont moraine but included in this section. This drift is now called Iowan,[1] but its topography is sufficiently indicated by the fact that it has at times been called Wisconsin. It has also been described as a poorly drained phase of the Kansan.[2] It differs from the main body of Iowan farther east[3] and differs strikingly from the adjacent Dissected Till Plains. A narrow strip of this type lies in front of the Bemis moraine on the Coteau.

On both sides of the Des Moines lobe in Iowa the outer moraine, though only a few miles wide, makes a conspicuous border, but marginal ridges are absent for 80 miles on the south. In northern Iowa and southern Minnesota, marginal moraines, Altamont and others, make a belt more than 20 miles wide east of the Blue Earth and Minnesota till plains.[4]

---

[1] F. Leverett, (U. S. Geol. Survey, *Prof. Paper* 161, p. 29) now calls this drift Iowan and gives some description of its topography. He also cites papers discussing the subject. His map of the Wisconsin moraines in Minnesota (Pl. 2) is the basis of statements made in the following paragraphs.

[2] CARMAN, J. E., Pleistocene Geology of Northwestern Iowa, *Ia. Geol. Survey*, vol. 26, pp. 233–445, 1915; ref. to p. 323.

[3] KAY, G. F., and E. T. APFEL, *Ia. Geol. Survey*, vol. 34, p. 53, 1928.

[4] LEVERETT, *op. cit.*, Pl. 3.

The middle part of eastern Minnesota, southwest of Lake Superior, is the area in which the slightly older mid-Wisconsin Patrician red drift remains uncovered (Fig. 155). The late Wisconsin Keewatin ice wrapped around it, depositing its gray drift on three sides, but built its conspicuous moraines some distance back (60 miles on the west) from its extreme edge. Here the great moraines, Altamont and others, make a wide irregular belt covering the higher, presumably hilly, districts of the granite surface. Apparently these hills checked the movement of the ice.

The drift of the Patrician lobe is similarly fronted by the strong St. Croix moraine. On the west it remains exposed or only partially covered by the thin edge of the Keewatin drift. On the north and south, however, the Keewatin sublobes mentioned on page 570 covered the moraines of red drift, at places so thinly that their forms are little altered although the surface carries the gray drift from the west.

Recessional Moraines.—Taken as a class, the recessional moraines show relatively little of the abrupt hummock and kettle topography which is so common (but not universal) in the great outer terminals including the Altamont. There are, however, exceptions, especially in localities where these moraines are more or less bunched, as is the case near Devils Lake.[1] The Big Stone moraine, where it lies near the Altamont in western Minnesota, is similar. So also is the Mille Lacs moraine, surrounding the lake of that name in the middle of the red drift north of Minneapolis. Such spots are too fortuitously distributed for enumeration or description. The one clear fact is that where the ice edge was looped back by high land, the moraines are closely bunched, and even those parts assigned to the recessionals are apt to have hummocks and kettles with 50 to 75 feet of relief. One such locality is the head of the Coteau des Prairies. The Turtle Mountains must have tended strongly to lobate the ice front, but accurate maps are wanting.[2] The drift that covers them has a strongly morainic surface in

---

[1] SIMPSON, *op. cit.*, p. 110.

[2] *Cf.* CHAMBERLIN, T. C., Preliminary Paper on the Terminal Moraine of the Second Glacial Epoch, U. S. Geol. Survey, 3d *Ann. Rept.*, Pl. 35, p. 382. The moraines are not shown on this map, but the arrows indicate that the ice closed around this highland from both sides.

which high knobs and lakes abound, at least one of the knobs rising to 2300 feet.

The Gary moraine, the first after the Altamont, and at many places contiguous with it, is the largest and best known of the recessionals. Like some of those in the Great Lake section, and perhaps some others in this section, it represents a slight readvance of the ice front, as indeed the Altamont does where the Bemis lies in front. At places, as west of the Coteau, it is separated from the Altamont moraine by 20 miles of smoothly rolling till plain. When it is remembered that 12 or more moraines have been recognized,[1] and that some of these have at places more than one crest, it will be seen that the intervening belts of ground moraine and outwash plains are rarely more than 20 miles wide. But it is also to be remembered that these moraines are often far from being continuous ridges. Where such ridges are a few miles wide and only 25 to 50 feet high, and have a surface of only gentle sags and swells, they are far less conspicuous on the open prairie than on the map.

Area of Iowan Drift.—Some 9000 square miles of ground moraine east of the Des Moines lobe in northeastern Iowa and a little in Minnesota have a surface that differs only in minor ways from the other till plains of this section. This is the area of Iowan drift.[2] Typically, its horizon is flat, its relief small and its surface mildly undulating where not flat. Streams are relatively few, and all but the larger ones run in shallow concave swales which the present drainage found and did not make. Some of the larger streams and the lower courses of their tributaries are in troughs whose depth approaches or even exceeds 100 feet, but the sides of these are smoothed and rounded, and the area having such pronounced relief is but a small part

---

[1] UPHAM, W., The Glacial Lake Agassiz, U. S. Geol. Survey, *Mon.* 25, p. 139, 1896.

[2] A classic description of this area (lacking its more recent interpretation) is given by W J McGee, the Pleistocene History of Northeastern Iowa, U. S. Geol. Survey, 11*th Ann. Rept.*, pp. 199–577, 1889. See especially pp. 394–396. Others are given by S. Calvin in his descriptions of the several counties in the reports of the *Iowa Geol. Survey*, *e.g.*, Mitchell County (vol. 13, p. 301, 1903), Dubuque County (vol. 10, pp. 395 and 470, 1900); also The Iowan Drift, *Jour. Geol.*, vol. 19, pp. 577–602, 1911. See also W. H. Norton and others, U. S. Geol. Survey, *Water Supply Paper* 293, p. 52, 1912, and descriptions of counties.

of the whole. In a few cases streams have removed the drift from preglacial rock valleys and re-exposed their walls. Except in these rare cases no stream has done much to make or modify its valley since the last glaciation. Everywhere there is a lack of small tributaries, though the swales which have streams branch out into smaller and still shallower swales without channels. Many of the interstream spaces are poorly drained. Permanent lakes do not exist, but there are broad panlike depressions of small depth which may hold water temporarily.

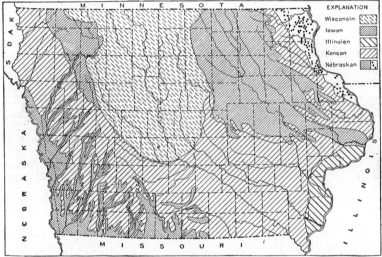

FIG. 157.—Drift sheets in Iowa. The Nebraskan in the southwest is exposed by erosion. In the northeast only scattered patches of boulders remain. (*G. F. Kay and E. T. Apfel; redrawn by F. Leverett, U. S. Geol. Survey.*)

The above description specifies the features which cause this district to be included in the Western Young Drift section, whose distinguishing characteristic is that its surface has been but little modified since the last glacial invasion. The Iowan drift has in common with the rest (1) a surface substantially as it was left by the last ice, (2) imperfect drainage, (3) early youth in the current erosion cycle, where a cycle can be said to have begun at all. This district is strongly contrasted with the mature surface of the Dissected Till Plains, whose features were made by running water. However, the two have something in common. Their plans are much alike, though their profiles differ strikingly. The shallow valleys or swales of the Iowan drift branch dendritically, even though streams are few and those that exist are merely obeying the surface slopes instead of producing them as in the Dissected Till Plains.

It is agreed among geologists that this district, previous to its last glaciation, was an integral part of the area of Dissected Till Plains, having an approximately mature topography and a relief which must in places have exceeded 150 feet. Relatively

Fig. 158.—Typical surface on uneroded Iowan drift. The nearly flat plain and the scattered boulders are equally characteristic. (*S. Calvin, Ia. Geol. Survey.*)

late in the Glacial epoch it was overridden by ice and covered by a drift sheet which, while necessarily extending north (beneath later drift) to the source of the ice, is not known to be exposed elsewhere than in northern Iowa and southern Minnesota.[1] The effect of the new cover was to mask and partially obscure the older topography by filling the valleys to various degrees and substituting for their former erosional profiles the flowing curves of drift deposition.[2] Depending on their size, the old valleys with definite axes were entirely obliterated, converted

[1] Leverett, in various papers, notably U. S. Geol. Survey, *Prof. Paper* 161, p. 29, expresses the opinion that the glacier here concerned has not yet been proved to be other than a Keewatin correlative of the Illinois glacial lobe which came from the northeast. In provinces farther west, a margin of the drift sheet is tentatively regarded as Iowan.

[2] ALDEN, W. C., and M. M. LEIGHTON, The Iowan Drift, A Review of the Evidences of the Iowan Stage of Glaciation, *Ia. Geol. Survey*, vol. 26, pp. 49–212, 1915.

into shallow swales, or merely modified in form. But the evidence of former dendritic dissection remains in the pattern of the depressions. It was this fact that once caused the Iowan drift to be included in the Dissected Till Plains section, with which it has a close historical relation, despite its present greater similarity to the rest of the young drift.[1]

In general the Iowan drift is thin. At places it would be difficult to identify were it not for the association of granite (or syenite) boulders, some of them of great size, which lie scattered over the area, particularly its northern part. Morainic ridges are all but wanting, but at places the loess, generally absent except near the edge, is accumulated in swells of considerable thickness, even in billowy hills simulating a terminal moraine.[2]

GLACIAL DRAINAGE AND LAKES

Glacial Lake Agassiz.—Streams flowing to Hudson Bay were necessarily ponded during the advance and recession of the ice front. Thus Lake Agassiz in the valleys of the Red, Saskatchewan, and upper Nelson rivers flooded an area of 110,000 square miles, which is greater than the combined areas of the present Great Lakes. It lay mainly in Canada but covered 15,000 squares miles of Minnesota and 6800 square miles of North Dakota (Fig. 159). It was more than 400 feet deep at the International Boundary and rose 650 feet above the level of Lake Winnipeg, its remnant and successor. Its surface, if restored at the level of the highest beach, would now be 1055 feet above sea level at its south end and 1230 feet on the Canadian border, indicating that the land surface has tilted.

Marginal lakes in side valleys appeared as soon as the final retreat of the ice front began to lay bare the north-sloping surface. Beaches of these earlier stages, higher than Lake Agassiz, are found at various places. All impounded waters necessarily overflowed to the south, except during an interval when the ice front receded so far as to open a northern outlet.[3]

---

[1] The area is so classified on the author's map of Physical Divisions of the United States, U. S. Geol. Survey, 1930.

[2] CALVIN, S., Concrete Examples from the Topography of Howard County, Iowa, *Amer. Geologist*, vol. 30, pp. 375–381, 1902.

[3] TYRRELL, J. B., The Genesis of Lake Agassiz, *Jour. Geol.*, vol. 4, pp. 811–

During that interval the lake was very low.   Beaches built at
that time were covered with clay when the ice again came south
as far as Winnipeg, burying and obscuring the northern outlet.

Lake Agassiz overflowed the lowest col in the divide between
the basins of the Red and Minnesota rivers (see map, Pl. 5).

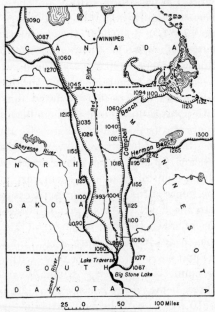

FIG. 159.—Map of glacial Lake Agassiz, showing two stages.   More than half
of the lake was north of the area represented.   Numbers indicate altitudes of
shore lines.   Note tilting toward the south.   (*Upham, revised by Leverett, U. S.
Geol. Survey.*)

The outlet, known as River Warren, followed the course now
marked by Traverse and Big Stone lakes and Minnesota River.
Its large volume is chiefly responsible for the 200 foot trench,
½ to 4 miles wide, through which the Minnesota River now
flows from Big Stone Lake to the Mississippi.

The col referred to, now cut down 95 feet below the level of the
highest beach, was at Brown's Valley between Traverse Lake
(975 feet A.T.) and Big Stone Lake (966 feet A.T.) on the Min-
nesota-South Dakota boundary.   The highest, or Herman,

815, 1896; JOHNSTON, W. A., The Genesis of Lake Agassiz; a Confirmation,
Jour. Geol., vol. 24, pp. 625–638, 1916.

beach (1065 feet A.T.) indicates the first long-continued level of the water surface. At that level the outlet was flowing on rock. The Herman beach is an impressive feature, traceable throughout the boundary of Lake Agassiz in the United States, and commonly used to define the lake's maximum altitude and extent. With progressive downcutting of the outlet, there appeared in succession the Herman beach (1065 ft.), the Norcross beaches (1040 to 1050 ft.), and the Tintah beaches (1000 to 1020 ft.). Then occurred the episode of the easterly outlet to Hudson Bay, during which beaches were built at low levels. With the return of the ice barrier and the renewal of overflow at the south, three Campbell beaches (980 to 990 ft.) were built, after which the northern outlet was resumed and the lake began its final fall, perhaps 8000 years ago (see footnote, page 586), its outlet being to Hudson Bay. It halted long enough at 960 feet to develop the McCauleyville beach. Later came a long series of beaches, 15 of which have been identified, some of them very faint.

It is not to be inferred that the water level dropped suddenly from one level to the next. In reality it fell 10 feet while constructing a series of seven Herman beaches. There are also two Norcross beaches 5 to 10 feet apart, two Tintah beaches 15 to 20 feet apart, and three Campbell beaches within 10 feet.

The beaches connected with the River Warren outlet are prominent features, being sandy belts several hundred feet wide and rising 5 to 10 feet above the land outside (away from the lake). When traced northward, all beaches are seen to rise, to become more widely spread, and to be split into a larger number of members. This is because of a northward differential uplift which was in progress during their development. With the southern outlet abandoned, side streams continued to drop their burdens in the wide flat valley, thus forming the dams that retain Traverse and Big Stone lakes.

The beach ridges represent the work of waves and shore currents on the till, mainly that beneath the water, for cliffs are rare. The clay was taken into suspension and allowed to settle elsewhere. The sand and gravel were washed along and accumulated under the water's edge and slightly above. With beach deposits rather abundant it is noteworthy that the offshore zones, in the wider strips between ridges, seem not to have been covered with either sand or mud. They are underlain directly by till[1] whose surface still has something left of the rolling character of the ground moraine, but less relief than the corresponding surface beyond the limits of the lake.

Deposits in Lake Agassiz.—Silt, much of it laminated, was deposited in the deeper, axial portions of the lake basin, often to depths of 30 to 50 feet. Above this is some alluvium of recent streams, for considerable areas are covered by floods. These

FIG. 160.—Lacustrine plain of Lake Agassiz in North Dakota. Aside from cultural features this view is representive of other lacustrine plains shown in fig. 129. (*Lantern slide issued by Howell's Microcosm.*)

deposits make the extensive and phenomenal flat for which this valley is proverbial. Silts in faint depressions also tend to even up the surface elsewhere. The limits of the silt plain are not everywhere topographically marked. The plain slopes north about 1 foot per mile and rises from the river to the beaches. From the Red River at Fargo west to the Campbell beach, the plain rises 100 feet in 40 miles,[2] the higher beaches being crowded into the next 5 miles, though at other places they are widely dispersed. A slope toward the middle of the basin is what might be expected in a lake that was shallowed but not filled by sediments washed in from the adjacent surface of very clayey till.

That the present flat is real lake bottom and not flood plain is made clear by its contrast with the extensive deltas of sand

[1] UPHAM, W., "Geology of Minnesota," vol. 2, p. 518, 1888; also U. S. Geol. Survey, *Mon.* 25, p. 21, 1896.

[2] See U. S. Geol. Survey, folio (No. 117).

built by the Sheyenne, Elk, and Pembina rivers (Pl. 5). The first-named delta covers 800 square miles and is clearly distinguished from the lake bottom, not only by its material but by a well marked front 60 to 70 feet high. The others are similar but smaller.

The northward slope of the plain was a little steeper before the postglacial southward tilt, which is made evident by the shore lines. However, the gradient has always been very small for a river no larger than the Red. Of necessity, the current is extremely sluggish and the stream meanders in intricate curves. Deposition, thus favored, has resulted in small natural levees. These local slopes away from the stream should not be confused with the main slopes of the valley, nor the material thus deposited with the much greater mass of lacustrine clay. Throughout much the larger part of the lacustrine plain erosion has not yet begun. Much of the area, especially in the north, is swampy.

Glacial Lake Souris.—A lake in the valley of the north-flowing Souris River was, in essential respects, the counterpart of Lake Agassiz. Fully half of it lies in Canada. It is said to have discharged its waters to the James River and later to the Sheyenne as the ice front receded.[1] Both of these streams flow in sharp trenches, 100 to 250 feet deep and ½ to 1 mile wide, which were probably cut by glacial waters, as the streams now, while classed as perennial, barely keep going during the summer.[2] The lacustrine plain of Lake Souris, which is 1100 feet high near the river, reaches 1600 feet where the shore is highest.

Glacial Lake Dakota.—Next to Lake Agassiz, the best known member of its class in this section is Lake Dakota. It covered what is now the immediate valley of the James River for 170 miles, with a maximum width of less than 30 miles. Throughout this distance the lacustrine plain varies little from 1300 feet in altitude. Its very small relief has been ascribed in part to pitting by the melting of buried ice[3] and in part to wind. Occasional swells reach 50 feet in height. The uniform altitude of the plain is believed by Todd to indicate that the lake was essentially filled with sediment. This flat is now trenched by the

[1] Upham, W., U. S. Geol. Survey, *Mon.* 25, p. 149.

[2] Jamestown-Tower folio (No. 168), U. S. Geol. Survey, 1909.

[3] Todd, J. E., The Moraines of Southeastern South Dakota, U. S. Geol. Survey, *Bull.* 158, p. 125, 1899.

James River, a few feet at the northern end, but increasing to
90 feet at the southern end.   The lake discharged to the south
by the James River.

The basin of Lake Dakota has been variously explained.
If the James River just previous to the Late Wisconsin substage
was flowing north (page 565), an ice dam at the north was all
that was necessary to retain a lake.   On the supposition that
the James was flowing south it has been assumed that glacial
erosion reduced the shale surface to a level below that of the
quartzite barrier south of Mitchell.[1]   The weighting of the
northern area by ice, with consequent depression, has also been
appealed to.[2]   It should be noted, however, that the subsequent recovery which tilted the shores of Lake Agassiz southward has not affected the plain of Lake Dakota.   If the pre-
Wisconsin James River flowed south the temporary basin of
Lake Dakota must be ascribed in part at least to the accumulation
of moraine at its southern end where the ice was checked by the
quartzite hills.

Glacial Lake Minnesota.—During the retreat of the ice front
from southern Minnesota, a lake of several hundred square
miles existed for a time in the valleys of southern tributaries
now entering the Minnesota at Mankato.   As the Minnesota
River turns to the north at that point its lower course remained
covered by ice, which caused the ponding and forced the lake to
discharge southward to the Des Moines River until an eastward
escape to the Mississippi was found at the edge of the ice.[3]
The former bed of this lake is relatively smooth, no doubt
evened up somewhat by sediments, but such deposits, while
noted locally, do not form an extensive sheet.   Only locally
are the old shores clear.

Postglacial Time.—More than local interest attaches to the
history of postglacial drainage around the mouth of the Minne-

[1] This was Todd's explanation in 1899 (U. S. Geol. Survey, *Bull.* 158,
p. 124).

[2] HARD, *op. cit.*, p. 40.

[3] A popular account with a map of this lake is given by C. W. Hall in his
"Geography of Minnesota," pp. 185–186 (Minneapolis, 1903).   A later
and more critical description is given by Leverett in U. S. Geol. Survey,
Prof. Paper 161 pp. 98–99.   Reference is here made to W. Upham who
originally described the lake, summarizing his observations in "Geology of
Minnesota," vol. 1, pp. 460–462. 1884.

sota River because of a time computation based on the recession of the Falls of St. Anthony.[1]   Southeastward from the sharp turn at St. Paul the Mississippi is in its wide preglacial valley

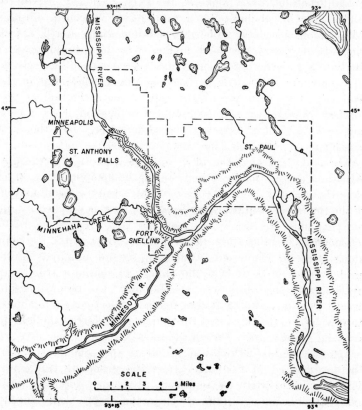

Fig. 161.—Sketch map showing valleys of the Mississippi and Minnesota rivers near their junction.   (*Data from U. S. Geol. Survey.*)

(Fig. 161).   The gorge upstream (southwest) from that point was cut by the powerful River Warren, flowing from Lake Agassiz.   It received the postglacial upper Mississippi near Fort Snelling at what is now the southern edge of the Twin Cities.   At this point both streams had their channels in the

[1] WINCHELL, N. H., The Geology of Hennepin County, "Geology of Minnesota," vol. 2, pp. 264–344, 1888.   Pages 313–344 contain an elaborate discussion of this subject.   See also F. W. Sardeson, Minneapolis-St. Paul folio (No. 201), U. S. Geol. Survey, 1916.

soft St. Peter sandstone, but the strong Platteville limestone, 30 feet thick, made the rim of the gorge and, except for its last mile, the bed of the upper Mississippi. Where that stream crossed the edge of the limestone the Falls of St. Anthony, 40 feet high, came into being. Their total recession to the center of Minneapolis has been at least 8 miles, and the rate of retreat since 1680, when they were first seen by Father Hennepin, is fairly well known. After making what was intended to be due allowance for complicating factors, Winchell computed that approximately 8000 years have passed since the ice left this locality and the falls were formed.[1] This evidence has its value, but such computations are accepted as suggestive rather than conclusive (*cf.* Niagara, page 499).

The first third of the total recession was covered before Lake Agassiz found its final northern outlet, while the copious River Warren was still deepening its channel. During the remainder of the time the enfeebled Minnesota River was unable to keep the old channel clean and, along with the Mississippi, aggraded at least 50 feet, making the extensive, poorly drained flats now seen along both streams. A second complication is found in the eroded upper surface of the limestone. On account of thinning upstream, the recession was accelerating. For 90 years previous to 1856 it was 6.73 feet per year. The falls seemed to be approaching extinction when, in 1871, they were protected by an artificial apron which checked the retreat.

Artesian Water.—The western margin of the Western Young Drift section is one of the great artesian basins of the world.[2] The area of originally flowing wells embraces much more than half of the Dakota portion of the section. The water-bearing stratum is the Dakota sandstone, which outcrops around the Black Hills and the Rocky Mountains and underlies this area in a syncline. It is reached by wells at depths ranging from several hundred to 2000 feet. Approximately 5000 wells have been drilled into this stratum in North Dakota, and probably a

---

[1] F. W. Sardeson, attaching different values to certain factors, makes the time 12,000 years since the falls originated, and 8000 years since Lake Agassiz found its northern outlet.

[2] For maps see N. H. Darton, U. S. Geol. Survey, 17*th Ann. Rept.*, pt. 2, Pl. 69, 1896; U. S. Geol. Survey, *Water Supply Paper* 227, Pl. 12; H. E. Simpson, U. S. Geol. Survey, *Water Supply Paper* 598, Pl. 1, 1929.

larger number in South Dakota. As the climate in these states
is semiarid (16 to 22 inches annual precipitation), streams few
and small, and the water of surface wells in the till, while com-

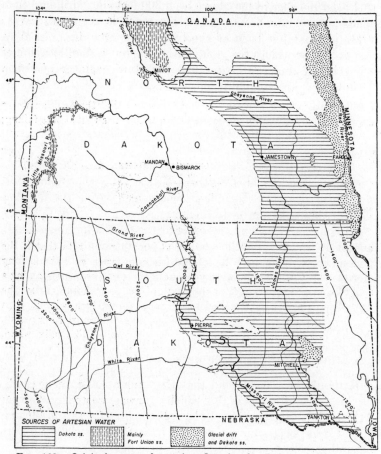

Fig. 162.—Original areas of artesian flow in the Dakotas. The original
artesian head (level to which the water would rise in a pipe) is shown for South
Dakota by 200-foot contours. (*Data for South Dakota mainly from N. H. Darton,
for North Dakota from H. E. Simpson.*)

monly usable, is often not free from ill-tasting salts, it is apparent
that a substantial part of the value of Dakota land lies in its
artesian water. Under such conditions waste is serious. Depletion is shown by loss of head and a narrowing of the territory of
flowing wells. In the last decade of the nineteenth century a

head sufficient to raise the water 300 feet above the surface was not uncommon in favored localities.   The loss of head in the Edgeley quadrangle of North Dakota by the year 1923 was at least 200 feet and may have been 300 feet since drilling began in this locality, and 250 feet over a much larger area.[1]   Wide areas in the outer parts of the basin have gone dry.   In areas where flow continues the yield of a well is but a small fraction of what it was.   As early as 1916 the state engineer of South Dakota[2] wrote:

There was a time when we did not know but that the artesian water supply was inexhaustible; later we began to surmise that it was failing;

Fig. 163.—Section of Red River Valley artesian basin.   (*Upham, U. S. Geol. Survey.*)

and today we know that it is failing at such a rapid rate that if the present waste continues to be tolerated in connection with the sinking of new wells it will only be a few years until there will not be remaining a single flowing artesian well in the State of South Dakota.   True, the water supply in the Dakota sandstone can never be exhausted, but when the last well in the valleys of the James and Missouri rivers quits flowing, it will be a sad day for the farmers in counties like Sully, where there are no running streams or surface wells to be had, and very deep pumping will have to be resorted to.

It should be remembered that the amount of water actually used is a small fraction of that which is (or was) wasted by allowing wells to flow continuously.   The only apology for this profligacy is that it has been common practice in artesian districts and that natural gas has been treated in the same manner.

THE DISSECTED TILL PLAINS

Distinctive Features.—The area designated as Dissected Till Plains is essentially that of the exposed Kansan glacial drift

---

[1] HARD, H. A., U. S. Geol. Survey, *Bull.* 801, p. 59, 1929.   Many interesting (and regrettable) statistics are given.

[2] Cited in U. S. Geol. Survey, *Water Supply Paper* 598, p. 59, from H. M. Derr, *6th Biennial Report of the State Engineer to the Governor of South Dakota*, p. 150, 1916.   As late as 1909 N. H. Darton (U. S. Geol. Survey, *Water Supply Paper* 227, pp. 64 and 146) saw no cause for alarm.

(Fig. 129), excepting only outlying patches of that sheet which are thrown in with adjacent sections of similar topography in order to obviate a multiplicity of areal units (page 455). This section is distinguished from the Till Plains on the east and from the Young Drift section on the north by the stage it has reached in the postglacial erosion cycle. It differs from the latter also in the almost complete absence of marginal moraines. If lakes ever characterized the surface, they must have been very shallow,

FIG. 164.—Dissected Till Plains in northeastern Kansas near the Missouri River where erosion is active. The same style of topography, but with gentler slopes and less forest, is prevalent. (*Kans. Geol. Survey.*)

and have long since disappeared. The original surface of the Dissected Till Plains must have been comparable to the undissected parts of the Illinoian ground moraine, or of the Wisconsin in central Ohio and Indiana. Broadly generalized, this section is a nearly flat till plain, submature to mature in its erosion cycle, with a present relief of 100 feet to 300 feet or even more; covered by loess, generally a few feet deep, but increasing to 30, 50, or even, in one locality, 90 feet near the large bordering rivers. Local variations and exceptions to this general formula will appear in the following discussion.

Boundaries.—In South Dakota the distinctive features of this section end at the foot of the Wisconsin terminal moraine. The same is true in part for western Iowa, but for 150 miles there is an intervening strip of Iowan drift not outlined by marginal moraines (page 577 and Fig. 157). The topography of this little eroded glacial plain readily differentiates it from the mature Kansan surface. On the south side of the Des Moines lobe, for 50 miles west of Des Moines and 30 miles east, the distinction is of the same character, there being no pronounced terminal moraine at the edge of the younger drift. The Raccoon River marks the boundary west of Des Moines. In eastern Iowa the Dissected Till Plains border the Driftless section for nearly 50 miles.

The eastern boundary is nowhere far from the Mississippi River. As stated on page 603, for a stretch of 100 miles in southeastern Iowa the Illinoian glacier crossed the present course of the river, thus imparting to a strip on the west, whose maximum width is 20 miles, the features of the Till Plains section. The old channel, occupied temporarily by the Mississippi River when crowded westward by the Illinoian ice sheet, an obvious trough now occupied in part by stretches of the Cedar and other rivers, is nowhere far from the boundary of this section. From Keokuk south to the Ozark province, the Mississippi may be taken as the section boundary.

The only part of this section that lies south of the Missouri River is a small area that lies west of St. Louis, which must be excluded from the Ozark Plateau. Farther west the Missouri River may be used for practical purposes.[1] As a strip near the river is much eroded, it is plain that the distinguishing features of till plains, whether young or old, will be absent there. For 150 miles westward from the center of the state, an old (perhaps in part Nebraskan) drift is found in patches south of the river, locally as much as 20 miles, but it is greatly wasted and very thin except where it fills a few old valleys. The Kansas River, like the Missouri, is the practical boundary from Kansas City to Manhattan, though scattered and deeply decayed boulders (perhaps Nebraskan) are found a dozen miles to the south.

The western boundary of this section, which is also the province boundary, is in part arbitrary. At the worst it may be said that the province on the east has a certain typical and prevailing

[1] In discussing the Ozark province this boundary is treated more critically. See p. 631.

character differing from that on the west, and that a line must be drawn somewhere. The boundary in the Dakotas is topographically justified. The same is true in Kansas, and the line is drawn across Nebraska to connect the other two. Drawn in this way, it is approximately at the edge of the known glacial drift, but for much of the distance the drift is buried by loess whose thickness at places approaches 100 feet and whose surface is a plain, stretching for miles on both sides of the line.

The western boundary is not everywhere so obscure or arbitrary. In northern Kansas the drift stops essentially at the eastern edge of the Dakota sandstone escarpment (Smoky Hills) which is taken as the edge of the Great Plains province.[1] West of Lincoln, Neb., the edge of the drift, and of the province, may be traced through several counties, being approximately at the Big Blue River. The surface to the east has at least 200 feet relief, cut into or through a thick, loess-mantled till sheet which presents an obscure morainal front to the west.[2] On the west is a youthful loess plain. Farther north in Nebraska the loess plain is uninterrupted, as shown in the first tier of counties south of the Missouri River where the edge of the drift is at Verdigre Creek.[3]

Underlying Rocks.—Most of the bedrock formations of this section impress their character but little on the surface forms. The older Paleozoics beneath the Mississippian appear only in narrow areas near the two great rivers. In the southeast they include the weak St. Peter sandstone and Maquoketa shale of the Ordovician, and some shale of the Devonian, but all

[1] See the author's companion volume, "Physiography of Western United States," p. 27, McGraw-Hill Book Company, Inc., New York, 1931. For the extent of the glacial drift in Kansas see W. H. Schoewe, Glacial Geology of Kansas, *Pan-Amer. Geol.*, vol. 40, pp. 102–110, 1923.

[2] DARTON, N. H., Underground Waters of a Portion of Southeastern Nebraska, U. S. Geol. Survey, *Water Supply Paper* 12, 1898, ref. to his Pl. 3, geologic and topographic map, also to Pl. 17.

[3] CONDRA, G. E., U. S. Geol. Survey, *Water Supply Paper* 215, 1908. This is one of those places in which the boundary line between two large provinces is less clear than the local boundaries of subdivisions. If Nebraska alone were to be described without reference to its larger relations, it might be advisable to regroup the small areal units, giving primary importance to certain prominent lines of division which have only minor significance when the entire country is considered. *Cf.* G. E. Condra, "Geography of Nebraska," Lincoln, 1906.

weak strata are either thin or local. Above them are the rocks of Mississippian age, mainly limestones, which underlie the upland near the Mississippi. They are relatively resistant and erode in angular forms. To the west they are overlain by the alternating shales and thin limestones of the Pennsylvanian which form the substratum of most of the section.

The Lower and Lower Middle divisions[1] of the Pennsylvanian north of the Missouri River embrace no formation of topographic significance. These divisions combined are familiarly known as the Lower (or Des Moines) Coal Measures. The overlying Upper (or Missourian) coal measures[2] are similar in composition, but a few of the limestone members are thick enough to offer more resistance to erosion and thus make escarpments and structural plains. The lowest of these is the Bethany Falls limestone (Bronson group in Kansas, page 613) near the base of the Kansas City formation and of the Missourian coal measures. Higher, and outcropping farther west, is the Oread limestone at the top of the Douglas group. Still higher and farther west is the Topeka limestone. The Pennsylvanian coal measures are overlain by the Permian, which is largely shale and soft sandstone. But in its lower part are beds of resistant, often flinty, limestone, notably the Cottonwood Falls limestone, which have a significant topographic effect here and make the prominent Flint Hills farther south (page 614). The resistant members of the Pennsylvanian and Permian mentioned here are only the thicker and more continuous representatives of their class. A complete list[3] would be bewildering, since many are merely local. It will be observed that in this section the strong members are almost exclusively limestone.

The Rock Surface.—The form of the rock surface suggests a former peneplain continuous with that already described on the

[1] These terms are used in order to facilitate reference to the standard geologic map of the United States, 1932.

[2] Indicated on the U. S. Geologic map as Upper and Upper Middle Pennsylvanian.

[3] Note the fuller description of rocks of the Osage section on pp. 606–610. An adequate picture of the succession of sediments with a suggestion of the topographic value of each member may be obtained from the diagrams in R. C. Moore's "Historical Geology" (McGraw-Hill Book Company, Inc., New York, 1933). Figures 165 and 175 are particularly valuable for this section.

east (page 503) and on the north (page 566). As elsewhere, it has been etched to a depth of several hundred feet, following a general uplift. It does not now appear that the main streams are degrading their channels, though headwaters in local uplands may be cutting in rock.

While practically the entire area has been carved into hills and valleys, the outcrops of the hard and soft rocks constitute belts differing in elevation. In the main, the belts of outcrop extend north and south, the dip being in a westerly direction with an average steepness reaching 10 to 15 feet per mile in Kansas, but less in Northern Missouri. The tendency of such structural conditions is to produce east-facing escarpments on the harder beds. This effect is very conspicuous in the Osage section to the south (page 611). It is less marked in the Dissected Till Plains, partly for stratigraphic reasons and partly because of the covering of drift and loess. In Iowa and Nebraska (within this section) the tendency is little observed. In Missouri the weak rocks of the Lower coal measures include no scarp makers and are so beveled as to disappear at the east where their thickness is reduced to zero. The more angular forms carved on the Mississippian and older Paleozoics give way gradually to the gentler slopes and smaller relief on the coal measures.

It is not until the Bethany Falls limestone is reached that a marked rise is observed. The Bethany escarpment crosses the Missouri River about 20 miles east of Kansas City and trends north-northeast, intersecting the Iowa boundary near its middle point and becoming less prominent and more obscured farther north. Everywhere in Missouri it marks a rise of 100 to 200 feet. It is described as abrupt but nowhere precipitous. Generally it may at least be called distinct, especially where streams follow its foot.[1] West of its crest an upland some miles in width is underlain by the Bethany Falls limestone, which farther west dips beneath soft shales. The Missouri River crosses this high belt between bluffs 300 feet high and 3 to 4 miles apart whereas, in the lowlands above and below, its valley is twice as wide and one third to one half as deep.

Escarpments and upland belts similar to those just described are seen west of Leavenworth and Lawrence, Kansas, on the

[1] MARBUT, C. F., Physical Features of Missouri, *Mo. Geol. Survey*, vol. 10, pp. 14–109, 1896. See pp. 45 and 68.

Oread limestone,[1] and west of Topeka on the Topeka limestone.[2] (*Cf.* Fig. 170, page 610). It must not be expected that abrupt slopes will appear everywhere at the outcrops of even these more prominent limestones. The outcrops of at least a half dozen more limestone members make local scarps and uplands. The flinty limestones near the base of the Permian underlie a characteristic upland but within this section they make no continuous escarpment as they do farther south.

In speaking of the surface as a former peneplain, it is not intended to assert that the belts of hard rock were ever reduced to the exact level of the soft rock. That would be rare on any peneplain. The subsequent lowering of the softer rocks and the carving of the valleys might conceivably have been accomplished in a single cycle,[3] but it would be in line with what has been assumed by Trowbridge and others farther north (page 567) to assume that the belts of softer rock were reduced to lowlands before the final rise that made the sharper valleys possible.[4] This question may be considered more profitably in connection with the driftless Osage section to the south.

The Drift Cover

Glacial Invasions.—Early in the Glacial epoch this area was covered by ice from the Keewatin center west of Hudson Bay. Probably the ice at that time covered most of the territory in the United States now known to have been glaciated, but its record outside of this section was largely obliterated by later invasions. Except for a limited area in northern New Jersey (page 452), this is the only region in which the ice is known to have advanced much farther than any subsequent ice sheet. Two stages, Nebraskan and Kansan, are recognized here. The ice of the former generally failed to reach the full extent of the latter. Probable exceptions to this rule, mentioned above, are

[1] Leavenworth-Smithville folio (No. 206), U. S. Geol. Survey, 1917.

[2] University Geol. Survey of Kan., vol. 1, 1896. Plate 6 shows a section along the Kansas River.

[3] This is Marbut's hypothesis (*op. cit.*, p. 26).

[4] *Cf.* HERSHEY, O. H., Preglacial Erosion Cycles in Northwestern Illinois, *Amer. Geologist*, vol. 18; 1896. Hershey here distinguishes five base levels but suggests that fewer would appear in northern Missouri. Probably the uplands in Missouri would correspond to his number 2, the lowlands to his number 3, and the stream valleys to his number 4 or 5.

found south of the Missouri and Kansas rivers. Another apparent exception is seen in the deeply loess-covered Platte Valley in southeastern Nebraska, where Nebraskan drift 100 feet thick is described as protruding from beneath the Kansan, both being deeply covered by loess.[1] Generally the Nebraskan drift is buried, or uncovered only in occasional valleys.

The area of exposed Kansan drift represents the southern end of a single glacial lobe, the movement being east toward and beyond the Mississippi, and south and west toward the Missouri. The ice of this stage, or of both Kansan and Nebraskan stages, advanced over the eroded peneplain described above.[2]

Thickness and Topographic Effect of the Drift.—Generally speaking, the thickness of the drift was sufficient to even up the eroded surface and make a smooth plain, much like the younger till plains in Illinois which still retain their flatness in large part. In Iowa, even the hills and ridges were well covered.[3] A thickness of 50 to 100 feet is even now not uncommon. It diminishes toward the edges, especially toward the south. The thickness in Kansas rarely reaches 20 feet; it is more generally 5 feet.[4] Where only thin and scattered patches now survive, it cannot be stated with confidence that the glacial surface ever was a good plain. Morainic ridges are all but unknown. In the Coteau des Prairies the combined Nebraskan and Kansan drifts are at

[1] LUGN, A. L., *Bull. Geol. Soc. Amer.*, vol. 41, pp. 171–172, 1930; vol. 43, p. 190, 1932.

[2] A. C. Trowbridge would make this statement applicable to the Kansan ice but not to the Nebraskan, believing that the latter advanced upon a peneplain whose dissection occurred in the ensuing Aftonian interglacial epoch. Leverett, on the other hand (Outline of Pleistocene History of Mississippi Valley, *Jour. Geol.*, vol. 29, p. 620, 1921; also U. S. Geol. Survey, *Prof. Paper* 161, p. 12, 1932), believes that the dissection came before the first ice invasion. The argument turns mainly on the presence of Nebraskan drift in valleys below the level of present streams.

[3] Much valuable information on the drift and the topography of the several counties in Iowa (arranged alphabetically) is given by W. H. Norton (and others) in Underground Water Resources of Iowa, U. S. Geol. Survey, *Water Supply Paper* 293, 1912.

[4] ADAMS, GEO. I., Physiographic Divisions of Kansas, *Bull. Am. Geog. Soc.*, vol. 34, pp. 89–104, 1902. The statement referred to here is credited by Adams to B. F. Mudge, Geology of Kansas, Kans. State Board Agr., *1st Bienn. Rept.*, pp. 51–52, 1878. An extreme thickness of 40 feet is allowed in U. S. Geol. Survey, folio No. 206.

places 300 to 500 feet thick,[1] thus making a continuous upland of what had been a belt of discontinuous rock masses. This upland, in so far as it is not covered by the younger drift sheets, constitutes a northward extension of the Dissected Till Plains section, trenched or dissected by the Big Sioux River and its tributaries.

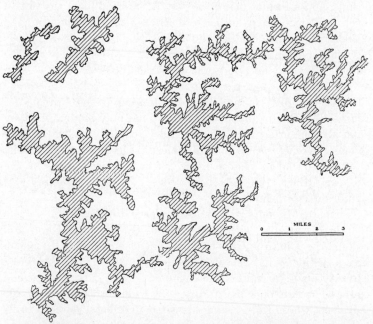

Fig. 165.—Remnants of level upland on the Loess-covered Kansan drift sheet in southern Iowa west of the Des Moines Valley. Blank spaces are areas reduced and roughened by post-Kansan erosion. Level upland remnants are more extensive farther east and less extensive or wanting in southwestern Iowa. (*G. F. Kay and E. T. Apfel.*)

Erosion of the Drift.—Much the larger part of the original Kansan till plain has been destroyed. It is incised by the larger streams to a depth of 200 to 400 feet. Many tributary valleys are at least 200 feet deep. Relief of 100 to 200 feet in a mile is common or general. No doubt, four fifths of the area has now an erosion surface. The remaining fifth is made up of many interstream remnants varying in width from that of a road to that of a township (Fig. 165). Slopes on the eroded Kansan

[1] Leverett, F., U. S. Geol. Survey, *Prof. Paper* 161.

till sheet are less steep than those on the rocks of the Driftless Area.

The largest of the flat uplands are found in Eastern Iowa and near the southern border east of the center of Missouri. Toward the west in Iowa, dissection is more and more complete. In parts of southwestern Iowa all divides are reduced to lines of hills, and a former plain can only be inferred from the nearly level horizon. Even in eastern Iowa, advancement in the postglacial erosion cycle is such that the larger creek valleys have flat bottoms, but the dominating plain there is on the divides. In Taylor and some other counties of the western part the dominating plain is made by the valley bottoms.[1] The Kansan drift of northwestern Iowa and the Coteau des Prairies is without tabular divides, and has only moderate valley flats, all the surface being valley side, generally of gentle slope though the relief is several hundred feet. Dissection in Nebraska is similar to that in western Iowa, but here, as well as east of the Missouri River, the influence of loess on the topography is significant (see below).

Northern Missouri is not distinguished topographically from southern Iowa, but within 50 miles of the Missouri River and east of the Chariton (Pl. 6) large uncut portions of the plain give a distinctly flat aspect to the landscape. This is Marbut's Moberly plain,[2] accounted for by him as due in part to water-laid drift. The Missouri River runs in a wide terraced trench 200 feet deep, whose rim is being dissected to a distance of 10 to 20 miles from the river. The exact original extent of the Kansan Till Plain is hard to determine. Superficially this margin differs little from that of the Ozark province on the opposite side.

In this latitude, as farther north, erosion is more advanced at the west. Near the Missouri and Kansas rivers north and west of Kansas City the glacial drift remains only in patches.[3] Elsewhere the sheet in Kansas may, in occasional spots, be more than 40 feet thick. Superficially the once drift-covered district in Kansas now resembles the driftless Osage section quite as much as it resembles the Dissected Till Plains of southern Iowa. At places only scattered boulders, mainly of Sioux

[1] KAY and APFEL, *op. cit.*, p. 44.
[2] MARBUT, *op. cit.*, p. 69.
[3] U. S. Geol. Survey, folio No. 206, 1917.

quartzite, some of them 10 feet in diameter, give evidence of a former till sheet.[1]

The Loess.—The Dissected Till Plains constitute the central part of the great loess-covered area of central United States.

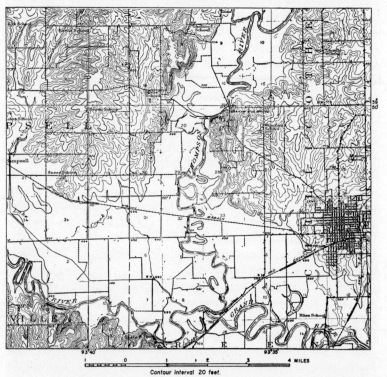

Fig. 166.—Map of part of the Chillicothe quadrangle in the Dissected Till Plain of northwestern Missouri, showing streams of low gradient carving shallow valleys (max. 200 feet) in the loess-covered Kansan drift. Intricate meanders and broad flood plains result. (*U. S. Geol. Survey.*)

They embrace perhaps half of its total area, which extends west on the Great Plains and east into the Driftless Area, beside covering all drift of Illinoian age and a wide strip along the Mississippi in the Coastal Plain province.

The origin of the loess is mentioned in connection with the Till Plains section (page 508). In this section as in that, the

[1] Schoewe, W. H., Glacial Geology of Kansas, *Pan-Amer. Geol.*, vol. 40, p. 102, 1923.

material is in the main "glacial flour" distributed first by water flowing from the ice, and later by wind which lifted it from flood plains. This process was not confined to any one glacial epoch, but the Iowan was much the most important and there has been very little deposition since that time. Hence the Young Drift section to the north is free from loess except a little on the edge of the Iowan. Farther west, mainly in the Great Plains province, a thick loess sheet derived its material from the dust of the Great Plains without the agency of ice. The loess of the Dissected Till Plains section shares this origin, but to separate the loess of glacial origin from that of the Great Plains type with exactness is not possible.

With respect to loess, Iowa is no doubt the most representative state. It is customary there to treat the loess-covered area under three heads, which are applicable likewise to other states. The first, erosional topography unmodified, includes surfaces covered by loess of fairly uniform thickness and therefore having little or no influence on the topography. The second includes surfaces on which the loess accentuates or otherwise modifies the topography. The third, loess depositional topography, includes surfaces whose present relief is largely constructional, *i.e.*, due to the deposition of loess.[1]

Most of the section falls in the first category. The loess has a fairly uniform thickness, rarely reaching 10 feet and generally not over 5 feet. From this relation it is plain that the main features of hill and valley were already carved in the Kansan till plain when most of the loess was laid down. Some loess, however, known as the Loveland, is very much older and occurs at the base of the formation.

A very different type of distribution is seen in a belt 5 to 15 miles wide on the east bluff of the Missouri River from South Dakota to Missouri, in which the loess is so thick as to obscure the older relief. A thickness of 40 to 50 feet is common, and it may reach twice that amount. The surface shows a moderate relief of steep slopes, mainly of irregular, broken, north-south ridges which, while roughened by erosion, are mainly due to wind deposition. Among the divides there is no plan or system. As the total relief may reach 200 feet in the eroded bluffs, it cannot be wholly depositional; still there are con-

[1] KAY and APFEL, *op. cit.*, pp. 38–65.

siderable areas in which the forms of drift beneath the loess are almost as much obscured as the forms of rock below the drift.

The largest area of loess-modified[1] topography is a belt with a maximum width of 40 miles, next east of the one just described. It represents the gradual thinning of the loess with distance from the river, *i.e.*, from the flood plain which furnished most of the dust.   Here the loess, being 10 to 30 feet thick on the hills and

Fig. 167.—Loess covering limestone near St. Louis.   The thickness indicated here by the height of the trees is very common near the larger rivers.

less than 10 feet thick in the valleys, accentuates and otherwise modifies the relief.   Comparable effects are seen in an east-west zone just south of the Iowan drift in eastern Iowa.   The loess thins with distance from that drift sheet as it does from the great rivers.   Here, dunelike accumulations are more frequent on slopes, increasing their number and complicating the relief. This belt overlaps the Iowan drift a very few miles and its northern edge is fairly definite.   On the south it merges into the unmodified erosion topography.

---

[1] The term "loess mantled," as used by the Iowa geologists to indicate "modified by loess deposition," is not wholly fortunate since it is equally applicable to the entire area of the loess and is apt to be so understood.

DRAINAGE

Most of the minor drainage lines of the present are consequent on the Kansan drift. This is strongly suggested by their parallelism. They seem to have been free to follow the regional slope without being seriously turned aside by minor relief features.[1] The drainage of the Coteau des Prairies was restrained on the west by the nearly straight Altamont moraine of the Dakota lobe, which interrupts the southwestward slope of the upland and compels the Big Sioux River to follow its front.

The course of the Des Moines River is not far from the axis of the depression in the underlying rock surface described on page 561. Trowbridge makes this the probable preglacial valley of the upper Mississippi, indicating that the river was crowded eastward by the Nebraskan ice sheet, which came from the northwest.[2] The present Des Moines River below Des Moines is believed by Lees[3] to have been consequent on the Nebraskan drift and to have returned to the course thus chosen when the Kansan ice melted. At least it is older than the Kansan drift. Its course north of Des Moines was subject to displacement by the Kansan glacier and again in part by the Wisconsin glacier.

By what lines the preglacial stream in the upper Des Moines Valley gathered its waters is poorly known. On evidence obtained by drilling it was suggested by Todd[4] that the preglacial Niobrara River continued eastward to the Raccoon valley (see map, Pl. 5) and joined the Des Moines. This is part of the larger problem, how the drainage from the northwest (south of the Hudson Bay drainage) reached the Mississippi and the Gulf. It is enough to say that the Missouri River in its present form represents an attempt to get around the ice. It must have picked its way at or near the edge of the glacier, following such valleys as it found, and receiving from the west the streams

---

[1] This may be seen on the Geological Map of the United States, 1932.

[2] TROWBRIDGE, A. C., Upper Mississippi Valley Structure, *Bull. Geol. Soc. Amer.*, vol. 45, pp. 519–527, 1934.

[3] LEES, J. H., Physical Features and Geological History of the Des Moines Valley, *Ia. Geol. Survey*, vol. 25, 423–615, 1914.

[4] TODD, J. E., Pleistocene History of the Missouri River, *Science*, vol. 39, p. 268, 1914.

whose lower courses were blocked by the ice.   For a considerable distance on the Nebraska boundary the present valley is so wide as to indicate that the river fell back to its old course, or at least to the course of *some* old river when the ice melted.

On the northeastern boundary of Kansas is one of the newer segments of the Missouri River, owing to displacement by the ice.   At Kansas City the river enters the wide preglacial valley of the Kansas River and follows it eastward for 70 miles, where it unites with the valley of another large preglacial stream from the northwest, which has been identified with the Platte.[1]

The Mississippi River seems to follow its preglacial course from near St. Paul to the vicinity of Clinton, Iowa.[2]   The narrow valley cut in rock between that city and Muscatine indicates that a new course was chosen.   This course includes the Upper Rapids and Rock Island.   Leading respectively southwest and southeast from near Clinton are two capacious drift-filled valleys known only by drilling, either of which may have contained the preglacial Mississippi (Fig. 168).   The smaller of the two filled valleys parallels the river on the Iowa side for 40 miles, *i.e.*, to a point above Muscatine, below which the present river follows it to southern Illinois, except for a 12-mile stretch (the Lower Rapids) above the mouth of the Des Moines River.

The larger of the buried valleys leads southeastward to the bend of the Illinois River at Hennepin.   It is at least probable that this valley, with its continuation along the lower Illinois, was the preglacial, or at least pre-Kansan, valley of the Mississippi.[3]   In that case the stream on the west side was a tributary (distinguished here as the Iowa Branch) draining eastern

[1] GREENE, F. C., Preliminary Sketch of the History of the Lower Missouri, *Bull. Geol. Soc. Amer.*, vol. 32, pp. 83–86, 1921.

[2] LEVERETT, F., Outline of Pleistocene History of Mississippi Valley, *Jour. Geol.*, vol. 29, pp. 615–626, 1921.   This paper is a convenient summary of much that Leverett has written on the history of the Mississipppi River. W. H. Schoewe (The Origin and History of Lake Calvin, *Ia. Geol. Survey*, vol. 29, Appendix *A*, 1924) gives a bibliography of contributions to the history of the Upper Mississippi River.

[3] The evidence for this consists largely in data obtained from borings. Consult Leverett's papers already cited for depths to bedrock along this course.   (See also page 517 of this book.)   Trowbridge's view, as stated above in connection with the Des Moines River, is that this easterly course of the Mississippi was a trunk stream when the river was crowded eastward by the Nebraskan ice sheet.

Iowa. The assumption is that these two important streams, the Mississippi-Illinois and the Iowa Branch, united at the present mouth of the Illinois. Both courses lead from the latitude of Clinton, Iowa, to the mouth of the Illinois, the distances being about the same. The switching of the Mississippi

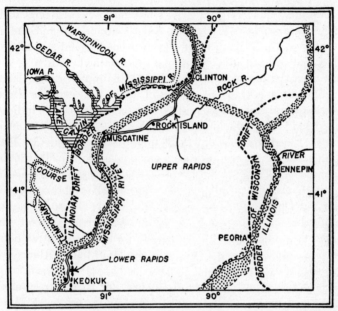

Fig. 168.—Sketch map showing possible preglacial courses of the Mississippi River in southeastern Iowa and northwestern Illinois. Dotted bands indicate large valleys, in part filled by drift and known only by drilling. The Illinoian drift border, Glacial Lake Calvin, and the temporary course of the Mississippi are also shown. (*Leverett, Jour. Geol. vol.* 29.)

from the one to the other (assuming that hypothesis to be correct) was the only really large change made by glaciation in the course of the Mississippi south of St. Paul.

The drainage line between Iowa and Illinois has been subject to pushing back and forth. The earlier ice came from the west, crowding the headwaters of the old Iowa branch eastward one or more times.[1] Much later the Illinoian ice came from the

[1] It is unnecessary in this discussion to consider the Nebraskan and Kansan epochs separately. It is not necessary to raise the question how far the old river was pushed to the east. The history of the river in each glacial and interglacial epoch is discussed by Leverett in his paper on the

northeast, crowding the streams westward. This unified the main flow of the Mississippi with the drainage of eastern Iowa. All together formed a single stream at the edge of the Illinoian ice. For a distance of more than 100 miles in eastern Iowa this temporary course lay west of the present Mississippi, but nowhere more than 20 miles. Some of its tributaries from the west were extensively ponded. The overflow of the Iowa and Cedar rivers coalesced, forming Lake Calvin.[1] When the ice disappeared, this stream found a lower course across the newly deglaciated surface, and there it has remained. Most of this course is in the preglacial valley of the old Iowa Branch. There the channel is cut in the filling of till. Between the valley of the ancestral Mississippi and that of the Iowa Branch a divide was crossed. Here the present river flows over a rocky bed which includes the Upper Rapids, 15 miles long, ending at Rock Island, and a longer section with a narrow valley from Davenport to Muscatine.

The Illinoian ice from the east did not cover the site of the Lower or Des Moines Rapids, and the stream in its detour around the ice came back to the present course above that point. This bit of the river therefore antedates the Illinoian ice epoch. Just when or how it was chosen as part of the course is not definitely known.[2]

Resources.—The resources of this section are related mainly to the Pleistocene mantle rock. Coal is by far the most important mineral resource from the consolidated rocks beneath. The parent material of most of the soil is loess, and the high standing of Iowa among agricultural states attests its fertility (*cf.* page 589). Like the sections on the east, the Dissected Till Plains are largely prairie (Fig. 196, page 690). Even in the parts mapped as originally forest there was always much grassland. On the other hand, trees covered the steeper slopes, especially those facing north, in the area classed as prairie. The aggregate of such areas in the Dissected Till Plains is con-

---

Lower Rapids of the Mississippi River, *Jour. Geol.*, vol. 7, pp. 1–22, 1899. See also A. C. Trowbridge, 9th Annual Field Conference of the Kansas Geological Survey, p. 62, 1935.

[1] SCHOEWE, *loc. cit.*

[2] This question is discussed by Leverett in the papers already cited; see also U. S. Geol. Survey, *Mon.* 38, pp. 89*ff.*, 1899.

siderable, and distinctly larger than in the newer and less eroded drift sheets.[1]

THE OSAGE SECTION

DEFINITION AND BOUNDARIES

A long southward extension of the Central Lowland, stretching from Kansas to Texas between the Interior Highland and the Great Plains, was never glaciated. This is the Osage section. It is a plain of low relief, interrupted at intervals by east-facing escarpments which indicate the presence of stronger strata in a great mass of relatively weak rocks dipping gently west or north-west toward the syncline of the Great Plains.

The Kansas and Missouri rivers approximately mark the much eroded edge of the glacial drift, which is the northern limit of this section. The eastern boundary against the Ozark Plateau is essentially at the edge of the Pennsylvanian rocks where these overlap the low Ozark dome. As the lowest formation of the Pennsylvanian is the weak Cherokee shale, its actual edge is generally inconspicuous, though not so along the Neosho River in Oklahoma. This line, despite its weakness in topographic expression, separates areas of decidedly different physiographic character.

The Osage section and the Arkansas Valley section of the Interior Highland (page 663) have much in common. A rather indefinite straight line or zone between Muskogee and McAlester, Okla., separates the Arkansas Valley, with its gently folded rocks and (mainly) east-west ridges, from the plain described above, with its east-facing escarpments. The separation of the Osage section from the Ouachita Mountains farther south is nowhere obscure. The remainder of the eastern boundary is against the seaward-dipping Cretaceous rocks of the Coastal Plain province (page 101). The lowest formation of this latter system is an easily eroded sandstone whose thin edge, resting on the Carboniferous substratum of the Osage section, is not strongly marked in a topographic way. A few miles east of the contact a strong limestone appears in an infacing escarpment (Fig. 28, page 103). In northern Texas the trend of the line

[1] For a classification and discussion of Iowa prairies see B. Shimek, The Prairies, Ia. State Univ. Lab. Nat. Hist., *Bull.*, vol. 6, pp. 169–240, 1911.

thus defined is north-south, but in central Texas it turns to the west and constitutes the southern boundary of the Osage section and of the Central Lowland.[1]

The western boundary of this section through much of its length is a definite east-facing escarpment several hundred feet high. It is popularly known as the "break of the plains," the "plains" in this case signifying the Tertiary mantle which here covers the interstream areas of the Great Plains province. Almost everywhere south of the Arkansas River the escarpment is either an abrupt rise, plainly seen from the lowland, or a belt of rough country. In Oklahoma and the Panhandle of Texas the wide valleys of east-flowing streams cause the escarpment to be deeply scalloped.

The province boundary in southern Kansas is a 10- to 30-mile zone of hills picturesquely carved in the edge of the Great Plains border and known as the Red Hills, their substratum being the red sandstone, shale, and gypsum of the Permian.[2] For a stretch of 50 miles north of these hills, the lowland of the Osage section rises westward without interruption, merging with the Great Plains in the so-called "Great Bend Lowland." The boundary here is necessarily arbitrary and is so drawn as to connect the Red Hills on the south with the Smoky Hills on the north, the latter being a much eroded cuesta of Dakota (Cretaceous) sandstone. (*Cf.* page 591, boundary of the Dissected Till Plains.)

Underlying Rocks

General.—The underlying rocks of the Osage section consist almost entirely of Pennsylvanian and Permian strata. Exception is made only of two local uplifts, the Arbuckle and Wichita Mountains, in which older rocks rise to the surface. The Pennsylvanian and Permian rocks vary somewhat from north to south, though characterized throughout by alternations of shales with stronger formations as well as by westerly dips.

Rocks of Pennsylvanian Age.—North of the Arkansas River much the larger part of the Pennsylvanian system is shale.

[1] For this and the western boundary against the Great Plains see the author's companion volume, "Physiography of Western United States," pp. 3–4, 25–30, McGraw-Hill Book Company, Inc., New York, 1931.

[2] Full description by C. S. Prosser, *Kans. Univ. Geol. Survey*, vol. 2, p. 85, 1897.

This is specially true in the lowest group (Cherokee) where only an occasional sandstone is a little more resistant. In the remainder of the column, limestones occur at frequent intervals (Fig. 169). They constitute in the aggregate only the smaller part of the system, but because of their greater resistance to erosion they are relatively conspicuous.[1] Toward the south, even before the Arkansas River is reached, the limestones become thin and some of them disappear. Concurrently, sandstone beds, which are relatively thin and unimportant in Kansas, thicken and take the place of the limestones as scarp makers. South of the Arkansas River in Oklahoma, limestone is very subordinate. Shale predominates while sandstone makes most of the stronger strata.[2]

[1] For the column of formations as known from drilling in southeastern Kansas, see Kans. Geol. Survey, *Bull.* 3, pp. 90–105, Figs. 14–19, 1917; also U. S. Geol. Survey, *Bull.* 296, Pl. 3, and folio No. 159. All Pennsylvanian formations in Kansas are shown diagrammatically by R. C. Moore in his "Historical Geology," p. 300, McGraw-Hill Book Company, Inc., New York, 1933.

[2] See GOULD, C. N., Index to the Stratigraphy of Oklahoma, Okla. Geol. Survey, *Bull.* 35, 1925, especially the table following p. 113.

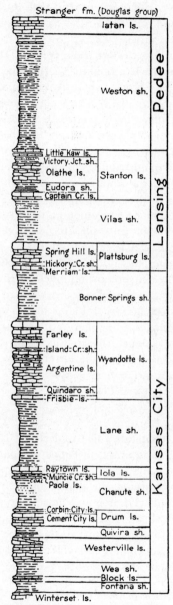

FIG. 169.—Partial column of the Missouri series of Pennsylvanian rocks in Kansas showing a preponderance of soft rocks. The harder formations (almost exclusively limestones in the part here shown) make the six escarpments marked *K* and *L* in Fig. 172. (*R. C. Moore and others.*)

In northern Texas[1] shale and sandy shale continue to be more abundant than any other type of rock, but thick, strong strata of limestone and sandstone are very important and are much in evidence.   In a total thickness of 5500 to 6500 feet, the lowest or Strawn group (3500 to 4000 ft.) outcropping at the east is largely dark shale with massive sandstone layers in the upper part. Then follow 950 to 1500 feet (Canyon group) in which massive limestone is most prominent, but thick, sandy shales and some sandstone are present.   In the remaining 820 to 1180 feet (Cisco group) outcropping farther west, red, sandy shale predominates, but sandstone strata are important and thin limestones occur.

Rocks of Permian Age.—The Permian in the Osage section north of Texas is in the main a great mass of shale.   However, at its base in Kansas and northern Oklahoma are at least 400 feet of beds in which limestone is more abundant.[2]   At several horizons this limestone is so full of chert that the latter is the most conspicuous substance seen.   Even the purer limestone is more resistant to weathering than shale.   South of the Arkansas River this limestone series is much less prominent.   Here, as in the Pennsylvanian rocks, sandstones take the place of limestones. Above these lower and harder beds, limited to a few hundred feet in thickness, is the Enid formation, which comprises some 1200 to 1500 feet of shale and shaly sandstone.   Hard rocks are negligible in this thick middle part of the Permian section. A red or ruddy color is almost universal in the Permian of Oklahoma, and even in the uppermost Pennsylvanian rocks. The eastern limit of red color, defined geographically, not stratigraphically, trends northwestward, entering Kansas near the meridian of 97°30′.[3]   The color of the rocks is preserved in the soil and imparts a distinctive aspect to the landscape.

The Permian rocks above this great mass of shale contain some more resistant beds of sandstone, gypsum, and dolomite.

---

[1] PLUMMER, F. B., and R. C. MOORE, Stratigraphy of the Pennsylvanian Formations of North-Central Texas, *Tex. Univ. Bull.* 2132, 1921.   See especially Tables 1 and 2, p. 23.   Thicknesses given here are taken from Sellards, *Tex. Univ. Bull.* 3232, 1932.

[2] See Cottonwood Falls folio, p. 6, U. S. Geol. Survey, 1904.   The section here referred to also includes a typical portion of the upper Pennsylvanian.

[3] AURIN, FRITZ, Geology of the Red Beds of Oklahoma, Okla.   Geol. Survey, *Bull.* 30, 1917.   Figure 1, p. 8, is a geologic map showing limits of red color.

In Kansas these are limited to the uppermost 400 or 500 feet. Their outcrop makes the Red Hills, mentioned above, which are the fringe of the Great Plains province. In Oklahoma the thickness of rocks above the Enid formation is much greater, it may be as much as 1000 feet,[1] and the surface on these beds, for reasons stated on page 619, is included in the Osage section of the Central Lowland. The lowest of these stronger formations is the Blaine, whose beds of gypsum are scarp makers.

The Permian of northern Texas is much like that of Oklahoma, red shales and weak sandstones predominating.[2] The striking red color gives out at the south near the 33d parallel. Near the top of the lowest division, the Wichita group, are beds of limestone, thick and resistant at the south and dying out toward the north. Another 2000 feet of red and blue clays, sandy shale, and sandstone constitute the Clear Fork group, roughly equivalent to the Enid. Above this (as in Oklahoma above the Enid formation) come more prominent sandstones and limestones with strong local beds of gypsum, constituting the lower part of the Double Mountain group, which also embraces several higher bands of strong limestone, or dolomite, and gypsum.

Quaternary Sediments. –Large spots in Texas west of the 99th meridian are covered by the Seymour (Pleistocene) formation which consists of sands and gravels overlain by silt. To a very large degree this formation consists of the worked-over and redeposited material of the late Tertiary mantle of the High Plains. The latter is not mapped in this area, but there is much gravel in both Texas and Oklahoma whose exact amount of rehandling is uncertain. Where it underlies a flat surface or is otherwise recognized as Quaternary, as in Texas, it is classed as Seymour. But a good deal of sand and gravel is also found in eroded areas where its chief topographic significance may be that it supplies material for the abundant bars in the streams,

---

[1] AURIN, *op. cit.*, diagram, p. 25, C. N. Gould in U. S. Geol. Survey, *Water Supply Paper* 148, gives numerous sections, Figs. 3–26, of the Permian in Oklahoma.

[2] For brief description see C. H. Gordon, Geology and Underground Waters of the Wichita Region, U. S. Geol. Survey, *Water Supply Paper* 317 1913.

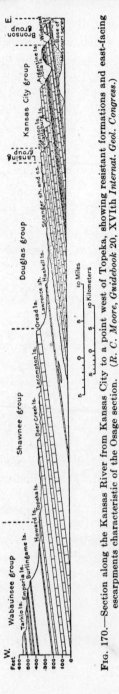

Fig. 170.—Section along the Kansas River from Kansas City to a point west of Topeka, showing resistant formations and east-facing escarpments characteristic of the Osage section. (R. C. Moore, Guidebook 20, XVIth Internat. Geol. Congress.)

and for the still more abundant dunes (page 621).

Structure.—The dominant direction of dip in this area is from the Ozark and Ouachita uplifts toward the axis of the broad syncline of the Great Plains. Near the northern end, dips rarely exceed 20 to 25 feet per mile, but they increase southward occasionally to 60 feet per mile in eastern Oklahoma and again decrease somewhat in Texas. From the eastern boundary of the province in Texas the beds dip in both directions. It is not an anticline, but the northwest-dipping rocks of the Osage section are overlain by the east-dipping rocks of the Coastal Plain province. At places their opposing outcrops form escarpments facing each other across the province boundary.

In general the strike is north-northeast and south-southwest, but in Missouri it wraps around the Ozarks, while in southern Oklahoma it is complicated by the Arbuckle-Wichita uplift. These mountain uplifts (see further mention under Topography) lie on an axis extending west by north from the Ouachita uplift. The effect of this axis is to make northerly (even northeasterly) dips from the Wichita Mountains, so that lines of outcrop in the upper Permian are offset to the west a full 100 miles, while a broad structural sag, the Anadarko basin, appears northeast of the Wichita Mountains. Most of the broad regional dips in the Osage section are here and there interrupted or otherwise affected by gentle folds of a lower order. These afford most of the requisite structures for the great oil fields for which the section is famous.

Topography

Southeastern Kansas and Adjacent Areas.[1]—From the Kansas River to the Arkansas, nowhere does a wide horizon deviate much from flatness. Local relief is generally less than 250 feet, this amount (which is exceptional) occurring only where the larger streams are cutting in the harder rocks. Strips of very mildly rolling surface on shale alternate with narrower, higher,

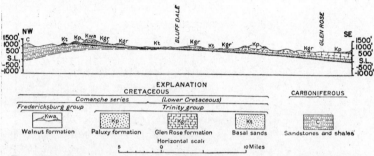

Fig. 171.—Cross section of the eastern boundary of the Osage section in Texas, showing the west-dipping Carboniferous beds of the Central Lowland and the east-dipping Cretaceous beds of the Coastal Plain. (*R. T. Hill.*)

and more hilly strips on the outcropping edges of limestones (and a few sandstones). These hilly belts, where well developed, constitute escarpments facing toward the Ozark uplift. Near streams their heights may reach 200 feet, but 50 feet is more common and most of them disappear locally. The outcrops of at least 18 limestone formations between the Flint Hills and the Ozarks cause escarpments in part or all of their extent. If the Flint Hills be included there are at least 25 fairly distinct limestone escarpments. A single straight line may cross as many as a dozen such belts (Fig. 172).[2] As the general horizon is nearly flat and the dip is very small, any one escarpment, though preserving its general direction across the state, is, in detail, an extremely crooked line, running up the valleys and

[1] ADAMS, GEORGE I., Physiographic Divisions of Kansas, *Bull. Amer. Geog. Soc.*, vol. 34, pp. 89–104, 1902. This paper is valuable for its descriptions, although the province boundaries given by Adams are not those used in this book.

[2] All of these are described by George I. Adams in his paper on the Physiography of Southeastern Kansas, *Trans. Kans. Acad. Sci.*, vol. 16, pp. 53–63, 1899.

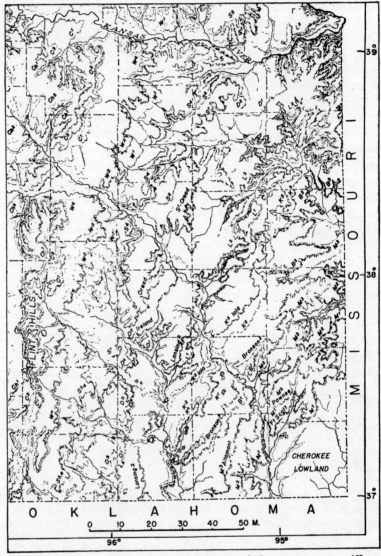

FIG. 172.—Map of eastern Kansas showing east-facing escarpments. (*Kans. Geol. Survey.*)

zigzagging back and forth in a zone as wide as a township.[1] On the shales between these outcrops of harder rock, the surface is not far from the local base level, as indicated by the beds of the larger streams. Divides within these shale belts are so low that further reduction is very slow. Each shale lowland is the bottom of a shallow trough, each cuesta-making limestone being stripped for a short distance back from its escarpment.

Among the more distinctive features is the Cherokee lowland, a strip 25 miles wide developed on the Cherokee shale at the base of the Pennsylvanian in southeastern Kansas and adjacent states. Its very gently rolling surface merges gradually into that of the stripped Mississippian limestone of the Ozark plateau. On the west it is limited by the escarpment of the Fort Scott limestone, 120 feet high near the Neosho River. In Missouri these same features in the same relations have been called the Nevada lowland and the Henrietta escarpment.[2] Both features also extend into Oklahoma. Toward the south the Cherokee formation thickens and its sandy members increase in importance, giving rise to local table lands and escarpments. Yet the general character is well preserved, even somewhat beyond the Arkansas River.[3]

West of the Fort Scott escarpment are others at intervals of 5 to 10 miles (Fig. 172). West of the Verdigris River, where it passes into Oklahoma, is the edge of the Bronson group. This may be traced, either as a single escarpment or along two or more lines, northeastward into Missouri (where it has been called the Bethany Falls escarpment) and less clearly to central Iowa.[4]

The Chautauqua Hills.—West of the 96th meridian the shales above the Iola limestone illustrate the gradual change from shale to sandstone as the beds are traced southward. Seventy five miles north of the state boundary the platform west of the Iola

[1] ADAMS, G. I., G. H. GIRTY, and D. WHITE, Stratigraphy and Paleontology of the Upper Carboniferous Rocks of the Kansas Section, U. S. Geol. Survey, *Bull.* 211, Pl. 3, 1903.

[2] MARBUT, C. F., Physical Features of Missouri, *Mo. Geol. Survey*, vol. 10, pp. 44, 67, 1896; *cf.* HAWORTH, E., *Kans. Univ. Geol. Survey*, vol. 3, pp. 85–86, 1898.

[3] TAFF, J. A., Muskogee folio (No. 132), U. S. Geol. Survey, p. 8, 1906. Note the topographic contrast along the Neosho River, which here marks the province boundary.

[4] MARBUT, *op. cit.*, p. 45, 1896.

escarpment is of the ordinary type described above. With increasingly arenaceous character toward the south, the plain becomes less perfect until on the Oklahoma line its place is taken by escarpments of sandstones in the Douglas group,[1] cut by narrow, steep valleys to a maximum depth of over 200 feet. These are the Chautauqua Hills.[2]   They are exceptional in Kansas but characterize a considerable area in Oklahoma (page 616).

The Chautauqua Hills are succeeded on the west by the Oread escarpment, one of the best in the series, well known farther north at Lawrence and Leavenworth. Others to the west of it are of the same type. Of the entire series very few are strong enough and continuous enough to be recognizable in the Dissected Till Plains north of the Kansas River.

The Flint Hills.—The Flint Hills cuesta, whose east-facing escarpment is near the meridian of 96°30′, is an exceptional feature of the Central Lowland. Only in size does it form an exception. Its structure, its reason for existence, its history and its geomorphic type are exactly those of the other east-facing escarpments already noted. Moreover, it is succeeded on the west by one of the most typical lowlands of the province. Yet its elevation approaches that of the Plains Border. The thinner soil and shorter grass cause the landscape of the cuesta to suggest that of the Great Plains. Moreover, the Flint Hills cuesta at the north (largely in the Dissected Till Plains) is contiguous with the Smoky Hills of the Great Plains province. For some such reasons the Flint Hills cuesta was at one time treated as a peninsula of the Great Plains.[3]

This feature owes its existence to the large proportion of limestone in the first 400 feet of Permian beds (page 608). Chert abounds at several horizons. The remains of flint quarries, exploited by Indians, may still be seen in the Kaw reservation at the south end.[4]   The limestone itself is sufficient to account for a ridge, but the protecting mantle of flints is an important

[1] Described as "Buxton formation" (obsolete term) in U. S. Geol. Survey Independence folio (No. 159), 1908.

[2] ADAMS, GEO. I., Physiography of Southeastern Kansas, *Trans. Kans. Acad. Sci.*, vol. 16, p. 60, 1899.

[3] ADAMS, GEO. I., Physiographic Divisions of Kansas, *Bull. Am. Geol. Soc.*, vol. 34, pp. 88–104, 1902.

[4] MEAD, J. R., The Flint Hills of Kansas, *Trans. Kans. Acad. Sci.*, vol. 17, pp. 207–208, 1901.

factor. As a result of eastward drainage from the Flint Hills, considerable areas were veneered with flint gravel, the remains of which still dominate the topography in some districts (notably in parts of Lyon and Greenwood counties) by constituting a protective cover. Where this cover remains, the alternating cuestas and lowlands failed to develop.[1] Historically therefore, these gravels are correlated with the extensive peneplain indicated by the tops of the cuestas.

From central Kansas to northern Oklahoma the Flint Hills upland has distinctly the form of a cuesta.[2] The summit

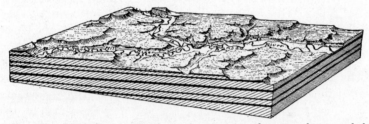

Fig. 173.—Block diagram showing rock structure and topography around the junction of the Kansas and Smoky Hill rivers. Hard strata shown in black. (*R. C. Moore.*)

elevation for most of the distance is between 1500 and 1600 feet. A slope to the east of 400 to 500 feet in 10 to 15 miles is common. Some narrow valleys like that of the Cottonwood River incise the escarpment several hundred feet with very steep slopes. The several strong limestones cause the general slope to be more or less distinctly terraced. The scarp slope is considerably dissected, and streams in the upland are sending out tributaries in steep-sided valleys, but the gently rolling summit upland merges on the west with the smooth and gentle dip slope which leads down to the Arkansas valley. At places the upland surface is pitted with sinkholes.

Northward from central Kansas the height of the cuesta diminishes and its form becomes less and less marked; the escarpment is most typical near the larger streams. In the

[1] R. C. Moore, personal communication.

[2] Henry Gannett in his Gazetteer of Kansas (U. S. Geol. Survey, *Bull.* 154, 1898), gives a contour map of Kansas on a scale of 1:750,000 with a contour interval of 100 feet. The map, being old, is necessarily much generalized, but the feature mentioned here is clear.

midst of this upland the Smoky Hill and Republican rivers unite to form the Kansas River, a thoroughly graded stream meandering between bluffs 150 to 200 feet high and 2 to 3 miles apart. In and near these bluffs is the typical scenery of the Flint Hills.[1] Dendritic tributaries are beginning to dissect the rolling limestone upland whose level, remote from rivers, reaches 1300 to 1400 feet, or 300 feet above that of the lowest valleys.

The use of the term "upland" in this district, which is a part of the "Central Lowland province," exemplifies the relative sense in which these terms are used. The Flint Hills Upland is not the typical Central Lowland, nor are the Smoky Hills on the west typical Great Plains, but the Central Lowland *province* includes some areas that are not good lowland, just as the Great Plains province includes much that is not plains.

Eastern Oklahoma.—Between Kansas and Texas both the rocks and the landscape undergo gradual changes. The dying out of limestone formations and the development of sandstones has already been mentioned. The latter make most of the escarpments south of the Arkansas River and west of the 96th meridian. The area east of this belt in Oklahoma, commonly called "prairie plains," differs little from the corresponding scarped plains in Kansas (Fig. 172). The delimitation of "sandstone hills" on the west and "prairie plains"[2] on the east cannot be expressed in terms of geological formations, since the dividing line crosses their outcrops diagonally.

At the north, the belt of "Sandstone Hills" is identical with the Chautauqua Hills, plus all the cuestas farther west, including the diminished southern end of the Flint Hills. It therefore includes some limestone cuestas, but with one or two exceptions these disappear at the Arkansas River. Within the area of sandstone cuestas a relief of 300 to 400 feet is not uncommon. The narrow shale lowlands are much like their more extensive analogues farther east, but the scarp slopes are often strewn with blocks of sandstone to such an extent as to exclude farming. The summits,

---

[1] HAY, ROBT., Geology of the Fort Riley Military Reservation, Kansas, U. S. Geol. Survey, *Bull.* 137; MOORE, R. C., The Environment of Camp Funston, Kans. State Geol. Survey, *Bull.* 4, 1918.

[2] These terms are used by L. C. Snider in his Geography of Oklahoma (Okla. Geol. Survey, *Bull.* 27, 1917) and are justified as a broad generalization empirically expressed.

where broad and smooth, are pastured rather than farmed.
The ridges, especially the scarp slopes, are in large part forested,
mainly with oak. The breadth of this belt is 50 to 60 miles.
At the south it is cut off by the Arbuckle Uplift (page 622). The
equivalent of this same belt in Texas is described on page 619.

The Redbeds Plains.—Extending 50 to 150 miles west from
the sandstone cuestas of Oklahoma and the Flint Hills of Kansas,

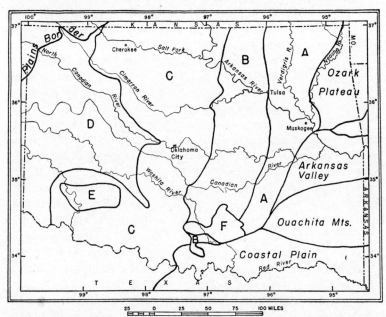

Fig. 174.—Sketch map of eastern Oklahoma showing minor divisions of the
Osage section; *A*, Prairie Plains; *B*, Sandstone Hills; *C*, Redbeds Plains; *D*,
Gypsum Hills; *E*, Wichita Mountain district; *F*, Arbuckle Upland. (*Altered
from L. C. Snider, Okla. Geol. Survey, Bull. 27.*)

is a great smooth lowland on the thick mass of Permian shale,
called the Enid formation in Oklahoma. Minor sandstones are
included, notably near the base, outcropping along the eastern
edge in line with the Flint Hills. Some of these make low
escarpments, but sufficiently prominent to contribute to the
vagueness of the eastern boundary. For the most part this belt,
stretching from central Kansas to north-central Texas (described
below) is a mildly rolling plain in which relief rarely reaches
50 feet. Only the main east-flowing streams have deeper valleys.

Except at the ends its soil, like the rocks beneath, is strikingly red.   The name Redbeds Plains is frequently used.[1]

The greater part of this plain in Kansas is comprised in that part of the Arkansas Valley where the river flows south to get around the end of the Flint Hills.   Its type is the smooth, rich plain of which Wichita is the center.   Farther north, with the thinning of the shales, the plain narrows and disappears between the Flint Hills upland and the Smoky Hills escarpment.   For a space of 50 miles between the Smoky Hills and the Red Hills this plain extends westward in the valley of the Arkansas with no topographic feature to divide it from the Great Plains province.

The Gypsum Hills.—West of the Redbeds Plains the more resistant beds, gypsum, sandstone, and dolomite, interbedded with soft shales in the upper part of the Permian, cause an alternation of escarpments and smooth plains, somewhat as on the Pennsylvanian rocks.   These escarpments differ from those farther east in being less continuous and less constant in direction.[2]   Lack of continuity is partly due to the fact that the gypsum itself (the chief scarp maker) grades laterally into other sediments even in very short distances.[3]   The inconstancy of direction is partly due to the fact that the beds in the west are so nearly parallel to the surface that outcrops must make long detours around the valleys.   Added to these factors is the northerly dip from the Wichita uplift, which causes the otherwise north-south lines of outcrop to run east-west, and thus to be offset 100 miles.   These conditions have caused the pattern of hilly belts and smooth belts in western Oklahoma to be somewhat patchy, and make their correct interpretation rather less obvious than that of similar features in eastern Oklahoma, or even of the same features on the Permian of Texas.

The area here concerned is geologically the southward extension of the Red Hills of Kansas (page 606).   In that state the belt of Red Hills, 20 to 30 miles wide, is contiguous with a typical portion of the Great Plains province, some 300 or 400 feet

---

[1] L. C. Snider in his "Geography of Oklahoma" gives good descriptions.

[2] FENNEMAN, NEVIN M., Physiographic Provinces and Sections in Western Oklahoma and Adjacent Parts of Texas, U. S. Geol. Survey, *Bull.* 730, pp. 116–124, 1922.

[3] GOULD, *op. cit.*, p. 59.

higher than the Redbeds Plains. The Red Hills are merely the dissected margin of the higher plain.[1] Near the Kansas-Oklahoma boundary, however, this broad belt of hills, or dissected escarpment, divides into two or more branches. The western branch (uppermost beds), trending southward just within the Texas panhandle, continues to mark the province boundary. The easternmost branch after entering Oklahoma turns to the southeast and makes the eastern escarpment of the Gypsum Hills. This escarpment, made by strong gypsum strata in the Blaine formation, is the most conspicuous of its class, being at places more than 100 feet high, but other escarpments of gypsum, sandstone, and dolomite occur farther west.

Plains on shale in this part of the section are locally quite as smooth as those on the Enid or the Cherokee. But they are less continuous and are, moreover, a little more deeply trenched by the main streams, hence more liable to dissection. Sand dunes are also more common.

Topography in Texas.—The massive and resistant limestones and sandstones in the Pennsylvanian of northern Texas give rise to a topography which is, at places, quite out of harmony with the general character of the section. Escarpments are more rugged, and partially dissected dip slopes are more like young plateaus. Stream valleys are relatively narrow and steep. In most of the area these differences are not so pronounced as to obscure the analogy of this district with the rest of the section. But the deep entrenchment of the Brazos River, especially in the limestones of the Canyon group (page 608), has so favored downcutting by tributaries as to allow unusual development of these aberrant features.[2] The river meanders over a 3- or 4-mile zone in a series of almost complete loops, entrenched to a depth of 500 feet in the highest cuestas, in a young valley so narrow as to exclude flood plains. This feature of rejuvenation is matched by the presence of tributary canyons and at places by the carving of the surface into steep-sided mesas; also by great development of scarps, one near Palo Pinto

[1] For more detailed statement see Nevin M. Fenneman, Physiographic Divisions of the United States, *Ann. Assoc. Amer. Geog.*, vol. 18, p. 311, 1928.

[2] Well shown on the Pickwick and adjacent topographic sheets. See also the Palo Pinto sheet, drawn on a smaller scale and more generalized. Also Plummer and Moore, *op. cit.*, p. 103.

being 300 to 400 feet high.   Between crests the northwesterly
dip slopes may have gradients up to 30 feet to the mile.[1]

The eastern half of the Permian plain in Texas is essentially
like the Redbeds Plains of Oklahoma, except that the red color
fails south of latitude 33°.   It is mildly rolling rather than flat;
and some weak sandstones in the great body of clay and shale
make low escarpments.   Near the Red River there is no prominent interruption until the Gypsum Hills are reached, a little east
of the 100th meridian.   Forty miles east of that line the Albany
escarpment, made by limestones near the top of the Wichita
group (page 609), begins as a faint rise near the Red River,
increases in height southward, and reaches the limit of the
province as a steep eastward slope 250 feet high.   It lies west of
the county seats, Seymour, Throckmorton, and Albany.   The
higher surface, which extends westward for the next 100 miles to
the "break of the plains," is much like the lowland farther east,
except that an occasional escarpment of gypsum, sandstone, or
dolomite, as in Oklahoma, is more prominent than those east of
the Albany escarpment.[2]

For a combination of reasons, including greater altitude,
stronger rocks, and increasing aridity toward the west, the
surface west of the Albany escarpment has a younger aspect than
farther east.   Its valleys are more angular, and there are more
flat areas not reached by erosion in the current cycle.

RIVERS AND VALLEYS

Drainage Lines.—Most of the main streams follow the regional
slope in unusually straight courses and with remarkable parallelism.   An exception is noted where the Arkansas turns south
from central Kansas as if to get around the Flint Hills.   The
parallelism of the streams suggests superposition.   Subaerial
deposition in the late Tertiary was very extensive.[3]   This seems
to have come after the last general peneplanation and probably

---

[1] *Cf.* HILL, R. T., Physical Geography of the Texas Region, U. S. Geol.
Survey Topographic Atlas, folio No. 3, p. 7, 1900.   Hill here describes the
roughest surface as the "Palo Pinto country," but this is only a limited
district within the larger area of Pennsylvanian rocks, most of which is
much less rugged.

[2] FENNEMAN, NEVIN M., U. S. Geol. Survey, *Bull.* 730, pp. 124–126.

[3] Gould (*op. cit.*, p. 83) thinks that Tertiary deposits once covered "nearly
the entire central and western parts of Oklahoma."

did much to relocate streams by superposition. Straightness and parallelism would thus be favored.

The southerly course of the Arkansas behind the Flint Hills suggests that that upland remained as a swell above the general level when the stream's course was adopted. The level of the river is now held up by its heavy load of sediment and consequent inability to cut deeper. The local and temporary base level thus provided is one of the reasons for the good development of the Great Bend lowland west of the Flint Hills.[1]

Valleys and Channels.—The channels of major streams lie 100 to 200 feet below the levels of the cuestas. Even in the lowlands there may be low bluffs 1 to 2 or 3 miles apart. Such shallow trenches are sufficiently marked off from the rest of the surface to suggest that they belong to a younger cycle. In Texas it is common to observe a gentle but distinct slope, as of an older valley, leading down to the top of the bluff.

All rivers except the Washita have their channels in wide beds of sand, often subdivided by bars, and at places typically braided. This becomes less marked in their lower courses.[2] The rock surface beneath channels is at fairly uniform depths, ranging from 15 to 30 or 40 feet, according to the size of the stream. This is little, if at all, below the depth of possible scour during floods; hence if the rivers are now filling their valleys (as is sometimes affirmed) the effect of such aggradation is as yet very small. An occasional clean-cut and obviously young terrace indicates that downcutting has been relatively recent.[3]

Sand Dunes.—The rivers of Oklahoma, from the Salt Fork of the Arkansas to the Canadian, inclusive, and with less regularity farther south, are bordered by belts of dunes up to 15 miles

[1] For the physiographic relation of this lowland, especially that part of it which lies within the Great Plains province, see the author's volume on the "Physiography of Western United States," pp. 27–28, McGraw-Hill Book Company, Inc., New York, 1931.

[2] *Tex. Univ. Bull.* 2327, 1923, by R. T. Hill, is a "Summary of Physiographic Investigations Made in Connection with the Oklahoma-Texas Boundary Suit," *i.e.*, by the physiographers engaged by the State of Texas. The testimony of these, and of others engaged by the State of Oklahoma and by the United States, contains a large amount of critical information regarding the behavior of the Red River and the features of its valley. See Records of the Supreme Court of the U. S. October Term, 1921.

[3] This question is more fully discussed by the author in U. S. Geol. Survey, *Bull.* 730, pp. 131–133, 1922.

in maximum width.   Some of the hills have the smooth bare surfaces and rounded forms of actively shifting dunes; others are covered with vegetation and are therefore "fixed."   Most of these belts are on the northeast sides of the rivers.   As the prevailing winds are from the southwest and the sands of the broad channels are frequently seen to be moved by wind, it cannot be doubted that a large part of the material of the dunes has come from the beds of the rivers.   On the other hand, it is pointed out[1] that some of the sand is gravelly.   Moreover, there are extensive dune areas along the edge of the Great Plains, quite independent of streams.[2]   These facts require that the sand hills be ascribed in part to mere rearrangement or combing out of the Tertiary and Quaternary formations by wind.

THE ARBUCKLE UPLAND[3]

General.—The Arbuckle upland is a gently inclined plain, sloping southeast and merging with the surface of the Red River Valley at about 750 feet.   Its extreme east-west length is 65 miles and its breadth 30 miles.   The canyon of the Washita River, west of the middle, divides the area into two distinct plateaus.   The so-called Arbuckle Mountains are mainly the 400-foot escarpment on the northern edge of the plateau (local only) or the dissected bluffs of the Washita River, nowhere more than 450 feet high.   The upland at the northwest is 1300 feet high and lies between plains 900 feet high on the south and 1000 feet high on the north, where stream valleys 100 feet deep increase the height of the escarpment.   Steep marginal slopes in the eastern part, except where the Washita Valley follows the edge, are almost limited to the northeastern edge, where a drop from 1100 feet to 750 feet occurs within 4 or 5 miles.   A southeastward slope of 10 feet to the mile on the upland is common.

Rocks and Structure.—The district here considered appears on the geologic map as an isolated area of rocks older than Car-

---

[1] GOULD, *op. cit.*, pp. 82–84.

[2] The Quaternary indicated on the new (1932) geological map of the United States is in part dune sand.   The map in U. S. Geol. Survey, *Water Supply Paper* 148, Pl. 1, is more expressive.

[3] Most of the facts on which the following discussion is based are summarized by J. A. Taff in his Preliminary Report on the Geology of the Arbuckle and Wichita Mountains, U. S. Geol. Survey, *Prof. Paper* 31, 1904. See also, Chester A. Reeds, Okla. Geol. Survey, *Bull.* 3, 1910.

boniferous. Cambrian and Ordovician limestones of the Arbuckle series, 4000 to 6000 feet thick, underlie most of the area. Above these, and outcropping around the margin, are several thousand feet of higher Ordovician and Silurian rocks, likewise mainly limestone but including the Sylvan shale which is 50 to 300 feet thick and topographically significant. Then

Fig. 175.—Gorge of the Washita River in the Arbuckle Upland. The river is here entrenched 350 feet, while running almost at the level of the plain before entering and after leaving the Arbuckle Upland. (*Okla. Geol. Survey.*)

follow the Hunton limestone and the Woodford chert, 600 feet thick and consisting of alternating thin chert beds and shale, hence not resistant. The Mississippian rocks belong mainly to the lowland, but the Sycamore limestone at the base (0 to 200 feet thick) makes an important marginal ridge where present. Second in area of outcrop to the Arbuckle limestone, and underlying a large area in the southeast, are Pre-Cambrian igneous rocks, mainly granite. The geologic column is as follows:

ROCKS OF THE ARBUCKLE UPLIFT[1]

Mississippian:
  Caney shale, maximum thickness, 1600 feet.
  Sycamore limestone; lentils of massive limestone up to 200 feet thick.

[1] Modified from J. A. Taff, *op. cit.*, pp. 17–34.

Mississippian or Devonian:
  Woodford chert; 200 to 700 feet; generally thin-bedded and containing
    much shale.
Devonian or Silurian:
  Hunton limestone group; 160 to 300 feet.
Ordovician:
  Sylvan shale; 50 to 300 feet
  Iola limestone, 500 to 700 feet.
  Simpson formation; sandstone, shale and limestone; 1200 to 2000 feet.
  Arbuckle limestone (lowest part probably Cambrian); 4000 to 6000 feet.
Cambrian:
  Reagan sandstone; thickness from near 0 to 500 feet.
Pre-Cambrian:
  Largely granite.

The Arbuckle Upland, despite its modest height and generally
plain surface, represents an orogenic uplift of 8000 to 10,000 feet.
Generalized and viewed as a whole, it is an anticlinorium whose
axis trends west-northwest. Marginal dips on the southwest
and northeast are steep, commonly 30 to 70 degrees. Dips
in the interior are generally, but not always, small. There are
some minor folds, in some of which the beds are closely corrugated. There are also profound faults, among which are those
by which the granite was brought to its present level. Reference
to structure is necessary to explain certain features, but most
of its details need no mention. A recognition of the general
complexity is useful mainly as a background in the consideration
of the remarkably smooth surface of the upland.

Topography.—To speak of the Arbuckle Upland as a "plain"
is justified (1) by its horizon, (2) by its history, and (3) by
the present character of a large part of it. Allowance must be
made for erosion, especially near the higher edges. In general
the horizon is almost flat, even where valleys are several hundred
feet deep. West of the Washita River, two broad swells, the
East and West "Wooded Hills," rise 50 to 100 feet above the
prevailing sky line. These are monadnocks of porphyry on an
old peneplain, whose residual relief may have been still further
reduced by the waves of an advancing sea as described below.
Over considerable areas mantle rock is almost absent. The
fresh edges of steeply dipping limestone beds appear in neatly
parallel and closely spaced white lines, numbered by the score
and extending for miles. The neatness and uniformity with
which these beds are truncated are noteworthy.

On account of its smaller area, greater altitude, and steeper edges, the western part retains its flatness only in the middle and on certain broad divides. Its margins, except on the west, are very rough.[1] Most of the valleys are dendritic, but the steeply dipping strata on the southern edge give rise to monoclinal ridges whose tops are approximately at the level of the upland. The ridges are made by three limestone formations, Iola, Hunton, and Sycamore. The intervening valleys are on the Sylvan shale and the Woodford chert. The first and second ridges occur again, but less conspicuously, east of the Washita River on the northeastern edge of the uplift.

The largest expanse of plains is found east of the Washita. On the granite in the southeastern part where there is no bordering escarpment, relief is very small. The same is true on the massive limestone to the north. The edges are dissected in proportion to their relative altitudes.

Interpretation.—That the upland surface is essentially a peneplain, truncating a huge structure, will not be questioned. There is, however, some question as to the part that wave erosion may have played, for the area was covered by the Cretaceous sea in which the Trinity sandstone was deposited. The surface thus produced, and still preserved beneath the Cretaceous sediments on the south, was not exactly that of the present upland, unless it be very near the southern edge where the protecting cover has but recently been stripped off. Farther north the surface made by wave planation has been lowered by an amount (at any one point) proportional to the time exposed and the amount of uplift. This erosion, which followed uplift, may have constituted a new cycle, beginning with youth and ending in a new peneplain. The material carried away in the new cycle would embrace the Cretaceous, with any younger sediments, and as much of the Arbuckle structure as lay above the new base level. On this assumption the present Arbuckle upland would be analogous, if not equivalent, to the Hot Springs peneplain of the Athens Piedmont (page 685).

It is also possible to assume that the rise was so small and so gradual that young valleys were never carved in the stripped sub-Cretaceous floor. Such an interpretation would identify the present upland with the sub-Cretaceous plain except for

[1] Well shown on the Ardmore topographic sheet of the U. S. Geol. Survey.

reduction by rainwash. As to whether erosion proceeded in one way or the other some inference may be drawn from the slopes of the two surfaces. The Cretaceous sediments dip south about 40 feet to the mile[1] and the slope of the floor beneath them is at least as much. The slope of the upland surface where exposed, even within the 5 to 10 miles of the contact, is less than that, and farther north it is about 5 feet per mile. It may be suggested that this represents the form of the uplift and that the stripping was recent enough to leave the newly exposed surface in essentially its original form. Such coincidences are possible rather than probable. The safer assumption is that the upland surface represents a more recent peneplain.

The former inland extension of Cretaceous sediments explains why the Washita River, flowing over a lowland in a wide, shallow valley, should suddenly enter and cross an isolated upland in a canyon 400 feet deep. The river was superposed on the Cretaceous cover when all the surrounding surface was at the same level.

THE WICHITA MOUNTAINS[2]

In line with the trend of the Arbuckle uplift, and 70 miles farther west, is a group of hills and mountains elongated in the same direction, N 70°W, and scattered through an area 60 miles long and 25 miles wide. Their forms vary from low, rounded hills to steep and rugged mountains rising 1500 feet above the plain. They differ wholly from the Arbuckles in having no uniform summit level. Around and between them stretches the nearly flat plain on the Permian Redbeds (page 617). The hills and mountains themselves consist mainly of Pre-Cambrian granite, gabbro, and porphyry. These rocks rise above the nearly horizontal Permian like islands, more than 250 of them, though the largest mass comprises most of the area and of the volume. One large group on the northeast side, including a single mass 20 miles long, consists of Ordovician limestone and dolomite (the Arbuckle group).

The areal plan of this uplift as a whole, as well as the distribution of its several constituent formations, indicates an

---

[1] Tishomingo folio (No. 98), p. 5, U. S. Geol. Survey, 1903.

[2] TAFF, *loc. cit.* The reader is referred to this paper for areal descriptions and details.

Fig. 176.—Northeastern face of the Wichita Mountains, probably in large part exhumed during the making of the peneplain on the "Redbeds" (Enid formation), which extends from Kansas to Texas, though not everywhere so flat as in this view. (*U. S. Geol. Survey.*)

orogenic uplift on an axis trending west-northwest. Near the east end, limestones on both sides of the median line dip away from it. The fold thus indicated is also known to pitch sharply to the east-southeast. That the structural elevation was large is evident from the fact that erosion has exposed a section of 4000 to 6000 feet in the Cambrian and Ordovician rocks.

In origin these mountains are much like the Arbuckles. The two uplifts have in common the deformation of all pre-Carboniferous rocks, so far as they are represented. The great difference between the two areas is seen in the failure of the Wichita Mountains to be base-leveled. The Arbuckle uplift, probably the higher of the two, was carried away. During the same time the Appalachian Highland was largely reduced to the best peneplain that is known to have been made in America, and the process was in large part repeated. No doubt the Wichita Mountains were, at least in part, buried by Permian sediments, but Taff does not conceive this burial to have been very much deeper than at present.[1] When one remembers the other mountain ranges that have been base-leveled in the more than 200 million years since the beginning of the Permian period, it is difficult to understand the survival of this group unless it was buried during a substantial part of that long time.

Summary of History

The structures which have determined the characteristic features of the topography of the Osage section were in large part completed before erosion began to make the present surface. The mountain structures were imparted by a series of deformations of which the last may have been coincident with the Appalachian Revolution. The general westerly dip dates from the pre-Cretaceous depression of the Great Plains.

The oldest erosion surface in the section is the southern margin of the Arbuckle Upland, where the Trinity sands have been but recently stripped away. The surface thus exposed is the pre-Cretaceous peneplain as modified by wave erosion.

The Osage section as a whole presents the spectacle of a large area of moderately hard and moderately soft rocks exposed

[1] Taff (*op. cit.*, p. 56) speaks of the outlines of all the groups in the region as dating from "a time when the Permian sea stood with its shores at the approximate position of the 'Red Beds' and porphyry contact."

to erosion for a hundred million years or more, never lifted very high, and without essential deformation during that time. The total amount of material above effective base level seems to have been well within the capacity of subaerial erosion to remove it. The altitude and rate of wasting have varied moderately, and there were probably intervals of approximate cessation in which the whole area was worn down to a nearly uniform lowland. In a region where uplifts have been so small, and where the effect of nearly horizontal rocks is to make structural and erosion plains difficult to distinguish, the discrimination of peneplains and their correlation with those of a wider area may well lack precision.

A small rise in the not distant past has enabled the major streams to lower their channels a little, but dissection resulting from this moderate uplift is small. Previous to this rise, the level was stationary long enough to allow the development of local peneplains on softer rocks, like the Cherokee shales and the Enid formation. Farther back in time a rather long interval of old age is suggested by the summit uplands of the cuestas. Absolute equality of height is not found either throughout a single ridge or in passing from one to another. It is not necessary to assume that these ridges were ever wholly obliterated.[1] Moreover, since the last considerable uplift they have been exposed a long time to erosion, and they vary in breadth and resistance, hence in liability to lowering. Some escarpments have retreated down the dip more than others and have lost more in height. Yet on the whole, when the extent of the area from northern Missouri to Texas is considered, uniformity of altitude is far more impressive than diversity. The upland represented by these crests was no doubt once a lowland which included the glaciated sections on the north and the Arkansas Valley on the east, in all of which areas are cuestas correlative with those of this section (see pages 593 and 667). The extraordinary meanders of the Brazos River, while perhaps of the "ingrown" type (page 445), and enlarged during entrenchment, strongly suggest a former condition of lower gradients and smaller relief.

It might be suggested with some plausibility that the surface beneath the late Tertiary gravels on the High Plains to the west (about 2000 feet high near the edge) represents the com-

[1] *Cf.* Marbut, C. F., *Mo. Geol. Survey*, vol. 10, pp. 19*ff.*, 1896.

pletion of an older cycle.   With that area might be included
the summit upland of the Flint Hills (1500 to 1600 feet high).
Refinements in future work may perhaps justify such fine discrimination, but it is not yet warranted.   The decline of summit
levels from west to east is due to crustal movement.   The
exceptional prominence of the Flint Hills is probably sufficiently
accounted for by assuming a greater residual swell on the peneplain and less loss since it was elevated and carved into cuestas.

CHAPTER XII

THE OZARK PLATEAUS

General Description.—An area of 40,000 square miles west of the Mississippi River and south of the Missouri consists of plateau, variously dissected and surrounded by lowlands. The form is that of an asymmetrical dome steeper on the east than on the west and breaking off rather abruptly on the south. On that margin, in Arkansas and Oklahoma, the dome form is impaired by the presence of a higher plateau 200 miles in length and averaging 35 miles in width, which rises abruptly some hundreds of feet above the rest. This plateau, known as the Boston Mountains, exceeds 2000 feet in altitude. The horizon at the top of the dome in Missouri is 1500 to 1700 feet high and declines to 400 feet or more on the east and 1000 feet on the west.

As the region is one of strong rocks and generally submature dissection, much of it is too steep for farming and remains in forest. Much also, where not too steep, has a soil so cluttered with chert as to be unproductive. Scattered through the whole are areas of good soil. Moreover, under scientific treatment much land that has little value for field crops is found to be excellent for fruit.

Boundaries.—The southeastern boundary of this section against the Mississippi Alluvial Plain is sharply marked. Farther north the Mississippi marks the boundary with sufficient accuracy for most geographical purposes. Actually, both the structural and the topographic limits of the dome are a little farther east, and it would be truer to say that the Mississippi follows a contour. Near the southern end of this stretch, Devonian and older rocks are exposed east of the river, and both structure and topography require that these be included in the Ozark province. On the north the Missouri River marks the boundary with sufficient accuracy for most purposes. This is very near the limit of the glacial drift and at the edge of the Dissected Till Plains. The area of Carboniferous rocks south

631

of the river, mainly in St. Louis County, must be allotted to the Dissected Till Plains. On the west, the Ozark Plateaus are essentially coextensive with the outcrop of Mississippian rocks.[1]

ROCKS AND STRUCTURE

Formations.—By far the most abundant rocks in the Ozarks are limestone and dolomite. Beneath them are igneous rocks,

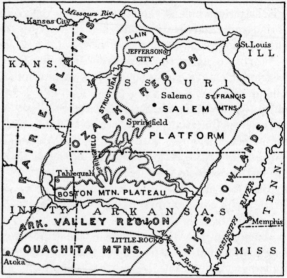

Fig. 177.—Sketch map of the Ozark and Ouachita provinces. (*U. S. Geol. Survey.*)

generally granite or porphyry, probably the most resistant rocks in the province. These protrude in the St. Francois Mountains and underlie the whole area at a depth which in most places is less than 2500 feet.

Overlying the Pre-Cambrian complex are Cambrian sediments with the La Motte sandstone at the base. Most of these rocks are dolomite without chert. Their thickness varies but is everywhere measured in hundreds of feet. Above them is the thick series of cherty dolomites known in geologic literature as

[1] All boundaries are discussed in more detail in the author's paper on Physiographic Divisions of the United States (revised edition), *Ann. Assoc. Amer. Geogr.*, vol. 18, pp. 261–353, 1928.

Cambro-Ordovician.[1] The Missouri Geological Survey now separates these rocks definitely into Cambrian and Ordovician.[2] Among the Cambrian formations the Potosi below and the Gasconade above will need separate mention in connection with topography. Then follow the Roubidoux (Ordovician) sandstone, rather widespread at the surface and averaging 150 to 200 feet thick; also the Jefferson City and other cherty dolomites to an aggregate thickness of about 600 feet, increasing toward the south. Nearly the whole of the area shown on the geologic map as Cambrian and Ordovician is underlain directly by the formations thus far mentioned. Overlying these is a friable sandstone, the St. Peter, ranging in thickness from 0 to 200 feet. It has great geographic extent, but its outcrop is generally limited to a narrow band.

The entire Ordovician column above the St. Peter sandstone is a succession of limestones with occasional thin sandstones or shales, of which the most important is the Maquoketa shale at the top. The entire series is 500 to 1200 feet thick on the east side, but the area of its outcrop is small, partly because of steeper dips than elsewhere. Much the same may be said of the Silurian and Devonian rocks, both as to character and as to outcrop.

At the bottom of the Mississippian is the Kinderhook group. Limestone predominates in this, but it is interbedded with shale and sandstone. The whole is thin and relatively weak. Its topographic importance consists largely in the fact that its wasting undermines the strong Boone chert and sharpens its escarpment, for, in western Missouri, the relatively weak Kinderhook is all that intervenes between the cherty dolomites of the Ordovician and the similar strong rocks of the Mississippian.

The Boone chert constitutes the great body of the Osage group of Mississippian rocks in this province, being equivalent to the Warsaw and Keokuk above and the Burlington below.

---

[1] ULRICH, E. O., Revision of the Paleozoic Systems in North America, *Science*, vol. 29, p. 630, 1901; *Bull. Geol. Soc. Amer.*, vol. 22, pp. 281–680, 1911.

[2] See Geological Map of Missouri, 1926; also DAKE, C. L., The Geology of the Potosi and Edge Hill Quadrangles, *Mo. Bur. Geol. Mines*, 2d ser., vol. 23, 1930; BRIDGE, J., Geology of the Eminence and Cardavera Quadrangles, *Mo. Bur. Geol. Mines*, 2d ser., vol. 24, 1930. Both of these Missouri reports contain valuable physiographic matter.

Locally there is also a shale (Fern Glen) at the base.   The strong limestone formations have a thickness of 250 to 400 feet, and form the substratum of a large part of the province.   The individual beds are thin, but the proportion of chert is very large, rising at places to one half the mass.   Higher Mississippian limestones, including the St. Louis and Spergen of the Meramec group, while important farther east, have very little to do with this province.   The 60 feet of Warsaw shale underlying them on the eastern side of the uplift may have been an important factor in the stripping of these formations from the Osage. The Chester group, at the top of the Mississippian column, outcrops mainly at the foot of the Boston escarpment, where it embraces the Batesville sandstone and, above it, the important Fayetteville shale which is locally 400 feet thick, evidently an important factor in the development of the great escarpment. The 100-foot Pitkin limestone above may (where present) make a rock terrace, but this is local.

Pennsylvanian formations on the west are excluded from the Ozark province, but they are faulted down and preserved in a considerable area on the northern part of the dome.   Their main importance is in the Boston Mountains, where they are of Pottsville age.   Several hundred feet at the bottom (Morrow group) consist largely of shale, but they include also sandstone and limestone members which stand out as terraces.   Between this group and the summit the rocks belong to the Atoka (Winslow) formation.   Its mass is largely shale, but at intervals there are sandstone members.   One at the base is especially thick and strong, though at the west a sandstone near the middle is more prominent.

Generalized Summary of Formations[1]

Pennsylvanian (Pottsville):
  Cherokee in Missouri (in part younger) and Atoka (Winslow) in Arkansas;
  mostly shale but having strong sandstone members.

---

[1] A composite of various columns for different localities.   Formations vary from place to place both in character and in thickness.   C. L. Dake and J. Bridge are cited above.   See also U. S. Geol. Survey folios, especially No. 202; also S. H. Ball and A. F. Smith, Geology of Miller County, *Mo. Bur. Geol. Mines*, 2d ser., vol. 1, 1903; also state geological maps of Missouri, (1926), Oklahoma (1926), and Arkansas (1929).   A description of formations with reference to their effects on physiography and soils, longer and more

Morrow group. Mainly shale, with minor sandstones and limestones.

Mississippian:

Limestone formations on east side (Ste. Genevieve, Meramec, and Chester groups); mainly shale and sandstone in Arkansas.

Boone chert of the Osage group (Warsaw, Keokuk, and Burlington formations).

Thin limestones and shales (mainly Kinderhook group).

Devonian:

Limestones with some "black shale" (may be mainly Kinderhook).

Silurian:

Limestones with minor sandstones and shale.

Ordovician:

Limestones with occasional thin sandstone or shale, especially at the top.

St. Peter sandstone.

Jefferson City and other cherty dolomites.

Roubidoux sandstone.

Cambrian:

Cherty dolomites, Potosi at base; Gasconade at top.

Dolomites with locally important shale (Davis shale, etc.).

Bonneterre dolomite relatively free from chert.

LaMotte sandstone.

Pre-Cambrian Crystalline rocks.

Structure.—In structure, as in topography, the Ozark uplift is a dome, though neither symmetrical nor simple. There are

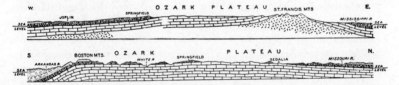

Fig. 178.—North-south and east-west sections of the Ozark uplift. Sections about 360 miles long and greatly exaggerated vertically. Block pattern, Cambrian and Ordovician; dark shading, mainly Mississippian; stippling, Pennsylvanian. (*U. S. Geol. Survey.*)

minor folds and also faults, though not of very large throw. A given stratigraphic horizon at the top of the dome is 2000 to 4000 feet lower beneath the surrounding lowlands.[1] The highest part of the structural dome is in the St. Francois Moun-

---

detailed than can be given here, is given by Carl O. Sauer, The Geography of the Ozark Highlands of Missouri, Geogr. Soc. Chicago, *Bull.* 7, 1920.

[1] Pre-Cambrian crystalline rocks are reached by wells at about 2000 feet in southwestern Missouri and are believed to have been reached at 3843 feet at St. Louis (U. S. Geol. Survey, Bull. 438, p. 17, 1911.)

tains, less than 50 miles from the Mississippi River, where knobs of crystalline rock rise through the sediments. From this locality the rocks dip in all directions, generally more steeply than the surface slopes. The eastward dip may average 75 feet to the mile. Toward the west it is more nearly 10 feet to the mile, but even this is twice the surface gradient, and the beds are therefore beveled. Dips to the north and south are intermediate in amount. Even in the central mass these dips give suggestions of low folds, domes, and sags. Generally, no system can be made out, but the compression was mainly in a north-south direction. At the eastern edge such folds are distinct. The geologic map of Missouri suggests the locations of four axes of uplift crossing the Mississippi River. Those opposite Grand Tower and Thebes, Illinois, are much deformed,[1] the former having overturned beds, and both being complexly faulted. The hard rocks cut by the river at Thebes cause the valley to be narrow and have thus fixed the site of a railroad bridge. At a few other places near the eastern margin, dips of 10 to 20 degrees are found, but these steep dips are features of the constituent folds, not of the dome as a whole.

The Boston Mountains at their western end are a low anticline or flat arch.[2] Farther east the plateau is monoclinal, but this monocline is only a generalization in which details are ignored. Contours on any single formation, as on the Boone chert,[3] show an undulating surface of domes and basins with a maximum relief of more than 800 feet, due in part to warping, in part to faulting. The generalized dip at the top of the Boston Mountains is small, but in western Arkansas the beds bend down near the southern margin, where an inclination of several hundred feet per mile is common. Local folds farther east show dips as high as 25 degrees.[4]

---

[1] FLINT, R. F., *Amer. Jo. Sci.*, 5th ser., vol. 12, pp. 37–40, 1926.

[2] PURDUE, A. H., Physiography of the Boston Mountains, *Jour. Geol.*, vol. 9, p. 695, 1901.

[3] U. S. Geol. Survey, folio No. 202, p. 16, Fig. 13.

[4] NEWSOM, J. F., and J. C. BRANNER, The Red River and Clinton Monoclines, Arkansas, *Amer. Geologist*, vol. 20, pp. 1–13, 1897. The axes of subordinate anticlines in the Boston Mountains and Arkansas Valley are shown on the geological map of Arkansas (1929). CRONEIS, C., Geology of the Arkansas Paleozoic Area, Ark. Geol. Survey, *Bull.* 3, 1930; ref. to p. 167, also to Pl. 1-*a*.

Throughout the province, is evidence of compressive forces in mild folding or in thrusting. There is also considerable brecciation,[1] especially where the rocks are cherty and brittle, but this is quite as apt to be related to the deformation attending solution. Brecciation is abundantly illustrated in the Joplin district, in which the crushed zones are in many cases filled with ores of lead and zinc.[2] Both normal and reversed faults are present, the former made by settling after compressive deformation, or perhaps during later warping.

Folding and warping have thus far been referred to as though indicated by inclined beds which were originally horizontal. It is necessary also to consider altitudes with reference to a peneplain which was developed and deformed after the rocks were folded. In this later deformation the peneplain was warped into domes and troughs which were much like the older structural features but less steep.

SURFACE OF THE OZARK DOME

Altitude, Slopes, and Relief.—Aside from the Boston Mountains the domed plateau reaches its highest level, 1700 feet, near its center, *i.e.*, in Wright County, Missouri, 40 miles east of Springfield, Mo. This is a local bulge and not the center from which the regional slopes diverge. The upland surface in Iron County, among the St. Francois Mountains, rises to 1500 feet and likewise slopes away in all directions. Between these two centers, 100 miles apart, is the main divide of the province, rarely falling below 1400 feet. This zone, rather than any one point, is the real top of the dome. For miles in all directions both the relief and the regional slope are small. The slope is steeper on the flanks of the dome, which is to say, they are convex upward. At the same time stream profiles are concave upward. They are incised but little in the central upland, and again on the adjacent lowlands, while their middle courses may be in valleys or gorges 300 to 500 feet deep. Those on the southeast have their deepest gorges 30 to 60 miles back from the edge.[3]

---

[1] BAIN, H. F., and G. I. ADAMS, Preliminary Report on the Lead and Zinc of the Ozarks, U. S. Geol. Survey, 22d *Ann. Rept.*, pt. 2, p. 92, 1901.

[2] SMITH, W. S. T., Zinc and Lead Deposits of the Joplin District, U. S. Geol. Survey, *Bull.* 313, p. 199, 1902.

[3] MARBUT, C. F., Physical Features of Missouri, *Mo. Geol. Survey*, vol. 10,

Topographic Effects of Solution.—The large admixture of chert in the limestones of this province affects not only the character of the soil but the topographic forms. Chert, being insoluble, accumulates at the surface as the limestone weathers away, leaving its insoluble constituents to form soil. Throughout much of this province north of the Boston Mountains, chert forms a substantial, at places a major, part of the mantle rock. The mere presence of flinty stones embedded in clay would not of itself make the soil more permeable, but the cherts weather and become porous, and the crumbling siliceous residue is not easily compacted. The flinty mantle covers hill and valley alike on the old rolling upland where active erosion has long been absent. Even on these moderate slopes the finer soil is to some extent washed into the gentle depressions, leaving the chert at the surface on the higher slopes. If the depressions are not reached by the head of a young valley, loam accumulates there and covers the chert. Thus it comes about that "the soil on the hills is beneath the chert-covered surface while that of the valley is above it."[1] Under such conditions it is not hard to see why the farms on the top of the plateau are largely in its nearly flat-bottomed valleys.

Even the chert fragments are subject to creep and are apt to form a thicker layer in depressions than on hills. Until such depressions are reached by valleys of a younger erosion cycle, all the water that falls as rain, or washes down the slopes, is generally absorbed by the mantle, from which it escapes either by entering the rock or by percolating down the slope. Only rains of extraordinary volume and density (amount per unit of time) are able to form surface streams, which may run for a few hours. A streak of bare chert may thus be exposed, but there is no true channel, no alluvium, no bluffs. Solution is, however, constantly lowering the level of the valley floors more than of the hills, and the thickness of the chert mantle in the depressions is thus increased. Some of these valleys approach 100 feet in depth. Their gradient need not be low. Often it is 25 feet per mile or even more. Corrasion is prevented only by percolation.

---

pp. 11–109, 1896. This paper, though written a long time ago, retains its value as a systematic scientific treatment of the subject.

[1] Marbut, C. F., *op. cit.*, p. 90.

The passage from this type of valley to that of the ordinary stream valley or gorge may be gradual or abrupt, more generally the former. Where the cherty limestone lies well above its local base level, the gentle slopes of the rolling upland often give way abruptly to narrow, straight, steep-sided trenches 50 to 100 feet deep. Near their heads these trenches also are generally without streams, their sides and bottoms being covered with chert. They are plainly the work of solution,[1] their steep heads having the form of one half of a sinkhole. Within a fraction of a mile, or at most a few miles, a channel appears and their character changes to that of the stream-cut gorge.

As might be expected, sinks are widely distributed on what remains of the upland, not on the steep valley sides of the present cycle. Some of them are of the familiar funnel form, having a definite and localized outlet. A few have almost vertical sides and were evidently made by the collapse of a cave roof. Many more are smooth shallow basins with nearly flat, chert-covered floors. When these are completely rimmed, the drainage necessarily escapes downward, but not by large or localized openings. Such basins may have diameters of 100 feet, of 100 yards, or of half a mile and any depth up to 100 or 200 feet. Like the valleys described above, they afford excellent farm lands when large enough.

The description given above of depressions, porous mantle rock, and percolation requires little distinction between valleys that are completely rimmed and have centripetal drainage, and others whose axial slopes decline continuously to an outlet. In the latter case, however, the similarity ceases where permanent stream channels begin. Large areas on the uncut upland, known as flatwoods, are partly of one type, partly of the other. Their essential characteristic is a lack of definite channels. The name is strictly applicable only to those that bear trees, but some similar areas are prairie.

As sinks are only the surface expression of subsurface drainage, springs abound on the lower valley sides and there are many caves.[2] Some large springs are called rivers and are used for

---

[1] Purdue, A. H., Valleys of Solution in Northern Arkansas, *Jour. Geol.*, vol. 9, pp. 47–50, 1901; also Bridge, J., *Mo. Bur. Geol. Mines*, vol. 24, pp. 42–43, 1930.

[2] Fayetteville folio (No. 119), U. S. Geol. Survey, 1905.

water power.[1] Big Spring in the gorge of the Current River has an average flow of 375 second-feet with a maximum of 840 second-feet.[2] In volume of discharge it is second only to Silver Spring in Florida (page 52) among the springs of the United States. Others, like the Eureka Springs in Arkansas, afford famous resorts. The water of the Eureka Springs descends

FIG. 179.—Upper outlet of Greer Spring, Oregon County, Missouri. The stream issues from the opening seen at the left.   (*H. C. Beckman, Mo. Bur. Geol. and Mines.*)

through the Boone chert and flows out at the top of the underlying shale. Other springs issue at different stratigraphic horizons, but the principle is general.

Stream Courses.—In the plan of drainage the most obvious fact is that streams flow outward from the top of the dome.

---

[1] ADAMS, G. I., U. S. Geol. Survey, *Water Supply Paper* 110, p. 181, 1905. CRANE, G. W., The Iron Ores of Missouri, *Mo. Bur. Geol. Mines*, 2d series, vol. 10, p. 3 , 1912; also U. S. Geol. Survey, folio No. 202, p. 2.

A list of 65 springs in Missouri, practically all in the Ozarks and having a discharge of 1 to 1000 second-feet, is given by H. C. Beckman, *Mo. Bur. Geol. Mines*, 2d ser., vol. 20, pp. 341–353, 1927.

[2] BRIDGE, J., *op. cit.*, p. 46.

In the main these radiating courses lead down the dip, and it is inferred that they are consequent on the main late Paleozoic uplift. They could not well be older, since it is apparent that the entire area was beneath the sea and covered by Pennsylvanian sediments just previous to that event.[1] Nothing later could have destroyed the essential pattern. However, the surface of the original dome has been much cut down, perhaps a full 1000 feet. In this long process rivers may have shifted their positions and many captures may have occurred in the effort to adjust the lines of drainage to the minor folds, domes, and fault blocks which originated with the uplift.[2]

The most striking fact about the White River in its middle course is its relation to the retreating edge of the obdurate Boone chert. It can scarcely be doubted that this stream has shifted down the dip of the Cherty Ordovician limestones that lie below the St. Peter sandstone.[3] Such a process would be facilitated by the relatively easy wasting of certain Ordovician formations and of the lowest Mississippian (Kinderhook) shale. The easy headward growth of streams on the outcrop of the same formations would favor the integration of a long subsequent stream in that position by the capture of earlier transverse streams. No evidence remains of such former streams. The Dry Fork-Spring-Neosho River also follows a strike valley at the margin of the plateau for 130 miles from southwestern Missouri to its junction with the Arkansas. Big River north of the St. Francois Mountains flows near the foot of a fault scarp. Farther east several streams, notably the south-flowing Whitewater, follow the lowland on the limestone, laid bare by the retreat of higher formations[4] (page 650). Near the Boston Mountains it is very common for tributaries to flow either down the escarpment or down the dip of the minor domes to join the main streams in their strike valleys.[5] However, after allowance is made for all cases of adjustment, there remains a large disregard of structure which suggests inheritance from a time antedating the last

[1] SCHUCHERT, CHARLES, "Outlines of Historical Geology," Pl. 18, p. 162, John Wiley & Sons, Inc., New York, 1931.

[2] *Cf.* PURDUE and MISER, Eureka Springs-Harrison folio (No. 202), U. S. Geol. Survey, 1916, p. 20.

[3] Correlation now changed; see U. S. Geol. Survey, *Bulls.* 734, 853.

[4] Most of these relations are pointed out by Marbut, *op. cit.*, pp. 77–84.

[5] PURDUE and MISER, *op. cit.*, p. 16.

deformation. A good illustration is afforded by the Osage
River, which is the most notable exception to the radial pattern.

VALLEY FORMS

Two-cycle Valleys.—Notwithstanding the noteworthy effects
of infiltration, the longitudinal profiles of rivers in the Ozarks
are of the usual type. Most of their descent is accomplished in
their upper courses. The gradient of the White River in most of
its course is not above $2\frac{1}{2}$ feet per mile, and of its larger tributaries 5 to 10 feet per mile, while among headwaters 25 feet per
mile is common, even where infiltration is dominant. The
gradient of the extremely crooked Osage River is less than half
that of the White.

The usual transverse profile indicates an upper and older
valley 3 to 5 miles wide, trenched by a younger valley or gorge
whose width ranges from several hundred feet to half a mile.[1]
The depth of the older valley is about 75 feet on the Osage,
Gasconade, and other tributaries of the Missouri. It is 300 feet
on the White River and reaches a maximum of nearly 400 feet
on the Current River in the Eminence quadrangle.[2] The
slopes of valley sides may also be interrupted by rock terraces,
but generally these are distinguishable. Tributaries entering
the main gorge have generally dissected the bottom of the
older valley and reach well back into the upland. Those of the
White have sharply dissected a belt 25 to 50 miles wide.

Entrenched Meanders.—The meandering of Ozark rivers and
of their gorges has inspired much of the scientific discussion of
entrenched, incised, and ingrown meanders.[3] These streams in
their elaborate windings occupy gorges whose bottoms have at
most only a few times the width of the streams themselves.
Each oxbow of the stream occupies a corresponding curve in the
gorge. Continued lateral cutting, since entrenchment, has

[1] Hershey, O. H., River Valleys of the Ozark Plateau, *Amer. Geologist*,
vol. 16, pp. 338–357, 1895.

[2] BRIDGE, *op. cit.*, p. 31.

[3] WINSLOW, ARTHUR, The Osage River and Its Meanders, *Science*, vol. 22,
pp. 31–32, 1893; DAVIS, W. M., Incised Meandering Valleys, *Bull. Phila.
Geog. Soc.*, vol. 4, pp. 1–11, 1906; also notes by Davis in *Science*, 1893; RICH,
J. L., Certain Types of Stream Valleys and Their Meaning, *Jour. Geol.*,
vol. 22, pp. 469–497, 1914; TARR, W. A., Intrenched and Incised Meanders,
Jour. Geol., vol. 32, pp. 583–600, 1934; also HERSHEY, *op. cit.*, pp. 347–348.

resulted in narrow and discontinuous strips of flood plain but, except near the low edges of the province, such bottomlands near present stream level are nowhere more than a minor fraction of a mile in width and they do not affect the truth of the preceding statements.

Agreement between the curves of the valley and those of the stream is limited to the narrow valleys of the last cycle. The

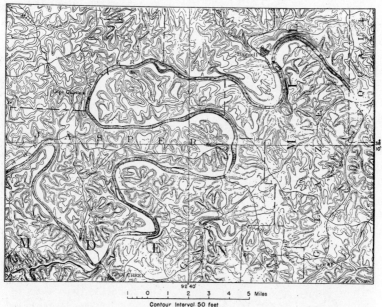

Fig. 180.—Entrenched meanders of the Osage River. The level of uplands on opposite sides is nearly the same, indicating that the meanders in this area have changed their form very little during entrenchment. (*U. S. Geol. Survey, Versailles, Missouri, topographic sheet.*)

upper, wider, and older valleys also meander, but their curves are larger in radius and occupy a broader belt. It is not necessary to assume that the streams were larger when these old valleys were made. Just as a river casts its course in curves, so the entire zone of meander, when once cleared of spurs, swings from side to side, imparting a sinuous form to its valley.[1]

---

[1] This principle is stated in some textbooks, notably by Longwell, Knopf and Flint, "Physical Geology," pp. 56–57, John Wiley & Sons, New York, 1932.

Discussion on this subject has related mainly to the origin of the curves. That the young valleys point to rejuvenation by uplift is not questioned. Where a river runs many miles in a simple gorge, whose two walls, rising to the level of the old

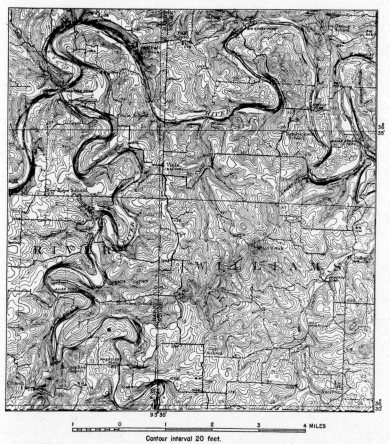

Contour interval 20 feet.

Fig. 181.—Entrenched meanders of the White and Kings Rivers. The striking development of slip-off surfaces indicates progressive lateral corrasion during entrenchment. (*U. S. Geol. Survey, Shell Knob topographic sheet.*)

upland or of the old valley floor, are essentially alike in steepness, it may be assumed that the stream followed its present curves on the floor of the old high-level valley, and that nothing has happened except downcutting as the result of uplift. Such is the case at some places, though not everywhere, on the Osage,[1] Gasconade, and other streams on the northern side of the dome.

Elsewhere on these same rivers, and generally on the White, Current, and Black rivers, *i.e.*, the streams draining the southern slope, the young valley has only one steep side, *i.e.*, the one on the outer or convex side of the curve. The inner, or concave, side is reached by a long, gradual, "slip-off slope," often bearing the remains of stream gravels. In such cases it is plain that downcutting has been accompanied by lateral shifting of the stream. The form of the curve must have altered materially during entrenchment. Arthur Winslow (cited above) suggested that the appearance of meanders was more or less incidental,[2] and that joints or tributary valleys to some extent imposed their pattern on the stream during its shifting and incision. "Developed meanders" were thus distinguished from "inherited meanders." To press the application of this principle to the Ozark rivers would be borrowing trouble, in view of the fact that the region is well known from other evidence to be an upraised peneplain on which meandering may safely be assumed. It is also true that much of the meandering in gorges is plainly a matter of inheritance.

ST. FRANCOIS MOUNTAINS

Near the eastern edge of the dome, separated from the Mississippi by not more than 30 miles, is an area of 1000 square miles within which Pre-Cambrian igneous rocks are not wholly covered. Swells, domes, and peaks of granite and porphyry rise to or above the surface, being separated and surrounded by Cambrian rocks which dip slightly outward from a center within the district. Within a fairly compact area of about 70 square miles known as the St. Francois Mountains, or familiarly as the "Iron Mountain country," hills or mountains of igneous rock occupy most of the surface, the valleys between them retaining the lowest of the sedimentary rocks, generally

---

[1] See Versailles, Mo., and adjacent topographic sheets of the U. S. Geol. Survey. The newer and larger scale maps of the U. S. Geol. Survey show slopes of equal steepness very sparingly. While exact equality of slopes is rare, there are numerous cases in which the inequality is wholly inadequate to explain the entrenched meanders without inheritance.

[2] See also BRANNER, J. C., *Ark. Geol. Survey*, vol. 5, p. 7, 1900.

dolomite or sandstone. The entire landscape is one of ancient mountains, buried while still moderately steep, and not yet fully exhumed.

Altitudes in the broader valleys range from less than 900 to more than 1000 feet. The mountains have all heights up to 1800 feet. The relief within a single view is frequently 500 to 800 feet. There is no general level either at the top, at the bottom, or at intermediate height, that can be traced from place to place and used as a plane of reference. The plateau surface on the south is at least 1500 feet high, and on the west about the

Fig. 182.—The St. Francois Mountains and the Arcadia Valley, a local peneplain above a water gap incident to superposed drainage. (*Marbut, Mo. Geol. Survey.*)

same. As this surface represents a peneplain, it must once have covered the mountain district except for the very few knobs that rose above it. It is completely destroyed there now, though still made evident elsewhere by a horizontal sky line.

The drainage of the mountain district is toward the east and south from the main Ozark divide. As the streams are only small headwaters near the main divide, it seems at first sight anomalous that their valleys should be so much more spacious here than in the adjacent plateau. However, as this district is on the apex of the structural dome, and local uplifts like the Farmington anticline are also present, it follows that the soluble Bonneterre limestone and the weak Davis shale (Cambrian) are found at higher levels here than elsewhere. They were therefore reached by a moderate amount of cutting. The result was a relatively rapid widening of valleys by the retreat of escarpments.

Lines of drainage were first adopted on a surface of sedimentary rocks. These mountains were not carved by the present streams but merely stripped. They guided the superposed streams into their courses by shunting them off from their sloping sides. Some streams, unable to shift their courses, cut gorges through granite masses which have since been left standing in the midst of lowlands. The term "shut-in" is in common use locally for gorges of this character. A well-known example is near Arcadia. On its upstream side the stream continued to work in softer sediments and developed the wide and fertile Arcadia Valley. Cases of such superposition are common.

A similar but very small group of Pre-Cambrian mountains is being exhumed in the valley of the Current River 60 miles southwest of the main mass of the St. Francois Mountains. All the features of the main mass are here exhibited.[1]

SALEM PLATEAU

The Upland.—In a geographic sense the term Salem Plateau is applied to the Ozark surface where carved on Ordovician and older rocks, including isolated patches of younger sediments and excluding the St. Francois Mountains. The Salem Upland is only that part of the Salem Plateau which embraces the remains of an old erosion surface, beneath which the valleys of later cycles are carved. This old surface of small relief is a modified peneplain. The modifications (continued solution and wash) may have either increased or decreased the original relief. Necessarily the entire surface has been somewhat lowered. This is not obvious where it parallels the bedding, but where the strata are cut across, cuestas appear, whose dip slopes plainly indicate renewed stripping.[2] The horizon of the former peneplain is essentially at the tops of these cuestas. As the local lowering effect of rainwash without streams is generally indistinguishable from the residual relief of the peneplain, the extent of alteration in form or lowering in level is very imperfectly known. Hence the existing upland is commonly spoken

---

[1] *Mo. Bur. Geol. Mines*, 2d ser., vol. 24, pp. 135–136.

[2] MISER, H. D., Deposits of Manganese Ore in the Batesville District, Arkansas, U. S. Geol. Survey, *Bull.* 734, pp. 13–15, 1922.

of as the peneplain. Such allowance must be made for all upraised peneplains. When not expressed, it is understood.

Local relief in most of the upland does not exceed 50 feet. Relief of 100 feet is exceptional, generally being limited to the harder rocks or to areas of rapid solution. Here and there are low monadnocks, mainly outliers of the Boone chert on the west. Occasional obscure sandstone cuestas assume some geographic importance, not from their height, but from the character of their soils and culture. A zone of woodland, brush, or wild pasture marks the low summit. The dip slope, often prairie, has a barren, sandy or cherty soil, cultivated only in valleys, while on the underlying limestone (or dolomite) at the foot of the obscure escarpment is generally a reddish limestone soil, easily tilled and moderately fertile.[1]

The uncut upland is most extensive on the axis of the dome, that is, on the main divide stretching west-southwest from the northern end of the St. Francois Mountains past Salem toward Springfield. The traveler in this zone sees most of the time only a boundless rolling plain varied by the solution features described on page 638. The heads of young valleys leading north or south, and having a maximum depth of 250 feet, invade the district but are overlooked in a wide view. They divide the plain into strips commonly spoken of as distinct "prairies." The plain is dominant in half a dozen counties. Next in extent are the broad divides between the main streams on the northern slope. That between the Osage and Gasconade rivers is followed for 70 miles by the St. Louis and San Francisco Railroad, with no bridge of importance and almost no hill in sight. Similarly, between south-east flowing streams there are many flat remnants. Here, however, the larger part of the area is comprised in steep-sided valleys, those of the larger streams being 300 to 500 feet deep. To a larger extent than on the main divide, farms on these remnants are in the shallow chert-covered valleys.

The Ozark Border.—Aside from the broad rolling plain remote from the larger streams, the irregular linear flat divides, and the scattered patches of upland, the Salem Plateau is roughly dissected. The White River in its middle course runs in a valley 500 feet deep, 300 feet of which belongs to its old valley and 200 feet to the young gorge. This depth of cutting is an index to the

[1] MARBUT, *op. cit.*, p. 59.

height of the nearby hills. Relief decreases with distance from
the main stream, but the tributaries have left little of the old
surface within a belt 20 to 50 miles wide. This belt comprises
much of southern Missouri and almost all of the Salem Plateau

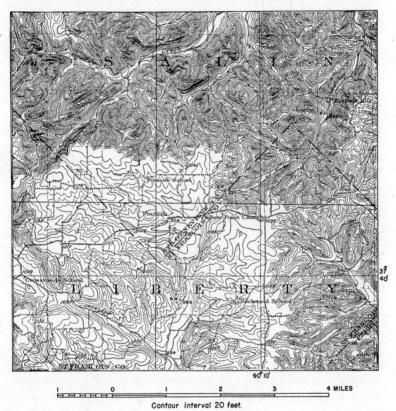

Contour interval 20 feet.

FIG. 183.—Topographic map of part of the Higdon, Mo., quadrangle on the
eastern slope of the Ozark dome. The rolling Salem upland, 1100 to 1200 feet
high, is being consumed by ravines leading down 400 to 500 feet to Greasy Creek
on the north and Whitewater River on the east. (*U. S. Geol. Survey.*)

in Arkansas. Similar statements might be made of the basins
of the smaller southeast-flowing rivers, the Current, the Black,
and the St. Francis, but they are too widely spaced to have
consumed all of the intervening uplands within the time allowed
since the last uplift.

On the north slope of the dome the main valleys, Gasconade
and others, rarely reach 350 feet in depth. They and their

tributaries have lower gradients than those in the south and southeast.   Flat divides are often found within a few miles of even the larger streams.   Many of them are followed by roads or railroads.   None the less, their aggregate area is a very small fraction of the whole.   It is a hilly country, though on the whole its slopes are less steep than on the east and south.

Cuestas on the East Side.—In Ste. Genevieve and adjacent counties north and east of the St. Francois Mountains, where the beds dip more steeply, cuestas are more strongly developed.[1] East of the main granite mass is a barren, brush-covered lowland

Fig. 184.—Avon escarpment, two miles west of Avon, Mo., looking south. (*Marbut, Mo. Geol. Survey.*)

on the LaMotte sandstone.   Beyond it, stretching in a curve for 50 miles, is the west-facing Avon escarpment (Figs. 184 and 185) several hundred feet high.   At its top is the strong cherty Potosi dolomite.   Dips in this escarpment range from almost 0 to 20 degrees.   While agreeing in direction with those of the entire Ozark dome, their steepness is due chiefly to a local uplift, the Farmington anticline, on the east side of the St. Francois Mountains.   A corresponding escarpment on the west side of this local uplift, *i.e.*, west of the sandstone lowland, is very irregular and due in part to the hard rocks of the mountains.   Other short escarpments farther west are apparently due to the local Farmington anticline.

[1] For fuller description see Marbut, *op. cit.*, pp. 34*ff*.

The dip slope of the Avon cuesta bevels in succession the Gasconade dolomite, the Roubidoux sandstone, and the Jefferson City limestone, the last sloping down to the foot of the Crystal escarpment. This feature, which may be traced with varying clearness and strength for more than 100 miles, owes its existence to the easily wasted St. Peter sandstone outcropping under the edge of the strong Middle Ordovician limestones. It contours the Ozark dome on its northeast side, wrapping around the north side almost to the middle of the state. On this side it lies north of the Missouri River, at places forming the bluff. Generally it lies a little farther north, the river valley proper being cut into the stripped surface of the Jefferson City limestone.[1] Nowhere on the north side is the Crystal escarpment more than several miles from the Burlington escarpment next to be described. At places they merge. A final merging is seen west of the mouth of the Gasconade River, where the Ordovician limestone is absent and the St. Peter sandstone appears intermittently. On the eastern side of the dome the Crystal escarpment is not everywhere clear, but at its southern end the Whitewater River marks its foot for 20 miles. The feature takes its name from the Crystal (St. Peter) sandstone, one of the leading glass sands of the United States. It is quarried in abundance from the escarpment at Crystal City and Pacific Junction.

The strong Ordovician limestones which make the Crystal cuesta are overlain by thinner and weaker Ordovician limestones and shales, these by the relatively nonresistant Kinderhook group, and these in turn by the cherty and resistant Burlington limestone. The last-named formation makes the most persistent escarpment in the Ozark province. With varying clearness and height it wraps entirely around the Salem Plateau except on the southeast side. For some miles south of St. Louis it lies just east of the Mississippi River. Farther south for a stretch of 40 miles it lies west of the river. This is in the latitude of the Avon cuesta only 10 to 20 miles away. In the northern half of this stretch the intervening Crystal cuesta is also fairly developed.

The Shawneetown Ridge.—East of the St. Francois Mountains, where the Ozark dome runs out in a more linear uplift (Shawneetown Ridge) across southern Illinois, almost all of

[1] MARBUT, *op. cit.*, p. 39.

the rocks, from Ordovician to Mississippian inclusive, are strong limestones. Alternating escarpments and lowlands are not developed on these rocks, but the transverse Mississippi trench, 400 feet deep, is between steep bluffs.   The dip of the beds in

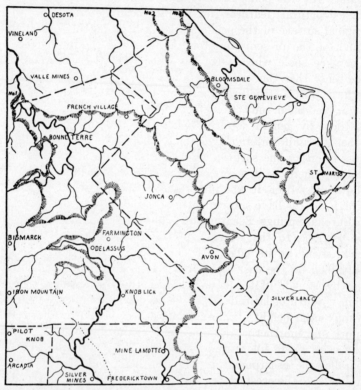

FIG. 185.—Sketch of Avon, Crystal, and Burlington escarpments facing inward toward the basin on the LaMotte (Lower Cambrian) sandstone.   (*Marbut, Mo. Geol. Survey.*)

the Shawneetown ridge in Illinois is northward toward the syncline of central Illinois. Its crest is on a great cuesta of Pottsville sandstone included in the Till Plains section and described on page 504.

SPRINGFIELD PLATEAU

Relation to the Peneplain.—The name Springfield Plateau is applied to that part of the Ozarks which is underlain by rocks of Mississippian age.   Its relation to the widespread peneplain is the same as that already stated for the Salem Plateau. Over wide areas the surface of the upland coincides so nearly with the bedding of the Boone chert that it is often called a structural plain. Its true peneplain character appears where it truncates the structural features made by local deformation.[1] The original surface of the peneplain lay a little higher. No doubt, much of the present limestone surface was thinly covered by Cherokee shale whose edge has since retreated westward. In the sense that the surface parallels the structure the upland is in large part a structural plain, but its history is that of a peneplain, modified only as all upraised peneplains are modified in time, by general lowering where the beds arc horizontal or otherwise uniform, and by etching where beds of unequal hardness intersect the surface. Beveling of strata is about as subordinate here as it is prevalent in the Salem Plateau, but as shown by Miser, it was important in the White River Valley, where cuestas have subsequently been developed.

Eureka Springs Escarpment.—The most obvious feature to be ascribed to the strength of the Boone chert is the great escarpment at its edge. It has already been described and explained on the east and north. It is absent or weak on the northwest side of the dome because the Boone chert there is thin. South of latitude 37°30′ it becomes prominent, attaining a maximum height of more than 300 feet in southwestern Missouri and northern Arkansas and again diminishing toward the east where all altitudes fall off. Just north of the 37th parallel the escarpment is 200 feet high, but the Springfield upland on the west slopes down within 30 miles to the level of the Salem upland on the east. In general it may be said that the edge of the Boone chert forms a cuesta which not only rises above the present upland level but which was present in more or less subdued form when the peneplain was at its best. Uplift, by stimulating erosion, freshened the escarpment. (*Cf.* edge of Highland Rim south of the Lexington basin, page 416.)

West of the 93d meridian the Eureka Springs escarpment surrounds and limits the broad, upper, and older valleys of the White River and its larger tributaries. As the result of a local uplift, the King's River anticline, an irregular branching area

[1] SMITH, W. S. T., and SIEBENTHAL, C. E., Joplin folio (No. 148), p. 11, U. S. Geol. Survey, 1907.

5 to 25 miles wide, is here denuded of its Mississippian rocks and reduced to a surface of moderate relief.[1] As this surface is underlain by Ordovician rocks the geologic map may suggest an extension of the Salem upland. Most of it, however, is to be correlated with the bottom of the old broad valley, here 300 feet deep, which indents that upland, and in which the narrow valley is cut. As pointed out above, the surface of the Boone chert near its eastern edge was probably not reduced quite to the level of the upland peneplain. The latter may also have suffered some differential uplift along the whole northern front of the Boston Mountains.[2] East of the 93d meridian the upland on the Boone chert continues to form a much frayed terrace 5 to 10 miles wide at the foot of the Boston Mountains. The Eureka Springs escarpment continues at its northern edge, which is the southern limit of the broad White River Valley (not the gorge). For a short distance the north side of this old valley can be traced in the Salem upland, but for the most part the hilltops rise without a decided break from the brink of the narrow valley to the level of the upland.

Erosion and Relief.—Relief on the Springfield upland is in part due to the incompleteness of base-leveling or of subsequent stripping. In part it is due to solution. Much the greater part is due to erosion since uplift. Evidence of the first is seen in occasional patches and strips of Cherokee formation which constitute the so-called "mounds."[3] Most of them are gently sloping swells, the most prominent being 50 to 100 feet high. Pea Ridge in northwestern Arkansas, remembered for a battle in the Civil War, is one of these remnants, capped with sandstone and forested.

Most of the White River drainage basin is maturely or submaturely dissected by steep valleys whose lower ends rival in

---

[1] Eureka Springs-Harrison folio (No. 202), U. S. Geol. Survey, 1916. *Cf.* Shell Knob topographic sheet (U. S. Geol. Survey) with the geologic map of Missouri.

[2] Such an uplift is assumed by O. H. Hershey (Peneplains of the Ozark Highlands, *Amer. Geologist*, vol. 27, p. 32, 1901) and stressed by A. H. Purdue (Physiography of the Boston Mountains, Arkansas, *Jour. Geol.*, vol. 9, pp. 699–701, 1901).

[3] Hershey, O. H., River Valleys of the Ozark Plateau, *Amer. Geologist*, vol. 16, pp. 338–357, 1895. See geologic map of Missouri, Mo. Geol. Survey, 1922; also geologic map of the United States, 1932.

depth the main gorge itself. In many distant views of this upland one sees only "a vast timbered plain, although it is one of the roughest regions east of the Rocky Mountains."[1] The drainage of the rest of the Springfield upland reaches the Mississippi by much more circuitous routes, either through the Missouri River or the Arkansas. It is estimated that half of the total area so drained retains the undulating form of the older surface. The rest is comprised in the steeper sided valleys of the current cycle. As streams are continuous from one type of topography to the other it is not always easy to make a sharp separation. The contrast described above between valley forms dominated by solution in their upper courses, and the same valleys trenched in their lower courses, is applicable mainly to the basin of the White River and others not far from the Boston Mountains. Valleys in the Springfield upland in Missouri rarely exceed 250 feet in depth and they become less deep toward the western edge.

The Neosho River, which marks the western boundary in Oklahoma, joins the Arkansas at an altitude of only 470 feet, or more than 400 feet below the level of the adjacent Springfield upland. Half of the latter is here cut away in valleys which, for depth and steepness, are much like those of the White River basin. Much of the area is still in forest.

BOSTON MOUNTAINS

Description.—In the general denudation of the Ozark dome, there was left resting on its southern margin an extensive remnant of Pottsville (Pennsylvanian) beds which seem once to have covered the province. They now constitute a dissected plateau known as the Boston Mountains, 200 miles long with an average width of 35 miles, limited on the north by a conspicuous escarpment. It is highest in the middle third, where the horizon for many miles is about 2250 feet.[2] This is 700 feet above the divides on the abutting Springfield plateau on the north, and 1000 feet above the upper, old, wide valley of the White River. Toward the east and west the summit level declines to that of the surrounding surface.

[1] HERSHEY, *op. cit.*, p. 338.
[2] U. S. Geol. Survey, folio No. 202, gives a generalized contour map.

The eastern third of the escarpment, when viewed from the north, appears as an almost simple even-topped wall without large outliers or deep reentrants, lowest at the east and increasing in height to 500 feet at the west. From the vicinity of Marshall, Ark., westward to near the meridian of 93°30′, the wall continues equally abrupt and even-topped, but fronted by outliers and gashed by reentrant gorges. The largest are 1000 to 1400 feet

Fig. 186.—View in the dissected northern escarpment of the Boston Mountains. (*Ark. Geol. Survey.*)

deep and 15 to 20 miles long. Farther west the smooth horizon continues, also the escarpment, but the latter is less simple and steep. Rock terraces are wider and outliers vary in height.[1] These terraces are sufficiently suggested in the mention of rocks on page 634.

The flat crests of the mountains represent the sandstone strata of the Atoka (Winslow) formation, especially the sandstone at the base, which is thickest and strongest (page 634). The summit slope, like the dip, is toward the south, being small near the main crest but steeper near the southern edge.[2] The slope is less steep than the dip, hence the crests at the southern margin are on higher strata. Along the greater part of the southern boundary the mountain upland merges with the hills of the Arkansas

[1] The escarpment is well described by J. C. Branner in "The Zinc and Lead Region of Northern Arkansas," Ark. Geol. Survey, vol. 5, p. 3, 1900.

[2] Winslow folio (No. 154), U. S. Geol. Survey, 1907.

Valley. At places the topographic break is abrupt, mainly where the boundary is against a local south-dipping monocline (page 636), but at places the break in topography follows a fault.[1]

There can be little doubt that the divides in the Boston Mountains represent a once old surface. Just how much of altitude and relief it retained when most worn down can not now be told, but the evidence of a former peneplain here is about the same as in the Allegheny and Cumberland Mountains (pages 288 and 332). Apparently the strata are beveled by the old surface.[2] At least they are not the same everywhere. Many of the divides are still flat, even where valleys are 500 to 1000 feet deep. Dissection is not more than submature. Highways on divides are quite as numerous as those in valleys. Valleys on both north and south slopes are characteristically young and have little if any flood plain. Their sides, like the northern escarpment, have rock terraces. Entrenched meanders are practically wanting.

Correlation of Surfaces.—Assuming a former summit peneplain, the question presents itself whether this is the one referred to above as surviving in modified form in the Salem upland. Or is it an older and higher surface? If the first supposition be true, there has been a relatively recent uplift to make the mountains. If the second be true, then this rugged plateau remained standing as such while the younger peneplain developed around it on all sides. Either assumption postulates an uplift. The first limits it strictly in area and makes it later than the Ozark peneplain. The second requires that the uplift should come after the first peneplain and before the second. Purdue[3] favored a single peneplain with uplift of the Boston Mountains in late Tertiary or post-Tertiary time, mainly because of the evident youth of the valleys and the absence of such forms as characterize two-cycle valleys. Hershey[4] elaborated the theory of

[1] The boundary may be traced on the topographic sheets of the U. S. Geol. Survey north of latitude 35°30′.

[2] HERSHEY, O. H., Boston Mountain Physiography, *Jour. Geol.*, vol. 10, p. 164, 1902.

[3] PURDUE, A. H., Physiography of the Boston Mountains, *Jour. Geol.*, vol. 9, pp. 694–701, 1901.

[4] HERSHEY, O. H., Peneplains of the Ozark Highlands, *Amer. Geologist*, vol. 27, pp. 25–41, 1902; also other papers cited above.

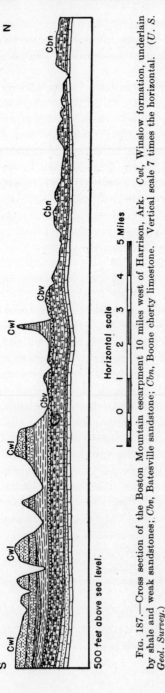

FIG. 187.—Cross section of the Boston Mountain escarpment 10 miles west of Harrison, Ark. *Cwl*, Winslow formation, underlain by shale and weak sandstones; *Cbn*, Batesville sandstone; *Cbn*, Boone cherty limestone. Vertical scale 7 times the horizontal. (U. S. Geol. Survey.)

two peneplains corresponding to those of the two prominent levels in the Ouachita Mountains (page 670) and in the Appalachians (Chap. 4). Both hypotheses have their difficulties. The first of necessity includes the outliers north of the mountain front in the recent uplift. But some of these are 20 miles away, surrounded by the Springfield upland. If time must be allowed since the uplift for the development of the wide lower-lying surface around these outliers, not much seems to be gained by denying a second cycle.

It may well seem that the youth of the Boston Mountain valleys is inconsistent with the assumption that their development was in progress throughout the cycle in which a new peneplain was produced on the north and south. However, with reference to both rocks and topography the case is similar to that of the Cumberland Mountains (page 332), which are believed without question to have survived the Harrisburg cycle.

That two base levels 1000 or more feet apart have left their records in the Ouachita Mountains is too plain to be denied. They must have had some northward extension. Only one general peneplain seems to have been developed on the top of the Ozark dome in Missouri. Hershey's hypothesis assumes that the uplift of 1000 feet or more, following the older cycle, diminished toward the north, and that, on the main Ozark dome, it was too small to be distinguished in the record. On this supposition the two peneplains, distinguished in Arkansas, merge in southern Missouri. The old surface in Missouri and adjacent states, having held over from one cycle to the next, is now classified as belonging to the newer cycle. Streams in that cycle succeeded only in cutting steep valleys in the strong rocks of the Boston Mountains, while the country on all sides was reduced to old age. This included a strip north of the present escarpment, where still later dissection by the vigorous White River and its tributaries has gone far in destroying the newer peneplain.

HISTORICAL SUMMARY

Ancient History.—In this province are relics of one of the oldest land areas in the United States. The St. Francois Mountains are the relics of a mass of unknown size, reduced to knobs not many hundred feet high before they were buried under the sediments of the Cambrian sea. There were other ups and downs, but in late Paleozoic time this region was still a flat sea bottom, beneath which were nearly horizontal sedimentary rocks, perhaps 1000 feet thicker than those that now remain north of the Boston Mountains. In the Appalachian Revolution the region was raised above the sea in the form of an asymmetrical dome, perhaps 3000 or 4000 feet high above its eastern base and having its highest point in or near the St. Francois Mountains. Since that time it is not known to have been beneath the sea. It was base-leveled more than once, and at different times the sea came in over a surface like the present flat uplands, filling ancient sinkholes with sediments of various Paleozoic periods. It may well have been base-leveled again when the margin of the continent, including the Mississippi Embayment and also the Great Plains, were reduced to a plain before the deposition of Cretaceous beds. All older peneplains were in turn lifted up and destroyed in the making of the oldest erosion surface suggested by the present topography.

Tentatively the surface at the top of the Boston Mountains may be looked upon as the oldest surface in the province. This would mean that the area was essentially peneplaned at some time in the Tertiary, perhaps at a time concurrent with the

Schooley cycle in the Appalachians. The peneplain was then upraised, but the uplift at this time centered in the Ouachita province to the south, diminishing toward the north to 500 feet in the Boston Mountains, to 100 feet on the Arkansas-Missouri boundary, and to zero a little farther north. In turn the new uplift was peneplaned[1] near all the larger streams and on the softer or more soluble rocks, but not in the Boston Mountains. Where these are highest, the newer peneplain appears at their base 500 feet below their summits, the interval decreasing northward and disappearing on the main Ozark dome. The surface here called the Ozark peneplain is, over a wide area, essentially the upper surface of the Boone chert. The high margin of this hard formation may have checked erosion at a level a little above its local base level, but farther west the base level is more apt to have been a little above the Boone surface than below it.

The Ozark peneplain is exemplified in the Salem upland, where its form is preserved despite continued solution and wash. It is here regarded as genetically the same as the Springfield upland. It is believed to have been completed in late Tertiary time,[2] but not so late as to exclude another partial cycle mentioned below.

The Ozark peneplain thus developed is, so far as known, the same as that which constitutes the uplands in adjacent states to the west, north, and east, designated in Wisconsin and Iowa as the Lancaster peneplain (or Dodgeville if that be recognized). It is clearest on the outcrops of the stronger formations, but it is possible that these never wholly lost their relative altitude. In the cases of the Niagara formation at the northeast, the Boone in the middle, and the lower Permian in the Flint Hills to the west, the residual relief was distinctly greater.

---

[1] Miser (U. S. Geol. Survey, *Bull.* 734) would have the peneplain on the Boston Mountains and the area at their northern foot cut down to a series of structural plains. His explanation does not call for any lower peneplain north of the Boston Mountains, though it does in the Ouachita Mountains to the south.

[2] Adams, G. I., and Ulrich, E. O., Fayetteville folio (No. 119), U. S. Geol. Survey, 1905; Bain, H. F., and G. I. Adams, U. S. Geol. Survey, *22d Ann. Rept.*, pt. 2, p. 71, 1901. Marbut, *op. cit.*, p. 26.

Hershey, in papers cited above, merely calls this peneplain Tertiary and the one on the Boston Mountains "Cretaceous" in accordance with the older usage in the Appalachians.

There followed a slight uplift of the Ozark peneplain, which made possible the development of the broad valleys. This rise, which was perhaps 75 feet near the Missouri River and 300 on the White, is noted also in the surrounding sections, but its amplitude was probably greatest in the southern Ozarks. These valleys, even if limited to alluvial bottoms between bluffs, required considerable time in the making. There must have been wide meandering, long enough continued to sweep away the spurs and push back the bluffs for several miles. The character of deposits left by the streams of that time would seem to indicate that their gradients were lower than those of present streams.[1] The older valley of the White River is more than a mere trench between bluffs. It is a strath or incipient peneplain, and this is probably true of others.[2]

The cycle of the old valleys is commonly ascribed to the Late Pliocene or "Lafayette."[3] It was followed by the rise that inaugurated the gorge cutting, commonly accepted as the beginning of the Quaternary. Following this rise, the channels of the lower Mississippi and its tributaries were cut down to depths that are now below base level. There has since been aggradation of 100 to 200 feet, raising the flood plain of the Mississippi (page 85) and partly filling the tributary valleys on the eastern and southeastern margins of the Ozark province.

Glacial ice did not reach this province, nor did it reach its borders until later, hence the gorges are sometimes said to have been cut in the "preglacial Quaternary." As gorge cutting was mainly in the Ozark province, this last uplift is also known to have been domelike in form. The final effect of all the uplifts that followed the first peneplaning was to restore roughly the outlines of the old structural dome. There were local maxima also in the later uplifts such as the one at Cedar Gap (page 637) where the upland surface is almost 1700 feet high.

Throughout both of the partial cycles, which have followed the uplift of the Ozark peneplain, its surface, even where there

[1] HERSHEY, O. H., River Valleys of the Ozark Plateau, *Amer. Geologist,* vol. 16, p. 350, 1895.

[2] *Cf.* MARBUT, C. F., Geology of Morgan County, *Mo. Bur. Geol. Mines,* 2d ser., vol. 7, p. 9, 1907.

[3] HERSHEY, O. H., Peneplains of the Ozark Highlands, *Amer. Geologist,* vol. 27, p. 32, 1901.

are no rejuvenated valleys, has been steadily wasting and lowering, especially by solution. Cuestas have gradually assumed greater prominence. The extent to which the Boone formation has, during this time, been stripped of Cherokee shale is uncertain. In any case the history of the Burlington cuesta is similar to that of the smaller cuestas of the Osage section (page 611).

CHAPTER XIII

OUACHITA PROVINCE

In central western Arkansas and eastern Oklahoma, between the Ozark Plateaus and the Gulf Coastal Plain, is the Ouachita province, an area much like the Folded Appalachians in both structure and topography. The name Ouachita Mountains originally designated the ridges in the Novaculite Uplift (page 676) which stretches westward from Little Rock and Hot Springs. It is now applied to all of the mountains carved from the closely compressed anticlinorium in the southern half of the province. Between these and the Boston Mountains is a synclinorium 30 to 50 miles wide, in which the folds are much more open, and the surface generally (not universally) lower. These two great structural features are roughly coextensive with the two sections of the province, the Ouachita Mountain section and the Arkansas Valley.

ARKANSAS VALLEY

Boundaries.—The distinction between the northern and southern sections has long been made by geologists on a structural basis, and the boundary in Arkansas defined as following parts of Petit Jean Creek, its tributary Dutch Creek, and the Poteau River[1] (Fig. 188). From Little Rock to Danville at the mouth of Dutch Creek, the boundary is described more accurately as following the Chicago, Rock Island, and Pacific Railroad. In the valley of the Poteau River, which flows westward into Oklahoma, the great Choctaw fault begins. It continues

---

[1] This line was defined by Arthur Winslow (Geotectonic and Physiographic Geology of Western Arkansas, *Bull. Geol. Soc. Amer.*, vol. 2, p. 225, 1891) and has been generally followed. The Chicago, Rock Island, and Pacific Railroad follows a nearly parallel course, deviating some 10 or 12 miles in Western Arkansas where the railroad runs north of Poteau and Petit Jean Mountains. Superficially these mountains appear to belong to the mountain province on the south, but in their structure and physiographic character they are like others of the Arkansas Valley.

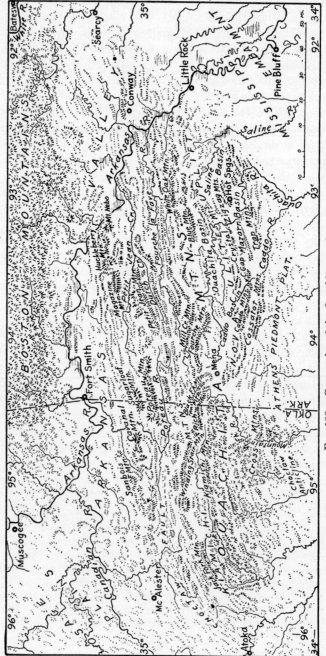

Fig. 188.—Geography of the Ouachita province.

westward and southwestward to the Gulf Coastal Plain, everywhere separating the linear Ouachita ridges, on steeply folded and faulted beds, from the isolated synclinal mountains and mesas which rise above the plain of the Arkansas Valley.[1]

The Arkansas Valley and the Osage section of the Central Lowland are described in much the same terms, except for the residual mountains in the former and the trend of escarpments. However, where the two are contiguous along a line between Muskogee and McAlester, there is only a narrow border that might be in doubt. Most of the surface west of the Arkansas and north of the Canadian River has the distinctive east-facing scarps of the Osage section. The northern boundary of the Arkansas Valley section is described on page 656. Its eastern boundary against the Tertiary lowland of the Mississippi Embayment is clear.

Rocks and Structure.—All of the consolidated rocks in the Arkansas Valley are of Pennsylvanian age. They constitute a great series of alternating sandstone and shale with valuable coal in both Arkansas and Oklahoma.[2] Resistance to erosion increases a little toward the south where closer folding has induced some incipient metamorphism.

Though the folding here is gentle in comparison with that of the Ouachita Mountains, it is none the less distinct and everywhere present. A width of 5 to 8 miles from one anticlinal axis to the next is common. In this spacing there is an element of regularity, but many of the axes curve. There are also short folds which overlap *en echelon*, and the amplitude of long folds differs from place to place. Near the northern boundary, dips of 3 to 6 degrees are most common. Folds increase in steepness toward the south. Several anticlines have dips between 45

---

[1] TAFF, J. A., and G. I. ADAMS, Geology of the Eastern Choctaw Coal Field, Ind. Territory, U. S. Geol. Survey, 21*st Ann. Rept.*, pt. 2, 1900; ref. to pp. 264, 267, and 270. For certain purposes these authors use the edge of the Savanna formation a few miles farther north. See also H. D. Miser, Structure of the Ouachita Mountains in Oklahoma and Arkansas, *Okla. Geol. Survey Bull.* 50, pp. 12 and 25, 1929.

[2] For data on stratigraphy and structure see U. S. Geol. Survey, 19*th Ann. Rept.*, pt. 3, 1898; 21*st Ann. Rept.*, pt. 2, 1900; *Bull.* 326, and folios No. 74 and 79. A summary treatment for Arkansas is given by C. Croneis, Geology of the Arkansas Paleozoic Area, Ark. State Geol. Survey, *Bull.* 3, 1930. Plates 1-*B*, 25, and 33 show stratigraphy and structure.

degrees and the vertical, but these do not make the mountains. There is also some thrust faulting near the mountains and normal faulting farther north.

Synclinal Mountains.—With rocks showing frequent alternation of shale and fairly strong sandstone, deformed as here described and reduced by erosion, the surface features found in the Arkansas Valley are the expectable result. The most prominent residual masses are synclinal mountains and mesas. These increase in magnitude toward the south, where folding was closest and the rocks indurated. Their present height is only in part due to better preservation. In part it is the result of recent regional uplift which was greater toward the south.

Among the typical and best known of these mountains are the Sansbois and Cavanal in Oklahoma, the Sugarloaf on the state boundary, and Magazine, Huckleberry, and Nebo Mountains in Arkansas. Poteau and Petit Jean Mountains on the southern border are of the same type structurally and morphologically but distinctly linear, having an east-west trend. In a purely descriptive or empirical treatment they would be classed with the Ouachita ridges. The mountains named range in height from 1800 to more than 2800 feet, Magazine Mountain (2823 feet) being one of the highest in Arkansas. Some others have heights of 1000 to 2000 feet.[1] All are isolated, and all are synclinal. The inward dipping beds in Magazine Mountain have a maximum steepness of 26 degrees. Dips of 10 to 25 degrees in this section are considered steep.

The general appearance of all these mountains is that of steep-sided buttes. Some are broad enough to have flat summits, and the slopes of all are more or less distinctly terraced by structural benches. Most of the slopes are forested but the benches and flat summits are in part farmed.

The above description is given here for mountains, but the same principle holds in all of the shallow synclines. A nearly horizontal sandstone in the axis of a syncline is likely to arrest erosion at a level somewhat higher than that of a peneplain on similar rocks in monoclines. Mesas of various height and extent are thus produced. They are not all made by the same stratum,

---

[1] A comparison of the Dardanelle and Magazine Mountain topographic sheets with the geological map of Arkansas is instructive.

and their heights are not limited by any single plane, either horizontal or sloping.

Monoclinal Ridges.—Below a certain level there is more consistency in the heights of ridges and mesas. Many of those in Oklahoma have their tops at an altitude of 800 to 850 feet. This is the same level as the peneplain already described (page 629) at the tops of the cuestas in the Osage section.[1] It rises a little toward the mountains on the south, and declines toward the Arkansas River and also eastward. Near the river in Arkansas some ridges are as low as 600 feet. Most that remains of this old surface is at the summits of the numerous cuestas of gently dipping sandstone strata, but some cuestas are higher and others lower. Synclinal mesas account for a smaller area, but the total surface at the old level is only a minor fraction of the section.

Cuestas necessarily have the same direction as the strike, hence an east-west trend here is more prominent than any other, but with folding so gentle, with axes often short and overlapping, and with cuestas supplemented by mesas, the east-west trend of the uplands must not be overemphasized. None the less the linear character is generally noticeable, the uplands often smooth and continuous, the scarps often distinct and occasionally precipitous. The height above the lowlands rarely exceeds 200 feet; near the Arkansas River it is not more than 100 feet. North of the Arkansas such ridges are almost wholly wanting, except near the eastern end where the river turns south at the edge of the mountain section. East of the river and north of Little Rock all the features of the Ridge and Valley province in Pennsylvania may be found reproduced in miniature.[2]

Lowlands.—A large part of the Arkansas Valley is a rolling lowland, 500 to 600 feet high, underlain mainly by shale, and lying between the low sandstone ridges just described. This is homologous with the Cherokee and other low strips in the Osage section (page 613). It is plainly the beginning of a younger peneplain than the one indicated by the uplands on the low cuestas. The streams which controlled its level in the making

[1] TAFF and ADAMS, *op. cit.*, p. 268; also U. S. Geol. Survey, Muskogee folio (No. 132), 1906.

[2] BRANNER, J. C., Geology in its Relation to Topography, *Amer. Soc. Civ. Eng.*, vol. 39, 1898.

now wind through alluvial plains which, near the Arkansas River, are sunk 100 feet below the general level. The descent from rolling peneplain to alluvial plain is such as to require the assumption of rejuvenation after a moderate rise.

The alluvial plain of the present cycle along the Arkansas itself, much of it swampy, is 2 to 6 miles wide. On tributaries it is much narrower and less deeply entrenched, and toward their heads it is not yet developed. Some small valleys, opening on the broad plain of the Mississippi and the Arkansas, have such sharp angles between their flat bottoms and steep sides as to indicate refilling after cutting to greater depths.[1] The diastrophic record indicated by the levels here described is summed up on page 97.

Drainage.—The eastward drainage of the Arkansas Valley may well have begun, perhaps on a peneplain, in Upper Cretaceous time, when the Mississippi Embayment came into existence by depression and the beds of former Cordilleran seas were elevated thousands of feet. A few northern tributaries of the Arkansas River near the eastern end of the section are so closely related to lines of folding as to suggest that they are consequent and have retained their positions ever since the late Paleozoic deformation.[2] Nearer the Tertiary lowland, and at a lower level, this relationship is lost, and it has been suggested that below the level of 500 feet the drainage was superposed on Tertiary sediments.

THE OUACHITA MOUNTAINS

General Statement.—The Ouachita Mountain section is a lens-shaped area having a width of 60 miles and a length of 225 miles from Little Rock, Ark., to Atoka, Okla. It is essentially coextensive with a closely compressed and faulted anticlinorium so far as that structure is exposed to view. It is somewhat arbitrarily delimited on the north and northwest by the line described on page 663 as the boundary of the Arkansas Valley section. On the east and south the section ends at the edge of the Coastal Plain, beneath which the mountain structure, worn down to its roots, no doubt continues for some distance. The

---

[1] NEWSOM, J. F., and J. C. BRANNER, The Red River and Clinton Monoclines, Arkansas, *Amer. Geologist*, vol. 20, p. 4, 1897.

[2] NEWSOME and BRANNER, *op. cit.*, p. 3. The geologic map of Arkansas issued in 1929 shows clearly both the drainage and the axes of anticlines.

entire area consists either of mountains, intermontane valleys, or piedmont from which mountains have been carried away by erosion. Most of the area is still in forest, having pines on the ridges, especially on south slopes, and much hardwood in the basins. Its western half was in the former "Indian Territory," in which most of the surface is classified as "grazing and timber lands."[1]

Description of Mountain Ridges.—The trends of the many mountain ridges are in general east-west, but deviations and inter-sections are frequent. Many of the ridges are short and over-lapping, curved, or hooked, following the outcrops of truncated pitching folds. Descriptions of these mountains as being even-topped, or having straight horizontal crests, must not be inter-preted in too strict a sense. At places this is literally true, and when viewed in the light of their long and eventful history the accordance of the highest summit levels throughout the province is noteworthy. In detail, however, there is much irregularity. In some cases this takes the form of isolated eminences rising above a consistent summit level. At other places the level itself is hard to detect.

Further difficulty in generalization arises from the fact that there are many even-crested mountain ridges whose tops do not reach the highest level of accordant summits. Some of the lower ones are essentially like the cuestas of the Arkansas Valley, and are probably to be explained in the same manner, though they are now several hundred feet higher. There are also mountains of intermediate height, and a continuous ridge may be high at one place and low at another. Diverse heights may generally be explained by the varying thickness and resistance of the ridge-making rocks.

The Summit Level.—If only the highest ridges are considered, those that determine the horizon in a very broad view, it may be said that the summit level at the east end is about 500 feet, or 250 feet above the adjacent plain. At the west end it is 750 feet, and again 250 feet above the Coastal Plain. From both ends it rises to a maximum of more than 2600 feet near the Oklahoma-Arkansas boundary. This point is near the axis of the uplift, from which altitudes decline both north and south. Broad

[1] HONESS, C. W., Geology of the Southern Ouachita Mountains in Oklahoma, Okla. Geol. Survey, *Bull.* 32, 1923; see Pl. 14.

valley floors are rarely higher than 1100 feet, hence relative heights in excess of 1500 feet are not uncommon.

It is commonly agreed that the summit level, generalized as above, is related to a former base level, and that such equality of height as now exists was inherited from an old-age topography. How much has been lost since uplift can not now be told; it cannot be told how much of the present irregularity of crests is due to incompleteness of peneplanation and how much to later

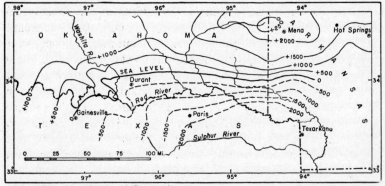

FIG. 189.—Contour map showing the elevation of the Ouachita peneplain (restored in the northern half, buried in the southern half). (*As devised by F. A. Melton and F. H. McGuigan, Amer. Assoc. Petrol. Geol. Bull., vol.* 12.) The contour at sea level is shown by a heavier line.

erosion. Adjacent even-topped ridges have been lowered unequally by later erosion. To postulate an erosion cycle for all cases of accordance would be unwarranted. Horizontal benches suggesting old base levels are best seen on the synclinal mountains of the Arkansas Valley, but it is in such relations also that the problem is most confused by structural benches.

Valley Levels.—The floors of the larger valleys or basins, without regard to definite stream valleys, are likewise highest near the center of the area. Around Mena, Ark., near the Oklahoma line, there are many square miles of mildly rolling surface not much above or below 1100 feet. In all directions from this locality the basin level declines to that of the surrounding lowlands. Narrow stream valleys indent this lower surface to a maximum depth of several hundred feet. All of these features are more fully described below under the several subdivisions.

Rocks.—Erosion, following close folding and elevation of the area, has exposed the edges of not less than 25,000 feet of Paleozoic strata,[1] ranging in age from Cambrian to Pennsylvanian. These formations cover the same range in age as those in the Ozarks where the total thickness is one fourth as much, but conditions of deposition were different; so also, has been the subsequent deformation. Not only are the sediments much thicker toward the south, but the proportion of sandstone is greater, indicating that they were derived from a highland farther south which no longer exists (page 686). Induration accompanying deformation has added to their resistance. In most cases metamorphism is only incipient but there is some quartzite and slate. In the order of their abundance the stratified rocks of the Ouachita province are shale (and slate), sandstone (and quartzite), chert, novaculite, tuff, limestone, and conglomerate.[2]

Among these rocks only novaculite is unfamiliar. It is an exceedingly dense, fine-grained rock composed of almost pure silica, and is the typical oilstone, honestone, and fine whetstone of commerce. Its origin has been much debated.[3] Some regard it as a variety of chert. Its abundance here, and the fact that it is almost unknown elsewhere in the world, give it special interest. As a mountain maker it is second only to the Jackfork sandstone. The following table of formations contains only such data as are needed in a physiographic discussion. Topographic value is the main consideration.

IMPORTANT FORMATIONS OF THE OUACHITA PROVINCE[4]

Carboniferous:
　Boggy shale; 2000 to 3000 ft.; Arkansas Valley in Oklahoma.
　Savanna sandstone; 750 to 2000 ft.; caps synclinal mountains in the Arkansas Valley.

---

[1] Maximum thicknesses in the table given below aggregate more than 30,000 feet but not all maxima occur at one place.

[2] MISER, H. D., and A. H. PURDUE, U. S. Geol. Survey, *Bull.* 808, p. 9, 1929.

[3] A brief summary with citations is given by C. Croneis, Geology of the Arkansas Paleozoic Area, Ark. State Geol. Survey, *Bull.* 3, p. 107, 1930.

[4] In part abbreviated from H. D. Miser, *Bull. Amer. Assoc. Petrol. Geologists*, vol. 18, p. 974, 1934. For pre-Carboniferous rocks see H. D. Miser, *Amer. Jour. Sci.*, 5th ser., vol. 2, pp. 64–65, 1921.

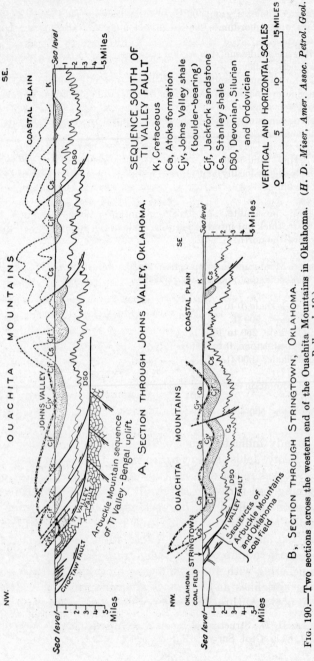

SEQUENCE SOUTH OF
TI VALLEY FAULT

K, Cretaceous
Ca, Atoka formation
Cjv, Johns Valley shale
   (boulder-bearing)
Cjf, Jackfork sandstone
Cs, Stanley shale
DSO, Devonian, Silurian
   and Ordovician

VERTICAL AND HORIZONTAL SCALES

A, SECTION THROUGH JOHNS VALLEY, OKLAHOMA.

B, SECTION THROUGH STRINGTOWN, OKLAHOMA.

FIG. 190.—Two sections across the western end of the Ouachita Mountains in Oklahoma.   (*H. D. Miser, Amer. Assoc. Petrol. Geol. Bull., vol. 18.*)

McAlester shale; a group of three formations of clay shale and sandy shale with subordinate sandstone and coal; 1150 to 2500 ft.; Arkansas Valley.

Hartshorne sandstone; 100 to 300 ft.; important in the low ridges of the Arkansas Valley.

Atoka formation. Sandy shale and sandstone in numerous alternations; maximum thickness 7800 ft.; its sandstone members are prominent in the lower ridges.

Jackfork sandstone; maximum thickness 6600 ft.; the substratum of all the most massive mountains.

Stanley shale; Clay shale with some sandstone; 6000 to 10,000 ft.

Hot Springs sandstone. A strong quartzitic formation 0 to 200 ft. thick, which occurs locally and unites its topographic effect with that of the novaculite.

Devonian:

Arkansas novaculite. A strong mountain-making formation nearly 1000 ft. thick but interbedded with shale in the upper part and thinning toward the north.

Silurian:

Missouri Mountain slate; maximum 300 ft.

Blaylock sandstone; maximum 1500 ft.

Ordovician:

Polk Creek shale, 0 to 400 ft.

Bigfork chert, 700 ft.

Womble shale, 250 to 1000 ft.

Blakeley sandstone, 0 to 500 ft.

Mazarn shale, 1000 ft.

Ordovician (?):

Crystal Mountain sandstone, 850 ft.

Cambrian:

Collier shale, 500+ ft.

As already indicated, the folding in these mountains is very close. Many folds are overturned and thrust-faulted. The entire belt was reduced to half its original width.[1] Most of the overturning and thrusting is toward the north, but where great compression resulted in fan folding some overturning was necessarily to the south, and the same is true of reversed faulting. Figures 190 and 192 show the deformation along selected lines. On the southern limb of the anticlinorium is a belt of remarkably close puckering with 40- to 90-degree dips, in which the ends of plunging anticlines and synclines alternate, making a structure like that of the Anthracite district of Pennsylvania, but on a small

[1] Miser, H. D., Structure of the Ouachita Mountains of Oklahoma and Arkansas, Okla. Geol. Survey, *Bull.* 50, p. 12, 1929.

scale with many more repetitions.   The resulting Zigzag Mountains are described on page 679.

The distribution of the rocks, as seen on the geologic map, explains the division of the Ouachita Mountain section into three districts whose distinctions have long been recognized, quite apart from scientific considerations.   In the middle, *i.e.*, on the top of the anticlinorium, and exposing the oldest rocks, are the mountains and basins of the Novaculite Uplift.   North and northwest of this area is a belt of mountains of Carboniferous rocks.   Within the state of Arkansas these have been called collectively the Fourche Mountains,[1] using the name of the principal divide for the entire group.   On the same principle the mountains in Oklahoma would bear the name Kiamichi. South of the Novaculite Uplift, mountains give way to the Athens Piedmont Plateau.

The Fourche-Kiamichi Belt

This belt comprises two thirds of the entire Ouachita section, including the highest and most massive mountains.   Among the best known are Rich and Black Fork Mountains, which cross the state boundary just north of latitude 34°40′, the former bearing the highest point in the province, somewhat above 2800 feet A.T.   These and the highest ranges to the east, the Fourche, Mill Creek, Blue, and Whiteoak (named in geographic order), are generally monoclinal ridges of Jackfork sandstone, which, farther north but still within the mountain section, is buried beneath the Atoka formation.   The sandstone members of the Atoka also make mountains of various structures, generally lower than those of the Jackfork sandstone.   None of them rise to the level of the synclinal mountains in the Arkansas Valley section (page 666).   Westward from Rich Mountain, the Winding Stair, Kiamichi, and Jackfork ranges carry the summit level, all composed of Jackfork sandstone.

The level crests of Rich and Black Fork Mountains for many miles are between 2500 and 2600 feet high.   They are a little higher and more even than the crest of Fourche Mountain, in

---

[1] Purdue, A. H., The Slates of Arkansas, *Ark. Geol. Survey*, pp. 26–28, 1909.   In Oklahoma this belt comprises so nearly all of the Ouachita system that the need has not been felt for a term to distinguish it from the Novaculite Uplift.   As Kiamichi is the most prominent geographic name in the Oklahoma section, it is here linked with Fourche to designate the belt.

line with them to the east. To the north there is nothing comparable until Poteau Mountain (page 666) is reached. Its long crest (2100 to 2300 ft.) is commonly correlated with the higher crest of Rich Mountain, and believed to indicate a northward slope of an old peneplain. Farther east in the longitude of Hot Springs, level crests above 1500 feet are short. The northward decline here is marked. Mountain ridges of the same character (Jackfork sandstone) continue eastward to Little Rock. Within sight of the city, where but little of the upland is above 600 feet A.T., they may still be regarded as the exact correlatives of the highest mountains in the province.

Westward from Rich Mountain, the Kiamichi range shows the same decline in altitude and undulation in crest line seen in Fourche Mountain to the east. Winding Stair Mountain north of Kiamichi and others south of it are distinctly lower and less even. Among the monadnocks of the Arkansas Valley, Cavanal Mountain near the Arkansas line is 2300 feet high, but it is quite isolated and affords no proof of a peneplain. Its correlatives farther west are much lower.

Jackfork Mountain on the axis of the uplift, and 60 miles west of the Arkansas-Oklahoma line, has a smooth crest, slanting southwestward from 1600 feet to 1300 feet in 12 miles. Smooth crests and declining altitude continue to the limits of the mountain section.

The Jackfork sandstone enters into all of the higher ridges here mentioned. North and south of them are similar mountains of lower altitude, generally in the Atoka or Stanley formations. Among some of these ridges in western Arkansas (Poteau Mountain and Mt. Ida quadrangles) there is so much consistency of altitude (1100 to 1300 feet) as to suggest that they are to be classed with the low ridges of the Arkansas Valley section, the plane of whose tops rises toward the south. Exact agreement with such a classification is not found. Nor is it to be expected, since such mountains, even if once peneplaned (which was only imperfectly done) lose height at different rates determined by the thickness of the stratum, its dip (breadth of outcrop), the local character of the rock, and the fortunes of drainage.

About half of the total area is an uneven valley floor, 1100 feet high around Mena at the east end of Rich Mountain where it is flattest, declining northward almost a foot per mile, and somewhat less in other directions. This surface is itself cut by valleys 100 to 200 feet deep and generally old enough to have flood plains.

THE NOVACULITE UPLIFT

On and near the axis of the Ouachita anticlinorium, where the uplift was greatest, Carboniferous rocks have been entirely eroded away. Rocks are thus exposed that give a distinctive character to the mountains and basins in a belt whose greatest width is about 25 miles, to which the name Ouachita Mountains was at first restricted.[1] The area here referred to is primarily the belt stretching west more than 100 miles from Little Rock, shown on the geologic map as older than Carboniferous. Just east of the Oklahoma boundary, the uplift sags and Carboniferous rocks still cover its crest. It rises again on the state line, turns southwestward, and soon disappears beneath the coastal plain formations.

Rocks.—The highest of the distinctive formations in this belt is the Arkansas novaculite (page 671). It outcrops in an almost continuous band on the borders of the district, except against the Coastal Plain. Reduplication of outcrops by close folding is common. The stratum comes to the surface with steep dips, and its resistant character is such that it makes a rim of mountains, at places double or multiple, uninterrupted for some long stretches, elsewhere broken, especially on the north side. Mountain ridges in and near the city of Hot Springs are made by the Hot Springs sandstone at the base of the Carboniferous. The Crystal Mountain sandstone (Ordovician?) has a similar topographic value. As most of the other rocks of the district are less resistant, a large part of the area is comprised of broad basins, separated and surrounded by mountains made by the two strong formations.

Mountain Ridges.—The general plan of the district is shown in Fig. 191. There is an interrupted line of mountains on the north where the novaculite emerges from beneath the Stanley shale, generally in minor anticlines. On the southern border, the Cossatot Mountains in the western half and the Trap

[1] PURDUE, A. H., The Slates of Arkansas, *Ark. Geol. Survey,* 1909. See footnote on p. 26.

Mountains in the eastern half are anticlines of the same novaculite formation. Between these rims on the north and south, and roughly parallel with them, the Caddo and Zigzag Mountains form a nearly continuous range made by the same formation. Its outcrop here divides the anticlinal basins on the north from the synclinal Mazarn basin on the south. The Caddo, Ouachita, and Saline basins north of this dividing ridge are all on the structural uplift and are separated, one from the other, by the Crystal Mountains (page 680), which cross the area twice.

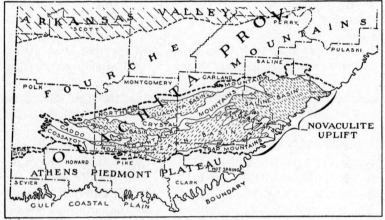

Fig. 191.—Map of the Novaculite Uplift showing mountains and basins. (*Ark. Geol. Survey.*)

The Novaculite ridges on the northern rim begin west of Little Rock as a group of flat-topped, parallel ridges rising only about 600 feet above sea level. At places single, at places multiple, the ridge continues westward, rising intermittently, but only in local swells or peaks does its altitude much exceed 1200 feet. Its relative height where it is well developed is not more than 300 to 400 feet. Exceptional swells may be 600 feet above the lowlands.

At the western end of the district all of the east-west ranges are closely crowded and the structure is highly complex.[1] Altitudes between 1500 and 2000 feet are frequent. Some crests are fairly even for considerable distances but their heights vary, and knobs, either isolated or on the crests of ridges, are very common. Most of the slopes are steep, the summits sharp and

[1] Good descriptions are given by Miser and Purdue, *op. cit.*, p. 14.

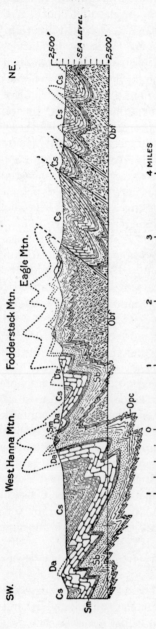

Fig. 192.—Section across the west end of the Novaculite Uplift in Arkansas, longitude 94°10′W, illustrating the fan-shaped folds. *Cs*, Stanley shale; *Da*, Arkansas novaculite; *Sm*, Missouri Mountain slate; *Sb*, Blaylock sandstone. (*Miser and Purdue, U. S. Geol. Survey Bull.* 808.)

Fig. 193.—Structure section across part of the Hot Springs district, Arkansas, showing how the folds of the Crystal Mountain anticlinorium on the north and the Trap Mountain anticlinorium on the south are overturned toward the Mazarn synclinorium. (*Purdue and Miser, U. S. Geol. Survey, Hot Springs folio.*)

barren, and talus slides abundant. For mountains of such moderate height these are very difficult to climb. This is true of all the Novaculite ridges in proportion to their altitude, which generally diminishes toward the east.

The Caddo Mountains, which form part of this complex belt at the west, are separate farther east, making a range 2 to 4 miles wide with a height which falls off to about 1200 feet in the Hot Springs quadrangle or 600 feet above the lowland. In general this is a monoclinal ridge of novaculite dipping south or southeast from the axis of the anticlinorium. In detail, the Novaculite and Hot Springs sandstone are closely folded. Examination of the geologic map[1] suffices to show how exceedingly complicated or kinky this folding is. What is actually truncated here is not a simple monocline but a thick stratum crumpled in a long succession of pitching anticlines and synclines.

Near Hot Springs the general direction of this outcrop changes from north of east to south of east. Here the kinks in the folding become still more pronounced, so much so that the outcrop of a single stratum makes a zigzag pattern, crossing back and forth several dozen times over a belt about 10 miles wide known as the Zigzag Mountains.[2] Near Hot Springs the general crest level, aside from local swells, is 1200 feet or more, *i.e.*, 500 to 700 feet above the lowland. All altitudes decline eastward to 700 feet or less before the Coastal Plain is reached.

In and near these mountains, are many dikes and some more massive intrusions of igneous rock. The residual heat of the larger masses is commonly assumed to be in some way accountable for the famous Hot Springs, but the exact relation is still in debate.[3] The springs are all on the nose of one of the plunging anticlines. Their temperatures range from 95° to 140°F., and the total discharge is 800,000 gallons daily.

Where the ranges are crowded together at the west the Cossatot Mountains constitute the southern half of the mountain belt. They embrace the highest ridges, an occasional crest reaching

[1] Geologic map of Arkansas, 1929; A. H. Purdue, The Slates of Arkansas, *Ark. Geol. Survey*, Pl. 3, p. 29, 1909.

[2] See map and sections in Hot Springs folio (No. 215), U. S. Geol. Survey, 1923.

[3] BRYAN, K., The Hot-water Supply of the Hot Springs, Arkansas, *Jour. Geol.*, vol. 30, pp. 425–449, 1922; also, *Jour. Geol.*, vol. 32, pp. 449–459, 1924.

2000 feet for several miles; also the highest peaks or knobs, some of which exceed 2300 feet.   Local relief of 800 to 1000 feet is common.   East of the 94th meridian this range becomes progressively separated from the Caddo Mountains by the broadening of the Mazarn Basin syncline.   South of that basin the Cossatot range is a closely compressed anticline.   It has a length of 45 miles, ending at the Caddo River on the east. After a gap of 7 miles the Trap Mountains begin, representing a continuation of the Cossatot anticline, so closely compressed that a fan structure is developed.[1]   These mountains consist of one to six or seven ridges in a belt not more than 5 miles wide. They nowhere exceed 1100 feet in altitude or rise much more than 500 feet above the lowland.

The Crystal Mountains are the only ones in the district not formed by the Arkansas novaculite or the closely associated Hot Springs sandstone.   They are due to anticlines which cross the main uplift diagonally, bringing to the level of erosion the massive Crystal sandstone (Ordovician?).   In their higher parts, crest levels up to 1500 feet, aside from exceptional swells, are not uncommon.   They are therefore somewhat higher than the Novaculite ridge on the north and less high than the Caddo and Cossatot Mountains.   Owing to the difference in weathering between sandstone and novaculite these mountains are more massive, their crests less sharp, and their slopes distinctly less rugged.

Basins of the Novaculite Uplift.—Four major basins are outlined by the mountains described above, and shown in Fig. 191.   The three basins north of the Caddo-Zigzag Mountains are on rocks (largely shale) older than the novaculite, hence with reference to the anticlinorium as a whole they are anticlinal. But this does not in all cases express their relations to their immediate rims, which are subordinate elements of the anti- clinorium.   All three basins are carved on the less resistant formations (page 673) between the Crystal Mountain sandstone and the novaculite.   These rocks are by no means uniformly weak, and the floors of the basins are far from being smooth lowlands.   All are more or less ribbed with divides in line with the strike, which probably were never wholly eliminated in any cycle of erosion.   Present streams are running from 100 to

[1] Croneis, *op. cit.*, p. 16.

200 feet below any possible peneplain, partly in broad valleys, partly in ravines.

Most suggestive of a uniform lowland is the Ouachita basin, whose elevation, except in the immediate Ouachita Valley, is mostly between 550 and 750 feet. Much of the Saline basin has small relief, 400 to 600 feet above sea level; there are also broad swampy valleys below 300 feet, also some areas of considerable extent several hundred feet above the general level. The Caddo basin is mainly a surface of moderate relief between 700 and 900 feet high, but higher and rougher near the mountains, and dropping to 600 feet near the Caddo River where it cuts through the mountains in Caddo Gap.

The Mazarn basin is in a synclinorium (Fig. 193) and is underlain throughout by the Stanley shale, the stronger members of which make low east-west ridges. The surface on divides is generally 500 to 600 feet high, but the area at that level is not large, since dissection is submature. The Ouachita River is incised 200 to 250 feet and its tribuaries are generally in narrow valleys. The general level rises northwestward and reached 1000 feet in the long westward extension between the Caddo and Cossatot Mountains.

It will be observed that the slopes of all basin floors are in the direction of the drainage, which is southeastward across the entire Novaculite Uplift.

Minor Uplift in Oklahoma.—Geologically the uplift in Oklahoma[1] is much like that in Arkansas. West of the sag mentioned on page 676 the Cross Mountains and others nearly in line with them stretch westward for 30 miles. They are made by a group of anticlines in which the Novaculite formation outcrops in ridges. Among them are some even crests 1500 feet high at the east and declining toward the west. Relative heights are 200 to 400 feet. The anticlines of the Cross Mountains are more or less separated from the main or Choctaw anticlinorium in Oklahoma which lies a few miles farther south and is clearly seen on the geologic map. The novaculite outcrop in that uplift surrounds an area of about 100 square miles of older rocks like those in Arkansas. Small overturned folds are so numerous that 50 of them have been counted within 20

---

[1] HONESS, C. W., Geology of the Southern Ouachita Mountains in Oklahoma, Okla. Geol. Survey, *Bull.* 32, 1923.

miles. The novaculite outcrop shows them in minute zigzags,[1] but the ridges characteristic of this hard formation become less and less marked as the Coastal Plain is approached. The surface of the whole uplift is plateaulike, its distant sky line being fairly even and declining from 1200 feet at the north to 500 feet, the level of the Coastal Plain, in 20 miles. Near the 400-foot trench of Mountain Fork River it is maturely dissected. Except for the diminished Novaculite ridges, the surface on the Choctaw anticlinorium merges with the Piedmont plateau next to be described.

The Athens Piedmont Plateau[2]

Description.—A strip 8 to 18 miles wide, lying between the Trap, Cossatot, and Cross ranges on the north and the Coastal Plain on the south, contains no mountains. Its rocks of Pennsylvanian age have the same character and diversity in hardness here as farther north. They include the Stanley shale and the Jackfork sandstone which makes the highest mountains of the province. The structure also is similar. Close folding, overturning and thrust faulting have left prevalent southward dips, generally between 45 and 90 degrees. Ashley states that in one section 24 miles long 39 anticlines were crossed. A broad outlook from an occasional knob or swell shows a landscape still largely in forest, stretching away to a nearly level horizon. The general slope is mainly toward the south but also toward the east. The altitude at the southeast is only 400 feet. It rises to the level of the Mazarn basin, 500 to 600 feet, at the foot of the Trap Mountains, and to 1100 feet around the Cross Mountains at the west. Through the sag in the uplift east of the Cross Mountains, the Piedmont surface on the south is continuous with Cove Basin, an extensive area north of the Cross Mountains in which the prevailing altitude is 1100 to 1250 feet.[3] The Jackfork sandstone makes low ridges or swells that rise above the general level of divides.

[1] Honess, *op. cit.*, p. 232.

[2] Ashley, Geo. H., Geology of the Paleozoic Area of Arkansas South of the Novaculite Region, *Proc. Amer. Phil. Soc.*, vol. 36, pp. 217–318, 1897; Miser and Purdue, *op. cit.*, 1929.

[3] Miser and Purdue, *op. cit.*, p. 17.

The Piedmont may be said to end at Mountain Fork River 10 miles west of the state line,[1] where Pennsylvanian rocks give way to the older rocks of the Novaculite Uplift. However, the same general level is continuous over the southern part of the Choctaw anticlinorium and over the low crests at the western end of the Ouachita Mountain section. The following description applies to the area east of Mountain Fork River.

The dominant feature of the topography of the Athens Piedmont Plateau is a series of east-west strike ridges and intervening valleys. The ridges increase in height from south to north, attaining in some cases a height of 300 feet above the valleys. Generally the horizon is nearly flat. Exceptions to this rule are seen on the Jackfork sandstone, which makes low ridges or swells above the general level. A few of the ridges are cuestas, scarping to the north, but, since dips are usually steeper than 45 degrees, most of the ridges are equally steep on both sides. The southern margin, a few miles wide, is almost flat, but with this exception there is little level country either on the ridges or in the valleys, though in a wide view the horizon is nearly flat.

Principal streams flow south across the district, generally in narrow valleys whose greatest depth reaches 350 feet. Tributaries, generally on shale, are chiefly in strike valleys, hence at right angles. They head at the main north-south divides. Where these divides have not yet suffered erosion, the upland is as continuous from north to south as it is on the ridges from east to west, but the total area of such level surface is small. The main south-flowing streams have rather steep gradients, as much as 15 to 25 feet per mile. As some of them are in entrenched meanders their former gradients must have been much less.

As in other areas on the same rocks in this province, the soil does not encourage farming, and population is sparse. Timber is still the main resource. Pine forests cover most of the south slopes. Elsewhere are hardwoods.

Origin of the Piedmont Surface.—The flatness of the horizon leaves no doubt of a peneplain. There is no evidence that the sea has covered this area since the indicated peneplain was

[1] HONESS, *op. cit.*, p. 276.

made.[1] The sea had indeed spread inland an unknown distance, perhaps to the mountains or even farther, in Cretaceous time when the oldest rocks of the Coastal Plain were laid down. The inland extension of those rocks, and the surface on which they were laid (itself an older peneplain), were destroyed by subaerial erosion in the making of the peneplain now indicated by the hill tops, which was vastly more extensive than the Athens Piedmont Plateau.

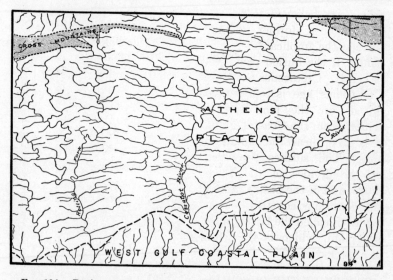

Fig. 194.—Drainage map of part of the Athens Plateau in Arkansas adjacent to the Oklahoma boundary, showing trellis pattern. (*Miser and Purdue, U. S. Geol. Survey Bull.* 808.)

As the edge of the Coastal Plain rocks retreats, the old hard-rock surface on which they rest is progressively laid bare. It is seen to slope southward about 80 feet to the mile, increasing to 100 feet per mile at the east, and decreasing to 40 feet south of the Arbuckle uplift (page 626). This is known mainly by data from wells, but the denuded sloping surface is preserved in a zone several miles wide, bearing fragments of the basal Cretaceous (Trinity) gravel. At the northern edge of this zone, which is generally a cuesta, the steep slope ends, and the hilltops fall in a plane which slopes seaward less than 20 feet in a mile.

[1] This whole subject is discussed by H. D. Miser in U. S. Geol. Survey, *Bull.* 808, pp. 144–146.

If the buried peneplain be projected northward to the mountains with a rise of 80 feet per mile, it would reach an elevation comparable to that of many of the more even-crested mountain tops[1] (Fig. 195). As those summits themselves are believed to be elements of a former old-age surface the implication is evident. If the buried peneplain of early Cretaceous or pre-Cretaceous age is represented at all on the land surface remote from the Coastal Plain, it is at or near the mountain tops. The surface preserved on the divides of the Piedmont, and of the basins among the mountains, constitutes what has been called the Hot Springs peneplain, which is the work of a later cycle.

HISTORY OF THE OUACHITA PROVINCE

Structural History.—The Ouachita province is not only analogous to the Folded Appalachians but is probably a part of the same system.[2] For aught that is known, a contin-

[1] MISER and PURDUE, *op. cit.*, p. 137 and their Fig. 7, p. 138. See also Hot Springs folio (No. 215), U. S. Geol. Survey, 1923.

[2] BRANNER, J. C., The Former Extension of the Appalachians across Mississippi, Louisiana and Texas, *Amer. Jour. Sci.*, 44th ser., vol. 4, pp. 357–371, 1897. Branner cor-

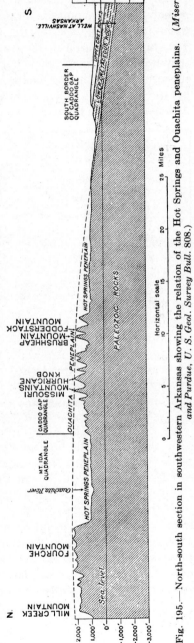

Fig. 195.—North-south section in southwestern Arkansas showing the relation of the Hot Springs and Ouachita peneplains. (*Miser and Purdue, U. S. Geol. Survey Bull. 808.*)

uous belt of folding may extend from Alabama to Arkansas. Mountains thus made had ample time to be base-leveled, as their correlatives were destroyed elsewhere, before subsidence made the Mississippi Embayment, in which the stumps of former mountains may be buried. As with the great geosyncline in the east, so here, the sediments were derived from an old Paleozoic land surface to seaward. In the former case the older land (Appalachia) is still in part exposed. In this case the older land (Llanoria[1]) has disappeared, partly by erosion, partly by submergence and burial. The sinking Ouachita trough accumulated some 30,000 feet of sediments before crustal movements were reversed, Llanoria sank, and the thick sediments of the geosyncline were folded into high mountains. In so doing a belt 100 to 120 miles wide was compressed into half its width.[2]

Ouachita Cycle.—Since the first upheaval, at least 18,000 feet of beds have been stripped from the top of the Novaculite district, but the height of the folds and fault blocks carried away is by no means limited to the thickness of the beds. That the entire structure above base level at some former time was essentially destroyed may safely be inferred, not only from the forms observed here, but from the analogy of the better known Appalachians. The more resistant formations are much alike in the two cases. In neither case was base-leveling complete or absolute. Yet when the hardness and thickness of the Jackford sandstone in Rich Mountain are considered, also its dip and the height of the folds thus indicated, the essential evenness of the crest line for 30 miles is very impressive. That many lumps should remain above base level, and many once-smooth crests should since have become irregular, these are only expectable details which do not impair the weight of evidence that a great erosion cycle was carried far toward completion, thus producing the Ouachita peneplain.

---

related the Ouachita system with the Cincinnati-Nashville anticline rather than with the main belt of Appalachian folding. H. D. Miser (Structure of the Ouachita Mountains, Okla. Geol. Survey, *Bull.* 50, p. 11, 1929) is inclined to correlate the Ouachita with the main Appalachian geosyncline.

[1] MISER, H. D., Llanoria, the Paleozoic Land Area in Louisiana and Eastern Texas, *Amer. Jour. Sci.*, 5th ser., vol. 2, pp. 61–89, 1921.

[2] MISER, *op. cit.*, p. 12, 1929.

Figure 195 illustrates the hypothesis that the summit level of the highest even-topped mountains represents the same peneplain that passes beneath the coastal plain sediments. This is a proposition that needs careful and critical consideration in view of the tendency among geologists to abandon a similar assumption with respect to the Northern Appalachians (page 256). It may be significant that the gradient of 80 feet per mile is measured, not on the unmodified peneplain but on the peneplain as modified by wave erosion during submergence and burial. One of the effects of wave erosion is to reduce the seaward slope, *i.e.*, to flatten the profile.[1] If allowance be made for such flattening, it is quite possible that the revised projection of the buried peneplain might pass well above the mountain tops and thus make possible the assumption that the Ouachita peneplain is younger than the buried surface, as the Schooley peneplain is believed to be younger than the buried surface east of it.

The correlation of summit peneplain with buried surface might still be maintained by assuming that the steepness of the uplift decreased inland, or that the mountains have been substantially lowered by erosion with sufficient uniformity to preserve the horizontality of their crests. Wasting and lowering, quite aside from carving, must be allowed for in any case. The validity of correlation in this case (as in some others) depends on quantitative studies in physiography not yet made. Hence it is not now possible to make a definite decision as to the geologic age of the Ouachita peneplain. However, if the Ouachita province were considered alone, *i.e.*, without regard to any analogy with the northern Appalachians, it is not probable that the correlation of the summit peneplain with the nearly Subcoastal plain floor would ever have been questioned.

Hot Springs Cycle.—The first uplift of the Ouachita surface was 1200 to 1500 feet in the vicinity of Rich Mountain, tapering off to little or nothing at the east, south, and southwest. No doubt, the uplift was also less in what is now the Arkansas Valley, but nothing remains there of the old surface to indicate its elevation. It has been tentatively assumed that it is represented by the summit plane of the Boston Mountains, where

---

[1] There are exceptions to this generalization, but probably none that apply to this case. The demonstration of the principle cannot be given here.

the first uplift was small, and north of which at no great distance it diminished to zero (page 658).

That the present drainage of the entire mountain section radiates from the locality where the old peneplain was raised highest strongly suggests that the drainage is consequent on the uplift.[1] The change from an older pattern to a radial pattern would be simple if superposition might be assumed, as has been suggested for the Northern Appalachians (page 258). There is no collateral evidence of that in this case (nor is there any evidence in the Appalachians, except inference from drainage). Barring superposition, it is necessary to assume that the outward slopes from the center of the dome were sufficiently steep to give decided advantage to radial streams. Drainage lines would then adjust themselves by shifting divides and captures, all tending toward a radiating pattern.

The uplift described above was followed by the development of the Hot Springs peneplain,[2] now best preserved in the vicinity of Rich Mountain, from which present drainage radiates, also on the divides of the Athens Piedmont. Presumably this is the surface indicated by the crests of the low sandstone ridges, cuestas, and uplands of the Arkansas Valley and the Osage section.[3] It has been most frequently referred to in the literature merely as the Tertiary or Late Tertiary peneplain. Tentatively, it may be identified with the dominant level of the horizon throughout the Central Lowland province.

As already pointed out, the Ouachita and Hot Springs peneplains intersect near the edge of the Coastal Plain (Fig. 195). Apparently they converge toward the north and merge in southern Missouri. They also converge toward the west and probably merge in eastern Oklahoma at an altitude of 800 to 900 feet. Where two peneplains merge, the name of the younger is applied.

It will be observed that the Hot Springs peneplain was not developed on the hardest rocks. The Arkansas novaculite

[1] *Cf.* Ashley, *op. cit.*, p. 228.

[2] The relations of both peneplains, Ouachita and Hot Springs, are explained in the Hot Springs folio (No. 215), U. S. Geol. Survey, 1923.

[3] J. A. Taff describes this surface in various papers already cited. See also J. A. Taff and G. I. Adams, Geology of the Eastern Choctaw Coal Field, U. S. Geol. Survey, 21*st Ann. Rept.* pt. 2, pp. 267–270, 1900. Also papers by O. H. Hershey cited above.

and the Jackford sandstone make ridges or swells at higher levels. These are not to be confused with the characteristic east-west divides of the Athens Piedmont, whose level is that of the Hot Springs peneplain. A later uplift raised the younger peneplain throughout this province and all of its neighbors. Subsequent erosion of the Athens Piedmont and the Arkansas Valley left the Hot Springs peneplain surviving mainly in narrow strips, generally located by the outcropping of the more siliceous members (or formations) in a mass of shale. Erosion in this last cycle did not generally make extensive lowlands south of the mountains, but much of the surface of the Arkansas Valley consists of wide valleys or straths cut 100 to 300 feet below the Hot Springs peneplain. These constitute Hershey's "Lafayette peneplain"[1] and are homologous with the wide, upper valleys in the Ozark Upland, the Cherokee Lowland, and other local or incipient peneplains of the Osage section.

All of the surfaces here mentioned are now trenched by stream valleys. Those of the Arkansas Valley section are described on page 667. Some alluvial terraces in both sections show that uplift has been intermittent. Even temporary subsidence is indicated by some valleys in which an alluvial surface abuts against steep sides.

[1] HERSHEY, O. H., Peneplains of the Ozark Highlands, *Amer. Geologist*, vol. 27, pp. 32*ff*, 1901.

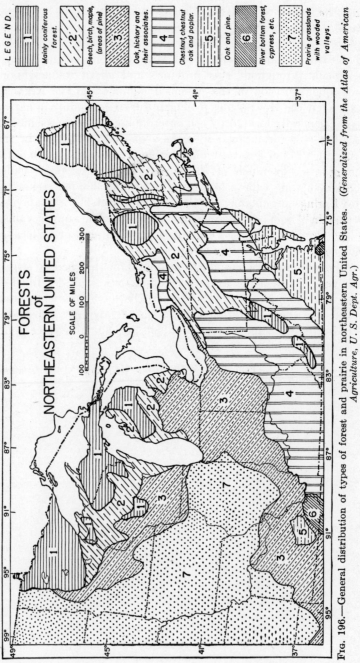

Fig. 196.—General distribution of types of forest and prairie in northeastern United States. (*Generalized from the Atlas of American Agriculture, U. S. Dept. Agr.*)

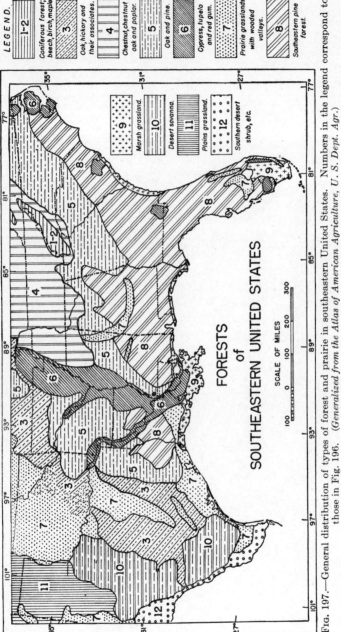

LEGEND.

1-2 *Coniferous forest; beech, birch, maple.*

3 *Oak, hickory and their associates.*

4 *Chestnut, chestnut oak and poplar.*

5 *Oak and pine.*

6 *Cypress, tupelo and red gum.*

7 *Prairie grasslands with wooded valleys.*

8 *Southeastern pine forest.*

9 *Marsh grassland.*

10 *Desert savanna.*

11 *Plains grassland.*

12 *Southern desert shrub, etc.*

FORESTS of SOUTHEASTERN UNITED STATES

SCALE OF MILES

100   0   100   200   300

FIG. 197.—General distribution of types of forest and prairie in southeastern United States. Numbers in the legend correspond to those in Fig. 196. (*Generalized from the Atlas of American Agriculture, U. S. Dept. Agr.*)

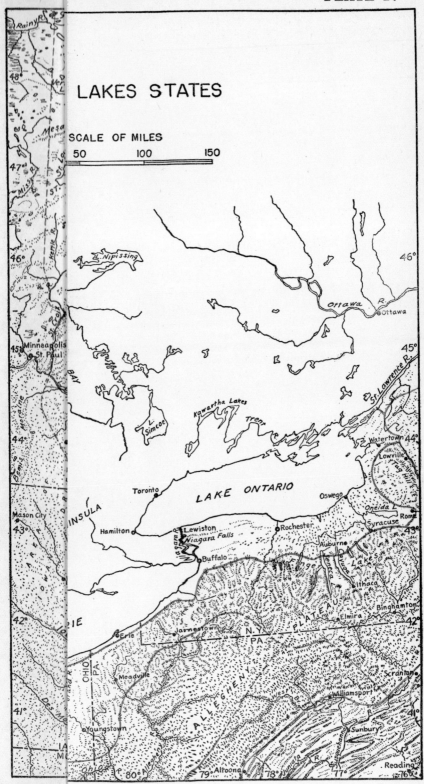

PLATE IV

LAKES STATES

SCALE OF MILES
50   100   150

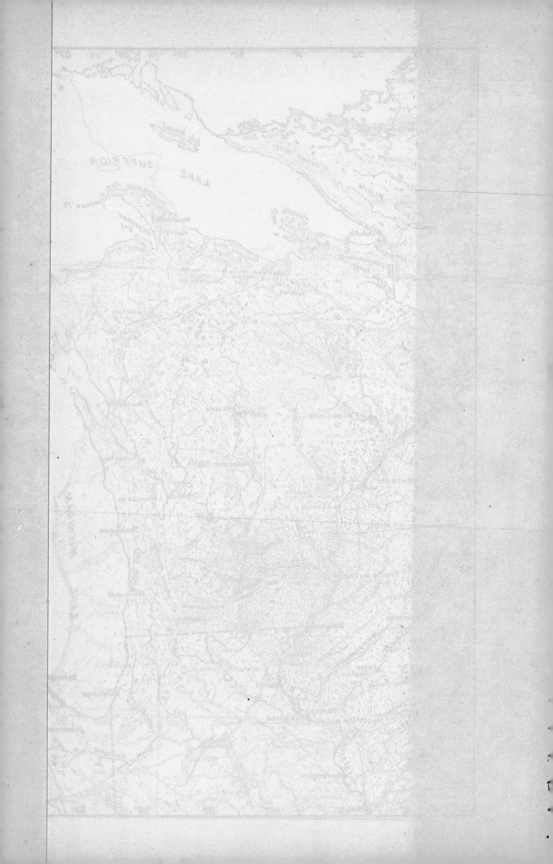

PLATE V

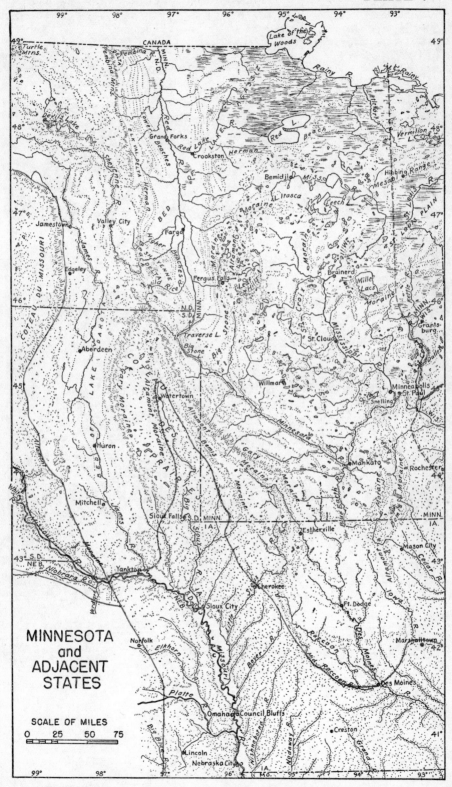

MINNESOTA
and
ADJACENT
STATES

SCALE OF MILES

0   25   50   75

PLATE VI

PLATE VII

TEXAS AND ADJACENT STATES

INDEX

693